AF572787

THEORY OF JETS IN IDEAL FLUIDS

THEORY OF JETS IN IDEAL FLUIDS

By M. I. GUREVICH

Translated from the Russian by

ROBERT L. STREET
STANFORD UNIVERSITY

KONSTANTIN ZAGUSTIN
UNIVERSIDAD CENTRAL DE VENEZUELA

1965

ACADEMIC PRESS New York and London

ACADEMIC PRESS INC.
111 FIFTH AVENUE
NEW YORK, NEW YORK 10003

United Kingdom Edition
Published by
ACADEMIC PRESS INC. (LONDON) LTD.
BERKELEY SQUARE HOUSE, LONDON W. 1

Library of Congress Catalog Card Number: 65-27087

This book was originally published as:
Teoriya Strue Ideal'noe Zhidkosti

Gosudarstvennoe Izdalel'stvo
Fiziko-Matematicheskoe Literaturÿ

Moscow, 1961

PRINTED IN THE UNITED STATES OF AMERICA

PREFACE

Jet theory is an important and extensively studied part of hydrodynamics. Helmholtz and Kirchhoff were, in the 1850's, the first to formulate and solve jet problems. It was expected that one of the results of the application of jet theory would be an explanation of D'Alemberts' paradox, and the drag forces on some simple bodies in an ideal fluid were computed using Helmholtz's and Kirchhoff's results. However, the calculated drag forces were considerably less than those measured experimentally. As a result, the assumptions of jet theory were criticized, and hydrodynamicists sought to create better models of the flow around a body. On the other hand, jet theory did accurately predict the contraction coefficients of streams flowing from vessels.

In the following years, hydrodynamicists studied many theories for the solution of jet problems. Meanwhile, the speeds of ships, propellers, turbines, etc., increased steadily, and hydroplanes appeared. With the increasing speed of objects moving through the water it became clear that the results of jet theory had previously been compared with experiments made at relatively low velocities, where the basic conditions of jet theory were, as a rule, not satisfied. This advent of higher velocities brought regimes under study in which the results of the jet theory coincided with the experimental results, and the solutions of many problems of jet theory that had previously seemed purely mathematical exercises now took on practical importance.

PREFACE

In the present book the author has tried to give a systematic exposition of contemporary jet theory. The first chapters give a relatively detailed exposition of classical jet theory. It is assumed that the reader is somewhat familiar with this theory, with basic hydrodynamics, and with the theory of complex variables. The later chapters become more specialized, and many problems are perforce treated only superficially. The very important part of jet theory dedicated to the problem of the existence and uniqueness of solutions is treated only briefly, and only superficial mention is made of supersonic jets, etc.

From another point of view, it was considered useful to present the solutions to certain particular problems of jet theory in those cases in which these solutions are relatively simple and, particularly, for which numerical results are obtained. This approach is required because of the complexity of many aspects of jet theory and of the impossibility of making short and simple presentations of these difficult areas. For instance, to understand the well-known work of Leray it is, in essence, necessary that one first study the extensive works of Leray and Schauder on functional analysis.

In order to read the present book the reader need be familiar only with the elements of complex variable theory, except that in some problems reference is made to special sections of mathematics (e.g., the theory of elliptic functions). A basis for understanding the main part of this book may be obtained from a study of Chapters I and II, and article 8 in Chapter III of Ref. [4] or Chapters I-V, VII, and article 1 in Chapter VIII and articles 1-3 of Chapter XI of Ref. [3].*

---

*Vallentine, Applied Hydrodynamics, Chapts. 1, 2, 4, 5, and 6, Butterworths, London, 1959 or Churchill, Complex Variables and Applications, 2nd ed., McGraw-Hill Book Co., Inc., New York,

PREFACE

The author hopes that the present book gives the general concepts of jet theory and also serves as an entry to a more extensive study of certain special problems.

The author takes this opportunity to express his gratitude to L. I. Sedov for his support and for many stimulating discussions. The author sincerely thanks G. A. Dombrovskii for his help in the writing of Section X.D and I. I. Moiseva, A. I. Sekerzh-Zenkovich, S. V. Falkovich, and L. A. Epshtein for their review of much of the book and their valuable comments. Thanks are also due N. A. Slezkin for the large bibliography on jet theory which he put at the author's disposal. With the same sincerity the author wants to thank all those other persons who gave him reprints of their works, bibliographic references, and other valuable help.

1960. Where appropriate, references to books more readily available to the English-language reader have been added to Russian references by the translators.

TRANSLATORS' PREFACE

This book, Theory of Jets in Ideal Fluids, by M. I. Gurevich, was first published in Moscow, Russia, in 1961, although it has never been generally available to the English-language reader. It is a comprehensive text on high-speed, incompressible hydrodynamics with a brief but significant chapter on compressible flow. The author's definition of jet theory is very broad, and he discusses a wide range of topics--e.g., "true" jets, hydrofoils, separated flow, and free-surface flow. Professor Gurevich is well-known in Russia and throughout the world as a mathematician and hydrodynamicist; he has published many papers on the theory of ideal fluid flow.

A particular strength of this book is its presentation of complete analyses with clear exposition of principles, and many examples, tabulated results, and comparisons of the theoretical results with experimental data. The book is basically theoretical and makes extensive use of complex-function theory.

We believe that this book is both a good reference work of lasting value and an excellent advanced theoretical-hydromechanics textbook. In addition, the literature list is extensive and current through 1960. The listed Russian works are, in general, available in either well-known Russian journals or in translated form. We have replaced original Russian references with their translated versions when possible.

In undertaking this translation, we were materially assisted by Professor Gurevich's transmittal of three original copies of the book and his personal list of errata. During the translation, our objective has been to present the translation in the

TRANSLATORS' PREFACE

form it would have taken were English Professor Gurevich's native tongue. Thus, while the basic organization and point of view have not been changed, the result is a free rather than a literal translation. Where our personal experience and knowledge permitted, we added English-languare references to aid the reader; however, none of the references in the original text were omitted.

For the reader seeking work accomplished in the field since this book was originally published in 1961, we suggest referral to the *Journal of Fluid Mechanics*, Cambridge University Press, London or New York, and the *Journal of Ship Research*, Society of Naval Architects and Marine Engineers, New York. Finally, we took the liberty of adding an index, which was not present in the Russian original.

We gratefully acknowledge the work of the following persons whose efforts were essential to the successful completion of the translation: Mrs. Robert Street, for editing and for typing part of the draft; Mrs. Byrne Perry, for typing the remainder of the draft; Mrs. Janet Gordon Berg, for preparing the draft for final typing and for layout of the illustrations; Mrs. Cathryn Adams for typing the final manuscript; and Professor Byrne Perry, for his review and comments on the translation. Finally, we acknowledge our deep appreciation to the U. S. Office of Naval Research, Fluid Dynamics Branch, and its Head, Mr. R. D. Cooper, for their support of our work through Contract Nonr 225(71).

Stanford, California
June 1965

R. L. Street
K. Zagustin

AUTHOR'S PREFACE TO THE ENGLISH EDITION

In the present book an attempt is made to set forth systematically the theory of jets in ideal fluids, an important area in hydromechanics with practical and theoretical significance. Jet theory has been developed in various countries, with significant contributions by Russian scholars. It is probable that the English-language reader will find references to publications that were heretofore unavailable to him because of the language barrier.

Some interesting developments on jet theory have appeared since 1961, but it was not generally possible to refer to them in the translation. However, the present book does provide a sufficient basis for understanding the more recent publications.

A number of minor errors in the original Russian book have been corrected in this English translation.

I wish sincerely to thank the translators for their efforts in preparing the English edition of this book.

Moscow, 1965 M. I. Gurevich

CONTENTS

CONTENTS

CONTENTS

Page

XII. FLOW OF A HEAVY FLUID AND THE EFFECTS OF SURFACE TENSION

CHAPTER I. INTRODUCTION TO THE THEORY OF PLANE, STEADY JET FLOWS

A. SOME INFORMATION ON KINEMATICS

This book is meant for a reader who is familiar with the elements of hydrodynamics; however, for the reader's convenience, some basic reference material on the theory of the plane, steady flow of an ideal, incompressible fluid is given here.

Consider a plane, steady flow of an ideal, incompressible fluid. It is said that the flow possesses a velocity potential φ, if

$$V = \operatorname{grad} \varphi \quad , \tag{1.1}$$

where V is the velocity vector. If we establish a fixed system of Cartesian coordinates x, y in the plane of the flow, then the continuity equation has the form [1, 2]

$$\frac{\partial^2 \varphi}{\partial x^2} + \frac{\partial^2 \varphi}{\partial y^2} = 0 \quad . \tag{1.2}$$

From this equation, we see that the velocity potential can be considered [3, 4] as the real part of the complex function $w(z) = \varphi + i\psi$, where $z = x + iy$. The function $w(z)$ is called the characteristic function or the complex potential, and its imaginary part ψ is called the stream function.

The conjugate functions φ and ψ satisfy the Cauchy-Riemman conditions [3]

$$\frac{\partial\varphi}{\partial x} = \frac{\partial\psi}{\partial y} , \qquad \frac{\partial\varphi}{\partial y} = -\frac{\partial\psi}{\partial x} , \tag{1.3}$$

which guarantee that, at a point z, the derivative dw/dz is independent of the direction along which the differentiation is performed. When the angle θ is defined as the angle between the velocity vector and the positive x-axis at some point z, the components v_x and v_y of the velocity vector along the coordinate axes are

$$\begin{aligned} v_x &= v \cos\theta = \frac{\partial\varphi}{\partial x} = \frac{\partial\psi}{\partial y} , \\ v_y &= v \sin\theta = \frac{\partial\varphi}{\partial y} = -\frac{\partial\psi}{\partial x} . \end{aligned} \tag{1.4}$$

For motion along a streamline--i.e., in the direction of the velocity vector--differential increments of the coordinates are given by $dx = \cos\theta\, ds_\varphi$, $dy = \sin\theta\, ds_\varphi$, where ds_φ is the differential arc distance measured perpendicular to equipotential lines. From Eq. (1.4) it follows that

$$d\varphi = \frac{\partial\varphi}{\partial x} dx + \frac{\partial\varphi}{\partial y} dy = v \cos^2\theta\, ds_\varphi + v \sin^2\theta\, ds_\varphi ,$$

$$d\psi = \frac{\partial\psi}{\partial x} dx + \frac{\partial\psi}{\partial y} dy = -v \sin\theta \cos\theta\, ds_\varphi + v \cos\theta \sin\theta\, ds_\varphi ,$$

i.e.,

$$d\varphi = v\, ds_\varphi , \qquad d\psi = 0 . \tag{1.5}$$

Thus, along every streamline, the stream function ψ is constant, and φ increases in the direction of the flow.

On the other hand, the differential coordinates along a line orthogonal to a streamline are

$$dx = \cos\left(\theta + \frac{\pi}{2}\right) ds_\psi = -\sin\theta \, ds_\psi \ ,$$

$$dy = \sin\left(\theta + \frac{\pi}{2}\right) ds_\psi = \cos\theta \, ds_\psi$$

where ds_ψ is a differential arc distance measured perpendicular to lines of constant ψ. Then, from Eq. (1.4) we find

$$d\varphi = 0 \quad , \qquad d\psi = v \, ds_\psi \ . \tag{1.6}$$

From Eqs. (1.5) and (1.6) it follows that the lines $\varphi = \text{const.}$ (equipotential lines) are orthogonal to the streamlines $\psi = \text{const.}$ The second of Eqs. (1.6) shows that ψ represents the flowrate. The stream function increases to the left when we look in the direction of the flow, and the flowrate between two streamlines is equal to the difference between the stream function values on these lines.

According to Eq. (1.4),

$$\frac{dw}{dz} = \frac{\partial\varphi}{\partial x} + i\frac{\partial\psi}{\partial x} = v_x - iv_y = ve^{-i\theta} \tag{1.7}$$

Obviously, the complex velocity dw/dz is the complex conjugate of the velocity

$$\overline{\frac{dw}{dz}} = v_x + iv_y \ . \tag{1.8}$$

Following are some simple, well-known examples of complex potentials that will occur frequently later in the text.

1. Uniform Flow Parallel to the x-Axis

The complex potential for this flow has the form

$$w = vz \qquad \text{or} \qquad \frac{dw}{dz} = v \ , \tag{1.9}$$

where the real constant v is equal to the velocity. From a comparison of Eqs. (1.9) and (1.7) we see that, everywhere in the z-plane,

$$v_x = v \ , \qquad v_y = 0 \ .$$

2. A Source Situated at a Point z_0

This complex potential is

$$w = \frac{q}{2\pi} \ln (z - z_o) \ . \tag{1.10}$$

During the process of passing around z_o in a counterclockwise direction on a closed contour--e.g., on a circle of radius r with center at z_o--the imaginary part of w increases by a constant amount q so that

$$w(r \exp [2\pi + \theta]i) - w(re^{\theta i}) = \frac{q}{2\pi} (\ln re^{2\pi i} - \ln r) = qi \ .$$

Therefore, according to Eqs. (1.6), $q > 0$ represents the discharge of a source, and if $q < 0$, then we have a sink.

3. Doublet (Dipole) at the Point $z = z_0$

If a sink and a source of equal intensity are placed on a line with a small distance separating them and we then pass to the limit by letting them come together while their intensity is increased in inverse proportion to the distance between them, the limiting flow will have a singularity called a doublet (dipole). The direction of the line from the sink to the source is called the axis of the doublet. The complex velocity potential of a dipole, situated at z_o with its axis forming an angle α with the x-axis, is

$$w = -\frac{M \exp[i\alpha]}{2\pi(z - z_o)} \quad . \tag{1.11}$$

The quantity M is called moment of the doublet.

4. A Vortex at the Point $z = z_o$

The complex potential of the vortex situated at z_o is expressed by

$$w = \frac{\Gamma}{2\pi i} \ell n \, (z - z_o) \quad . \tag{1.12}$$

The real part of w increases by a constant amount Γ while passing in a counterclockwise direction around the point z_o. The circulation [1,2] around the vortex is

$$\oint v_x \, dx + v_y \, dy = \oint \frac{\partial\varphi}{\partial x} dx + \frac{\partial\varphi}{\partial y} dy = \oint d\varphi = \Gamma \quad .$$

5. Sources and Vortices in a Fluid Bounded by a Straight Wall

Let the fluid fill the upper half-plane $y > 0$ and let the x-axis represent a solid wall. In addition, let a source with discharge q be placed at the point $z_1 = x_1 + iy_1$. To obtain the velocity potential of this flow we assume that in the lower half-plane there also exists a fluid flow, chosen such that the x-axis will be a streamline. The velocity potential of the resulting flow will be known, because a streamline in an ideal fluid can always be replaced by a solid wall. In order to produce such a flow, we place at the point

$\bar{z} = x_1 - iy_1$ a source with discharge q. The complex potential of the flow with the sources at points z_1 and $\bar{z}_1$ has the form

$$w = \frac{q}{2\pi} \ln (z - z_1) + \frac{q}{2\pi} \ln (z - \bar{z}_1) \quad . \tag{1.13}$$

This is the complex potential that we sought.

In fact, the complex potential

$$w = \frac{q}{2\pi} \ln \left[z^2 - z(z_1 + \bar{z}_1) + z_1\bar{z}_1\right] = \frac{q}{2\pi} \ln \left(z^2 - 2zx_1 + x_1^2 + y_1^2\right)$$

is real when $z = x$--i.e., the x-axis is a streamline $\psi = 0$. Evidently, in the region of the flow, w has a logarithmic singularity not only at the point z_1 but also at infinity, where there is a sink. Of course, it could not be otherwise, because the flow of the sources cannot disappear. It is possible to avoid having the sink at infinity by translating it into a finite distance from the origin--e.g., to the point $z = z_2$. The characteristic function of this flow has the form

$$w = \frac{q}{2\pi} \ln (z - z_1) + \frac{q}{2\pi} \ln (z - \bar{z}_1) - \frac{q}{2\pi} \ln (z - z_2) - \frac{q}{2\pi} \ln (z - \bar{z}_2)$$

$$= \frac{q}{2\pi} \ln \frac{(z - z_1)(z - \bar{z}_1)}{(z - z_2)(z - \bar{z}_2)} \quad . \tag{1.14}$$

It is also easy to find the complex potential of a vortex located at a point z_1 with circulation Γ under the condition that the x-axis represents a solid wall. To accomplish this, the flow should be extended into the lower half-plane, and a vortex with circulation $-\Gamma$ should be placed at $\bar{z}_1$ so that

$$w = \frac{\Gamma}{2\pi i} \ell n \frac{z - z_1}{z - \bar{z}_1} = \frac{\Gamma}{2\pi i} [\ell n (z - z_1) - \ell n (z - \bar{z}_1)] \quad . (1.15)$$

Actually, $\ell n (z - \bar{z}_1)$ does not change while passing counterclockwise around the point z_1 on an infinitely small circle, and $\ell n (z - z_1)$ increases by $2\pi i$; it follows that w increases by an amount Γ, i.e., at z_1 a vortex exists with circulation Γ. Furthermore, the x-axis is a streamline, since on the x-axis

$$\text{Im } w = - \frac{\Gamma}{2\pi} \ell n \left| \frac{x - z_1}{x - \bar{z}_1} \right| = - \frac{\Gamma}{2\pi} \ell n \, 1 = 0 \quad .$$

In the above method the complex potentials of sources and vortices in the presence of a wall are constructed by placing image sources and vortices at points that are symmetrically located with respect to the wall. From the mathematical point of view, this method represents a particular application of the Riemman-Schwarz Symmetry or Reflection Principle (see for example the following references on the theory of functions [3,4, or 5]. We shall apply this principle to one example.

6. Source and Sink within a Circle

Assume that we have a solid wall in the shape of the circle $|z| = 1$; at the points $z_1 = r_1 \exp [i\sigma_1]$ and $z_2 = r_2 \exp [i\sigma_2]$ within the wall, let there exist respectively a source and a sink of equal intensity q. The complex potential $w(z)$, extended to the whole z-plane, must have logarithmic singularities corresponding to the source and sink, at the points outside the wall that are symmetric to z_1 and z_2 with respect to the circle $|z| = 1$. Points P and P' are said to be reciprocally symmetric to the circle C if they lie on a straight line radiating from the center of C, and the product of their distances from the center of circle C is equal to the square of its radius [3,4]. In this way, points $\exp[i\sigma_1]/r_1$ and $\exp[i\sigma_2]/r_2$ will be symmetrical to points $r_1 \exp[i\sigma_1]$ and $r_2 \exp[i\sigma_2]$ respectively. Thus, we obtain

$$w(z) = \frac{q}{2\pi} \ell n \frac{(z - r_1 \exp[i\sigma_1])(z - \exp[i\sigma_1]/r_1)}{(z - r_2 \exp[i\sigma_2])(z - \exp[i\sigma_2]/r_2)} . \quad (1.16)$$

The function $w(z)$ obviously possesses the proper singularities within the circle $|z| = 1$. To verify finally that $w(z)$ is the correct function, we need only to prove that, on the circle $|z| = 1$, the imaginary part of $w(z)$ is constant--i.e., that the circle is a streamline. For a point on the circle $|z| = 1$ we can set $z = e^{i\sigma}$, where σ is real. Then

$$\operatorname{Im} w(z) = \operatorname{Im} \frac{q}{2\pi} \ell n \frac{\left(e^{i\sigma} - r_1 \exp[i\sigma_1]\right)\left(r_1 e^{i\sigma} - \exp[i\sigma_1]\right) r_2}{\left(e^{i\sigma} - r_2 \exp[i\sigma_2]\right)\left(r_2 e^{i\sigma} - \exp[i\sigma_2]\right) r_1}$$

$$= \operatorname{Im} \frac{q}{2\pi} \ell n \frac{\left(e^{i\sigma} - r_1 \exp[i\sigma_1]\right)\left(r_1 \exp[-i\sigma_1] - e^{-i\sigma}\right) \exp[i\sigma_1]\, e^{i\sigma} r_2}{\left(e^{i\sigma} - r_2 \exp[i\sigma_2]\right)\left(r_2 \exp[-i\sigma_2] - e^{-i\sigma}\right) \exp[i\sigma_2]\, e^{i\sigma} r_1}$$

$$= \frac{q}{2\pi} (\sigma_1 - \sigma_2) = \text{const.}$$

B. A REMARK ABOUT THE SYMMETRY PRINCIPLE

The symmetry principle is formulated for single-valued and holomorphic functions, but we have just now applied it to functions possessing singularities. The justification for such an operation was found by direct verification of the result. While this is not the place to study the purely mathematical question of a general formulation of the symmetry principle, we shall derive a result that will be useful later.

Let AB be a segment of a straight line or of a circular arc; then assume that AB corresponds simultaneously to a part of the boundary of the region D of the independent complex variable z, on which region a function f(z) is prescribed and is required to be real on AB. Furthermore, let the function f(z) have at point z_o of the region D a singularity of a type $(z - z_o)^\alpha$ or, in other words, in the vicinity of point z_o, it has the expansion

$$f(z) = (z - z_o)^\alpha \left[a_o + a_1(z - z_o) + a_2(z - z_o)^2 + \ldots\right] ,$$

where α is a real number.

Then the function f(z) can be continued through AB to the region D^*, symmetrically located with respect to D relative to AB. It is necessary to put with D^* a singularity of the form $(z - z_o^*)^\alpha$ at z_o^* which is symmetric to z_o relative to AB. If the modulus $|f(z)|$ of the function is constant on AB, then at z_o^* there will exist a singularity of the form $(z - z_o^*)^{-\alpha}$.

By a linear fractional transformation of the independent variable, it is always possible to map AB onto a segment of a real axis while keeping symmetric points symmetric. Assume that this transformation has been accomplished and then that $z_o^* = \bar{z}_o$. First, we let $\text{Im}\,[f(z)] = 0$ on AB. We represent f(z) in the form

$$f(z) = (z - z_o)^\alpha (z - \bar{z}_o)^\alpha P(z)$$

where $P(z)$ is a holomorphic and single-valued function in D. Obviously,

$$(z - z_o)^\alpha (z - \bar{z}_o)^\alpha = \left[z^2 - z(z_o + \bar{z}_o) + z_o\bar{z}_o\right]$$

is real on AB, where $\mathrm{Im}\,[z] = 0$. Then, in order that $f(z)$ be real on AB, the function $P(z)$ must be real on this segment. But in this case $P(z)$ can be extended by the symmetry principle to the region D^*. Since $(z - z_o)^\alpha (z - \bar{z}_o)^\alpha$ takes symmetric (conjugate) values at symmetric points, the whole function $f(z)$ can be continued symmetrically into D^*.

Analogously, if $|f(z)| = 1$ on AB, then $f(z)$ can be given in the form

$$f(z) = \left(\frac{z - z_o}{z - \bar{z}_o}\right)^\alpha Q(z) \quad , \tag{1.17}$$

where the function $Q(z)$ is single-valued and holomorphic in D. Since $|[(z - z_o)/(z - z_o)]^\alpha| = 1$ on AB, then $|Q(z)| = 1$ on AB. Accordingly, the function $Q(z)$ can be extended into the region D^* by the symmetry principle. Thus, in accordance with the above-mentioned concept of symmetry relative to the circle $|f(z)| = 1$, the values $f(z)$ at points of symmetry relative to AB will be inversely proportional in their modulus and will have equal arguments. It should not be difficult for the reader to prove that the function $[(z - z_o)/(z - \bar{z}_o)]^\alpha$ possesses this type of symmetry relative to the real axis. From Eq. (1.17) it can be seen that $f(z)$ has at the point $\bar{z}_o$ a singularity of the form $(z - \bar{z}_o)^{-\alpha}$. It is no more difficult to analyze in the same manner the case for which $f(z)$ possesses several similar singularities in the region D.

C. BASIC ASSUMPTIONS

In jet theory the flows considered are bounded partly by solid walls and partly by free surfaces on which the pressure is constant. As an example, consider the flow shown in Fig. 1. A weightless fluid flows against the plate AB and is divided into two parts by the plate. On the free surfaces BD and AD the pressure is constant. Behind the plate there is a zone of static fluid in which the pressure is constant. The region of the moving fluid is to be studied, and the fluid is considered to be ideal and without viscosity. Although there have been attempts to solve jet problems with the consideration of gravity (see Chapter XII), in the majority of works the fluid is considered to be weightless.

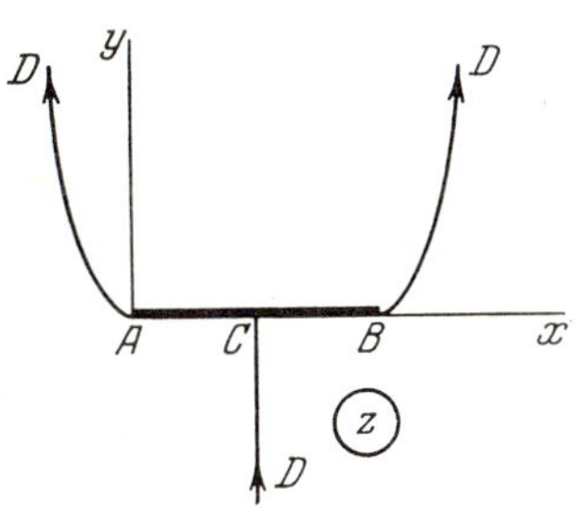

Fig. 1

The foundations of the jet theory of compressible fluids were given by Chaplygin [6]. The theory of gas jets has now been developed considerably and can serve as a subject for a special monograph. With the exception of Chapter X, in which Chaplygin's basic ideas are explained, the present exposition is limited to the jet theory of incompressible flow. For steady flows* this last assumption imposes limitations only on the flow velocity, which should be considerably less than the speed of sound (i.e., the propagation velocity of small disturbances in the medium). For gases this limitation is considerable, but for liquids it has no practical importance.

*Until recently in jet theory only steady flows were investigated. In Chapter IX, we consider also some current work about unsteady flows.

It is useful to make some preliminary remarks in regard to other assumptions. The substitution of an ideal fluid for a fluid that possesses only a low viscosity is quite common. However, it is important to remember that, with fluids of low viscosity, the viscous effects occur in two ways. First, as a consequence of the internal friction of the flow, thin boundary layers develop in which tangential forces occur at the surface of the body. Second, the boundary layer may separate and deform the flow outside the body. The boundary layer is laminar or turbulent depending on the Reynolds number, and the point of boundary layer separation from the body will vary accordingly. The picture of the flow around a body depends on many factors, such as the shape of the body, the Reynolds number of the flow, etc. It is also possible to have flows in which not only the boundary layer but also the whole flow separates from the body (see Fig. 1). Only this last type of flow is studied in jet theory. The points of flow separation in the jet flow about a body or a flow from a vessel may not depend on the characteristics of the boundary layer. For example, in the flow of a jet about a cylinder the flow separation point is considerably closer to the forward critical (stagnation) point (see Chapter IV, Section B) than the separation point of the boundary layer in an infinite fluid flow about the cylinder.

The above indicates the manner in which the hypothesis of an ideal fluid is used in jet theory. This hypothesis is valid in those cases in which the flow regimes and the shape of the body are such that the boundary layer does not separate. These cases are quite realistic and, under these conditions, according to boundary-layer theory, the friction forces can be computed separately after the solution of the ideal fluid-flow problem.

The assumption of the absence of vorticity is closely related to the assumption of an ideal fluid. The absence of vorticity simplifies considerably the mathematical solution of the problem. In fact, in an incompressible fluid flow without vorticity, a velocity potential φ exists, which satisfies Laplace's equation, Eq. (1.2). As we know, with a given velocity potential it is possible to compute the velocity and pressure field, and then to determine any of the summable characteristics of the motion: the discharges, the resultant forces and moments acting on a wall, etc. The velocity potential must also satisfy some definite boundary conditions on solid walls and on free surfaces. Neglecting the weight of the fluid greatly simplifies the boundary conditions on the surfaces of jets.

Consider, as an example, a steady flow. In this case the boundaries of the flow must be stream surfaces on which the following conditions are satisfied:

1. The normal velocity (the normal derivative of φ) is equal to zero on the given solid walls and on the unknown free surfaces.
2. On free surfaces the pressure is constant.

The uncommon feature of these conditions lies in the fact that, on the free surfaces, boundary condition 2. is given instead of the shape of the free surfaces.

The magnitude g of the gravity acceleration evidently does not appear either in the continuity equation, Eq. (1.2), or in condition 1. above. However, since the pressure on the free surface is constant, it follows from the Bernoulli equation [1,2] that, on the free surface,

$$\frac{v^2}{2} + gy = \text{const.} \quad , \tag{1.18}$$

where v is the velocity on the free surface and y is the vertical coordinate. Thus, the acceleration due to gravity enters into condition 2. It is obvious that neglect of the fluid's weight is equivalent to the assumption that the flow velocity on the jet surface is relatively large.* In the consideration of the flow around bodies in an infinite fluid this assumption is valid only at a sufficiently short distance from the body.

By accepting the assumption of the weightlessness of the fluid, it is possible to replace condition 2. with the simplified condition of constant velocities on free surfaces. If this velocity is too low, this assumption of fluid weightlessness will not be valid; if this velocity is too high, the fluid cannot be considered as incompressible. This double limitation is easily satisfied in a great number of important cases.

It was mentioned above that a specific difficulty, with which we must deal in the study of free surface flows, is the necessity of solving boundary-value problems in a region of complex and unknown shape. In the case of plane problems this difficulty can be overcome in a very effective and elegant manner because invaluable help is rendered by the theory of complex variables and, in particular, the application of conformal-transformation techniques.

In summary, we introduce the following assumptions, which will be used throughout the text except in the last four chapters. The fluid is weightless, ideal, and incompressible. Vortices are absent. The flow is steady, and only plane flows are considered. Thus, the flow is fully determined if a

---

*In theoretical-mechanics terms, this assumption becomes a requirement that the Froude number $F = v^2/g\ell$, where ℓ is a characteristic linear dimension, be large.

velocity potential is known, the potential being the real part of a complex potential $w(z) = w(x + iy)$, where x and y are the cartesian coordinates in the flow. On the body surface in a limited flow, the normal component of the velocity is zero; on each free surface the modulus of the velocity is constant.

In order to avoid any difficulties that may arise as a result of the abstract nature of the exposition in later chapters, some of the basic methods of plane jet theory are now applied to some simple examples.

D. KIRCHHOFF'S METHOD

Kirchhoff's method [7,8] is basically an enlargement and extension of Helmholtz's first solutions to jet problems [9].

Consider the irrotational flow of a weightless, ideal incompressible fluid around a plate with separation of the jet (see Fig. 1). On the surfaces of the jets AD and BD the modulus of the velocity is equal to the modulus of the velocity of the approaching stream v_o. The region of constant pressure behind the plate extends to infinity. The plate is perpendicular to the direction of the velocity of the approaching stream. In lieu of determining the complex potential $w = \varphi + i\psi$ as the function of the complex variable $z = x + iy$, it is possible to find the function

$$v_o \frac{dz}{dw} = \zeta(w) \quad . \tag{1.19}$$

If $\zeta(w)$ is found, then, with a single integration, it is possible to find $z(w)$. Actually

$$z = \frac{1}{v_o} \int \frac{v_o dz}{dw} dw = \frac{1}{v_o} \int \zeta \, dw \quad . \tag{1.20}$$

By inverting $z(w)$, it is possible to find $w(z)$. However, as will be seen at the end of the section, the inversion of $z(w)$ is an unnecessary and at the same time, practically speaking, a very difficult operation. Thus, we turn back to the problem of finding $\zeta(w)$. The geometric significance of $\zeta(w)$ lies in the fact that it gives a conformal transformation of the region of change of w onto the region of change of ζ. We can now determine these regions.

The complex potential is determined only up to an additive constant of the form $C = C_1 + iC_2$. We can always choose the real constant C_1 so that φ will be equal to zero at the critical (stagnation) point C on the plate (see Fig. 1). The real constant C_2 can be chosen so that the bifurcated streamlines CBD and CAD represent the line $\psi = 0$. Similarly, it will be considered that the fluid flowrate ψ is measured from this line. Because along the line $\psi = 0$ we have $d\varphi = vds_\varphi$, and because the velocity $v > 0$ approaches a finite value v_0 at infinity, it is obvious that, along DC, φ varies from $-\infty$ to 0; along CBD and CAD it varies from 0 to $+\infty$. As we move along the equipotential lines $\varphi = \text{const.}$ from the streamline $\psi = 0$ to the left and to the right up to infinity, where $v = v_0$ (Fig. 1), the magnitude of ψ changes monotonically from 0 to $-\infty$ and from 0 to $+\infty$ respectively.

To every point in the z-plane there corresponds a point in the w-plane with coordinates φ, ψ. Conversely, to every point in the w-plane, excluding those points on the real, positive semi-axis, there corresponds one point in the region of flow z. For every point of the real semi-axis $\psi = 0$, $\varphi > 0$, in the region of the flow, there are two corresponding points--one on CBD, the other on CAD--since one is on one branch and the other on another branch of $\psi = 0$ and $0 \leq \varphi < \infty$. If we now cut the region of w along the real, positive semi-axis and let the upper side of the cut conform to the branch CAD and the lower side to the branch CBD, then the relation between the regions of change of w and z becomes one to one. Because of the symmetry of the flow, the points A and B have the same values of $\varphi = \varphi_o$. In this way, the region of change of w is made to consist of the entire plane, with the exception of a cut along the real, positive semi-axis. The cut corresponds to the boundaries of the flow (Fig. 2).

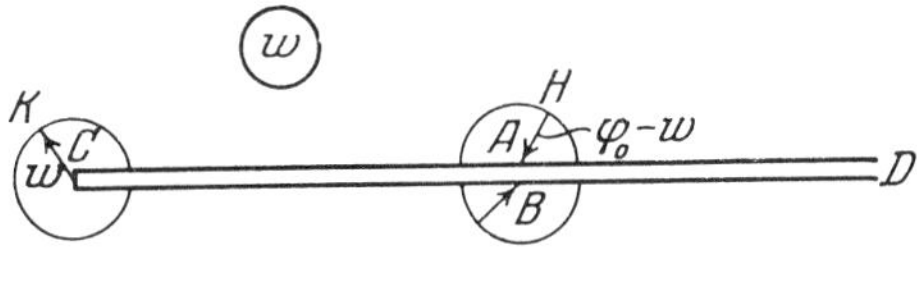

Fig. 2

Consider now the function

$$\zeta = \frac{v_o \, dz}{dw} = \frac{v_o \, e^{i\theta}}{v} ,$$

where θ is the angle between the velocity and the x-axis [see Eq. (1.7)]. Along CB, where $\theta = 0$, v_o/v changes from infinity at point C to 1 at point B. The section CB of the plate corresponds to a part of the real axis $1 \leqq \zeta < \infty$ in the ζ-plane. Along the free surface BD the angle θ changes from 0 to $\pi/2$, and $|v_o/v| = 1$; furthermore, along DA, θ continues to grow and reaches π, while $|v_o/v|$ remains equal to unity. Hence, the free surface corresponds to the upper half of a circle of unit radius in the ζ-plane. Finally, the segment AC of the plate corresponds to a part of the real axis $-\infty < \zeta \leqq -1$. In the whole plane of flow $0 \leqq \theta \leqq \pi$, $1 \leqq v_o/v < \infty$ and the region of flow corresponds in the ζ-plane to the upper half-plane from which a semicircle of unit radius is cut (Fig. 3).

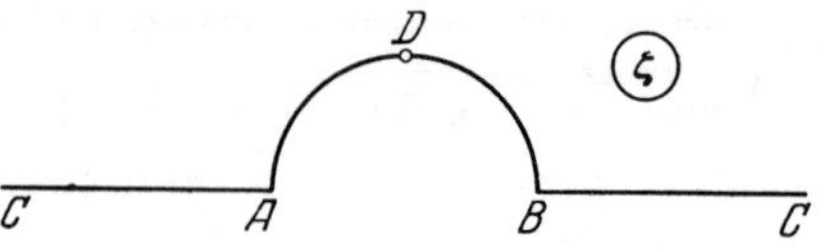

Fig. 3

To obtain the general solution of the present problem, it is sufficient to map a known region w (a plane with the cut along the positive real semi-axis) onto a known region of change of ζ (Fig. 3). This problem is completely elementary and, because of its simplicity, cannot be compared with the problem of finding a harmonic function in a region, the boundary of which is not known in advance but can be determined only with the help of additional conditions. This replacement of a complicated boundary problem with a simple one is the primary concept of Kirchhoff's method.

We will determine the conformal transformation of w onto ζ with the help of several successive conformal transformations. Under the linear-fractional transformation

$$\tau = \frac{\zeta - 1}{\zeta + 1} , \tag{1.21}$$

the corresponding parts of the plate on the real axis $1 \leqq \zeta < \infty$ and $-\infty < \zeta \leqq -1$ are mapped onto the real, positive semi-axis of the τ-plane, and the semicircle $\zeta = e^{i\theta}$ is mapped onto the upper imaginary semi-axis

$$\tau = \frac{e^{i\theta} - 1}{e^{i\theta} + 1} = i \tan \frac{\theta}{2}$$

where $0 \leqq \theta \leqq \pi$. In this way, the region of change of ζ maps onto the upper right quadrant of the τ-plane (Fig. 4.) The region of change of $\tau_1 = \tau^2$ is the upper half-plane

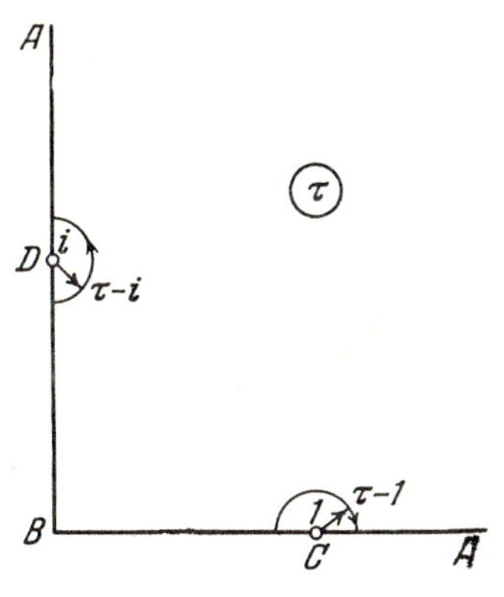

Fig. 4

(Fig. 5), because the argument of each point τ is doubled by the squaring of τ. The positive imaginary semi-axis of τ corresponds to the negative, real semi-axis in the τ_1-plane; the real

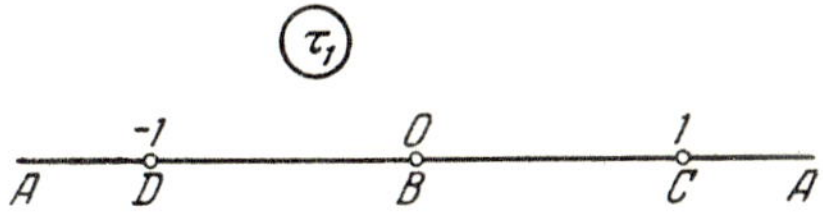

Fig. 5

positive semi-axis of τ corresponds to the same semi-axis in the τ_1-plane.

On the other hand, the cut w-plane is mapped onto the upper half-plane by the transformation $(w/\varphi_0)^{1/2} = t$ [at each point the argument of w/φ_0 is decreased by half and the points of the cut $w = \varphi_0$ map to the points $t = \pm 1$ (Fig. 6)]. Now, it is necessary to map the upper half-plane τ_1 so that the points $D(t = \infty)$, $B(t = -1)$, $C(t = 0)$, $A(t = 1)$ of the t-plane are mapped to

$$D(\tau_1 = -1), \qquad B(\tau_1 = 0), \qquad C(\tau_1 = 1), \qquad A(\tau_1 = \infty)$$

of the τ-plane; it is sufficient to put

$$\tau_1 = \tau^2 = \frac{1 + t}{1 - t} \quad . \tag{1.22}$$

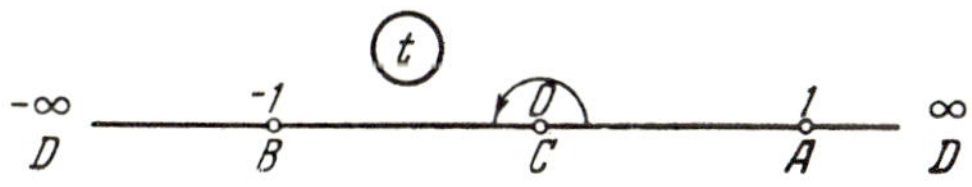

Fig. 6

In accordance with Eq. (1.21),

$$\left(\frac{\zeta - 1}{\zeta + 1}\right)^2 = \frac{1 + (w/\varphi_o)^{1/2}}{1 - (w/\varphi_o)^{1/2}} .$$

On solving this equation for ζ, we find

$$\zeta = \frac{\left[1 - (w_o/\varphi_o)^{1/2}\right]^{1/2} + \left[1 + (w/\varphi_o)^{1/2}\right]^{1/2}}{\left[1 - (w/\varphi_o)^{1/2}\right]^{1/2} - \left[1 + (w/\varphi_o)^{1/2}\right]^{1/2}}$$

$$= - \left(\frac{\varphi_o}{w}\right)^{1/2} - \left(\frac{\varphi_o}{w} - 1\right)^{1/2} , \qquad (1.23)$$

where the radicals are positive on AC. In order to obtain the values of ζ at any point in the flow it is necessary each time to consider the following: what value do the radicals have under the mapping of the points located on AC? For these points, Eq. (1.23) is easily checked directly. The function ζ obtained from Eq. (1.23) is analytic everywhere except at the cut CD. Consequently, it remains only to check the boundary conditions or, equivalently, the correspondence of Eq. (1.23) with our given Figs. 2 and 3.

In accordance with Eq. (1.23) ζ can be presented in the form

$$\zeta = - \left(\frac{\varphi_o}{w}\right)^{1/2} \exp\left[\frac{i}{2} \arg \frac{\varphi_o}{w}\right]$$

$$- \left(\frac{|\varphi_o - w|}{|w|}\right)^{1/2} \exp\left[\frac{i}{2} \arg \frac{\varphi_o - w}{w}\right] . \qquad (1.24)$$

An analysis of this equation shows:

1. On AC (i.e., for $0 \leqq w \leqq \varphi_o$) we have $\arg w = 0$; $|w| = w$; $\arg(\varphi_o - w) = 0$; and $|\varphi_o - w| = \varphi_o - w$. It follows, of course, that Eq. (1.24) completely agrees with Eq. (1.23). Along the upper border of the cut AC, the function ζ is real and changes from $-\infty$ (where $w = 0$) to -1 (where $w = \varphi_o$). Under these changes the velocity v varies from 0 to v_o.
2. We now examine the difference $(\varphi_o - w)$ in the neighborhood of the point A. This difference is represented by a vector, the origin of which is located at H and the end at A (see Fig. 2). On AC, $(\varphi_o - w)$ is real and positive. As the point H passes in the clockwise direction on an infinitesimal semicircle about A, the argument of $(\varphi_o - w)$ decreases by π and becomes $-\pi$. On the other hand, on AD, $|\varphi_o - w| = w - \varphi_o$. Thus, Eq. (1.24) gives on AD,

$$\zeta = -\left(\frac{\varphi_o}{w}\right)^{1/2} + i\left(\frac{w - \varphi_o}{w}\right)^{1/2} . \qquad (1.25)$$

From Eq. (1.25) it is easy to see that, with the movement of w along the upper border of the cut AD, ζ moves on the quadrant AD of the circle $|\zeta| = 1$ (Fig. 3). Actually, on AD,

$$|\zeta|^2 = \left[-\left(\frac{\psi_o}{w}\right)^{1/2}\right]^2 + 1 - \frac{\varphi_o}{w} = 1 .$$

In accordance with this, when $w = \varphi_o$, we have $\zeta = -1$, and when $w = \infty$, we have $\zeta = i$. It is scarcely necessary to remind the reader that $|\zeta| = 1$ represents the physical condition that the absolute value of the velocity is equal to a constant value v_o.

3. If we pass around the point C in a counterclockwise direction on a circle of infinitesimal radius (i.e., we pass onto CB from AC), the argument of the vector w, having its origin in C and its end at K (Fig. 2), increases by 2π. It follows that Eq. (1.24) gives, on CB,

$$\zeta = \left(\frac{\varphi_o}{w}\right)^{1/2} + \left(\frac{\varphi_o - w}{w}\right)^{1/2} \quad ; \qquad (1.26)$$

Thus, it is evident that, during the change of w from 0 to φ_o, the value of ζ is real and decreases from ∞ to 1, as shown in Fig. 3.

4. The analysis of the behavior of ζ in the neighborhood of B is substantially the same as the above analysis of its behavior in the neighborhood of A. On BD

$$|\varphi_o - w| = w - \varphi_o \quad , \qquad \arg(\varphi_o - w) = \pi \quad ;$$

and Eq. (1.24) gives

$$\zeta = \left(\frac{\varphi_o}{w}\right)^{1/2} + i\left(\frac{w - \varphi_o}{w}\right)^{1/2} \quad ,$$

i.e., it leads to Eq. (1.23). Hence, on BD (in accordance with Fig. 3),

$$|\zeta|^2 = \frac{\varphi_o}{w} + 1 - \frac{\varphi_o}{w} = 1 \quad ,$$

i.e., the boundary condition $dw/dz = v_o$ is satisfied.

Thus, our direct check confirms the validity of Eq. (1.23). We will see now that, with the above equations, it is possible to compute the pressure on the plate and to find the geometric elements of the flow--the length of the plate and the equations of the free streamlines. It will also be shown that, because $\zeta(w)$ and therefore $z(w)$ are known, it is not necessary to invert $z(w)$. The solution can be fully determined in terms of the following parameters: ρ--the density of the fluid; p_o, v_o--the pressure and velocity at infinity, and ℓ--the length of the plate. However, instead of ℓ the quantity φ_o appears in the equations, thus making it necessary to eliminate φ_o. For this purpose we compute the length of the plate using Eqs. (1.20) and (1.23). It is obvious that

$$-\frac{\ell}{2} = \frac{1}{v_o}\int_0^{\varphi_o} \zeta \, dw = -\frac{1}{v_o}\int_0^{\varphi_o}\left[\left(\frac{\varphi_o}{w}\right)^{1/2} + \left(\frac{\varphi_o}{w} - 1\right)^{1/2}\right] dw \quad . \tag{1.27}$$

By putting $w/\varphi_o = t^2$, we easily find that

$$\frac{\ell}{2} = 2\,\frac{\varphi_o}{v_o}\int_0^1 [1 + (1 - t^2)^{1/2}]\, dt \quad , \tag{1.28}$$

from which we obtain

$$\ell = 4\,\frac{\varphi_o}{v_o}\left[t + \frac{1}{2}\,t(1 - t^2)^{1/2} + \frac{1}{2}\arcsin t\right]_0^1 = 4\,\frac{\varphi_o}{v_o}\left(1 + \frac{\pi}{4}\right)$$

or

$$\varphi_o = \frac{\ell v_o}{4 + \pi} \quad . \tag{1.29}$$

The pressure p is found by using the Bernoulli theorem

$$p - p_o = \frac{\rho}{2}\left(v_o^2 - v^2\right) = \frac{\rho}{2} v_o^2 \left(1 - \frac{1}{|\zeta|^2}\right) . \qquad (1.30)$$

In our case, in accordance with Eq. (1.23), Eq. (1.30) takes the form

$$p - p_o = \frac{\rho v_o^2}{2}\left[1 - \frac{1}{\left\{(\varphi_o/w)^{1/2} + [(\varphi_o/w) - 1]^{1/2}\right\}^2}\right] . \qquad (1.31)$$

The total pressure force P on the plate is given by the integral

$$P = \int_{-\ell/2}^{\ell/2} (p - p_o)\, dx . \qquad (1.32)$$

If we consider the symmetry of the flow and the fact that along the plate $\zeta dw = v_o dx$, then, from Eqs. (1.23) and (1.31) it follows that

$$P = \frac{2}{v_o} \int_{\varphi_o}^{0} (p - p_o)\zeta\, dw$$

$$= \rho v_o \int_0^{\varphi_o} \left[\left(\frac{\varphi_o}{w}\right)^{1/2} + \left(\frac{\varphi_o}{w} - 1\right)^{1/2}\right]\left[1 - \left\{\left(\frac{\varphi_o}{w}\right)^{1/2} + \left(\frac{\varphi_o}{w} - 1\right)^{1/2}\right\}^{-2}\right] dw$$

$$= \rho v_o \int_0^{\varphi_o} \left[\left(\frac{\varphi_o}{w}\right)^{1/2} + \left(\frac{\varphi_o}{w} - 1\right)^{1/2} - \left\{\left(\frac{\varphi_o}{w}\right)^{1/2} + \left(\frac{\varphi_o}{w} - 1\right)^{1/2}\right\}^{-1}\right] dw$$

$$= \rho v_o \int_0^{\varphi_o} \left[\left(\frac{\varphi_o}{w}\right)^{1/2} + \left(\frac{\varphi_o}{w} - 1\right)^{1/2} - \left\{\left(\frac{\varphi_o}{w}\right)^{1/2} - \left(\frac{\varphi_o}{w} - 1\right)^{1/2}\right\}\right] dw$$

$$= 2\rho v_o \int_0^{\varphi_o} \left(\frac{\varphi_o}{w} - 1\right)^{1/2} dw .$$

This elementary integral has already been evaluated [see Eq. (1.27)]. By taking advantage of this fact, we can write immediately

$$P = \pi\rho v_o\varphi_o \tag{1.33}$$

or, by Eq. (1.29),

$$P = \frac{1}{2}\rho v_o^2 \ell \frac{2\pi}{4+\pi} . \tag{1.34}$$

The coefficient $2\pi/(4 + \pi) \approx 0.88$ is called the drag coefficient of the plate. In order to find the location of some streamline $\psi = \psi_o$, it is sufficient to evaluate the integral that occurs in Eq. (1.20). We put $w = \varphi + i\psi_o$ in Eq. (1.20) and, after separating the real and imaginary parts, we find the equation of a streamline in a parametric form to be

$$x = x(\varphi), \qquad y = y(\varphi) .$$

At this time it is not necessary to carry out this operation in detail. We extract only the result of the integration of Eq. (1.20), so that the difficulty of inverting $z = z(w)$, even for the very simple problem presented here, can be clearly seen. It follows from Eq. (1.20) that on AC

$$z = \frac{\varphi_o}{v_o}\left[2\left(\frac{w}{\varphi_o}\right)^{1/2} + \left(\frac{w}{\varphi_o}\right)^{1/2}\left(1 - \frac{w}{\varphi_o}\right)^{1/2} + \arcsin\left(\frac{w}{\varphi_o}\right)^{1/2}\right] . \tag{1.35}$$

Obviously, w cannot be expressed in an explicit way in terms of elementary functions of z.

E. ZHUKOVSKII'S METHOD

After the works of Kirchhoff and Helmholtz, the next big step ahead was taken in 1890 by Zhukovskii [10]. The Zhukovskii method is concerned with the case in which the region occupied by the fluid flow is simply connected, and the solid walls that bound the flow consist of a finite number of straight lines. Instead of using $\zeta = v_o dz/dw$, where v_o is the velocity on the surface of the jet, Zhukovskii introduced

$$\omega = \ln \zeta = - \ln \frac{dw}{v_o dz} = - \ln \frac{v}{v_o} + i\theta \quad , \qquad (1.36)$$

where θ is the angle between the velocity and the x-axis.

Furthermore, Zhukovskii applied the following valuable method. Instead of finding the relation between ω and w directly, he expressed both functions in terms of a parametric variable t that varies over the upper half-plane. If $\omega(t)$ and $w(t)$ are known, it is then possible, by eliminating t, to obtain a solution by the Kirchhoff method. However, the elimination of t is sometimes quite difficult, and actually unnecessary. From knowledge of $\omega(t)$ and $w(t)$ it is possible to compute, through the parameter t, both the pressure in the fluid and the geometric elements of the flow. For these calculations it is sufficient to find for each t the position of the point in the z-plane and the velocity at this point--i.e., to determine $\zeta(t)$ and $z(t)$. This is easily done because

$$\zeta = e^{\omega(t)} \quad ; \qquad z = \frac{1}{v_o} \int \zeta \, dw = \frac{1}{v_o} \int e^{\omega} \frac{dw}{dt} \, dt \ . \qquad (1.37)$$

Now we will examine in detail the ideas contained in the method introduced by Zhukovskii. As we mentioned before, the boundaries of the region of change of w consist of straight lines on which $\psi = \text{const}$. On the other hand, when the solid walls consist of straight lines, then the boundaries of the region of change of ω also consist of straight lines, since along the free surfaces the real part of ω is constant and along the walls its imaginary part is constant. Therefore, the mapping of the regions of change of w and ω onto the upper half-plane of the parametric variable t can be accomplished by the Schwarz-Christoffel formula (see, e.g., [3,4]). This formula was first applied to jet theory by Michell [11]. Zhukovskii, without using the Schwarz-Christoffel formula, indicated a general form that gave the desired relations for $w(t)$ and $\omega(t)$ for a large class of problems considered by him.* Thus the introduction of ω makes the method of finding the general solution to many problems so clear that the main difficulties lie in the determination of the constants which enter into the solution.

Another advantage of Zhukovskii's method, especially stressed in his monograph [10], is that the applicability of the method does not depend on the number of critical points--i.e., points at which the velocity is equal to zero. (Sketches of typical flows are presented in Figs. 121, 122, and 144.) It is evident that if in the region of the flow there are several critical points, then in the region of change of ζ these points correspond to only one point, $\zeta = \infty$. Thus, the region of change of ζ will not be contained on a single

*Zhukovskii gave an elegant geometric interpretation of his formulas, which will not be expressed here because it does not make the solution of the problems easier. The formulas alone will be presented at the end of this section.

sheet. The problem of finding the conformal transformations of these regions is difficult because of the complicated geometric configuration. On the other hand, the Schwarz-Christoffel formula is suitable for a polygon with any number of sides, each one of which corresponds to a jet or a solid wall; furthermore, on a wall it is possible to have any number of critical points.

Working with his method, Zhukovskii recreated the solutions of all the specific problems that had been treated by his predecessors and solved many new problems that had presented difficulties when solution was attempted by the Kirchhoff method.

We will now use Zhukovskii's method to obtain the solution to the problem presented above, concerned with jet flow around a plate. It is easy to see that the mapping of the region of change of w (Fig. 2) to the region of change of t (Fig. 6)* is given by the formula

$$w = \varphi_o t^2 \quad . \tag{1.38}$$

The function w is analytic everywhere in the upper half t-plane. On the real t-axis, w is positive. The conformality of the mapping breaks down only at the points $t = 0$ and $t = \infty$ because dw/dt is zero at the first of these points and is infinite at the second. Under these conditions, when we pass around the point $t = 0$ in the upper half-plane on a semicircle with an infinitesimal radius, the argument of w changes by 2π. Thus, the upper border of the cut, made along the positive, real semi-axis in the w-plane, corresponds to the positive real semi-axis in the t-plane; the

*We note now that the corresponding points of the mapped regions are designated on different figures by the same letters.

lower border of the cut corresponds to the negative, real semi-axis in the t-plane. Note that, in the neighborhood of $t = 0$,

$$\frac{dw}{dt} = 2\varphi_o t = O(t) \quad , \tag{1.39}$$

where, as always, the symbol $O(t)$ represents a magnitude of the order of t.

We examine now the region of change of w. Along the streamline BD the velocity $v = v_o$; hence, $\ln (v_o/v) = 0$. On the other hand, θ changes from 0 to $i(\pi/2)$ (Fig. 7). Similarly, we find that along DA, w changes from $i(\pi/2)$ to $i\pi$. On CB, ω is real and changes from ∞ at C to 0 at B. Along AC the imaginary part of ω is constant and equal to π, and the real part changes from 0 to ∞. In passing through C the magnitude of θ changes abruptly. Thus, the region of change of ω is represented by a semi-infinite strip, which can be treated as a triangle ABC, whose vertex C is at infinity.

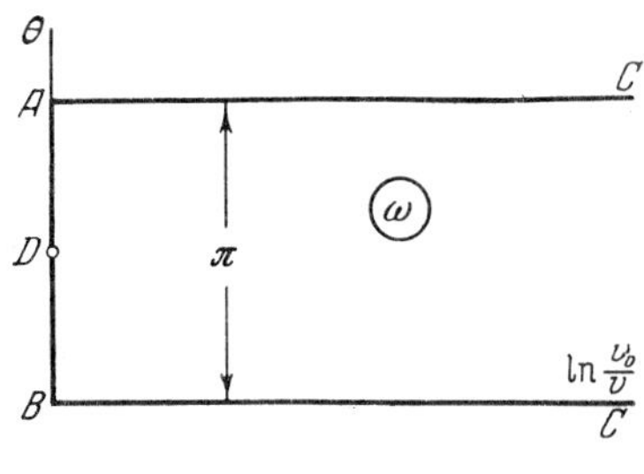

Fig. 7

To obtain the mapping of the triangle ABC (Fig. 7) onto the upper half of the t-plane (Fig. 6), it is possible to use the Schwarz-Christoffel formula [3,4]. For the convenience of the reader we will give the formula in its general form. Assume that in the w-plane there exists a polygon with interior angles $\alpha_1, \alpha_2, \ldots, \alpha_n$, none of which exceeds 2π. The mapping of the interior of the polygon onto the upper half-plane is accomplished by

$$\omega = C_1 \int (t - t_1)^{(\alpha_1/\pi)-1} (t - t_2)^{(\alpha_2/\pi)-1} \ldots (t - t_n)^{(\alpha_n/\pi)-1} dt + C_2 . \tag{1.40}$$

The perimeter of the polygon corresponds to the entire real axis in the t-plane whose points $t_1, t_2, t_3, \ldots, t_n$ correspond to the vertices of the polygon; the constants C_1 and C_2 depend on the location and orientation of the polygon on the ω-plane. If $t_k = \infty$, then the factor $(t-t_n)^{(\alpha_k/\pi)-1}$ is absent in the product standing under the integral sign in Eq. (1.40). In the right side of Eq. (1.40) there are $2n+3$ independent parameters:

1. n real numbers $t_1, t_2, \ldots, t_n$
2. $n-1$ of the n angles $\alpha_1, \alpha_2, \ldots, \alpha_n$ that are related by the known geometric relation

$$\alpha_1 + \alpha_2 + \ldots + \alpha_n = (n - 2)\pi$$

3. four real constants, defined by the two complex constants C_1 and C_2.

Since the aspect and position of the polygon is fully determined if the $2n$ coordinates of the vertices are given, we conclude that, when using the Schwarz-Christoffel formula, three parameters may be arbitrarily prescribed. For instance, t_1, t_2, and t_3 may be given and the conformal transformation will be fully determined (see, e.g., [3,4]).

We return now to the problem that we are solving. The angles of the triangle at the vertices A, B, and C are equal to $\pi/2$, $\pi/2$, and 0 respectively. In accordance with the above, we assume that, at the vertices of the triangle, t has the values: $t_A = 1$, $t_B = -1$, and $t_C = 0$. Thus Eq. (1.39) gives

$$\omega(t) = C_1 \int \frac{dt}{t(t^2 - 1)^{1/2}} + C_2 \quad .$$

The constants C_1 and C_2 are determined as follows: at point A, $\omega(1) = \pi i$; hence,

$$\omega(t) = C_1 \int_1^t \frac{dt}{t(t^2 - 1)^{1/2}} + \pi i \quad .$$

Upon evaluating the integral, we obtain

$$\omega(t) = C_1 \left(-\arcsin \frac{1}{t} + \frac{\pi}{2}\right) + \pi i \quad . \tag{1.41}$$

From Figs. 6 and 7 it is seen that, at point B, $\omega(-1) = 0$. Accordingly, Eq. (1.41) gives $C_1 = -i$. Thus,

$$\omega(t) = i \arcsin \frac{1}{t} + \frac{\pi i}{2} \quad . \tag{1.42}$$

By using known formulas relating the logarithmic function with the inverse of the trigonometric functions [4], Eq. (1.42) can be presented in another form as

$$\omega(t) = \ln \left[\left(1 - \frac{1}{t^2}\right)^{1/2} + \frac{i}{t}\right] + \frac{\pi i}{2} \quad . \tag{1.43}$$

The equivalence of Eqs. (1.42) and (1.43) can be easily checked by direct differentiation. With t real and less than 1 in absolute value, $\omega(t)$ can be conveniently given as

$$\left.\begin{aligned} \omega(t) &= \ln \frac{1 + (1 - t^2)^{1/2}}{t} + \pi i \ , \qquad & 0 < t \leqq 1 \ , \\ \omega(t) &= \ln \frac{1 + (1 - t^2)^{1/2}}{-t} \ , \qquad & 0 > t \geqq -1 \ . \end{aligned}\right\} \tag{1.44}$$

From Eqs. (1.44) and (1.36) it follows that

$$\frac{dw}{v_o dz} = \frac{(1 - t^2)^{1/2} - 1}{t} = - \frac{t}{(1 - t^2)^{1/2} + 1} \qquad (1.45)$$

or, according to Eq. (1.38)

$$\zeta = \frac{v_o dz}{dw} = \frac{t}{(1 - t^2)^{1/2} - 1} = - \frac{(1 - t^2)^{1/2} + 1}{t}$$

$$= - \left(\frac{\varphi_o}{w}\right)^{1/2} - \left(\frac{\varphi_o}{w} - 1\right)^{1/2} , \qquad (1.46)$$

which coincides with Eq. (1.23). Further computation of the length of the plate and of the pressure force on the plate can be carried out either in the same way (as in Section D) or directly by integration in terms of the parametric variable t. As an example, we compute the length of the plate ℓ by direct integration.

From Eq. (1.38) and (1.46) it follows that

$$z = \int \frac{dz}{dw} \frac{dw}{dt} dt = - \frac{2\varphi_o}{v_o} \int [(1 - t^2)^{1/2} + 1] dt \quad .$$

By integrating along AC (Fig. 1) we find half of the plate length. As was pointed out above (see also Fig. 6), the values of t at A and C are equal to 1 and 0, respectively. Thus

$$\frac{\ell}{2} = - \frac{2\varphi_o}{v_o} \int_1^0 [(1 - t^2)^{1/2} + 1] dt \quad .$$

This equation agrees with Eq. (1.28) and after integration gives, as in Section D, for the length of the plate

$$\ell = 4 \frac{\varphi_o}{v_o}\left(1 + \frac{\pi}{4}\right) .$$

By using the Bernoulli integral in the same manner, it is possible to find the pressure force P on the plate. From Eqs. (1.26) and (1.43), by considering the symmetry of the flows, we have

$$P = \int_1^{-1} (p - p_o) \frac{dz}{dw}\frac{dw}{dt}\, dt = 2 \int_1^0 \frac{\rho v_o^2}{2}\left(1 - \frac{1}{\zeta^2}\right)\frac{1}{v_o}\,\zeta\,\frac{dw}{dt}\, dt .$$

By combining the different expressions for ζ given by Eq. (1.46), we obtain

$$P = 2\rho v_o \varphi_o \int_0^1 \left[1 - \frac{1 - (1 - t^2)^{1/2}}{1 + (1 - t^2)^{1/2}}\right][(1 - t^2)^{1/2} + 1]\, dt ,$$

or

$$P = 4\rho v_o \varphi_o \int_0^1 (1 - t^2)^{1/2}\, dt = \pi\rho v_o \varphi_o ,$$

which fully agrees with Eq. (1.28). It is worth noting the coincidence that the integrals in Section D were actually computed with the help of the change of variables from ω to t.

We examine now the example of a jet flow from an orifice in a plane (Fig. 8). Let the stream function $\psi = 0$ on the boundary streamline CBD; on the other boundary streamline CAD, $\psi = -q$. On the surfaces AD and BD, of the jet, the absolute value of the velocity is v_o. With movement downstream along a streamline the velocity potential changes from $-\infty$ to ∞. In this way, we see that the region of change of

w consists of a strip (Fig. 9) of width q. The mapping of this strip onto the upper half-plane of the variable t (Fig. 6) is accomplished by

$$w = \frac{q}{\pi} \ln t - qi \quad . \tag{1.47}$$

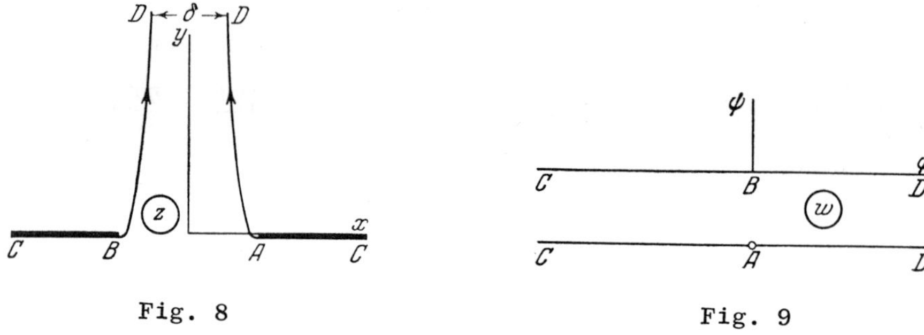

Fig. 8

Fig. 9

On CAD the imaginary part of w is equal to $-q$, and the real part changes from $-\infty$ at $t = 0$ to $+\infty$ at $t = \infty$. When passing in a counterclockwise direction around the point $t = 0$ along an infinitesimal semicircle (see Fig. 6), the complex potential

$$w = \frac{q}{\pi} [\ln |t| + i \arg t] - qi$$

changes by qi; along CBD the complex potential $w = (q/\pi) \ln |t| = \varphi$ will be real, and φ will change from $-\infty$ at $t = 0$ to $+\infty$ at $t = -\infty$. In the upper half-plane, w is analytic. Equation (1.47) can be obtained from the Schwarz-Christoffel Eq. (1.40) by considering the strip ABCC'B'A' as a figure with only two corners. Equation (1.47) can also be interpreted from the hydrodynamic point of view. In the flow plane (Fig. 8) there is a source at infinity (at point C) and a sink at point D. The function $w(t)$, determined by Eq. (1.47), can be considered a complex potential of the flow produced by a sink at infinity (point D) and a source at the origin C (Fig. 6). Equation (1.47) can be obtained directly from Eq. (1.13) up to a constant difference qi by replacing z by t and putting $z_1 = \overline{z_1} = 0$.

We find now the function $\omega = \ln (v_o/v) + i\theta$. On the free surfaces BD and AD, $\text{Re}\,\omega = \ln (v_o/v) = 0$. On the wall BC, $\text{Im}\,\omega = 0$, and on the wall CA, $\text{Im}\,\omega = \pi$ (see Fig. 8). Since the velocity v is equal to 0 at infinity (point C), the region of change of ω will be a semi-infinite strip (Fig. 7) coinciding exactly with the region of change of w for the problem of flow around a plate. Because of this $\omega(t)$ or dw/dz can be obtained by taking advantage of Eqs. (1.42) - (1.44) or (1.45) to give

$$\frac{dw}{v_o dz} = \frac{(1 - t^2)^{1/2} - 1}{t} = \frac{-t}{(1 - t^2)^{1/2} + 1} \quad . \tag{1.48}$$

The equations obtained permit us to find the most interesting characteristic value of our problem--the coefficient of contraction of the jet which is equal to the ratio of the width of the jet at infinity to the width of the aperture AB in the wall. From Eqs. (1.47) and (1.48) we have

$$dz = dx + i\,dy = -\frac{q}{\pi v_o}\,[(1 - t^2)^{1/2} + 1]\,\frac{dt}{t^2} \quad . \tag{1.49}$$

In order to find a streamline location it is sufficient to integrate Eq. (1.49) along this streamline and, after separating the real and imaginary parts, to find the equation for the streamline in a parametric form. Considering, for example, the streamline BD, we see that, along this line, t is real and varies from -1 to $-\infty$. Under these conditions, $(1 - t^2)^{1/2}$ is a purely imaginary quantity and Eq. (1.49) gives

$$dx = -\frac{q}{\pi v_o} \frac{dt}{t^2} \quad . \tag{1.50}$$

The width δ of the jet at infinity is equal to the ratio of the discharge q to the velocity on the jet v_o so $\delta = q/v_o$. From the symmetry of the flow picture with respect to the y-axis, it follows that BA is equal to the sum of twice the projection of the streamline on the x-axis and the width of the jet at infinity δ; thus, according to Eq. (1.50), we have

$$BA = \delta + \frac{2\delta}{\pi} \int_{-1}^{-\infty} \frac{-dt}{t^2} = \delta \left(1 + \frac{2}{\pi}\right) ,$$

from which it may be deduced that the coefficient of contraction k_o is

$$k_o = \frac{\delta}{BA} = \frac{\pi}{2 + \pi} \approx 0.61 \quad . \tag{1.51}$$

Let us consider yet one more example. Let a jet with a free surface flow against an infinite plate (Fig. 10), installed close to the surface of the jet. The jet bifurcates when it meets the plate. A jet with a finite flowrate moves up the plate while a jet containing an infinite amount of fluid passes under the plate. In Chapter VII, the reader will see that the example treated here corresponds to the problem of a planing plate. There, computations of the drag, the lift, and the position of the center of pressure on the planing plate

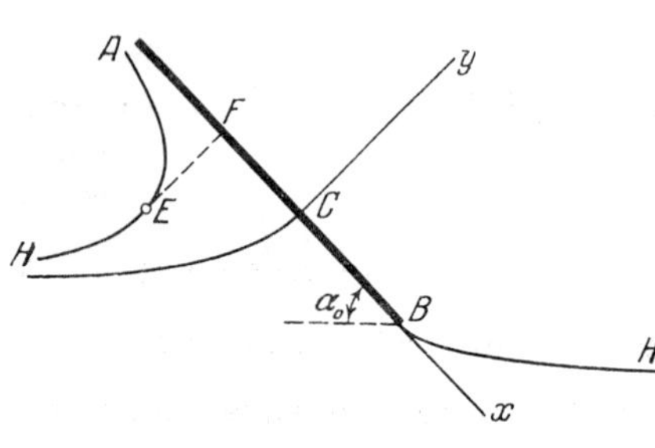

Fig. 10

will be carried out. Now, we are interested only in finding ω and $dw/v_o dz$ in a parametric form, which will help us in our analysis of the method of singular points to be given below.

Let the stream function $\psi = 0$ on the bifurcated streamline HCA and HCB. Then on HA the stream function $\psi = \delta v_o$, where v_o is the velocity on the free surface and δ is the width of the jet at infinity. If we put $\varphi = \varphi_o$ at point C, then along CA and CBH φ will change from φ_o to infinity. Therefore, the region of change of w will be a half-plane with a cut that corresponds to the plate and the free surface BH (Fig. 11).

It is easy to see that the conformal transformation of the region of change of w (Fig. 11) onto the upper half t-plane (Fig. 12)* is given by

$$w = \frac{N}{t + h} - \frac{\delta v_o}{\pi} \ln \frac{1 - t}{t + h} \quad . \tag{1.52}$$

On the upper half-plane, $w(t)$ is an analytic function. Along ACBH $(-h < t < 1)$, $w(t)$ is real. As the point $t = -1$ is approached, the velocity potential $\varphi = \text{Re}\, w \to +\infty$.

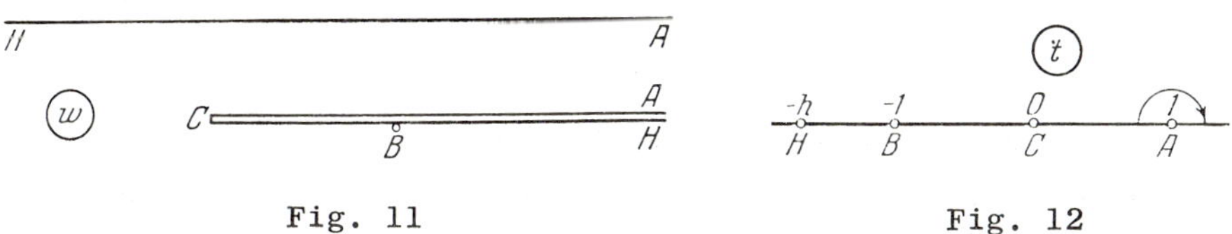

Fig. 11 Fig. 12

*Recall that on the boundaries of the t-plane the position of three points can be chosen arbitrarily. Here it is again assumed that the points B, C, and A correspond to the points $t = -1$, $t = 0$, $t = 1$.

If $N > 0$, then as $t \to -h + 0$ the velocity potential $\varphi \to +\infty$, and as $t \to -h - 0$ the velocity potential $\varphi \to -\infty$. When passing around $t = 1$ in a clockwise direction on an infinitesimal semicircle, $\ln(1-t)$ becomes $\ln(t-1) - \pi i$, from which, with $t > 1$, we obtain

$$w = \frac{N}{t + h} - \frac{\delta v_o}{\pi} \ln \frac{t - 1}{t + h} + i\, \delta v_o \quad . \tag{1.53}$$

i.e., on HA, $\operatorname{Im} w = \psi$ has a constant value δv_o. Since the flowrate of fluid in the jet $\psi = \delta v_o$, δ represents the width of the jet at infinity.

At point C, where $t = 0$, we have

$$w(0) = \varphi_o = \frac{N}{h} + \frac{\delta v_o}{\pi} \ln h \quad .$$

Thus, $w(t)$, determined by Eq. (1.52) or (1.53), is analytic and satisfies all the boundary conditions. However, the transformation of $w(t)$ in the neighborhood of C is not conformal, as can be seen from Figs. 11 and 12. Because of this nonconformality at C,

$$\left(\frac{dw}{dt}\right)_{t=0} = 0 \quad . \tag{1.54}$$

We are easily convinced of this if we follow the turning of the vectors $w(t) - w(0)$ and t when they pass around C in a counterclockwise direction with t infinitely small. It is obvious that the argument of $w(t) - w(0) = \Delta w$ increases by 2π while the argument of $\Delta t = t - 0$ increases only by π (see Figs. 11 and 12). Thus, in the neighborhood of $t = 0$,

$$w(t) - w(0) = O(t^2) \quad ,$$

from which it follows that

$$\frac{dw}{dt} = o(t) \quad .^{*} \tag{1.55}$$

From Eq. (1.54) it is easy to find N, which until now was unknown, since

$$\left[\frac{dw}{dt}\right]_{t=0} = \left[-\frac{N}{(t+h)^2} + \frac{\delta v_o}{\pi}\left(\frac{1}{1-t} + \frac{1}{t+h}\right)\right]_{t=0} = 0 \quad .$$

Thus,

$$N = \frac{\delta v_o}{\pi} h(1+h) \quad .$$

From this result, Eq. (1.52) can be rewritten in the form

$$w = \frac{\delta v_o}{\pi}\left[\frac{h(1+h)}{t+h} - \ell n \frac{1-t}{t+h}\right] \quad . \tag{1.56}$$

Equation (1.56) can be obtained also by use of the Schwarz-Christoffel Eq. (1.40). But here we must generalize the understanding of a polygon and consider that, in the triangle ACH (Fig. 11), the angles of the vertices A and C are equal to 0 and 2π respectively and that the angle at vertex H is equal to $-\pi$ because the sum of the interior angles of a triangle is π (see [12 or Ch. II § 38 of 4]). Then Eq. (1.40), with an obvious change of notation, gives

$$w(t) = C_1 \int (t+h)^{-2}\, t(1-t)^{-1}\, dt + C_2 \quad .$$

---

*It is recommended that the reader compare Eqs. (1.41) and (1.55) and note the equality of the order of the derivatives dw/dt when $t \to 0$ in the first example and the example considered here.

The evaluation of this integral with a proper choice of constants C_1 and C_2 brings us again to Eq. (1.56).

We turn now to the consideration of the ω function. Its region of change is the same as that given in Fig. 7 for the two preceding problems. The function $\omega(t)$ does not depend on the position of H. Points B, C, and A are located in Fig. 12 in the same way as in Fig. 6. Then, $\omega(t)$ is determined, as before, by Eq. (1.42), or by (1.43) and (1.44), and $dw/v_o dz$ by Eq. (1.45).

By using Eq. (1.45) it is easy to find the direction of the flow at infinity. On passing around $t = -1$ (point B) in a counterclockwise direction on an infinitesimal semicircle, we find that, on BH,

$$\frac{dw}{v_o dz} = e^{-i\theta} = -\frac{1}{t} + i\,\frac{(t^2 - 1)^{1/2}}{t} \; . \qquad (1.57)$$

It follows that θ (the angle of inclination of the velocity on the free surface BH with respect to the x-axis) is

$$\theta = \arctan\,(t^2 - 1)^{1/2}$$

At the point at infinity H, $t = -h$; hence, the angle of inclination θ_∞ at infinity is

$$\theta_\infty = \arctan\,(h^2 - 1)^{1/2} \; . \qquad (1.58)$$

This represents the angle of attack of the plate: $\alpha_o = \theta_\infty$.

We could map the regions of change of w and ω onto the upper half-plane in another way by assuming that, as before, A and B correspond to ± 1 and that H corresponds to a point at infinity in the t_1-plane. Then, it is possible to show that

$$w(t_1) = -Mt_1 - \frac{v_o \delta}{\pi} \ln(1 - t_1) \quad , \qquad (1.59)$$

where M is a constant. Equation (1.59) may be checked directly by studying the change of $\text{Im}\, w$ as t_1 moves along the real axis. As a consequence of the flow asymmetry in the t_1-plane, C no longer corresponds to $t_1 = 0$, and it is necessary to find a new expression for ω in the t_1-plane.

Now we are prepared to undertake an analysis of Zhukovskii's general formulas. Even though they are equivalent to the Schwarz-Christoffel formula, an analysis of them is useful as a natural transition of Chaplygin's method.

Zhukovskii examined the class of problems in which $w(t)$ and $\omega(t)$ are determined by the following:

$$w(t) = F(t) + \alpha_1 \ln \frac{t - \gamma_1}{\beta_1} + \alpha_2 \ln \frac{t - \gamma_2}{\beta_2} + \alpha_3 \ln \frac{t - \gamma_3}{\beta_3} + \dots \quad , \qquad (1.60)$$

$$\omega(t) = m \int \frac{f(t)\, dt}{[(t - c_1)(t - c_2)(t - c_3) \dots]^{1/2}} \quad . \qquad (1.61)$$

In Eq. (1.60), $F(t)$ can have the form $Mt^2 + Nt$ or $[M/(t - a)^2] + [N/(t - a)]$, where all α_k, β_k, γ_k, as well as M and N, are real numbers. By comparison of Eq. (1.60) with those equations for w obtained during the solution of three particular problems considered above, it is clear that:

1. If the flow is bounded by one streamline that passes at a finite distance from the origin of the coordinates, then $M = 0$ and $F(t)$ is equal to Nt or $N/(t - a)$, depending of the place to which we map the point at infinity of the main flow--i.e., to $t = a$ or to $t = \infty$. We saw an example of such a flow in the analysis

of the planing-plate problem--see Eqs. (1.56) or (1.59). As a result of the above, we discover that, in passing around the point $t = a$ (or $t = \infty$), the argument of w changes by π; recall that, when $t \to a$ (or $t \to \infty$), then $w \to \infty$.

2. If the approaching flow covers the entire physical plane, as in the first problem considered, where an infinite flow passed around a plate (Fig. 1), then $M \neq 0$ and $F(t)$ has a pole of the second order. In passing around such a pole, the argument of w changes by 2π and, as $t \to a$ (or $t \to \infty$), $w \to \infty$.

3. To each point $t = \gamma_k$ there corresponds a point at infinity on a jet with a finite flowrate [see Eqs. (1.47) and (1.56) in the section concerning flow from an orifice or a planing plate].* In passing around a point at which w has a logarithmic singularity, the imaginary part of the logarithm experiences a jump that leads to a jump in ψ which is equal to the flowrate of the fluid in the jet.

Equation (1.60) may be interpreted hydrodynamically in the following way: since $w(t)$ is an analytic function of the complex variable t and $\operatorname{Im} w$ has constant values on all segments of the real axis between the singular points, w can be considered a complex potential of a flow in the t-plane that is produced by sources and sinks with finite or infinite discharges. The sources and sinks are located, obviously, on the real axis.

---

*In the case of the planing plate, we have at infinity (point H) the junction of two jets: one with a finite width and another with an infinite width.

In the Levi-Civita and Chaplygin methods, which will be considered later, the region of change of the parametric variable t is taken to be a region different from the upper half-plane (e.g., in the Levi-Civita method a semicircle of unit radius is chosen). In these methods, w is given the same hydrodynamic sense--i.e., $w(t)$ is imagined to be a complex potential of a flow in the domain of t.

Now we analyze Eq. (1.61). Here $f(t)$ represents an algebraic, rational function with real coefficients; the function can have simple poles on the real axis or at infinity. In the latter case the order of the infinity must be less than the order of the infinity in the radical in the denominator of Eq. (1.61), but not less than unity. This must be true since $\omega(t)$ can have infinite singularities only of logarithmic order that correspond to angular and critical points on the contours [cf., the further analysis of Eqs. (1.64) and (1.65) below]. The quantities c_1, c_2, c_3, ... are all real; m is equal to i or unity. Integration is accomplished on some contour located inside the region, from some constant point located on the real axis, to the variable point t. Since all the points at infinity and the branches of the function under the integral lie on the boundary of the region under consideration, the value of the integral does not depend on the path of integration. Along the real axis the function under the integral will be either real or imaginary, since each time a point $t = c_k$ is passed (more precisely, after passing around each one of these points on an infinitesimal semicircle in the upper half t-plane), the sign of the expression under the radical changes. The real and imaginary parts of $w(t)$ always change in this way, and we are successively on the straight walls or the free surface.

The $f(t)$ function can be given in the form

$$f(t) = f_1(t) + \frac{A_1}{t - a_1} + \frac{A_2}{t - a_2} + \frac{A_3}{t - a_3} + \ldots , \qquad (1.62)$$

where $f_1(t)$ is a polynomial. It is assumed that points a_1, a_2, a_3, ... are located on only those segments of the real axis that correspond to the walls.

In the neighborhood of $t = a_k$, $\omega(t)$, according to Eq. (1.61), has the form

$$\omega(t) = m \int_{t_o}^{a_k - \epsilon} \frac{f(t)\,dt}{[(t - c_1)(t - c_2)(t - c_3) \ldots]^{1/2}}$$

$$+ m \int_{a_k - \epsilon}^{t} \frac{f(t)\,dt}{[(t - c_1)(t - c_2)(t - c_3) \ldots]^{1/2}} , \qquad (1.63)$$

where ϵ is a very small, positive quantity. The first of these integrals has a constant value for a constant ϵ. If, in the second integral, we perform the integration along a semicircle of small radius ϵ with $\epsilon \to 0$, then this integral will give a jump in $\omega(t)$ as we pass through $t = a_k$. After computing this integral, we can show that, as we pass through a_k, the angle θ (which determines the direction of the velocity) experiences a finite jump. Since we know the limiting value of the integral as $\epsilon \to 0$ and $t \to a_k$, we can immediately set $t = a_k$ in the expression under the radical, and $f(t)$ can be replaced by the principal term of its expansion, Eq. (1.62) in powers to $t - a_k$. Thus, the jump in $\omega(t)$ at $t = a_k$ is equal to

$$\lim_{\epsilon \to 0} \frac{mA_k}{[(a_k - c_1)(a_k - c_2) \ldots]^{1/2}} \int_{a_k-\epsilon}^{a_k+\epsilon} \frac{dt}{t - a_k} = \Delta\omega \quad .$$

By putting $t - a_k = \epsilon \exp [i\sigma]$, where σ varies from π to 0, we find that

$$\Delta\omega = \frac{mA_k}{[(a_k - c_1)(a_k - c_2) \ldots]^{1/2}} \int_{\pi}^{0} i \, d\sigma$$

$$= - \frac{\pi i m A_k}{[(a_k - c_1)(a_k - c_2) \ldots]^{1/2}} \quad .$$

It follows that $\theta = \text{Im}\ \omega(t)$ changes suddenly during passage through $t = a_k$ along the wall of the vessel. Thus,

$$\Delta\theta = \frac{A_k m\pi}{[(a_k - c_1)(a_k - c_2) \ldots]^{1/2}} , \tag{1.64}$$

where $\Delta\theta$, by our conditions, is a real quantity.

By substituting $A_k/(t - a_k)$ for $f(t)$ in the second integral of Eq. (1.63) and replacing the expression under the radical by $(a_k - c_1)(a_k - c_2) \ldots$ the magnitude of the velocity in the neighborhood of $t = a_k$ can be computed from the relation

$$\ell n \frac{v_o}{v} = - \frac{\Delta\theta}{\pi} \ell n \left| t - a_k \right| + B \quad , \tag{1.65}$$

where B is a finite quantity. If $\Delta\theta > 0$, then $\ell n\ (v_o/v) \to +\infty$; thus $v = 0$ at $t = a_k$. With $\Delta\theta > 0$, there is a critical (stagnation) point at the vertex of the angle. With $\Delta\theta < 0$, the fluid passes around the corner through the greater of the two angles, and the velocity at the vertex of the corner is infinite (Fig. 13).

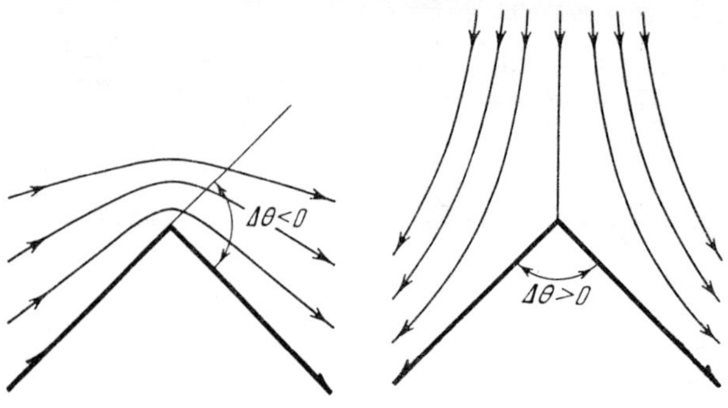

Fig. 13

Equations (1.60) and (1.61) give the general solution to problems of a particular type. To make numerical computations, it is necessary to express the mathematical parameters as functions of the geometric quantities for each particular problem--e.g., the angles, the length of the walls, and the distance between them. It is evident that, in a general case, it is quite difficult to find the resultant expressions. Therefore, the values of the parameters in Eqs. (1.60) and (1.61) are usually given and the corresponding geometric quantities are computed. Some examples of such computations are given later.

In the case of flow from vessels having straight walls, or in the case of flow around one polygonal obstacle, the Levi-Civita method is often used. For flow about a polygonal obstacle, Levi-Civita's method differs from Zhukovskii's method because the region of change of the parametric variable is taken to be a semicircle of unit radius. Although Levi-Civita's method, which first allowed solution of problems of flow around curved obstacles, came first historically, we postpone its discussion until Chapter IV and pass now to a discussion of the singular-point method.

F. CHAPLYGIN'S SINGULAR POINT METHOD

Chaplygin astonished his contemporaries with his ability to solve complicated hydrodynamic problems quickly. These were often two-dimensional problems in the theory of ideal, incompressible fluids, which can be solved by complex-variable theory. Chaplygin used the method of singular points and usually formed the solution of such problems in his mind; only afterward did he check the results that he obtained. Although he used the method systematically, Chaplygin himself never published a paper in which the method appeared as an understandable mathematical entity that could be attributed to him. The method of singular points and its application to jet theory are presented here in a separate section since, after its introduction by Chaplygin, this method has been widely used by both hydro- and aerodynamicists.

The singular-point method is based on an analysis of the behavior of the unknown complex-variable function; the objective is to find all of the function's zeros and singularities in the flow region and correspondingly in the region of change of the parametric variable. Any variety of regions may be chosen as the region of change of the parametric variable. There is great flexibility in this choice; it is necessary only that the boundaries of the region be composed of straight-line segments and arcs of circles in such a way that the whole region of the complex variable can be covered simply by the use of mirror images of the region of change. Usually this type of region is a semicircle, square, circle, strip, half-strip, rectangle, sector of a circle (half- or quarter-circle), etc. The advantage of choosing one of these regions of change is related to the particular singularities of each problem. If the region of change of the function is also bounded by straight lines and arcs of circles, then, by choosing one of the indicated regions of change of the parametric variable and by using the symmetry principle, it is possible to find all the zeros and singularities of the unknown function, as analytically extended to the whole plane of the parametric variable. Furthermore, it is necessary to construct a function with these zeros and singularities. In particular, if the singular points are poles and if we know the principal part of the function's expansion in the neighborhood of the poles, then we can construct the function without knowing its zeros. The Liouville Theorem assures the uniqueness of the result.

It is easy to see that the singular-point method is applicable when the walls that bound the fluid flow are represented by segments of straight lines (polygonal contours). Then, as was pointed out above (see Section E), the boundaries of the w and ω regions of change are also straight lines. In the case of polygonal contours, the boundaries of dw/v_0dz will consist of straight lines, corresponding to the walls,* and an arc of a unit radius circle on which $|dw/v_0dz| = 1$.

Chaplygin chose the unknown functions with a certain freedom; he sometimes used the ω function and sometimes dw/v_0dz. Instead of w, Chaplygin often looked only for its derivative in terms of the parametric variable. This approach proved to be sufficient for the computation of all geometric and hydrodynamic characteristics. It is not difficult to show that by introducing Eqs. (1.60) and (1.61), Zhukovskii was practically using a particular form of the singular-point method.

---

*Since on straight walls the argument of dw/v_0dz is constant, the walls correspond in the region of change of dw/v_0dz to rays that come from the origin of the coordinates.

Before attempting to solve a problem by the singular-point method, it is useful to list the types of singular points that are most frequently met in jet theory. Actually, we used all of the singularities in the previous section. In most cases, the types of singular points, located on the boundaries, will be the same for straight and curvilinear boundaries of the parametric-variable's regions.

Let $w(t)$ give a mapping of the region of change of w into the region of change of the parametric variable t; then:*

1. For a jet with infinite flowrate, $w(t)$ has poles of the first and second order (cf. 1. and 2., Section E, p.).
2. For a jet with finite flowrate, $w(t)$ has a logarithmic singularity (cf. 3., Section E, p. 42).
3. At those points where the wall forms an angle, $w(t)$ has a logarithmic singularity, and accordingly $dw(t)/dz = v_o e^{-\omega}$ becomes zero or infinite--see Eq. (1.65).
4. Assume there is a cut beginning at the point w_o of the w-plane corresponding to the bifurcation of the streamline. The point w_o maps onto a point in the auxiliary t-plane, and the tangent to the arc onto which the cut is mapped turns continuously at the point t_o. Then, in passing in a counterclockwise direction around point t_o on an infinitesimal contour, the $(t-t_o)$ vector turns through an angle π, and the $(w-w_o)$ vector in the w-plane turns through an angle 2π, (see, as an example, Figs. 2 and 4). The conformality of the mapping is violated and $w - w_o = O(t-t_o)^2$, while $dw/dt = O(t-t_o)$--i.e.,

*The listed points could alternatively be formulated and proved in the form of theorems.

$$\left(\frac{dw}{dt}\right)_{t=t_o} = 0 \quad .$$

Examples of these points are the C points in the problems considered above [see also Eqs. (1.38) and (1.54)]. These are the critical (stagnation) points, and the bifurcation of the streamline takes place there. Sometimes the bounding streamline may bifurcate at a noncritical point (see, as an example, point O on Fig. 41). In this case dw/dt will also become 0 at the point of the streamline bifurcation.

5. At those points where a junction of jets occurs, the conformality of the mapping of $\omega = \ln (v_o/v) + i\theta$ and $dw/v_o dz$ is frequently violated. Actually, the boundaries of the ω and $dw/v_o dz$ regions form a right angle at these points since the lines $\ln (v_o/v)$ = const. and the lines θ = const. are orthogonal to each other in the ω and $dw/v_o dz$ planes.* [As an example, in Eq. (1.61) these points of jet juncture correspond to points $t = c_1$, $t = c_2$, ... At these points dw/dt

*In the $dw/v_o dz$ plane the lines

$$\ln \frac{v_o}{v} = -\ln \left| \frac{dw}{v_o dz} \right| = \text{const.}$$

correspond to circular arcs with their centers at the coordinate origin, and the lines

$$\arg \left(\frac{dw}{v_o dz} \right) = \theta = \text{const.}$$

correspond to rays coming from the coordinate origin.

becomes infinite.] If we choose the t-plane so that those of its boundaries which correspond to the jet juncture regions form right angles, then at these juncture points there will not be a violation of the conformality of the mapping. Conversely, in the mapping functions, the singularities appear at such points where the conformality of the mapping is violated because the boundaries of the region of change of the parametric variable contain corners while the corresponding boundaries of the region of change of the unknown function do not.

As an example of the application of Chaplygin's method we consider the problem of flow around a plate (Fig. 1). We choose as a region of change of the parametric variable τ the right-hand upper quadrant (Fig. 14). The locations of points A, B, and C on the boundaries of the quadrant are chosen arbitrarily. The position of D and $w(\tau)$ must be determined as part of the solution.

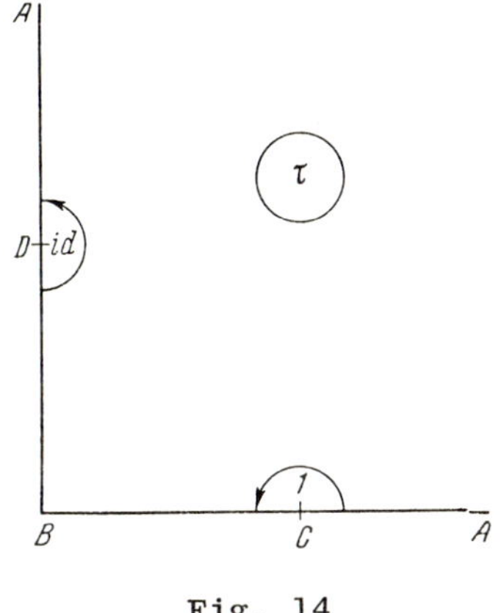

Fig. 14

The w function can be determined only up to an arbitrary constant. Therefore we can assume that at point C the complex potential is zero; then we have $\psi = 0$ everywhere on the bifurcated streamline. On this streamline it is not possible for w to be zero, since any movement along the streamline causes the potential φ to change monotonically. Furthermore, w cannot be equal to zero on the other streamlines, since there $\psi \neq 0$. Thus, the only zero of w must be at C where $\tau = 1$. Furthermore, at C the mapping is not conformal, since with passage around C on an infinitesimal semicircle in the t-plane the argument of $(\tau-1)$ changes by π (Fig. 14), while the corresponding change in the argument of w is 2π (cf. Fig. 2). In other words, the argument of $w(\tau)$ changes twice as fast as the argument of $(\tau-1)$ at point C.

The same property is possessed by $(\tau-1)^2$ and, in general, by any analytic function whose expansion in a Taylor series in powers of $(\tau-1)$ begins with a term containing $(\tau-1)^2$. It follows that w has, at the point C, a zero of the second order and that the derivative $dw/d\tau$ has a zero of the first order (cf. Section E above).

In the flow region $w(\tau)$ has only one pole of second order (cf. 1. of the present section or 2. of Section E). Thus, during passage in a counterclockwise direction around point D on an infinitesimal contour (Fig. 14), arg $(\tau-id)$ increases by π, while arg $[1/(\tau-id)^2]$ and, with it, arg (w) (Fig. 2) decrease by 2π (we pass about the point at infinity in the w-plane).

Thus, in the region of flow, $w(\tau)$ has only one zero of second order at $\tau = 1$ and a single pole of second order at $\tau = id$. Because the lines $\psi = 0$ are the boundaries of the w region (the two sides of the cut along the real semi-axis, see Fig. 2), $w(\tau)$ can be analytically extended by the symmetry principle [4] to the whole τ-plane. After a reflection mapping relative to the real and imaginary axes, we determine that $w(\tau)$ has zeros of second order in the τ-plane at $\tau = \pm 1$ and poles of second order at points $\tau = \pm id$. We now form the relation

$$\frac{[(1-\tau)^2 (1+\tau)^2]/[(\tau - id)^2 (\tau + id)^2]}{w} = F(\tau) \quad .$$

In the entire τ-plane, including the point at infinity, $F(\tau)$ will be holomorphic and bounded; it follows that, according to Liouville's Theorem [4], $F(\tau) = \text{const.}$ Thus, we have

$$w = \varphi_o d^4 \frac{(1 - \tau^2)^2}{(\tau^2 + d^2)^2} , \tag{1.66}$$

where φ_o is the value of w at point $B(\tau = 0)$. It is immediately seen that $(1-t^2)^2/(d^2+\tau^2)^2$ is real--i.e., $\psi = 0$ on the boundaries of the upper right quadrant--and possesses the required singularities.

We can now find $dw/v_o dz$. Everywhere in the flow region $dw/v_o dz$ is bounded. It becomes zero only at the one point, $\tau = 1$ (point C). On the plate BCA (real axis of τ) $dw/v_o dz$ is real, and on the free surface BDA (imaginary axis of τ) we have $|dw/v_o dz| = 1$--i.e., the boundaries of the region of change of $dw/v_o dz$ are composed of a part of the real axis and a circular arc of unit radius. Because of this, according to the symmetry principle, the zeros of $dw/v_o dz$ become zeros and its poles become poles under a mapping relative to the real axis of τ; under a mapping relative to the imaginary axis of τ the zeros become poles and the poles become zeros, since the reflection mapping of the points relative to the circle $|dw/v_o dz| = 1$ is obtained by an inversion (see the example in Section A). Thus, $dw/v_o dz$ as extended to the whole τ-plane has a unique zero at $\tau = 1$, and a unique pole at $\tau = -1$. Proceeding in the same way as we did to find $w(\tau)$, we can obtain

$$\frac{dw}{v_o dz} = \frac{1 - \tau}{1 + \tau} . \tag{1.67}$$

It is easy to see that $(1-\tau)/(1+\tau)$ is real on the real axis and its modulus is equal to unity on the imaginary axis of τ.

Equations (1.66) and (1.67) give, practically speaking, a solution to a much more general problem than the one we had posed. To clear up this difficulty, we determine the direction of the velocity of the approaching flow. According to Eq. (1.67), at the point at infinity of the flow--i.e., at point D,

$$\left(\frac{dw}{v_o dz}\right)_{\tau=id} = \frac{1 - id}{1 + id} = \exp\,[-2i \arctan d] \quad ;$$

but, on the other hand, at infinity $dw/dz = \exp\,[-i\theta_\infty]$, where θ_∞ is the angle between the approaching flow velocity and the plate (Fig. 15). Thus, $\theta_\infty = 2 \arctan d$, and, generally speaking, we obtain an oblique flow around a plate [8,13] with an angle of attack $\alpha_o = \theta_\infty$. If $d = 1$, we have $\theta_\infty = \pi/2$, and the flow around the plate is symmetric. In this case, Figs. 14 and 15 can be replaced by Figs. 1 and 4. If we set $d = 1$ and $w/\varphi_o = t^2$ in Eq. (1.66) and $dw/v_o dz = 1/\zeta$ in Eq. (1.67), then these equations are easily reduced to Eqs. (1.21) and (1.22), from which a solution of the problem was obtained in the form of Eq. (1.23).

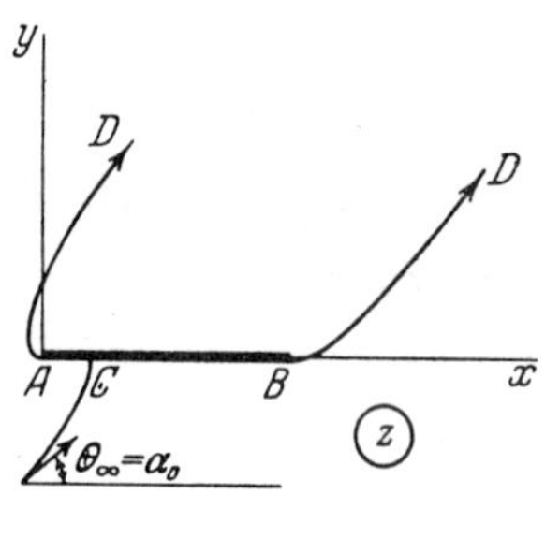

Fig. 15

The function $dw/v_o dz$ could have been determined quite simply from Eq. (1.67). To a considerable extent this simplicity is attributed to the choice of a parametric-variable region, not as an upper half-plane, but as a quadrant with right angles at the boundary points B and A that correspond to the separation points of the jet. Since the boundaries of the $dw/v_o dz$ region form right angles at these points also, then the mapping remains conformal there. The w and $dw/v_o dz$ functions were found without computations. With some practice in finding the zeros and the singularities of these or other convenient hydrodynamic functions, one is able to find the general solution to many problems directly.

It is possible to solve a series of problems by the singular-point method, but here we limit ourselves to only one more example. We consider once more the problem of a jet coming from a wall (Fig. 8, Section E). We map the region of change of w and $dw/v_o dz$ onto the upper right quadrant of the parametric variable τ-plane (Fig. 14). The location of three points B, C, and A on the boundaries can be chosen arbitrarily. The w function has logarithmic singularities at point C (source) and at point D (sink). On extending w, according to the symmetry principle (see Example 5, Section A), over the real axis of τ, we find that there must also be a sink at a point symmetric to D, $\tau = -id$. On extending w over the imaginary axis of τ, we see that a source must be at a point symmetric to C, $\tau = -1$.

Thus, w must have four logarithmic singularities on the entire τ-plane, corresponding to the two sources and two sinks of equal intensities. From this we obtain

$$w = \frac{q}{\pi} \ln (\tau - 1) + \frac{q}{\pi} \ln (\tau + 1) - \frac{q}{\pi} \ln (\tau + id) - \frac{q}{\pi} \ln (\tau - id) + w_o$$

$$= \frac{q}{\pi} \ln \frac{\tau^2 - 1}{\tau^2 + d^2} + w_o \quad , \qquad (1.68)$$

where w_o is an arbitrary constant that we may set equal to qi.

It is easy to check the accuracy of Eq. (1.68). First, its righthand part is holomorphic everywhere inside the upper right quadrant of the τ-plane. On $CA(\tau > 1)$, $\text{Im } w = -q$.

During passage in a counterclockwise direction around $C(\tau = 1)$ on an infinitesimal semicircle, the argument of $(\tau-1)$ increases by π, while the arguments of $(\tau+1)$ and (τ^2+d^2) do not change. Because of this, we have $\mathrm{Im}\, w = 0$ on CB. Along BD the argument of w is constant, but as we pass in a counterclockwise direction around point D along an infinitesimal contour, $\arg(\tau+id)$ increases by π. It follows that the imaginary part of w experiences a jump of q, and on DA we have $\mathrm{Im}\, w = -q$.

As in the previous problem, $dw/v_o dz$ has a unique zero at $C(\tau = 1)$ and, after analytic extension to the entire τ-plane, a unique pole at $\tau = -1$. This procedure again brings us to Eq. (1.67)--i.e., in the problem of flow from an orifice in a wall $dw/v_o dz = (1-\tau)/(1+\tau)$ also. Again, it is possible, by use of the arbitrary d, to obtain solutions for a more general nonsymmetric problem (Fig. 16) than the one whose solution we seek. As before, to obtain a solution for a symmetric problem (as treated in Section E) from the general solution, it is sufficient to set $d = 1$ in Eq. (1.68). If we put $d = 1$ and $\tau = (1+t)^{1/2}(1-t)^{-1/2}$ in Eqs. (1.67) and (1.68)--i.e., we choose a new variable t (see Fig. 6)--then these equations will reduce to Eqs. (1.47) and (1.48), which were obtained by the Zhukovskii method.

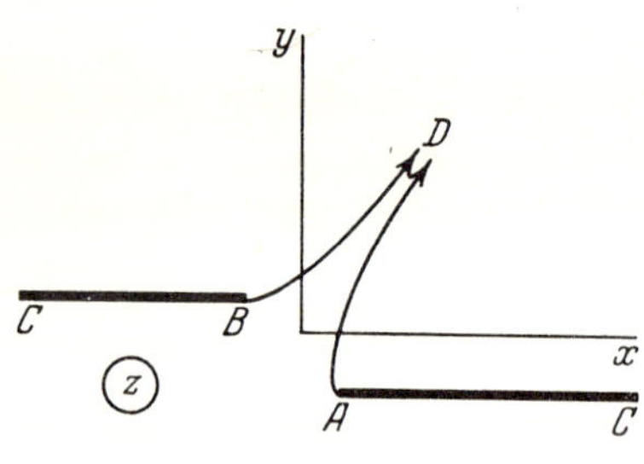

Fig. 16

CHAPTER II. FLOW FROM A VESSEL

A. FLOW FROM A VESSEL WITH OBLIQUE WALLS

In this chapter a series of problems about the flow from vessels is discussed. In each case we seek a general solution that permits us to ascertain the streamline shape and the velocity at any point in the flow field. However, our principal interest is to determine discharge and jet-contraction coefficients.

As von Mises [14] demonstrated, most of the interesting problems* about flow from vessels are particular cases of the following problem. Figure 17 shows an infinitely large vessel BCHA with an oblique plane bottom CB, from which a jet of fluid is flowing. It is assumed that the velocity on the jet's surface is constant and equal to v_o. To solve the problem, the regions of change of $dw/v_o dz$ and w are mapped onto a semicircle of unit radius (Fig. 18) in the t-plane ($|t| \leqq 1$; $\text{Im } t \geqq 0$). Since we may arbitrarily choose the location of three points on the mapped contour [3,4], we let the points B, C, and A correspond to $t_B = -1$, $t_C = 0$, and $t_A = 1$ respectively. The function $dw/v_o dz$ is 0 only at C (Chapter I, Section F.3). We now analyze the behavior of $dw/v_o dz$ in the neighborhood of C.

*Many of those problems were first solved, not by von Mises, but by other scientists, (e.g., see Zhukovskii's work [10]); however, von Mises gave a systematic presentation of the solutions, provided numerical computations, and compared the computed results with experimental data.

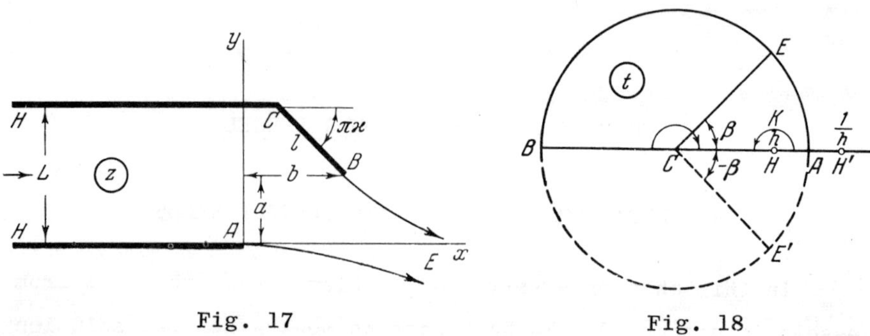

Fig. 17   Fig. 18

If the angle between the wall HC and the bottom CB of the vessel is $\pi-\pi\kappa$, where $0 \leq \kappa \leq 1$, then, in passing from HC to CB the angle of the velocity changes from 0 to $-\pi\kappa$. Under these circumstances the argument of $dw/v_o dz = ve^{-i\theta}/v_o$ changes by $\pi\kappa$. It is easy to see that $dw/v_o dz = \zeta^{-1}(t)$ has a singularity of the order t^{κ} at C. Actually, at point $C(t = 0)$, $t^{\kappa} = 0$, and, as we pass counterclockwise around this point on an infinitesimal semicircle, the argument of t^{κ} increases from 0 to $\pi\kappa$.

When $\zeta^{-1}(t)$ is extended by the symmetry principle [3,4] into the lower half of the circle $|t| \leq 1$, no new singularities are formed. On the other hand, in continuing $\zeta^{-1}(t)$ over the circle $|t| = 1$ into the entire t-plane, we see that $\zeta^{-1}(t)$ must have a singularity of the order t^{κ} at infinity. It is obvious that Nt^{κ}, where N is a constant, possesses all the singularities of $\zeta^{-1}(t)$, and hence it is possible to set $\zeta^{-1}(t) = Nt^{\kappa}$. At $t = 1$ we have $\zeta^{-1}(1) = 1$; it follows that $N = 1$, and finally

$$\frac{dw}{v_o dz} = t^{\kappa} \quad . \tag{2.1}$$

This result can be verified immediately. Inside the upper half of the semicircle $|t| \leqq 1$, t^{κ} is holomorphic. Thus, it remains only to check the boundary conditions. On the circle $|t| = 1$ we have also $|t^{\kappa}| = 1$. Furthermore, on the real axis $0 \leqq t \leqq 1$, t^{κ} is real and positive. Finally, it is clear that on BC $(-1 \leqq t \leqq 0)$ $\arg(t^{\kappa}) = \kappa\pi$--i.e., the boundary conditions are satisfied everywhere.

The function $w(t)$ is determined in the same way as it was in the solution of the problem of flow from a wall (Chapter I, Section F). In the region of flow $w(t)$ has two logarithmic singularities: one at H (a source) and another at E (a sink). Obviously, the source and the sink have equal intensities. In extending $w(t)$ to the lower half of the circle, we see that there must be a sink at $E'(t = e^{-i\beta})$; in extending $w(t)$ outside the circle $t = 1$, we find that there must also be a source at $H'(t = 1/h)$ that is symmetric to H relative to the unit circle. Knowing now all the singular points of $w(t)$ in the t-plane, we construct w, up to the unessential constant, and

$$w = \frac{q}{\pi} \ln (t - h) + \frac{q}{\pi} \ln \left(\frac{1}{h} - t\right) - \frac{q}{\pi} \ln (t - e^{i\beta}) - \frac{q}{\pi} \ln (t - e^{-i\beta}) \quad . \tag{2.2}$$

To establish the accuracy of Eq. (2.2), it is sufficient to check for the fulfillment of the boundary conditions. In the interval HA $(h < t < 1)$ we have

$$\operatorname{Im} w = \operatorname{Im} \frac{q}{\pi} \ln \frac{(t - h)(h^{-1} - t)}{(t - \cos \beta)^2 + \sin^2 \beta} = 0 \quad .$$

By putting $t = e^{i\sigma}$ we have on the arc AE $(\sigma < \beta)$

$$\operatorname{Im} w = \operatorname{Im} \frac{q}{\pi} \ln \frac{(e^{i\sigma} - h)(e^{-i\sigma} - h)\, h^{-1}}{\left\{\exp\left[\frac{i(\sigma - \beta)}{2}\right] - \exp\left[\frac{-i(\sigma + \beta)}{2}\right]\right\}\left\{\exp\left[\frac{i(\sigma + \beta)}{2}\right] - \exp\left[\frac{-i(\sigma - \beta)}{2}\right]\right\}}$$

$$= 0 \ .$$

In exactly the same way we find that, on the streamline HCBE, the imaginary portion of the complex potential $\psi = q$. We may now compute the discharge coefficients by using Eqs. (2.1) and (2.2).

It is most natural to assume that the geometric elements of the vessel are given--i.e., the angle $\pi\kappa$, the length ℓ of CB, the distance L between walls, the abscissa b of point B, and the ordinate $a = L - \ell \sin \pi\kappa$ of point B, as well as the flowrate q. However, if these quantities are specified in advance as a system of independent parameters, we are led to a system of complicated transcendental equations that must be solved to obtain the discharge coefficients. This difficulty, which is characteristic of all jet-theory problems, is circumvented by choosing another set of independent parameters. From Eqs. (2.1) and (2.2) it is clear that a most convenient system will include κ, q, v_o, h, and β. All the desired characteristics of the flow can be expressed in terms of this new set of independent parameters. Furthermore, selection of a set of values allows determination of all the remaining geometric elements of the flow.

First, we establish the physical meaning of h and β, included in Eq. (2.2). On the jet at infinity (i.e., at E) we have $(dw/v_o dz)_E = \exp[-i\theta_o]$, where θ_o is the angle between the jet and x-axis at infinity. But at E, $t = e^{i\beta}$; hence

$$\left(\frac{dw}{v_o dz}\right)_E = \exp[-i\theta_o] = e^{i\beta\kappa} \qquad \text{or} \qquad \theta_o = -\beta\kappa \ , \quad (2.3)$$

i.e., the parameter β determines the direction of the jet at infinity. Now we find the magnitude v_H of the jet velocity at infinity (point H). From Eq. (2.1) and Fig. 17 we have

$$\frac{v_H}{v_o} = \left(\frac{dw}{v_o dz}\right)_H = h^{\kappa} \quad ; \qquad (2.4)$$

thus, h determines the velocity in the vessel at upstream infinity.

The geometric elements ℓ, L, and b are found next. Obviously, $q = Lv_H$, and according to Eq. (2.4), we have

$$L = \frac{q}{v_o h^{\kappa}} \quad . \qquad (2.5)$$

To compute ℓ and b it is necessary to find z(t). From Eqs. (2.1) and (2.2) it follows that

$$z(t) = \frac{1}{v_o} \int \frac{v_o dz}{dw} dw$$

$$= \frac{q}{\pi v_o} \int \frac{dt}{t^{\kappa}} \left[\frac{1}{t - h} + \frac{1}{t - (1/h)} - \frac{1}{t - e^{i\beta}} - \frac{1}{t - e^{-i\beta}}\right] \quad . \qquad (2.6)$$

Considering that on $\overrightarrow{CB}$ $t^{\kappa} = e^{i\pi\kappa}(-t)^{\kappa}$, one can easily obtain

$$\overrightarrow{CB} = \frac{qe^{-i\pi\kappa}}{\pi v_o} \int_0^1 \frac{dt}{(-t)^{\kappa}} \left[\frac{1}{t - h} + \frac{1}{t - (1/h)} - \frac{2t - 2\cos\beta}{t^2 - 2t\cos\beta + 1}\right],$$

from which, by replacing $-t$ with ξ; we find:*

$$\ell = |\overrightarrow{CB}| = \frac{q}{\pi v_0} \int_0^1 \frac{d\xi}{\xi^{\kappa}} \left[\frac{1}{\xi + h} + \frac{1}{\xi + (1/h)} - \frac{2(\xi + \cos\beta)}{\xi^2 + 2\xi\cos\beta + 1}\right], \tag{2.7}$$

From Figs. 17 and 18 it is seen that

$$b + ia = \int_1^{-1} \frac{dz}{dt}\, dt \quad , \tag{2.8}$$

where the integral is over that portion of the diameter of the unit circle (Fig. 18) joining the points A and B. In particular, on this contour we take a segment of the real t-axis from A to B with the condition that the pole of the integrand at $t = h$ is passed along an infinitesimal semicircle K with its center at H (Fig. 18). Clearly, it is sufficient to find the real part of the integral in Eq. (2.8), since its imaginary part is known and, as was pointed out above (see Fig. 17), is equal to

$$a = L - \ell \sin \pi\kappa \quad . \tag{2.9}$$

Furthermore, from Figs. 17 and 18 it is seen that

$$\mathrm{Re} \int_0^{-1} \frac{dz}{dt}\, dt = \ell \cos \pi\kappa \quad ,$$

and then that

$$b = \ell \cos \pi\kappa + \mathrm{Re} \int_1^0 \frac{dz}{dt}\, dt \quad .$$

*It is possible to prove that, with $0 < \xi < 1$, the quadratic term in the brackets under the above integral is positive.

A direct computation establishes that the integral along K gives in the limit a purely imaginary result when the radius of the semicircle tends to 0.* Therefore, we finally obtain

$$b = \ell \cos \pi\kappa + \text{V.P.}\ \frac{q}{\pi v_o} \int_1^0 \frac{dt}{t^\kappa} \left[\frac{1}{t - h} + \frac{1}{t - (1/h)} - \frac{2t - 2\cos\beta}{t^2 - 2t\cos\beta + 1} \right], \tag{2.10}$$

where the Cauchy principal value, indicated by V.P., must be taken in Eq. (2.10). Instead of a, b, ℓ, L, it is convenient to consider the dimensionless quantities a/L, b/L, ℓ/L; Eqs. (2.5), (2.7), (2.9) and (2.10) then become

$$\frac{\ell}{L} = \frac{h^\kappa}{\pi} \int_0^1 \frac{d\xi}{\xi^\kappa} \left[\frac{1}{\xi + h} + \frac{1}{\xi + (1/h)} - \frac{2(\xi + \cos\beta)}{\xi^2 + 2\xi\cos\beta + 1} \right], \tag{2.11}$$

$$\frac{a}{L} = 1 - \frac{\ell}{L} \sin \pi\kappa , \tag{2.12}$$

$$\frac{b}{L} = \frac{\ell}{L} \cos \pi\kappa - \frac{h^\kappa}{\pi}\ \text{V.P.} \int_0^1 \frac{dt}{t^\kappa} \left[\frac{1}{t - h} + \frac{1}{t + (1/h)} - \frac{2(t - \cos\beta)}{t^2 - 2t\cos\beta + 1} \right]. \tag{2.13}$$

We may now introduce the <u>discharge coefficients</u> k_a and k_b [14], which are defined as follows:

$$k_a = \frac{q}{a v_o} = \frac{L h^\kappa}{a}, \qquad k_b = \frac{q}{b v_o} = \frac{L h^\kappa}{b}. \tag{2.14}$$

*This result is obvious geometrically, and it is possible to show that the imaginary result is iL.

Since q/v_0 represents the width δ of the jet at infinity, k_a and k_b are the ratios of δ and the projections a and b of the opening on lines parallel and perpendicular to the walls of the vessel.

The coefficients k_a and k_b can be computed from Eqs. (2.11) through (2.13). Thus, when $\kappa = p/q$, where p and $q \geqq p$ are positive whole numbers, the integrals of Eqs. (2.11) through (2.13) are reduced to integrals of rational fractions by the change of variables $\xi = \xi_1^q$ and $t = t_1^q$. The computation of these integrals has been analyzed in detail by von Mises [14]. Since the methods for reduction of integrals of rational fractions are generally known, though sometimes difficult, we will use von Mises' final numerical values and omit the intermediate computations.

A systematic computation can also be made by another method, suggested by Birkhoff and Zarantonello [5]. For this it is necessary to tabulate the incomplete Beta-functions

$$B_\gamma(\tau) = \int_0^\tau \tau^{\gamma-1} (1 - \tau)^{-1} \, d\tau \quad ,$$

to which the integrals appearing in Eq. (2.6) can be reduced by a simple change of variables. For real values of the argument, these Beta-functions are tabulated by Pearson [15].

B. SYMMETRIC ORIFICE IN A RECTANGULAR VESSEL

If in Fig. 18, the bottom CB forms a right angle with the wall HC, then $\kappa = 1/2$. Furthermore, assume that the lower wall of the vessel extends to infinity, not only to the left but also to the right; then A and E coincide $(\beta = 0)$, and we obtain the flow represented by the solid lines in Fig. 19. If we reflect the flow about the HA axis, then a

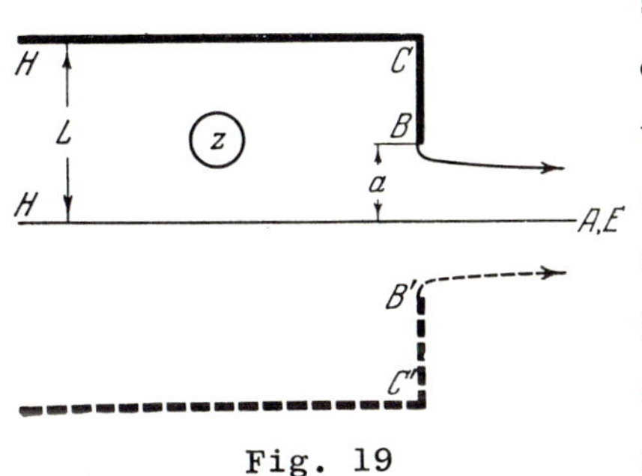

Fig. 19

symmetric flow (dotted line) is obtained; it is the flow from a vessel with width 2L, with a symmetric opening of width 2a in the bottom. The wall HA can be replaced by a streamline without changing the flow. Consider now the form that the above-mentioned general formulas take under these conditions. Instead of Eqs. (2.1) and (2.2), we have, obviously,

$$\frac{dw}{v_o dz} = t^{1/2} \tag{2.15}$$

$$w = \frac{q}{\pi} \ln (t - h) + \frac{q}{\pi} \ln \left(\frac{1}{h} - t\right) - \frac{2q}{\pi} \ln (1 - t). \tag{2.16}$$

Equations (2.12) and (2.13) are simply replaced by $a = L - \ell$ and $b = -\infty$; Eq. (2.11) takes the form

$$\frac{\ell}{L} = \frac{h^{1/2}}{\pi} \int_0^1 \frac{d\xi}{\xi^{1/2}} \left[\frac{1}{\xi + h} + \frac{1}{\xi + (1/h)} - \frac{2}{\xi + 1}\right]. \tag{2.17}$$

The integral in Eq. (2.17) is easily computed after changing the variable ξ to η^2 and

$$\frac{\ell}{L} = \frac{2h^{1/2}}{\pi} \left[\frac{1}{h^{1/2}} \arctan \frac{1}{h^{1/2}} + h^{1/2} \arctan h^{1/2} - \frac{\pi}{2}\right]. \tag{2.18}$$

By replacing $\arctan (1/h^{1/2})$ by $(\pi/2) - \arctan h^{1/2}$ we find

$$\frac{2a}{2L} = 1 - \frac{\ell}{L} = h^{1/2} \left[\frac{2}{\pi}\left(\frac{1}{h^{1/2}} - h^{1/2}\right) \arctan h^{1/2} + 1\right]. \tag{2.19}$$

In determining the discharge coefficients, we see (Figs. 17 and 19) that k_b has a trivial value zero, and k_a represents the jet-contraction coefficient equal to the ratio of the jet's width $\delta = 2q/v_o$ at infinity to the width of the opening 2a. According to Eq. (2.14), we have

$$k_a = \frac{h^{1/2}}{2a/2L} \quad . \tag{2.20}$$

The only geometric characteristic of the vessel is the ratio of the opening width 2a to the width 2L. Generally speaking, it is possible to consider Eq. (2.19) as an equation for the determination of $h^{1/2}$. There is, of course, no need to solve this complicated transcendental equation. It is sufficient to specify various values of $h^{1/2}$ and then to compute $2a/2L$ and k_a. Several important results and conclusions can be drawn from the numerical computations [14]. First, we note that as $h^{1/2} \to 0$ the quantity $2a/2L$ obviously tends to 0, and for small $h^{1/2}$

$$\frac{2a}{2L} \approx h^{1/2}\left[\frac{2}{\pi} + 1\right] \quad . \tag{2.21}$$

From Eqs. (2.20) and (2.21) it follows that

$$\lim_{(a/L)\to 0} k_a = k_o = \frac{\pi}{2 + \pi} \approx 0.611 \quad . \tag{2.22}$$

Naturally, the limiting value of k_a for the rectangular vessel under consideration coincides with the value k_o obtained in Chapter I, Eq. (1.51), for the contraction coefficient of a jet flowing from an opening in a wall. The values of k_a for different a/L are presented later in Table 3 under $\kappa = 1/2$. Experimentally, it is more convenient, however, to determine

$$k'_a = q\left\{a\left[\frac{2(p_H - p_o)}{\rho}\right]^{1/2}\right\}^{-1},$$

a coefficient related to k_a. Here, p_H and p_o are the pressures at points H and E (Fig. 19).

The Bernoulli integral now gives

$$\frac{v_H^2}{2} + \frac{p_H}{\rho} = \frac{v_o^2}{2} + \frac{p_o}{\rho},$$

and we obtain

$$\frac{2(p_H - p_o)}{\rho} = v_o^2 - v_H^2 . \qquad (2.23)$$

Since the flowrates through each complete cross section of the flow are equal, then denoting the width of the jet at infinity (point E) by 2δ leads to

$$v_H 2L = v_o 2\delta$$

or

$$v_H = \frac{v_o \delta}{L} = v_o \frac{a}{L} k_a . \qquad (2.24)$$

From Eqs. (2.23) and (2.24) it follows that

$$\frac{2(p_H - p_o)}{\rho} = v_o^2\left[1 - \left(\frac{a}{L} k_a\right)^2\right],$$

and

$$k'_a = \frac{q}{a\left[\dfrac{2(p_H - p_o)}{\rho}\right]^{1/2}} = \frac{k_a}{\left[1 - (k_a\, a/L)^2\right]^{1/2}} . \qquad (2.25)$$

Obviously, for a vessel of infinite width $k' = (k'_a)_{a/L=0} = k_a$. The values of the ratio k'_a/k'_o as computed by von Mises are presented in Table 1.

TABLE 1

a/L	k'_a/k'_o	$\bar{k}'_a/\bar{k}'_o$
0.1	1.004	1.006
0.2	1.016	1.026
0.3	1.04	1.058
0.4	1.07	1.103
0.5	1.11	1.160

In the third column of the table we give the values of $\bar{k}'_a/\bar{k}'_o$ obtained from a rearrangement of Weisbach's experimental data for circular and rectangular openings. Of course, the shape of the opening has an essential influence on the contraction coefficient and therefore a direct comparison of the theoretical k'_a and the experimental $\bar{k}'_a$ is not permissible.

In the table, the comparison between k'_a/k'_o and $\bar{k}'_a/\bar{k}'_o$ serves not only to point out where two-dimensional jet theory can be applied approximately to real flows, but also to confirm that, at least for flows from vessels, jet theory has a firm physical basis and accurately represents the essential character of real flow.

C. FLOW FROM THE OPENING BETWEEN TWO FLAT PLATES

We wish to examine a symmetric flow from a slot between two walls. To obtain such a flow, we move points A and C to infinity (Figs. 17 and 20) and form the joint points C;H C;H and A;E. Then, as before, we replace the lower wall HA by a streamline and attach a reflected symmetric flow to the original one. Thus, we obtain the symmetric flow picture we

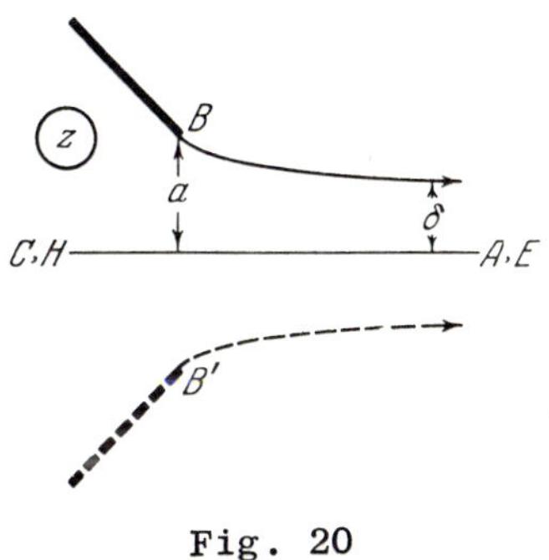

Fig. 20

sought. Because C and A are together with H and E respectively at infinity, we must set $h = \beta = 0$ in the Eqs. of Section A, while Eq. (2.1) is unchanged. After adding the constant $(q/\pi)\ \ln h$ (it has no physical meaning) and passing to the limit $h \to 0$ and $\beta \to 0$, w will be expressed by

$$w = \frac{q}{\pi} \ln t - \frac{2q}{\pi} \ln (t - 1) \quad . \tag{2.26}$$

Equation (2.26) is easily checked directly, if we trace the change in w as we pass over the unit semicircle in the upper half-plane. Since L, ℓ, and b are infinitely large in the present particular case, the equations derived in Section A are unsuitable. It is better to determine the value 2a directly. To do this, we find dy on the streamline BE. From Eqs. (2.1) and (2.26) it follows that

$$dz = \frac{v_o\, dz}{dw} \frac{1}{v_o} \frac{dw}{dt}\, dt = \frac{t^{-\kappa}}{v_o} \frac{q}{\pi} \left[\frac{1}{t} - \frac{2}{t - 1}\right] dt \quad .$$

Thus, assuming that on the free surface $t = e^{i\sigma}$, we have

$$dy = \text{Im}\, dz = - \text{Im} \frac{q}{\pi v_o} \frac{(t+1)\, dt}{t^{1+\kappa}(t - 1)} = \frac{q}{\pi v_o} \cot \frac{\sigma}{2} \sin \kappa\sigma\, d\sigma \quad .$$

From Fig. 20 it is seen that the half width a of the opening is equal to the half-width $\delta = q/v_o$ of the jet at infinity plus the difference in elevation between points B and E--i.e.,

$$a = \delta + \frac{q}{\pi v_o} \int_0^{\pi} \cot \frac{\sigma}{2} \sin \kappa\sigma\, d\sigma \quad , \tag{2.27}$$

and hence the jet-contraction coefficient is equal to

$$k_a = \frac{2\delta}{2a} = \frac{2q}{2v_o a} = \pi\left[\pi + \int_0^\pi \operatorname{ctn}\frac{\sigma}{2}\sin\kappa\sigma\, d\sigma\right]^{-1} . \quad (2.28)$$

For $\kappa = 1/2$ we obtain the results for the problem of flow from a slot in a plate considered earlier; thus Eq. (2.28) gives [compare with Eq. (2.22)]

$$(k_a)_{\kappa=1/2} = \frac{\pi}{\pi + 2} .$$

For $\kappa = 1$, the flow through the Borda nozzle is obtained (Fig. 21). We will return to this problem in Section D. When $\kappa = 1$, the integral in Eq. (2.28) is easily computed and

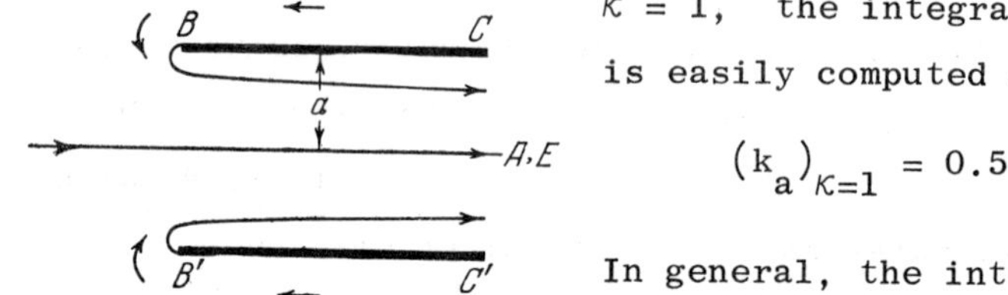

Fig. 21

$$(k_a)_{\kappa=1} = 0.5 . \quad (2.29)$$

In general, the integral in Eq. (2.28) is easily handled in all the cases when κ is a rational fraction.* The computed results are given in Table 2.

In Column 3 of Table 2 Weisbach's experimental data for a circular funnel appear, as corrected for gravity effects by Zeuner [14]. With $\kappa = 1/2$ the experimental coefficient of contraction is $(k_a^*)_{\kappa=1/2} = 0.632$. The results presented in the table are shown graphically in Fig. 22.

*If we put $\kappa = p/q \leqq 1$, where p and q are positive whole numbers, then to reduce the integral to one known from ordinary mathematics courses, one need only introduce a new variable $\sigma_1 = \sigma/2q$ and represent $\sin\kappa\sigma = \sin 2p\sigma_1$ by a trigonometric polynomial in powers of $\sin\sigma_1$ and $\cos\sigma_1$.

TABLE 2

$180\ \kappa$ (deg)	$k_a/(k_a)_{\kappa=1/2}$	$k_a^*/(k_a^*)_{\kappa=1/2}$
22.5	1.40	1.39
45	1.22	1.19
67.5	1.09	1.08
90	1	1
112.5	0.93	0.96
135	0.88	0.915
157.5	0.845	0.865
180	0.819	0.855

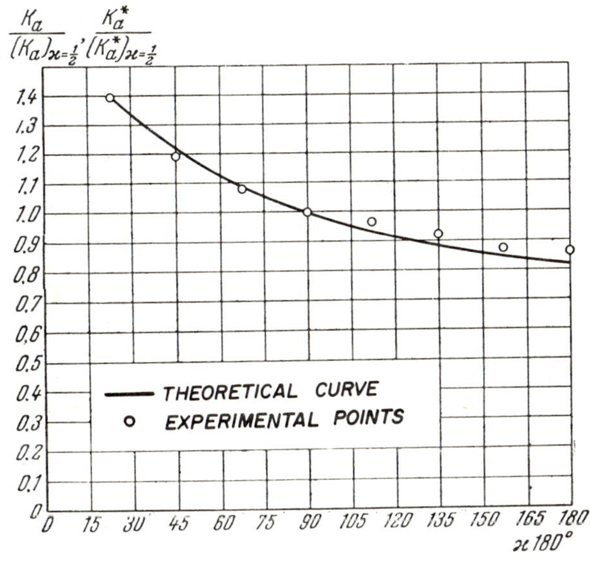

Fig. 22

D. VESSEL WITH A FUNNEL-SHAPED BOTTOM AND BORDA'S NOZZLE

As in Section B, point A is moved to infinity ($\beta = 0$), but the magnitude of κ remains arbitrary. After a symmetric extension of the flow to the lower half-plane, we obtain the flow shown in Fig. 23. We must remember that, although we

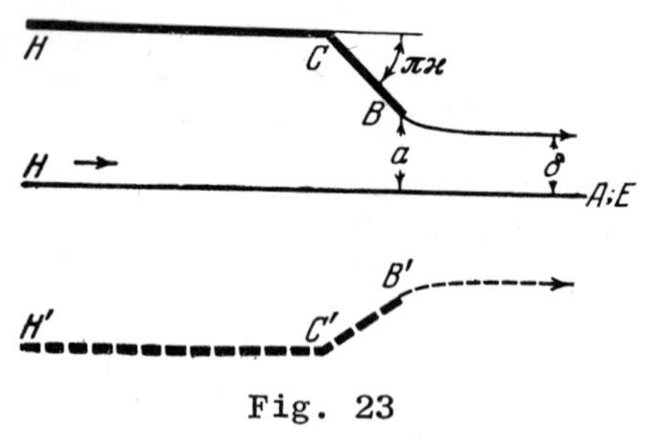

Fig. 23

refer to flow from a vessel with a funnel-shaped bottom, the problem considered is two-dimensional, not three-dimensional and axisymmetric.

In the problem, Eq. (2.1) is unchanged, but Eq. (2.2) changes to Eq. (2.16). As in Section B, $b = -\infty$, and Eq. (2.11) takes the form

$$\frac{\ell}{L} = \frac{h^{\kappa}}{\pi} \int_0^1 \frac{d\xi}{\xi^{\kappa}} \left[\frac{1}{\xi + h} + \frac{1}{\xi + (1/h)} - \frac{2}{\xi + 1} \right] . \quad (2.30)$$

As noted in Section A, the integrals in Eq. (2.30) are easily evaluated when κ is a rational fraction. von Mises [14] calculated the jet contraction coefficient for $\kappa = 1/4$; $1/2$; and $3/4$.

By assuming different values of h, with constant κ, one can obtain all possible values of ℓ/L from Eq. (2.30). With ℓ/L known, it is easy to find a/L [see Eq. (2.12)] and k_a [see Eq. (2.14)]. The results of von Mises' computations are given in Table 3. The values of k'_a are obtained from Eq. (2.25), whose derivation in the present case is the same as that presented in Section B. The data for $\kappa = 1$ are also given in the table. A special solution for this case is given below. A solution for $\kappa = 1/2$ was given in Section B.

As mentioned above, a special solution is required in the case of $\kappa = 1$, when the flow becomes one from the so called "Borda nozzle" or "Borda tube." This flow, with symmetric extension, is shown in Figs. 21 and 24. The flow in Fig. 21 $(L = \infty)$ is the first problem solved by Helmholtz in 1868 using jet theory [9].

TABLE 3

a/L	κ = 1/4		κ = 1/2		κ = 3/4		κ = 1	
	k_a	k'_a	k_a	k'_a	k_a	k'_a	k_a	k'_a
0	0.746	0.746	0.611	0.611	0.537	0.537	0.500	0.500
0.1	0.747	0.749	0.612	0.613	0.546	0.547	0.513	0.514
0.2	0.747	0.759	0.616	0.621	0.555	0.558	0.528	0.531
0.3	0.748	0.767	0.622	0.633	0.569	0.578	0.544	0.551
0.4	0.749	0.785	0.633	0.653	0.580	0.597	0.564	0.578
0.5	0.752	0.812	0.644	0.681	0.599	0.628	0.586	0.613
0.6	0.758	0.851	0.662	0.721	0.620	0.668	0.613	0.659
0.7	0.765	0.906	0.687	0.783	0.652	0.710	0.646	0.724
0.8	0.789	1.015	0.722	0.885	0.698	0.841	0.691	0.820
0.9	0.829	1.242	0.781	1.097	0.761	1.048	0.760	1.041

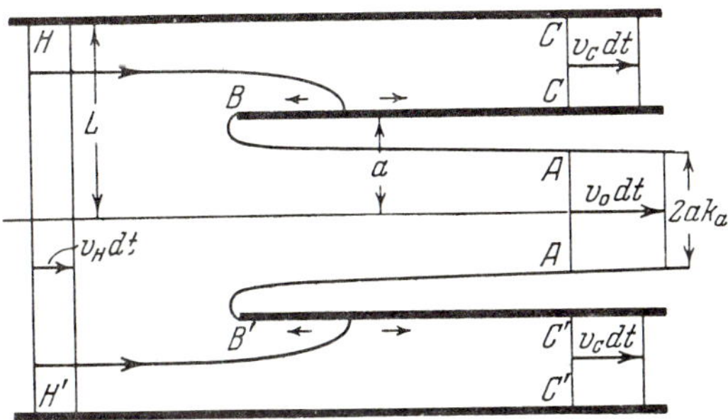

Fig. 24

The following are obtained from Eqs. (2.1) and (2.2) for the Borda tube:

$$\frac{dw}{v_0 dz} = t \quad , \tag{2.31}$$

$$\frac{dw}{dt} = \frac{q}{\pi}\left[\frac{1}{t - h} - \frac{1}{(1/h) - t} + \frac{2}{1 - t}\right] \quad . \tag{2.32}$$

According to Eq. (2.31) the velocity at infinity--i.e., point C(t=0), is zero.

For Borda's nozzle, Eq. (2.30) must naturally give an infinite value of ℓ/L and Eqs. (2.12) and (2.14) for a/L and k_a become indeterminate. Thus, it is convenient to turn immediately to Eqs. (2.31) and (2.32) to determine k_a. From these equations we obtain

$$dz = \frac{q}{\pi v_o}\left[\frac{1}{t - h} - \frac{1}{(1/h) - t} + \frac{2}{1 - t}\right]\frac{dt}{t} \quad . \tag{2.33}$$

Since $q = v_H L$, it follows from Eq. (2.4) or (2.31) that

$$\frac{q}{v_o} = \frac{v_H}{v_o} L = hL \quad . \tag{2.34}$$

Therefore

$$z = \int dz = \frac{hL}{\pi}\int\left[\frac{1}{t - h} - \frac{1}{(1/h) - t} + \frac{2}{1 - t}\right]\frac{dt}{t} \; . \tag{2.35}$$

The contraction coefficient k_a is now easily found from Eq. (2.35) as a result of manipulations with the parameter h. The final result is obtained as a function of a/L. From Fig. 24 it is seen that the distance between the interior wall BC and the exterior wall HC is L-a. This distance is equal to $\text{Im} \int dz$, where the integral is taken along an infinitesimal semicircle around C (see Fig. 18). The integration is made in the clockwise direction because we must pass from the interior to the exterior wall. In passing to the limit* we may immediately set $t = 0$ in the differences $t-h$, $(1/h)-t$, $1-t$; then, from Eq. (2.35) we obtain

$$L - a = \text{Im}\, \frac{hL}{\pi}\left[-\frac{1}{h} - h + 2\right]\int\frac{dt}{t} \quad .$$

*Cf. the end of Section E, Chapter I.

After computation of $\int (dt/t)$ and simplification of the above expressions, we have

$$h^2 - 2h + \frac{a}{L} = 0 \quad , \tag{2.36}$$

which is a quadratic equation in h. Solution of the equation with the restriction that $h < 1$ produces

$$h = 1 - \left(1 - \frac{a}{L}\right)^{1/2} \quad . \tag{2.37}$$

Since $q = v_H L = v_o \delta$, then $\delta/L = v_H/v_o = h$. Consequently, $k_a = (\delta/a) = (\delta/L)(L/a) = h\ L/a$ and, according to Eq. (2.37),

$$k_a = \frac{1 - [1 - (a/L)]^{1/2}}{a/L} \tag{2.38}$$

or

$$k_a = \frac{1}{1 + [1 - (a/L)]^{1/2}} \quad . \tag{2.39}$$

Clearly, when $a/L = 0$, the contraction coefficient is $1/2$.

Determination of the jet-contraction coefficient for the Borda nozzle is one of the few hydrodynamic problems that can be solved without resorting to conformal mapping. A solution is obtained by using the momentum and energy theorems as well as the continuity equation for the jet flowrate. We will examine, as examples, the solutions to several more general problems obtained by Konovalov [16].

Consider the flow produced by the existence of a pressure differential between the infinitely separated sections HH', CC, C'C', and AA (see Fig. 24). We designate the pressures and velocities at these sections by p_H, p_C, $p_A = p_0$

v_H, v_C, $v_A = v_o$. Thus, in contrast to the Borda-nozzle conditions, the velocity v_C is not necessarily 0 at infinity on the right (at sections CC and C'C'). The pressure difference between the sections can be expressed by the Bernoulli integral in terms of the velocities and the fluid density ρ as

$$p_H - p_o = \frac{\rho}{2}\left(v_o^2 - v_H^2\right), \qquad p_C - p_o = \frac{\rho}{2}\left(v_o^2 - v_C^2\right). \quad (2.40)$$

At a time when $t = 0$ there is a fixed volume of fluid confined between the walls HD, CB, C'B', H'C'; the free surfaces BA, B'A; and the sections HH', CC, C'C', AA. A small interval of time ΔT later, this fixed fluid volume occupies a new position--i.e., the section HH' moves a distance $v_H\Delta T$, sections CC and C'C' move a distance $v_C\Delta T$, and section AA moves a distance $v_o\Delta T$ (see Fig. 24). Since the flow is steady, the horizontal (x-axis) component of momentum of the fixed fluid volume receives an increment $(-\rho q_H v_H + \rho q_C v_C + \rho q_o v_o)\Delta T$, where q_H and q_o are the discharges through HH' and AA' respectively, and q_C is the discharge through both CC and C'C'. This increase in momentum occurs, obviously, as a result of the pressure difference action on the jet surfaces BA, B'A, and at sections HH', CC, C'C', AA. By equating the impulse of the horizontal components of the pressure forces to the increase in momentum of the fluid volume, we get

$$\rho\Delta T(q_o v_o + q_C v_C - q_H v_H) = [p_H 2L - p_C 2(L - a) - p_o 2a]\Delta T$$

or

$$\rho(q_o v_o + q_C v_C - q_H v_H) = (p_H - p_o)2L - (p_C - p_o)2(L-a) \ . \quad (2.41)$$

Furthermore, from Fig. 24 it is easily seen that

$$q_H = 2Lv_H; \qquad q_C = 2(L - a)v_C; \qquad q_o = 2k_a av_o, \tag{2.42}$$

where k_a is the jet-contraction coefficient. By use of Eqs. (2.40) and (2.42), Eq. (2.41) is transformed into

$$2k_a av_o^2 - Lv_H^2 + (L - a)v_C^2 - v_o^2 a = 0 \quad . \tag{2.43}$$

If the ratio of discharges q_H and q_o is now denoted by

$$n = \frac{q_H}{q_o} = \frac{v_H L}{k_a av_o} \quad ,$$

then

$$v_H = \frac{nk_a av_o}{L} \quad . \tag{2.44}$$

Since the discharge through section HH' equals the sum of the discharges through sections CC, C'C', and AA, we have $q_C = q_H - q_o$, and [see Eq. (2.42)]

$$(L - a)v_C = \frac{q_o}{2}(n - 1) = k_a av_o(n - 1) \quad . \tag{2.45}$$

Equation (2.43) is nondimensionalized by using Eqs. (2.44) and (2.45) and the result is

$$\frac{2k_a a}{L} - n^2 k_a^2 \left(\frac{a}{L}\right)^2 + \frac{k_a^2 (a/L)^2 (n - 1)^2}{1 - (a/L)} - \frac{a}{L} = 0$$

or

$$\frac{1}{k_a^2} - \frac{2}{k_a} - A = 0 \quad , \tag{2.46}$$

where

$$A = \frac{a}{L} \frac{1 - 2n + n^2(a/L)}{1 - (a/L)} .$$

Equation (2.46) is quadratic in the inverse of the magnitude of k_a. From Eq. (2.46), with the physical requirement that $k_a \geqq 0$, we find

$$\frac{1}{k_a} = 1 + (1 + A)^{1/2} . \qquad (2.47)$$

The von Mises problem for $v_C = 0$, as examined above, is obtained when $n = 1$, according to Eq. (2.45). Under this condition Eq. (2.47) agrees with Eq. (2.39). When the velocity v_C in sections CC and C'C' (see Fig. 24) is directed from right to left, $v_C < 0$ and $n < 0$.

E. LATERAL FLOW FROM A CHANNEL

In the previous section the problem of flow from a Borda nozzle, located between two walls (see Fig. 24), was examined. For that problem we moved points A and C to infinity and set $\kappa = 1$ (see Fig. 17). If we now set $\kappa = 1$ and move only C to infinity, then the resulting flow is as shown in Fig. 25. The general problem solution is given in this case by Eqs. (2.1) and (2.2) with $\kappa = 1$. However, then the velocity at infinity (point C) is 0 [see Fig. 17 and Eq. (2.1)]. In reality it is possible to solve a problem of practical value and more general type, which

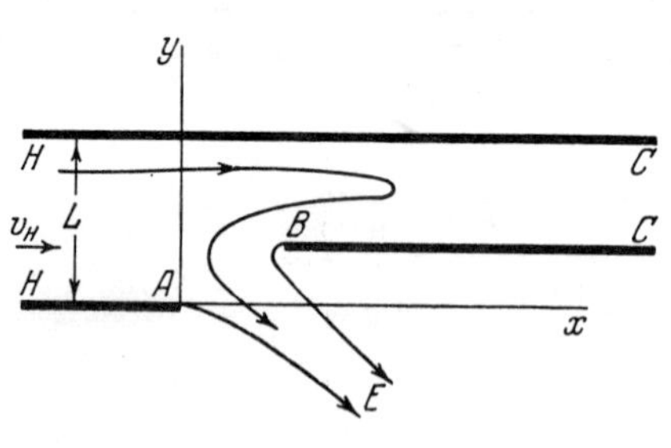

Fig. 25

consists of a flow from an opening between walls, such that the critical point (i.e., the point at which the velocity is 0) is located not at C but rather at some arbitrary point on one of the walls--e.g., at D (see Fig. 26). It is

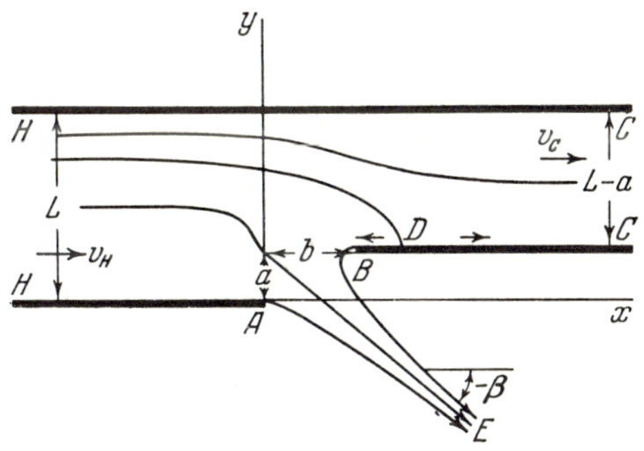

Fig. 26

obvious that the velocity at C is not 0 and can generally be either positive or negative. Also, D can be located on any one of the walls. As an example, consider the flow where the velocities at H and C are positive and D is located on BC. The equations obtained will be valid for the other cases; however, the constants appearing in the equations have different values that are easily determined. This problem has been investigated by Konovalov [17], Taliev [18] and several other authors [19]. It is interesting to note that the general-solution outline to this problem (without numerical computations) was displayed recently in some rough notes written by Zhukovskii and found after his death. Our discussion is based on references [17] and [18].

In our approach to the solution we make use of many previous results and definitions. It is easy to see that the region of change of $dw/v_o dz$ is the upper half of a unit circle with its center at the coordinate origin (Fig. 27). On the jet AEB, $|dw/v_o dz| = 1$, and at D, $dw/v_o dz = 0$. If at infinity (point E) the jet forms an angle $-\beta$ with the x-axis, then at that point $dw/v_o dz = e^{i\beta}$. On the walls $\text{Im}\ dw/v_o dz = 0$; hence on BD, $dw/v_o dz < 0$, and on the remaining parts of the walls (i.e., on DC, HC, and HA), $dw/v_o dz > 0$. Then, if we set

$$\frac{dw}{v_o dz} = t \quad , \tag{2.48}$$

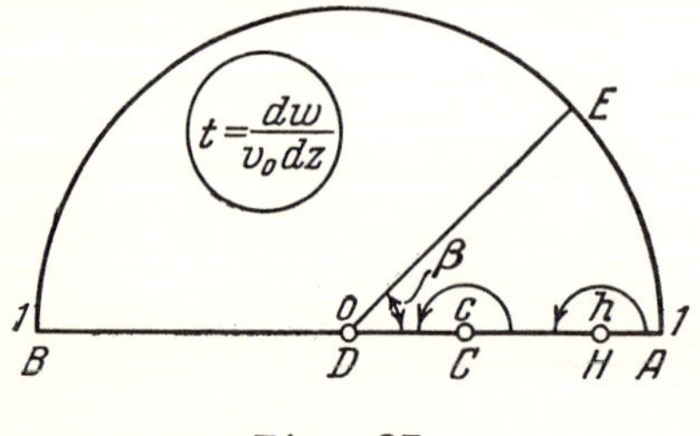

Fig. 27

a semicircle designated as the domain G (Fig. 27) serves as the region of change of t. Clearly, Figs. 18 and 25 can be considered particular cases of Figs. 26 and 27 in which D and C coincide (or the critical point D coincides with the infinitely distant point C). Here w(t) is determined in precisely the same way as in Section A. If we designate the discharge through HH (Fig. 26) by q and the jet discharge by $q_E = q/n$, then the discharge through CC is $q - q_E = q_E(n-1)$ because all fluid flowing in through HH and not flowing out through EE must flow through CC. Thus, inside G, w(t) has logarithmic source-sink singularities at points H(t=h), C(t=c), and $E(t=e^{i\beta})$. After we extend w(t) to the lower unit semicircle and subsequently to the entire t-plane, we observe that w(t) has the same type of singularities at points $E'(t=e^{-i\beta})$, C'(t=1/c), and H'(t=1/h).

Since all the singularities of w(t) are known, it is easy to construct (except for unessential constants)

$$w(t) = \frac{q}{\pi}\ \ell n\ (t - h) + \frac{q}{\pi}\ \ell n \left(\frac{1}{h} - t\right) - \frac{q - q_E}{\pi}\ \ell n\ (t - c)$$

$$- \frac{q - q_E}{\pi}\ \ell n \left(\frac{1}{c} - t\right) - \frac{q_E}{\pi}\ \ell n\ (t - e^{i\beta})$$

$$- \frac{q_E}{\pi}\ \ell n\ (t - e^{-i\beta}) \quad . \tag{2.49}$$

When $q = q_E$, Eq. (2.49) is transformed into Eq. (2.2). Also, two new constants, q_E and c, appear in Eq. (2.49) as compared to (2.2). These two constants cannot be chosen arbitrarily because they are interdependent and are related by an extra condition which we will now derive.

If we examine the streamlines of Figs. 25 and 26, we see that, in the flow represented in Fig. 25, all the fluid flowing in through section HH is flowing out through the slot; there are no bifurcated streamlines. However, in Fig. 26 there is a streamline that bifurcates at point D. The flow passing above this streamline leaves through section CC, while the flow passing below leaves through the slot.

At point D

$$\left(\frac{dw}{dz}\right)_{t=0} = \left(\frac{dw}{dt}\right)_{t=0} \left(\frac{dt}{dz}\right)_{t=0} = 0 \quad ;$$

and, since the mapping of the z-plane (see Fig. 26) onto the t-plane (see Fig. 27) is conformal at D, $(dt/dz)_{t=0} \neq 0$. Thus,

$$\left(\frac{dw}{dt}\right)_{t=0} = 0 \quad . \tag{2.50}$$

The same result can be obtained by a more detailed method analogous to that used to obtain condition (1.55) (see also Chapter I, Section F.4). Since from Eq. (2.49) it follows that

$$\frac{dw}{dt} = \frac{q}{\pi}\left(\frac{1}{t - h} - \frac{1}{(1/h) - t}\right) - \frac{q - q_E}{\pi}\left(\frac{1}{t - c} - \frac{1}{(1/c) - t}\right) - \frac{q_E}{\pi}\left(\frac{1}{t - e^{i\beta}} + \frac{1}{t - e^{-i\beta}}\right) , \tag{2.51}$$

then Eq. (2.50) becomes

$$\frac{q}{q_E}\left(h + \frac{1}{h}\right) - \left(\frac{q}{q_E} - 1\right)\left(c + \frac{1}{c}\right) = 2 \cos \beta \quad . \qquad (2.52)$$

It is interesting to note that a transformed form of Eq. (2.52) is easily obtained by using the momentum and Bernoulli theorems in a manner analogous to that used in the previous section to get Eq. (2.43) [14,17].

It is simple to establish the hydrodynamic significance of h and c. If v_H and v_C are the velocities at the infinitely distant sections HH and CC, then from Eq. (2.48) it follows that

$$h = \frac{v_H}{v_o} , \qquad c = \frac{v_C}{v_o} \quad . \qquad (2.53)$$

In addition, we designate the jet's width at infinity by $\delta = q_E/v_o$.

The basic problem before us consists in finding the coefficient $k_b = \delta/b$ as a function of the given dimensionless quantities: b/L, a/L, $q/q_E = n$, where L is the distance between walls at the left of the opening (see Fig. 26) and a and b are the vertical and horizontal projections of the opening (the walls of the channel are arranged horizontally). The solution is found in a parametric form by expressing k_b, b/L, and a/L in terms of $n = q/q_E$, c, h. First, we find dz/dt and z as functions of t. From Eqs. (2.48) and (2.51) it follows that

$$\frac{dz}{dt} = \frac{dz}{dw}\frac{dw}{dt}$$

$$= \frac{1}{v_o t}\left\{\frac{q}{\pi}\left[\frac{1}{t - h} - \frac{1}{(1/h) - t}\right] - \frac{q - q_E}{\pi}\left[\frac{1}{t - c} - \frac{1}{(1/c) - t}\right]\right.$$

$$\left. - \frac{q_E}{\pi}\left[\frac{1}{t - e^{i\beta}} + \frac{1}{t - e^{-i\beta}}\right]\right\} . \tag{2.54}$$

Since this equation must be integrated, it is convenient to expand dz/dt in partial fractions as

$$\frac{dz}{dt} = \frac{A_1}{t} + \frac{A_2}{t - h} + \frac{A_3}{t - (1/h)} + \frac{A_4}{t - c} + \frac{A_5}{t - (1/c)}$$

$$+ \frac{A_6}{t - e^{i\beta}} + \frac{A_7}{t - e^{-i\beta}} .$$

The constants $A_1, A_2, \ldots, A_7$ are determined by the usual methods. From Eqs. (2.54), (2.48), and (2.50) we have:

$$A_1 = \left(t\,\frac{dz}{dt}\right)_{t=0} = \frac{1}{v_o}\left(\frac{dw}{dt}\right)_{t=0} = 0 \quad ;$$

$$A_2 = \left[\frac{dz}{dt}(t - h)\right]_{t=h} = \frac{q}{v_o \pi h} \quad ;$$

$$A_3 = \frac{q}{\pi v_o} h \quad ;$$

$$A_4 = -\frac{q - q_E}{\pi v_o c} \quad ;$$

$$A_5 = \frac{q - q_E}{\pi v_o} c \quad ;$$

$$A_6 = - \frac{q_E e^{-i\beta}}{\pi v_o} ;$$

$$A_7 = - \frac{q_E e^{i\beta}}{\pi v_o} .$$

Finally, by combining the last two terms of the dz/dt expansion, we find

$$\frac{dz}{dt} = \frac{q}{\pi v_o h} \frac{1}{t - h} + \frac{qh}{\pi v_o} \frac{1}{t - (1/h)} - \frac{q - q_E}{\pi v_o c} \frac{1}{t - c}$$

$$- \frac{(q - q_E)c}{\pi v_o} \frac{1}{t - (1/c)}$$

$$- \frac{2q_E}{\pi v_o} \frac{\cos \beta(t - \cos \beta) + \sin^2\beta}{(t - \cos \beta)^2 + \sin^2\beta} . \quad (2.55)$$

To find the width L of the channel at the left of the slot we divide the discharge q by the velocity at infinity (point H). Thus $L = q/v_H$ and, by using Eq. (2.53) to replace v_H, we have

$$L = \frac{q}{v_o h} . \quad (2.56)$$

Similarly, the width of the channel at the right of the slot is found to be

$$L - a = \frac{q - q_E}{v_o c} . \quad (2.57)$$

Equations (2.56) and (2.57) are also easily obtained by integrating Eq. (2.55) along an infinitesimal semicircle around points H and C (see Fig. 27). From Eqs. (2.56) and (2.57),

$$n \frac{1 - (a/L)}{n - 1} = \frac{h}{c} \quad . \tag{2.58}$$

Now, by assigning values to $n = q/q_E$ and a/L, it is possible to find for each h the corresponding value of c. Next, we find b, the projection on the horizontal x-axis (see Fig. 26) of the opening between the lower walls of the channel. If we integrate Eq. (2.55) from $A(t=1)$ to $B(t=-1)$ and take the real parts on both sides of the equal sign, then

$$b = \text{Re} \int_1^{-1} \frac{dz}{dt}\, dt$$

$$= \text{Re} \left[\frac{q}{\pi v_o h} \int_1^{-1} \frac{dt}{t - h} + \frac{qh}{\pi v_o} \int_1^{-1} \frac{dt}{t - (1/h)} \right.$$

$$- \frac{q - q_E}{\pi v_o c} \int_1^{-1} \frac{dt}{t - c} - \frac{(q - q_E)c}{\pi v_o} \int_1^{-1} \frac{dt}{t - (1/c)}$$

$$- \frac{2q_E}{\pi v_o} \cos\beta \int_1^{-1} \frac{t - \cos\beta}{(t - \cos\beta)^2 + \sin^2\beta}\, dt$$

$$\left. - \frac{2q_E}{\pi v_o} \sin^2\beta \int_1^{-1} \frac{dt}{(t - \cos\beta)^2 + \sin^2\beta} \right] .$$

Since all the resulting integrals are tabulated, it is possible after elementary computations to write the final formula for b as

$$b = \frac{q}{\pi v_o} \left(h + \frac{1}{h}\right) \ln \frac{1 + h}{1 - h} - \frac{q - q_E}{\pi v_o} \left(c + \frac{1}{c}\right) \ln \frac{1 + c}{1 - c}$$

$$+ \frac{q_E}{\pi v_o} \left[2 \cos\beta \ln \tan \frac{\beta}{2} + \pi \sin\beta\right] ,$$

from which, by using Eq. (2.56), we get

$$\frac{b}{L} = \frac{h}{\pi}\left(h + \frac{1}{h}\right) \ell n \frac{1 + h}{1 - h} - \frac{n - 1}{\pi n} h \left(c + \frac{1}{c}\right) \ell n \frac{1 + c}{1 - c}$$

$$+ \frac{h}{\pi n}\left[2 \cos \beta \ \ell n \tan \frac{\beta}{2} + \pi \sin \beta\right] . \tag{2.59}$$

The system of equations for our computations is finally completed with the equation for the coefficient $k_b = \delta/b = q_E/v_o b$ or

$$k_b = \frac{h}{n}\frac{L}{b} . \tag{2.60}$$

Calculations can be accomplished in the following order. We are given the values a/L, n, and h. From Eq. (2.58) we find c; from Eq. (2.52) we find β. Subsequently, from Eq. (2.59) we determine b/L, and from Eq. (2.60), k_b. When $n = 1$, indeterminate expressions appear in the above equations; however, they are easily evaluated. We point out that, with $n = 1$, the discharge through CC is 0; hence $v_c = 0$ and, according to Eq. (2.53), $c = 0$. From Eq. (2.58) it follows that

$$\lim_{n \to 1} \frac{n - 1}{c} = \frac{1}{h}\left(1 - \frac{a}{L}\right) . \tag{2.61}$$

Therefore, with $n = 1$, Eq. (2.52) takes the form

$$h + \frac{a}{hL} = 2 \cos \beta , \tag{2.62}$$

and Eqs. (2.59) and (2.60) are replaced by

$$\frac{b}{L} = \frac{h}{\pi}\left(h + \frac{1}{h}\right) \ell n \frac{1 + h}{1 - h} + \frac{h}{\pi}\left[\cos \beta \ \ell n \frac{1 - \cos \beta}{1 + \cos \beta} + \pi \sin \beta\right] , \tag{2.63}$$

and

$$k_b = h \frac{L}{b} \quad . \tag{2.64}$$

A more interesting case is the flow from a channel of constant width--i.e., when $a/L = 0$. In this case k_b can be called the jet-contraction coefficient. Equation (2.58) then gives

$$c = h \left(1 - \frac{1}{n}\right) \quad . \tag{2.65}$$

By putting c from Eq. (2.65) into (2.52), we find

$$h = \frac{\cos \beta}{1 - (1/2n)} \quad . \tag{2.66}$$

As a result, Eqs. (2.59) and (2.60) take the forms [18]

$$\frac{b}{L} = \frac{1}{\pi} \left\{ \frac{\pi \sin \beta}{n} - \frac{\cos \beta}{n} \ln \frac{1 + \cos \beta}{1 - \cos \beta} \right.$$

$$+ \frac{[1 - (1/2n)]^2 + \cos^2 \beta}{[1 - (1/2n)] \cos \beta} \ln \frac{1 - (1/2n) + \cos \beta}{1 - (1/2n) - \cos \beta}$$

$$- \frac{[1 - (1/2n)]^2 + [1 - (1/n)]^2 \cos^2 \beta}{[1 - (1/2n)] \cos \beta}$$

$$\left. \cdot \ln \frac{1 - (1/2n) + [1 - (1/n)] \cos \beta}{1 - (1/2n) - [1 - (1/n)] \cos \beta} \right\}$$

$$\cdot \frac{\cos \beta}{1 - (1/2n)} \quad , \tag{2.67}$$

and

$$k_b = \frac{L}{b} \frac{2 \cos \beta}{2n - 1} \quad . \tag{2.68}$$

Thus, when $a/L = 0$, Eqs. (2.67) and (2.68) are the complete solution to the problem. With these equations the values b/L and k_b are computed from given values of n and β. Konovalov [17] computed k_b for $b/L < 0.1$, while Taliev [18] computed k_b for the range $0.15 \leqq b/L \leqq 1.98$. In the latter report a systematic experiment about air flow from a slot into open air is discussed. Table 4 presents the theoretical (upper numbers) and experimental (lower numbers) values of the jet-contraction coefficient.

TABLE 4

1/n	b/L					
	0.15	0.32	0.62	1.03	1.51	1.98
0.2	0.540 0.535	0.414 0.400	0.278 0.279	0.186 0.185	0.128 0.127	0.100 0.101
0.4	0.590 0.616	0.544 0.541	0.445 0.440	0.330 0.331	0.242 0.241	0.196 0.196
0.6	0.602 0.653	0.580 0.597	0.524 0.522	0.436 0.433	0.342 0.335	0.287 0.282
0.8	0.606 0.675	0.594 0.615	0.566 0.560	0.506 0.500	0.422 0.406	0.370 0.356
1.0	0.609 0.714	0.604 0.660	0.584 0.597	0.546 0.544	0.480 0.461	0.432 0.411

As Taliev's photographs showed [18], the jet of air flowing into ambient air was strongly diffused; as a result the experimental conditions were not sufficiently similar to the conditions implied by application of jet theory. Nevertheless, with small $1/n$ and large b/L the agreement between results was satisfactory. For more extensive checking of the theory, it would be desirable to have some experimental data available for flow of a more dense fluid into a less dense one (e.g., water into air).

F. FLOW FROM A RECTANGULAR VESSEL WITH AN ORIFICE AT A CORNER

The flow from a symmetric rectangular vessel (Fig. 28) is well suited for computations. If we replace the middle streamline by a solid wall, then Fig. 29 shows the resulting

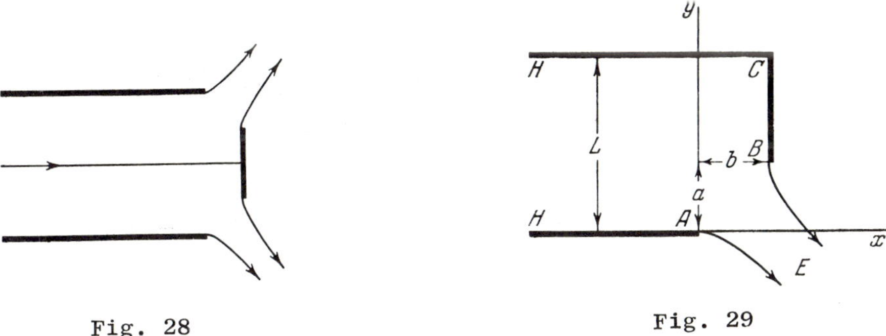

Fig. 28 Fig. 29

flow. This figure is a particular case of the von Mises flow (see Fig. 17) which he solved in detail [14]. A solution is obtained from the equations of Section A with $\kappa = 1/2$; hence, we may compute very easily all the necessary integrals. After setting $\kappa = 1/2$ in Eqs. (2.11) through (2.13) and replacing the variable of integration t and ξ by u^2, we obtain

$$\frac{a}{L} = 1 - \frac{\ell}{L}, \tag{2.69}$$

$$\frac{\ell}{L} = \frac{2h^{1/2}}{\pi} \int_0^1 \left[\frac{1}{u^2 + h} + \frac{1}{u^2 + (1/h)} - \frac{2(u^2 + \cos\beta)}{u^4 + 2u^2\cos\beta + 1}\right] du, \tag{2.70}$$

$$\frac{b}{L} = -\frac{2h^{1/2}}{\pi}\, \text{V.P.} \int_0^1 \left[\frac{1}{u^2 - h} + \frac{1}{u^2 - (1/h)} - \frac{2(u^2 - \cos\beta)}{u^4 - 2u^2\cos\beta + 1}\right] du, \tag{2.71}$$

The integrals in Eqs. (2.70) and (2.71) are computed by expanding the functions under the integral in partial fractions and

$$\frac{\ell}{L} = \frac{2h^{1/2}}{\pi} \int_0^1 \left[\frac{1}{u^2 + h} + \frac{1}{u^2 + (1/h)} + \frac{u \sin(\beta/2) - 1 + 2\sin^2(\beta/2)}{u^2 + 2u\sin(\beta/2) + 1} + \frac{-u\sin(\beta/2) - 1 + 2\sin^2(\beta/2)}{u^2 - 2u\sin(\beta/2) + 1} \right] du ,$$

$$\frac{b}{L} = -\frac{2h^{1/2}}{\pi} \text{ V.P.} \int_0^1 \left\{ \frac{1}{2h^{1/2}} \left[\frac{1}{u - h^{1/2}} - \frac{1}{u + h^{1/2}} \right] + \frac{h^{1/2}}{2} \left[\frac{1}{u - (1/h^{1/2})} - \frac{1}{u + (1/h^{1/2})} \right] + \frac{u\cos(\beta/2) - 1 + 2\cos^2(\beta/2)}{u^2 + 2u\cos(\beta/2) + 1} + \frac{-u\cos(\beta/2) - 1 + 2\cos^2(\beta/2)}{u^2 - 2u\cos(\beta/2) + 1} \right\} du .$$

Now we easily obtain

$$\frac{\ell}{h} = \frac{2h^{1/2}}{\pi} \left[\frac{1}{h^{1/2}} \arctan\frac{1}{h^{1/2}} + h^{1/2} \arctan h^{1/2} + \frac{\sin(\beta/2)}{2} \ln\frac{1 + \sin(\beta/2)}{1 - \sin(\beta/2)} - \frac{\pi\cos(\beta/2)}{2} \right] . \quad (2.72)$$

$$\frac{b}{L} = \frac{2h^{1/2}}{\pi}\left[\frac{1}{2}\left(\frac{1}{h^{1/2}} + h^{1/2}\right) \ln \frac{1 + h^{1/2}}{1 - h^{1/2}}\right.$$

$$\left. - \frac{\cos(\beta/2)}{2} \ln \frac{1 + \sin(\beta/2)}{1 - \cos(\beta/2)} + \frac{\pi \sin(\beta/2)}{2}\right] . \qquad (2.73)$$

From Eqs. (2.69) and (2.74) it follows that

$$\frac{a}{L} = \frac{2h^{1/2}}{\pi}\left[\left(\frac{1}{h^{1/2}} - h^{1/2}\right) \arctan h^{1/2}\right.$$

$$\left. - \frac{\sin(\beta/2)}{2} \ln \frac{1 + \sin(\beta/2)}{1 - \sin(\beta/2)} + \frac{\pi}{2}\cos(\beta/2)\right] . \qquad (2.74)$$

Equations (2.73) and (2.74) can be briefly presented in the form

$$\frac{b}{L} = h^{1/2}\left[g_1(h^{1/2}) + g_2(\beta/2)\right] , \qquad (2.75)$$

$$\frac{a}{L} = h^{1/2}\left[f_1(h^{1/2}) + f_2(\beta/2\beta\right] , \qquad (2.76)$$

where

$$f_1(h^{1/2}) = \frac{2}{\pi}\left(\frac{1}{h^{1/2}} - h^{1/2}\right) \arctan h^{1/2} ,$$

$$g_1(h^{1/2}) = \frac{1}{\pi}\left(\frac{1}{h^{1/2}} + h^{1/2}\right) \ln \frac{1 + h^{1/2}}{1 - h^{1/2}} ,$$

$$f_2(\beta/2) = \cos(\beta/2) - \frac{\sin(\beta/2)}{\pi} \ln \frac{1 + \sin(\beta/2)}{1 - \sin(\beta/2)} ,$$

$$g_2(\beta/2) = f_2\left(\frac{\beta}{2} - \frac{\pi}{2}\right) = \sin(\beta/2) + \frac{\cos(\beta/2)}{\pi} \ln \frac{1 - \cos(\beta/2)}{1 + \cos(\beta/2)} .$$

By prescribing values of h and β, it is possible to compute a/L and b/L, and then with the help of Eq. (2.14) to find the discharge coefficients k_a and k_b [14]. Of particular interest are the cases $a/L = 0$ (an opening in the wall) and $b/L = 0$ (an opening in the bottom). When $a/L = 0$, the coefficient k_b becomes the jet-contraction coefficient; when $b/L = 0$, the jet-contraction coefficient is k_a. To complete the computations we first construct the graphs of the functions $f_1(h^{1/2})$, $g_1(h^{1/2})$, $f_2(\beta/2)$ (Fig. 30). If we consider the case when $a/L = 0$, then we must, given β, pick h from the graph (Fig. 30) such that $f_1(h^{1/2}) = f_2(\beta/2)$.

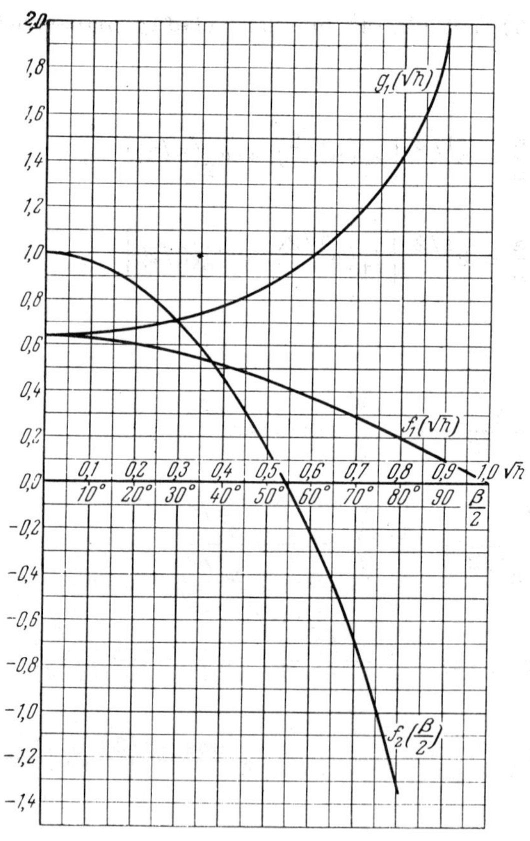

Fig. 30

Furthermore, with the pair of values h and β obtained from the graphs, b/L is found from Eq. (2.75), and then, from Eqs. (2.14) and (2.75), we obtain

$$k_b = \frac{Lh^{1/2}}{h} = \frac{1}{g_1(h^{1/2}) + g_2(\beta/2)} . \qquad (2.77)$$

It is convenient to proceed in an analogous manner in the case of $b/L = 0$. Then, it is necessary to determine h and β so that $g_1(h^{1/2}) = -g_2(\beta/2)$; for the contraction coefficient

$$k_a = \frac{Lh^{1/2}}{a} = \frac{1}{f_1(h^{1/2}) + f_2(\beta/2)} . \qquad (2.78)$$

The results of von Mises' computations are given in Tables 5 and 6 and in Figs. 31 and 32.

TABLE 5
($b/L = 0$)

a/L	0	0.1	0.2	0.3	0.4	0.5	0.6	0.7	0.8	0.9
k_a	0.673	0.676	0.680	0.686	0.693	0.702	0.720	0.740	0.782	0.842

TABLE 6
($a/L = 0$)

b/L	0	0.5	1.0	1.5	2.0	2.5	3.0	3.5	4.0	4.5	5.0
k_b	0.673	0.640	0.582	0.504	0.438	0.363	0.320	0.281	0.250	0.220	0.200

k_a
0,9
0,8
0,7
0,6
0,5
0,4
0,3
0,2
0,1
0
0,1 0,2 0,3 0,4 0,5 0,6 0,7 0,8 0,9
$\frac{a}{L}$

Fig. 31

k_b
0,9
0,8
0,7
0,6
0,5
0,4
0,3
0,2
0,1
0
0,5 1,0 1,5 2,0 2,5 3,0 3,5 4,0 4,5
$\frac{b}{L}$

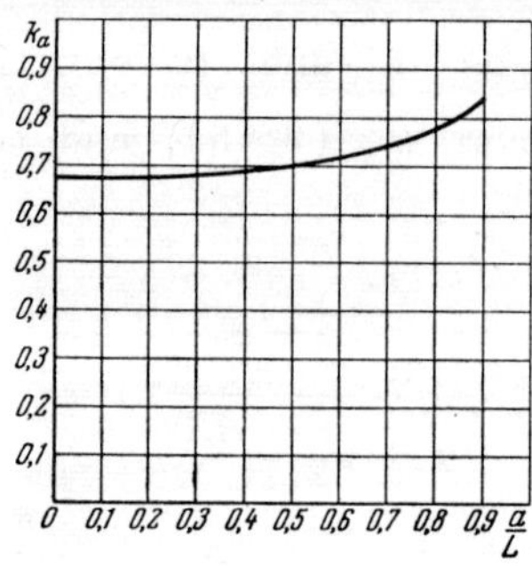

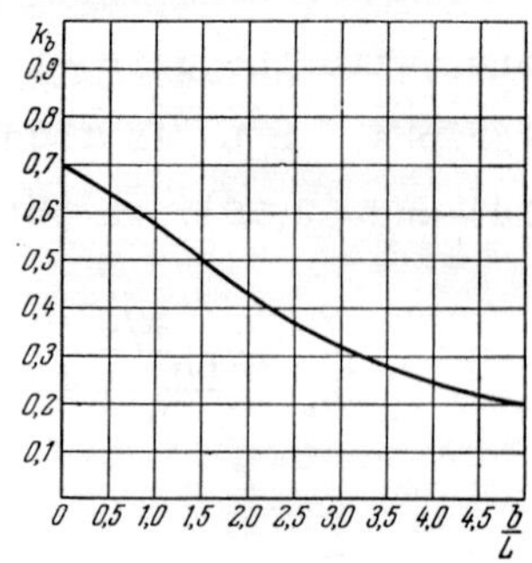

Fig. 32

CHAPTER III. INFINITE FLOW PAST A POLYGONAL OBSTACLE

A. FLOW AROUND A WEDGE

In Chapter I we discussed the flow of an infinite jet past a plane plate (Fig. 1). Now we consider the more general problem of flow past an asymmetric wedge with a central angle $2\pi\kappa$. Particular cases of this problem are flow around a symmetric wedge and flow past a plate inclined to the stream.

Many have studied this particular class of problem. Both Bobylev [20] and Rethy [21] solved the problem of symmetric flow past a wedge. The specific problem of asymmetric wedge flow was solved by Gerlach [22], but a more general one was studied by Meshcherskii [23]. And, of course, the particular case of an oblique jet flow past a plane plate was studied by Rayleigh [13]. The first flow considered is shown in Fig. 33, and it is now appropriate to define our basic terms. The flow velocity and the angle between the velocity and the x-axis at infinity will be designated as v_0 and θ_0 respectively. At the vertex C of the wedge the streamline bifurcates. In accordance with the selected coordinate axes (Fig. 33), the argument of the complex velocity dw/v_0dz is 0 on CB and is $-2\pi\kappa$ on AC. Although our present flow is not necessarily symmetric, the complex velocity must be 0 at point C. On the streamlines AD and BD, $|dw/v_0dz| = 1$.

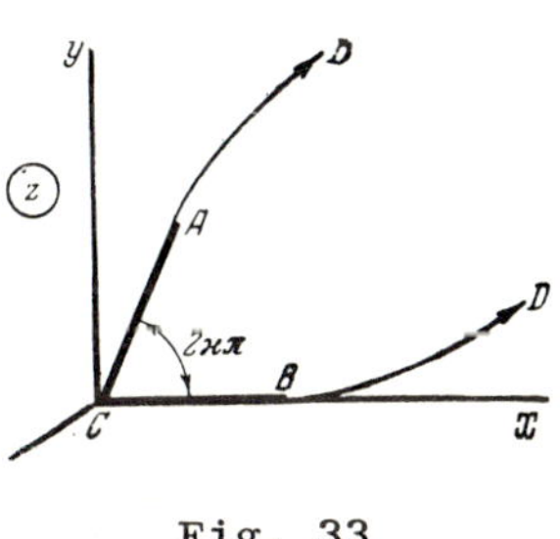

Fig. 33

Thus, the region of change of $dw/v_o dz$ is a sector of a unit circle (Fig. 34). We now introduce the auxiliary function

$$u = \left(\frac{dw}{v_o dz}\right)^{1/2\kappa} , \tag{3.1}$$

whose region of change is, obviously, a unit-radius semicircle (Fig. 35). We shall find the complex potential as a function of u.

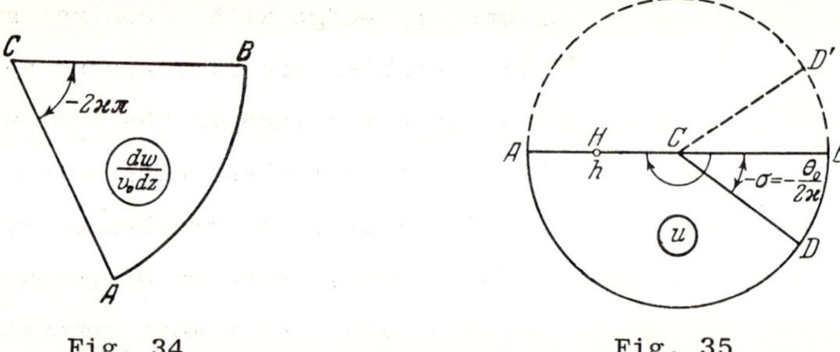

Fig. 34 Fig. 35

Since w need be determined only up to an unessential constant term, we can set w = 0 at C. (Hence, $\psi = 0$ along the entire streamline that bifurcates at C.) Now the region of change of w coincides exactly with the region shown in Fig. 2. At the critical point C, $dw/du = 0$ (see Chapter I, Section F.4), and the complex potential has a second-order zero at C.

At D ($u = \exp[-i\theta_o/2\kappa] = e^{-i\sigma}$), corresponding to the point at infinity, the complex potential has a second order pole (cf. Chapter I, Sections E, p. 42, and F, p. 49). Since w is real on the boundaries CAD and CBD, w(u) is easily extended over the entire u-plane by the symmetry principle.* On extending w through AB to the upper half

*See the remark in Chapter I, Section B, regarding the symmetry principle.

of the circle $|u| \leq 1$, we find that, at $D'(u = e^{i\sigma})$, symmetric to D, $w(u)$ has a second-order pole. No new singularities appear as a result of the extension of w through the boundaries of the unit circle to the entire u-plane. At the point at infinity in the u-plane, corresponding to point C, w has a second order zero—i.e., its expansion in negative powers of u must begin with a term containing u^{-2}.

Since we know all the zeros and poles of the complex potential w, it is easy to find its analytical expression. Clearly, the ratio $w(u - e^{i\sigma})^2 (u - e^{-i\sigma})^2/u^2$ must be finite and holomorphic on the entire u-plane. Thus, according to the Liouville theorem, the ratio must be equal to a constant. If we designate this contant by N, we have

$$w = \frac{Nu^2}{(u - e^{-i\sigma})^2 (u - e^{i\sigma})^2}$$

or

$$w = \frac{Nu^2}{(u^2 - 2u \cos \sigma + 1)^2} \ . \tag{3.2}$$

Since $\operatorname{Im} w = 0$ on the real axis, N is a real constant. Furthermore

$$\frac{dw}{du} = \frac{2Nu(1 - u^2)}{(u^2 + 1 - 2u \cos \sigma)^3} \ . \tag{3.3}$$

The lengths of the wedge sides $CB = \ell_1$ and $CA = \ell_2$ do not appear directly in Eqs. (3.1) or (3.3). Therefore, it is more convenient to prescribe the central angle of the wedge $2\pi\kappa$, the direction of the velocity at infinity (the angle θ_0), and the constant N, and then to determine the parameters ℓ_1 and ℓ_2 from

$$z(u) = \int \frac{dz}{dw}\frac{dw}{du}\,du = \frac{2N}{v_o}\int \frac{u^{1-2\kappa}(1 - u^2)}{(u^2 + 1 - 2u\cos\sigma)^3}\,du \quad . \qquad (3.4)$$

From Eq. (3.4) (see Fig. 35) it follows that

$$\ell_1 = \frac{2N}{v_o}\int_0^1 \frac{u^{1-2\kappa}(1 - u^2)}{(u^2 + 1 - 2u\cos\sigma)^3}\,du \quad . \qquad (3.5)$$

After passage around C along an infinitesimal semi-circle in the clockwise direction (Fig. 35), $u^{1-2\kappa}$ takes the form $\exp[-\pi i(1 - 2\kappa)](-u)^{1-2\kappa}$. From Eq. (3.4) we then obtain

$$\ell_2 \exp[2i\pi\kappa] = \exp[2\pi i\kappa - \pi i]\,\frac{2N}{v_o}\int_0^1 \frac{(-u)^{1-2\kappa}(1 - u^2)}{(u^2 + 1 - 2u\cos\sigma)^3}\,du \;,$$

or, after a change of variables from u to $-\xi$ and obvious simplifications,

$$\ell_2 = \frac{2N}{v_o}\int_0^1 \frac{\xi^{1-2\kappa}(1 - \xi^2)}{(\xi^2 + 1 + 2\xi\cos\sigma)^3}\,d\xi \quad . \qquad (3.6)$$

From Eqs. (3.5) and (3.6) it follows that the ratio ℓ_1/ℓ_2 depends only on κ and $\sigma = \theta_o/2\kappa$. Therefore, if the angle between the sides of the wedge and the angle of inclination θ_o of the velocity vector at infinity are given, then the lengths ℓ_1 and ℓ_2 cannot be chosen arbitrarily. This does not mean, of course, that an arbitrary wedge cannot be placed in a flow at an arbitrary angle, it does mean, however, that for every wedge with given 2κ and ℓ_1/ℓ_2 there exists only one angle θ_o for which the bifurcation of the flow occurs at the nose of the wedge. For other angles of attack, the critical (stagnation) point C, where the streamline bifurcates, is located on one of the wedge sides, and the nose H does not coincide with the stagnation point C. If the wedge is placed with a side against the approaching flow, then the velocity at H is infinite (Fig. 36). If the wedge is placed with the opening against the approaching flow (Fig. 37), then the velocity at H remains 0.

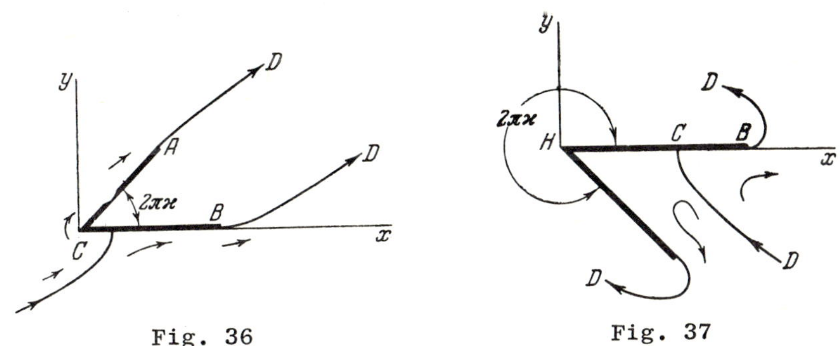

Fig. 36

Fig. 37

The problems shown in Figs. 36 and 37 can be solved. However, while the flow in Fig. 37 may have immediate physical significance, the flow in Fig. 36 has questionable significance because of the infinite velocity at H. On the other hand, one cannot reject completely the possibility of the latter's practical application. In wing theory, for example, such a flow is known to exist—namely, the flow around a thin wing with an infinite velocity at the leading edge [24, cf. 25].

We will give the general solution to the problem when the critical (stagnation) point C is not at the vertex H of the wedge. The flows in Figs. 36 and 37 differ only in that in Fig. 36 $0 < 2\kappa < 1$, while in Fig. 37 $1 < 2\kappa < 2$. Therefore, the general solutions to these problems are essentially the same. We turn then to Fig. 36 and map the regions of change of w and $dw/v_0 dz$ onto the same region of the parametric variable u—i.e., onto the lower unit semicircle of Fig. 35. Thus the points A, C, and B have the corresponding values -1, 0, and 1 in the u-plane. Consequently, the vertex H of the wedge corresponds to some point $u = h$, not to $u = 0$. If the critical point C is located on HB (Fig. 36), then h is positive. If C is located on HA, then $h < 0$.

Clearly, the region of change of w is identical to that obtained when the flow split at the vertex of the wedge (Fig. 33). Therefore, Eqs. (3.2) and (3.3) remain valid for the general case (Figs. 36 and 37). However, the relation between dw/v_0dz and u is not given by Eq. (3.1) in the general case. At C, dw/v_0dz has a first-order zero since C is a critical point where $dw/v_0dz = 0$. As we pass completely around C along a very small contour in a clockwise direction, the argument of the velocity vector increases by π (Fig. 36) and, consequently, the argument of dw/v_0dz decreases by π. Also arg(u) in the u-plane (Fig. 35) decreases by π as we pass around $C(u = 0)$ in a clockwise direction. Under similar circumstances, passage around H through the exterior wedge angle (Fig. 36) produces a decrease of $(\pi - 2\pi\kappa)$ in the argument of the velocity vector, and $\arg(dw/v_0dz)$ increases by $(\pi - 2\pi\kappa)$. The corresponding clockwise passage around H in Fig. 35 causes $\arg(u - h)$ to decrease by π. Thus, dw/v_0dz has a singularity of the type $(u - h)^{2\kappa-1}$ at H $(u = h)$—i.e., $dw/v_0dz = O[(u - h)^{2\kappa-1}]$. On the circle $|u| = 1$, $dw/v_0dz = 1$. Consequently, according to the symmetry principle (see Chapter I, Section B) dw/v_0dz must have a singularity of the type $(u - 1/h)^{-(2\kappa-1)}$ at $H'(u = 1/h)$. According to the same symmetry principle, dw/v_0dz has a second-order pole at the point $u = \infty$ after analytical extension to the entire u-plane.

A study of the flow region reveals clearly that in the extended region (the entire u-plane) the only zeros and singularities of $dw/v_o dz$ occur at the above-mentioned points $u = 0$, $u = h$, $u = 1/h$, and $u = \infty$. It follows immediately that $dw/v_o dz$ must have the form

$$\frac{dw}{v_o dz} = M \frac{u(u - h)^{2\kappa - 1}}{(u \quad 1/h)^{2\kappa - 1}} ,$$

where M is a real constant. This constant is easily determined because at $B(u = 1)$ the complex velocity must be unity. Thus, $M = (-h)^{1-2\kappa}$ and finally

$$\frac{dw}{v_o dz} = u\left(\frac{u - h}{1 - hu}\right)^{2\kappa - 1} . \tag{3.7}$$

It is easy to see that Eq. (3.7) gives the proper values of $dw/v_o dz$ on the lower unit semicircle. Clearly, in Eq. (3.7) $dw/v_o dz$ has the proper singularities and zeros, the proper arguments on AHCB, and, on the arc ADB, $|dw/v_o dz| = 1$.

When $2\kappa > 1$ the velocity at H is 0 and the flow pattern changes from that of Fig. 36 to that of Fig. 37. When $h = 0$, points H and C coincide and the flow pattern returns to that in Fig. 33. Furthermore, Eq. (3.7) becomes (3.1). Equations (3.2) and (3.7) give the general solution to the problem and it is easy to use them to compute $z(u)$ and the pressure at each point in the flow region.

In 1915 Bryan and Jones [26] made numerical calculations from the theory for the case when the vertex H and stagnation point C do not coincide and the wedge is positioned with the opening against the flow (Fig. 37). In the ensuing discussion we consider only those flows in which the flow bifurcation occurs at the wedge nose and κ is a rational fraction.

When κ is a rational fraction, evaluation of the integrals in Eqs. (3.5) and (3.6) gives elementary functions. Computations for a symmetric case were done by D. K. Bobylev [20] and for the general case by I. V. Meshcherskii [23]. Besides determing the ratio ℓ_1/ℓ_2, it is important to find the pressure force acting on the wedge. The difference between the pressure p at an arbitrary point and the constant pressure p_o on the jets' surfaces behind the wedge is determined from the Bernoulli integral

$$p - p_o = \frac{\rho}{2}\left(v_o^2 - v^2\right) = \frac{\rho v_o^2}{2}\left(1 - |u|^{4\kappa}\right) , \qquad (3.8)$$

where ρ is the density of the fluid and $v = |dw/dz|$.

First, we analyze in detail the flow past a plane plate* [13]. The results of Bobylev's and Meshcherskii's computations will be given without any intermediate calculations.

For flow past a plane plate $\kappa = 1/2$ and $\sigma = \theta_o/2\kappa = \alpha_o$, where α_o is the angle of attack of the plate. The length of the plate is $\ell = \ell_1 + \ell_2$ and, according to Eq. (3.4), ℓ is expressed by

$$\ell = \frac{2N}{v_o} \int_{-1}^{1} \frac{1 - u^2}{(u^2 + 1 - 2u \cos \sigma)^3} du = \frac{2N}{v_o} I . \qquad (3.9)$$

After a change of variables

$$\frac{u - \cos \sigma}{\sin \sigma} = \tan t ,$$

*In Section VI.A, the final equations are given for the forces acting on a wedge located in a jet of arbitrary discharge.

the integral in Eq. (3.9) takes the form

$$I = \frac{1}{\sin^4\sigma} \int_{-(\pi/2)+(\sigma/2)}^{\sigma/2} \cos^4 t \; [\sin\sigma\,(1 - \tan^2 t) - 2\cos\sigma\tan t]\; dt$$

or

$$I = \frac{1}{2\sin^4\sigma} \int_{-(\pi/2)+(\sigma/2)}^{\sigma/2} [-\sin\,(2t - \sigma) + \sin\sigma\cos^2 2t - \cos\sigma\cos 2t\sin 2t]\; dt\,.$$

Hence, by taking into account that $\sigma = \alpha_o$, we have

$$\ell = \frac{N}{v_o \sin^4\alpha_o}\left(1 + \frac{\pi\sin\alpha_o}{4}\right)\,. \tag{3.10}$$

Along the plate $dz = dx$; thus, the force P, normal to the plate, is given by

$$P = \int_{-1}^{1} (p - p_o)\,\frac{dz}{du}\,du = \rho N v_o \int_{-1}^{1} \frac{(1 - u^2)^2}{(u^2 + 1 - 2u\cos\sigma)^3}\,du\;,$$

where use has been made of the Bernoulli integral (3.8). By changing u to the variable t, introduced above, we obtain

$$P = \rho N v_o \frac{1}{\sin^3\sigma} \int_{-(\pi/2)+(\sigma/2)}^{\sigma/2} \sin^2(2t - \sigma)\;dt = \frac{\rho N v_o \pi}{4\sin^3\sigma}\,.$$

From this result, by taking into account that $\sigma = \alpha_o$ and by using Eq. (3.10), we obtain the well-known Rayleigh result [13]

$$P = \frac{\rho v_o^2 \ell}{2}\,\frac{2\pi\sin\alpha_o}{4 + \pi\sin\alpha_o}\,. \tag{3.11}$$

For $\alpha_o = \pi/2$ we obtain, as expected, Eq. (1.33) for a plate located normal to the flow. The quantity

$$C_n = \frac{2P}{\rho v_o^2 \ell} = \frac{2\pi \sin \alpha_o}{4 + \pi \sin \alpha_o}$$

is called the normal pressure coefficient. The drag and lift coefficients of the plate are obtained by multiplying C_n by $\sin \alpha_o$ and $\cos \alpha_o$ respectively.

It is also easy to compute the position of the center of pressure $\bar{x}$ for the above flow. Until now there have been no essential restrictions placed on the location of the coordinate origin. In the above equations for wedge flow the only condition imposed was that the x-axis lie along the side CB of the wedge C. It was not essential that the coordinate origins on Figs. 33, 36, and 37 be chosen at the wedge vertex. For the plane-plate case we place the coordinate origin at the end A of the plate (Fig. 38). Then the location of the center of pressure is expressed by

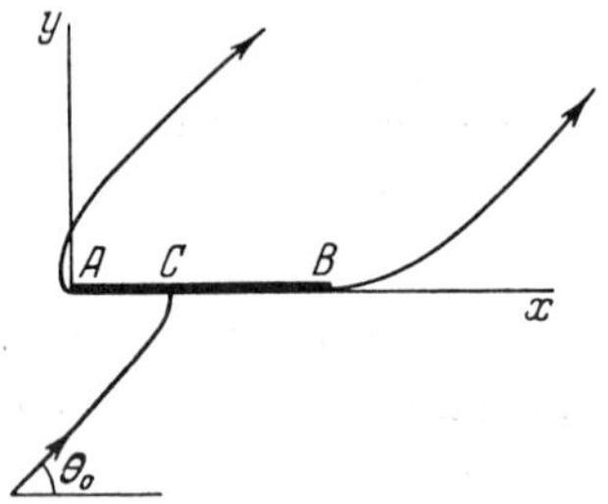

$$\bar{x} = \frac{1}{P} \int_{-1}^{1} (p - p_o)\, z \frac{dz}{du}\, du \quad . \quad (3.12)$$

By performing the indicated integration we are led to [2]

$$\bar{x} = \frac{\ell}{2}\left(1 - \frac{3}{2}\,\frac{\cos \alpha_o}{4 + \pi \sin \alpha_o}\right) \quad . \quad (3.13)$$

Fig. 38

The normal pressure-force coefficient C_n and the location of the center of pressure $\bar{x}$ are given in Table 7 for various values of $\alpha_o = \theta_o$ [2,27,28].

Now we consider a symmetric flow around a symmetric wedge. Accordingly, the wedge-side lengths (Fig. 33) $\ell_1 = CB$ and $\ell_2 = CA$ are equal and the velocity at infinity forms

TABLE 7

α_o (deg)	$C_n = \frac{2P}{\rho \ell v_o^2}$	$\bar{x}/\ell$	α_o (deg)	$C_n = \frac{2P}{\rho \ell v_o^2}$	$\bar{x}/\ell$
90	0.88	0.5	30	0.563	0.383
70	0.849	0.463	20	0.423	0.361
50	0.751	0.425	10	0.24	0.337

equal angles $\theta_o = \pi\kappa$ with the wedge sides. Then P_1 and P_2, the normal pressures on the wedge sides, are also equal. The wedge's drag X is directed along the axis of symmetry of the wedge and is, obviously,

$$X = (P_1 + P_2) \sin \pi\kappa = 2P_1 \sin (\pi\kappa) \quad .$$

The base width of the wedge is $2\ell_1 \sin (\pi\kappa)$. The drag coefficient C_X, related to the wedge's base width, is expressed by

$$C_X = \frac{2X}{\rho v_o^2 2\ell_1 \sin \pi\kappa} = \frac{2P}{\rho v_o^2 \ell_1} \quad .$$

The values of C_X obtained by Bobylev are given in Table 8 [2, 23], in which the values κ 180 deg are equal to one-half the included angle of the wedge, measured in degrees. Thus, for a plane plate, $\kappa = 1/2$ and κ 180 deg = 90 deg.

It is appropriate to examine next Meshcherskii's computations [23] for a nonsymmetric wedge (Fig. 33). He computed the ratio $P_1 \sin \theta_o / \rho v_o^2 \ell_1$ for various included angles of the wedge and different angles of attack. After multiplying this ratio by $2/\sin \theta_o$ we obtain the normal pressure coefficient on one side of the wedge

$$C_{n_1} = \frac{2P_1}{\rho v_o^2 \ell_1} \quad ,$$

whose values are given in Tables 9 through 11. It is unnecessary to compute the pressure coefficient C_{n_2} on the other side of the wedge because the values C_{n_1} and C_{n_2} are symmetric in the sense that, for an attack angle θ_o at infinity, C_{n_2} is equal to the C_{n_1} corresponding to an angle of attack $2\pi\kappa - \theta_o$.

TABLE 8

κ 180 deg (deg)	C_X	κ 180 deg (deg)	C_X
10	0.199	100	0.907
20	0.359	110	0.931
30	0.489	120	0.950
40	0.593	130	0.964
45	0.637	135	0.970
50	0.677	140	0.975
60	0.745	150	0.984
70	0.800	160	0.990
80	0.844	170	0.996
90	0.879		

TABLE 9. WEDGE WITH INCLUDED ANGLE 45 deg (κ = 1/8)

θ_o (deg)	ℓ_1/ℓ_2	C_{n_1}
5	782.0	0.1263
10	45.59	0.229
15	7.974	0.3085
20	1.237	0.37
22.5	1.0000	0.3945
25	0.5162	0.415
30	0.1254	0.448
35	0.0215	0.471
40	0.0013	0.483

TABLE 10. WEDGE WITH INCLUDED ANGLE 90 deg ($\kappa = 1/4$)

θ_o (deg)	ℓ_1/ℓ_2	C_{n_1}
5	8661.0	0.1285
10	567.2	0.237
15	115.4	0.329
20	36.89	0.407
25	14.92	0.472
30	6.926	0.525
35	3.493	0.569
40	1.848	0.606
45	1.0000	0.637
50	0.5411	0.662
55	0.2863	0.683
60	0.1443	0.7
65	0.0670	0.713
70	0.0271	0.724
75	0.0087	0.731
80	0.0017	0.737
85	0.0012	0.741

TABLE 11. WEDGE WITH INCLUDED ANGLE 135 deg ($\kappa = 3/8$)

θ_o (deg)	ℓ_1/ℓ_2	C_{n_1}	θ_o (deg)	ℓ_1/ℓ_2	C_{n_1}
10	1863.0	0.2495	75	0.5719	0.81
20	130.4	0.417	85	0.2615	0.831
30	28.05	0.547	90	0.1705	0.8408
40	9.334	0.637	95	0.1071	0.85
50	3.824	0.71	105	0.0357	0.861
60	1.748	0.758	115	0.0077	0.868
67.5	1.0000	0.787	125	0.0005	0.873

The next wedge flow to be studied is shown in Fig. 39—i.e., the wedge is located with its opening against the flow. The angle of attack of side CB is $180 - \theta_o$ deg. Also, for an angle of attack of $(2\pi - 2\pi\kappa) - (\pi - \theta_o) = \pi + \theta_o - 2\pi\kappa$, the normal pressure coefficient C_{n_1} on CB is equal to the normal pressure coefficient C_{n_2} on CA for an angle of

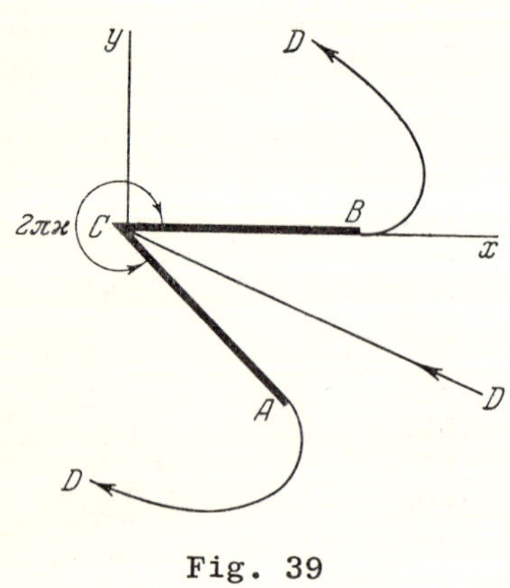

Fig. 39

θ_o (the angle made by the velocity at infinity and the x-axis)—i.e., for an angle of attack of the first side CB of $\pi - \theta_o$ (see Tables 12 and 13). Finally, Meshcherskii computed the wedge drag coefficient, defined with respect to the length ℓ_2 of the side CA, when the flow approaches along one of the wedge's sides ($\theta_o = 0$). The length of CB, which is parallel to the flow velocity at infinity, is infinite (Table 14).

TABLE 12. WEDGE WITH INCLUDED ANGLE 90 deg ($\kappa = 3/4$)

$180-\theta_o$ (deg)	ℓ_1/ℓ_2	C_{n_1}
5	0.4114	0.985
10	0.4665	0.984
15	0.5258	0.982
20	0.5895	0.98
25	0.6583	0.979
30	0.7328	0.977
35	0.8138	0.975
40	0.9024	0.973
45	1.0000	0.97
50	1.108	0.968
55	1.229	0.965
60	1.365	0.96
65	1.519	0.956
70	1.696	0.951
75	1.9029	0.945
80	2.143	0.939
85	2.431	0.93

Flows around various polygonal obstacles have been studied by numerous authors. For example, Zhukovskii [10]

TABLE 13. WEDGE WITH INCLUDED ANGLE 135 deg ($\kappa = 5/8$)

$180-\theta_o$ (deg)	ℓ_1/ℓ_2	C_{n_1}
10	0.1003	0.968
20	0.1699	0.967
30	0.2650	0.964
40	0.3917	0.958
50	0.5592	0.952
60	0.7822	0.943
67.5	1.0000	0.937
75	1.278	0.927
85	1.788	0.913
90	2.130	0.903
95	2.553	0.894
105	3.773	0.865
115	5.877	0.829
125	9.966	0.779

TABLE 14

$360\ \kappa$ (deg)	C_X	$360\ \kappa$ (deg)	C_X	$360\ \kappa$ (deg)	C_X
10	0.0240	60	0.5120	120	0.7262
20	0.0878	70	0.6096	130	0.6608
30	0.1796	80	0.6878	135	0.6176
40	0.288	90	0.7414	140	0.5678
45	0.3448	100	0.7668	150	0.4506
50	0.4020	110	0.7620	160	0.3134
				170	0.1614

[In Table 14 C_X is defined to be

$$C_X = \frac{2P_2 \sin(\kappa\ 360)}{\rho v_o^2 \ell_2}$$]

examined in detail the flows in Figs. 40 and derived the equations required to describe them. Also, Bryan and Jones [26] outlined a general solution for the flows in Fig. 40 for obstacles consisting of an arbitrary number of connected

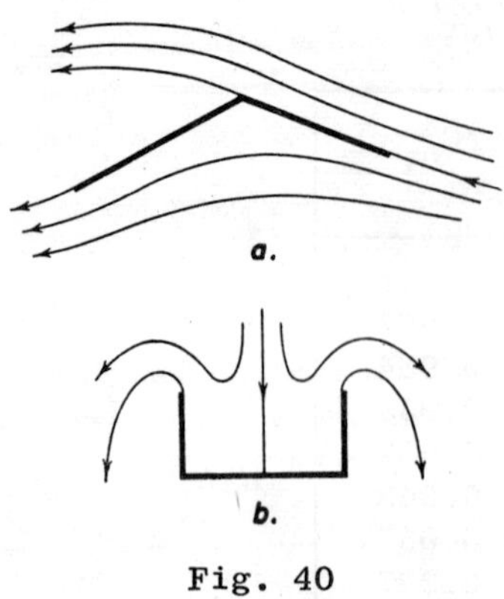

Fig. 40

plates. Other similar and old works may also be cited. However, such efforts have only narrow or special interest, and the particular problem solutions required can usually be obtained by application of the methods that we have examined in detail above. Hence, we will now consider some problems whose solutions give us further insight into the methodology of jet theory.

B. JET FLOW AROUND A PLATE WITH A STAGNATION REGION IN FRONT OF IT

In 1899, Chaplygin [29] considered the flow shown in Fig. 41. This flow is distinguished by the presence of two zones of constant pressure that are bounded by split streamlines, where the magnitude of the velocity v is constant. One zone is located behind the plate (as expected); the other, bounded by A'OAA', is in front of the plate.

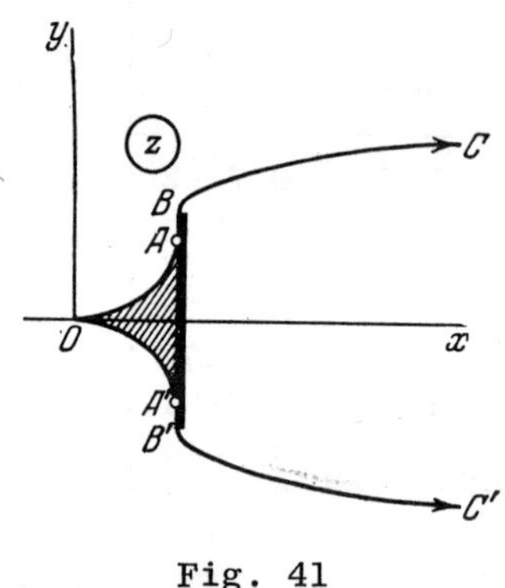

Fig. 41

Consider the function

$$\tau = \ell n\ (v_o dz/dw) = \ell n\ (v_o/v) + i\theta\ ,$$

where v_o is the flow velocity at infinity.* On the jets BC and B'C', $\mathrm{Re}\ \tau = \ell n\ (v_o/v) = 0$, where θ changes along

*In Chapter I, ω was used in lieu of τ. In this Chapter, ω is used (in conformance with standard notation) to denote the half-period of the Weierstrass function.

BC from $\pi/2$ to 0 and along B'C' from $-\pi/2$ to 0. On AB and A'B', θ is equal respectively to $\pi/2$ and $-\pi/2$, while v varies from v_o to some value $v_1 < v_o$. On OA' and OA, θ varies, but $\operatorname{Re} \tau = \ln (v_o/v_1) > 0$ remains constant. Thus, the region of change of τ is a rectangle, as shown in Fig. 42.

We choose as a parametric variable

$$t = \frac{2\omega i}{\pi} \tau \; ; \qquad \tau = - \frac{i\pi}{2\omega} t \quad . \tag{3.14}$$

Obviously, the region of change of t is the rectangle shown in Fig. 43. The height of this rectangle is ω'/i so that, in accordance with (3.14),

$$\omega' = \frac{2\omega i}{\pi} \ln \frac{v_o}{v_1} \quad . \tag{3.15}$$

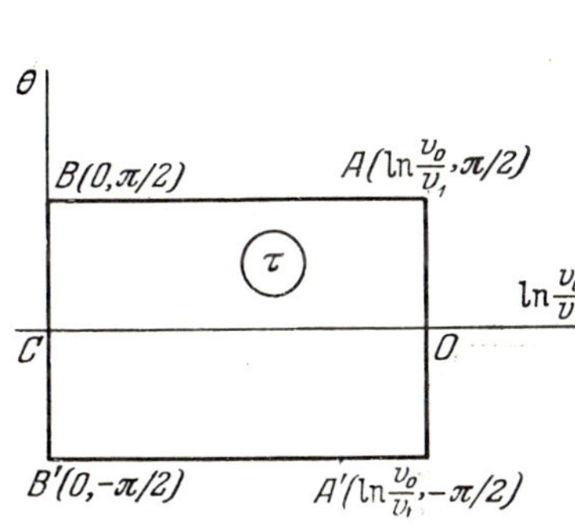

Fig. 42

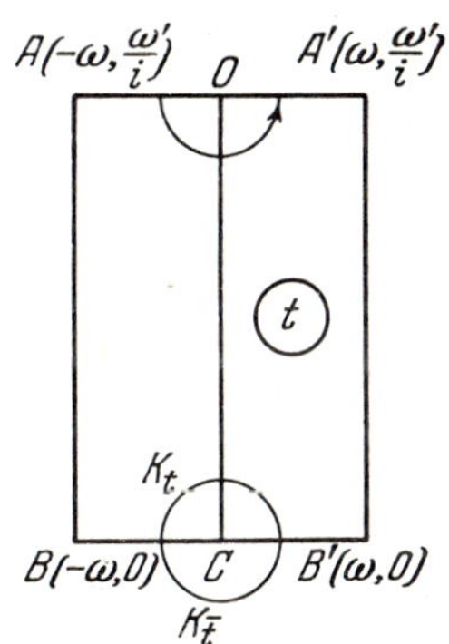

Fig. 43

Since the complex potential w is determined only up to a constant term, we can choose this term so that at point O, $[w(t)]_{t=\omega'} = 0$. Since the streamline bifurcates at point O, $(dw/dt)_{t=\omega'} = 0$ there; hence, w has a second-order zero at point O (Chapter I, Section F.4). We now repeat briefly the arguments of Section I.F. The region of change of w in this problem is exactly the same as that for flow around a plate* (see Fig. 1). These regions are planes with a cut along the real axis corresponding to the bifurcated parts of the streamlines OABC and OA'B'C' (Fig. 44). If we allow for the difference in nomenclature, we observe that Fig. 44 is identical to Fig. 2. Passage along an infinitesimal semicircle at 0 in the t-plane corresponds to passage along an infinitesimal circle at 0 in the w-plane and, clearly, when the infinitesimal vector $(t - \omega')$ turns through an angle π, the equivalent infinitesimal w turns through 2π. Thus, $w = O(t - \omega')^2$. On the other hand, in the neighborhood of point C (the point at infinity in the z-plane), $w = O(1/t^2)$ (cf. Chapter. I, Sections E or F.1). The function w has no other zeros or singular points in the rectangle BB'A'A.

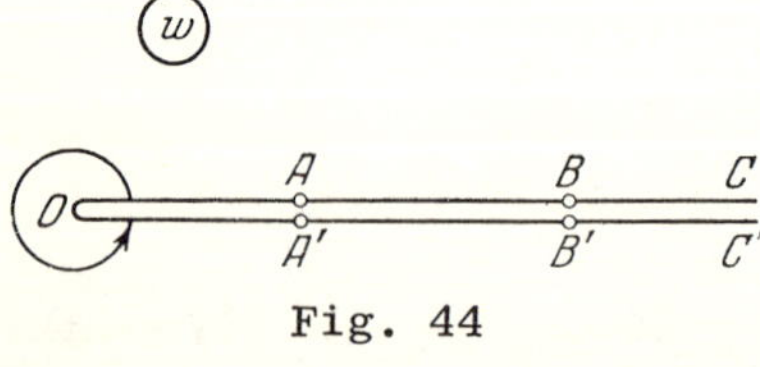

Fig. 44

On the boundaries of ABB'A' the complex potential w is real $(\psi = 0)$. As a result $w(t)$ can be extended by the symmetry principle to the adjacent rectangle with sides ω and ω'/i. Continuous repetition of this process leads to coverage of the entire t-plane with equal rectangles. We find that $w(t) = w(t + 2\omega) = w(t + 2\omega')$ because of the symmetry of the analytic extension of w. Hence, $w(t)$ is a doubly periodic function with second-order poles at $t = \pm 2m_1\omega \pm 2m_2\omega'$ and second-order zeros at $t = \omega' \pm 2m_1\omega \pm 2m_2\omega'$, where m_1 and m_2 are whole numbers. It follows that $w(t)$ is an elliptic function given by the Weierstrass function $\wp$ [30] with periods 2ω and $2\omega'$;

$$w = B[\wp(t) - e_3] \quad , \tag{3.16}$$

*The corresponding regions of change of $\ln (v_0 dz/dw)$ are, however, different.

where B is a real constant and $e_3 = \wp(\omega')$. Actually, the elliptic function is determined up to a constant term by its zeros and poles in the periodic array of rectangles. In this array, the function, $B[\wp(t) - e_3]$ has a unique second-order pole at the origin, where $\wp(t) = (1/t^2) + O(t)$, and a unique second-order zero at $t = \omega'$, where $\wp'(\omega') = 0$.

Equations (3.14) and (3.16) give a general solution in parametric form. With them it is possible to compute the plate dimensions as well as those of the stagnation region in front of the plate and the fluid-pressure force on the plate. Obviously,

$$z = \frac{1}{v_o} \int \exp\left[\ell n \frac{dzv_o}{dw}\right] dw = \frac{1}{v_o} \int \exp\,[\tau]\, \frac{dw}{dt}\, dt$$

$$= \frac{B}{v_o} \int \exp\left[-\frac{\pi i t}{2\omega}\right] \wp'(t)\, dt \quad . \tag{3.17}$$

If the coordinates of point A' in the z-plane are (x_1, y_1), then

$$z_1 = x_1 + iy_1 = \frac{B}{v_o} \int_{\omega'}^{\omega+\omega'} \exp\left[-\frac{\pi i t}{\omega}\right] \wp'(t)\, dt \quad . \tag{3.18}$$

Similarly, if the coordinates of point B' are $(x_1, -\ell/2)$, where ℓ is the length of the plate $B'B$, then

$$x_1 - \frac{i\ell}{2} = \frac{B}{v_o} \int_{\omega'}^{\omega'+\omega} \exp\left[-\frac{\pi i t}{2\omega}\right] \wp'(t)\, dt$$

$$+ \frac{B}{v_o} \int_{\omega'+\omega}^{\omega} \exp\left[-\frac{\pi i t}{2\omega}\right] \wp'(t)\, dt \quad . \tag{3.19}$$

To compute x_1, y_1, and ℓ Chaplygin expressed $\wp'(t)$ as a series of trigonometric functions, substituted the series in (3.18) and (3.19), and integrated by parts. The details are in Ref. [29]. Here we give only the final series used for computation of the stagnation-region length $a = x_1$, the stagnation-region width $b = -2y_1$, and the length ℓ of the plate; hence,

$$\left.\begin{aligned}
a &= \frac{\ell}{2q^{1/2}} \; \frac{64 \sum_{1}^{\infty} [n^3/(4n^2 - 1)][q^n/(1 - q^{2n})]}{\pi + 4 + 64 \sum_{1}^{\infty} (-1)^{n-1} [n^3/(4n^2 - 1)][q^n/(1 - q^{2n})]} \\
b &= \frac{\ell}{q^{1/2}} \; \frac{64 \sum_{1}^{\infty} (-1)^{n-1} [n^3/(4n^2 - 1)][q^n/(1 - q^{2n})]}{\pi + 4 + 64 \sum_{1}^{\infty} (-1)^{n-1} [n^3/(4n^2 - 1)][q^{2n}/(1 - q^{2n})]} \\
\ell &= \frac{2B}{v_o} \left(\frac{\pi}{\omega}\right)^2 \left[\frac{\pi + 4}{8} + 8 \sum_{1}^{\infty} (-1)^{n-1} \frac{n^3}{4n^2 - 1} \, \frac{q^{2n}}{1 - q^{2n}}\right] \\
q &= \frac{v_1^2}{v_o^2} = \exp\,[i\omega'\pi/\omega] \quad .
\end{aligned}\right\} \tag{3.20}$$

The pressure distribution on the plate is given by the Bernoulli integral. The resultant pressure force is obtained by integration. However, these calculations can be reduced considerably by use of the method described below—one that we will use extensively in the future.

Consider the flow past the arbitrary solid arc AOB in Fig. 45. We examine the fluid mass M, bounded at the present instant of time by the contour AOB, the surfaces of the jet AC' and BC, and the contour K, with infinitely large radius and center at the coordinate origin.

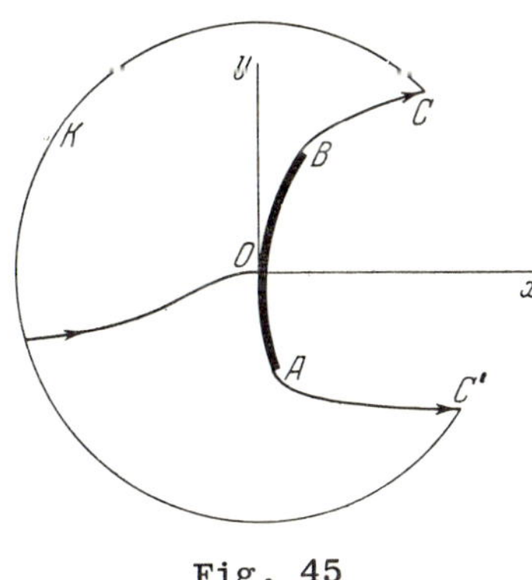

Fig. 45

We now apply the momentum theorem to the mass M of the fluid. It is known that the resultant of a constant pressure acting on a closed contour is 0. Therefore, we can subtract from the external forces acting on M the constant pressure p_o at infinity or, for simplicity, set $p_o = 0$. Thus there are no forces acting on the jets BC and AC'. If the resultant of the pressures acting on AOB is $X + iY$, then the resultant of the pressure forces due to the contour acting on the fluid is $-(X + iY)$. The quantity dz can be represented on an arc in terms of its length ds and a tangential direction. An interior normal vector with magnitude dx is given by idz. If p is the magnitude of the pressure, then the normal pressure vector on an arc element ds of the contour K is ipdz. The total pressure on K will be $i \int_K p\,dz$. During an infinitesimal time interval δT the impulse $(-X - iY + i \int_K p\,dz)\, \delta T$ acts on the fluid M.

Also, during the time δT the fluid particles move. The fixed contour—consisting of K, the surfaces of the jets BC and AC', and the contour AOB—is called the control surface. The flow is steady; hence, the momentum of the fluid within the control surface must be constant. Thus, the change in momentum of the particular collection of fluid M is computed in terms of the net flux of momentum through the control surface—i.e., the change is equal to the momentum of fluid coming into the control surface plus the change in the momentum of the particles of M displaced but still inside the control surface, less the momentum of fluid particles leaving the control surface. The result is expressed by

$$\rho \int (v_x + i v_y)\, d\psi\, \delta T \quad ,$$

taken along the control surface. Since there is no flow through the streamlines BC, AC', and AOB $(d\psi = 0)$, the only contribution to the integral comes from integration along the contour K. According to the momentum theorem, equating the impulse of the external forces acting on M to the change of momentum of M, and cancelling δT, we obtain

$$-X - iY + i \int_K p\, dz = \rho \int (v_x + i v_y)\, d\psi \quad . \tag{3.21}$$

With $p_o = 0$ the Bernoulli integral gives

$$p = \frac{\rho}{2}\left(v_o^2 - v^2\right) = \frac{\rho}{2}\left(v_o^2 - \frac{dw}{dz}\,\overline{\frac{dw}{dz}}\right) \quad .$$

The introduction of this result in Eq. (3.21) produces

$$X + iY = \frac{\rho}{2}\left[i v_o^2 \int_K dz - i \int_K \overline{\frac{dw}{dz}}\, dw - 2 \int_K \overline{\frac{dw}{dz}}\, d\psi\right]$$

or

$$X + iY = \frac{i\rho}{2}\left[v_o^2 \int_K dz - \int_K \overline{\frac{dw}{dz}}\,(d\varphi + i\, d\psi - 2i\, d\psi)\right] ,$$

from which we get

$$X + iY = \frac{i\rho}{2}\left[v_o^2 \int_K dz - \int_K \overline{\frac{dw}{dz}}\, dw\right] . \qquad (3.22)$$

Thus, with Eq. (3.22) we can calculate the resultant pressure force on a solid contour by integration at infinity. This equation also arises as an intermediate result in the derivation of the Levi-Civita equation [31], which will be discussed in Chapter IV. Now, however, we use Eq. (3.22) to find the force X acting on the plate $B'B$ (Fig. 41).

The contour K corresponds to the semicircle K_t with infinitesimal radius in the t-plane (Fig. 43). The center of K_t is at $C(t = 0)$, and the integration proceeds (from C to C') in a clockwise direction.

Consider the expression under the second integral in Eq. (3.22). On BCB', $\text{Im}\, dw = 0$. Thus, the values of dw and $\overline{dw}$ are equal on K_t (which corresponds to a part of BCB'). Also,

$$(dw/v_o dz)\overline{(dw/v_o dz)} = |dw/v_o dz|^2 = 1$$

on BCB'. From this and the symmetry principle [3,4], it follows that $\overline{dw/v_o dz} = dw/v_o dz$ on $K_{\bar{t}}$. Thus, $v_o[\overline{(dw/v_o dz)dw}]$ on K_t can be replaced by $v_o[(dz v_o/dw)dw] = v_o^2\, dz$ on $K_{\bar{t}}$. Accordingly, since passage along K_t in a clockwise direction is equivalent to counterclockwise passage along $K_{\bar{t}}$, the second integral in Eq. (3.22) can be given as $-v_o^2 \int_{K_{\bar{t}}} dz$. A similar change of contour may be introduced into the first integral in Eq. (3.22) and the pair of integrals reduced to one. Thus, Eq. (3.22) becomes

$$X + iY = -\frac{i\rho v_o^2}{2} \oint dz \quad , \tag{3.23}$$

where the integral is to be taken counterclockwise over an infinitesimal contour about $t = 0$ in the t-plane. By using Eq. (3.17) to express z as a function of t, we are led to

$$X + iY = \frac{-i\rho v_o^2}{2} \frac{B}{v_o} \oint \exp\,[-\pi i t/2\omega]\, \wp'(t)\, dt \quad . \tag{3.24}$$

Since

$$\wp'(t) = -\frac{2}{t^3} + O(t)$$

and

$$\exp\,[-\pi i t/2\omega] = 1 - \frac{\pi i t}{2\omega} + \frac{1}{2}\left(-\frac{\pi i t}{2\omega}\right)^2 + \ldots \quad ,$$

Eq. (3.24) gives

$$X = \frac{\rho v_o B \pi^3}{4\omega^2} \quad ; \qquad Y = 0 \quad .$$

The coefficient B is expressed in terms of ℓ through Eq. (3.20). Then,

$$X = \frac{\rho}{2} v_o^2 \ell 2\pi \left\{\pi + 4 + 64 \sum_1^\infty (-1)^{n-1}[n^3/(4n^2 - 1)][q^{2n}/(1 - q^{2n})]\right\}^{-1} . \tag{3.25}$$

From Eqs. (3.20) and (3.25) it is clear that the dimensions of the stagnation region in front of the plate and the force X depend on the arbitrary parameter q. With $q = 0$,

$a = 0$ and $b = 0$; hence, we obtain the common case of flow past a plate (Chapter I, Section D). In this case Eq. (3.25) becomes equal to Eq. (1.34). However, Chaplygin [29] does not limit himself only to solution of the above problem. Using Zhukovskii's general formulas [see Chapter I, Eqs. (1.60) and (1.61)], Chaplygin concludes, "In any jet flow problem the neighborhood surrounding any critical point (points with zero velocity) on a wall can be replaced by a finite mass of stagnant fluid; the dimensions of the stagnant mass in the x-y plane generally depend within certain limits on some arbitrary parameter."

It certainly has long ago occurred to the reader to ask, "What kind of flow really occurs at these critical points or stagnation regions in the flow?" The same question can, of course, be asked about nonseparated flow--e.g., flow past a wing. Some discussion will be given regarding these questions in the chapter on cavitation, Chapter V.

C. FLOW PAST A PLATE WITH THE SEPARATION FROM ITS UPPER SURFACE

A flow with velocity v_o at infinity approaches a plate BD of length ℓ (Fig. 46). The velocity vector forms an angle α_o with the x-axis at infinity as shown. The flow separates from the plate at points C and D. Point D is located at the trailing edge of the plate, and point C, in contrast to our previous problems (e.g., Fig. 38), is located somewhere on the upper surface of the plate. This problem was first solved in 1933 by Chaplygin and Lavrentiev [32] with the hope of improving the picture of flow around

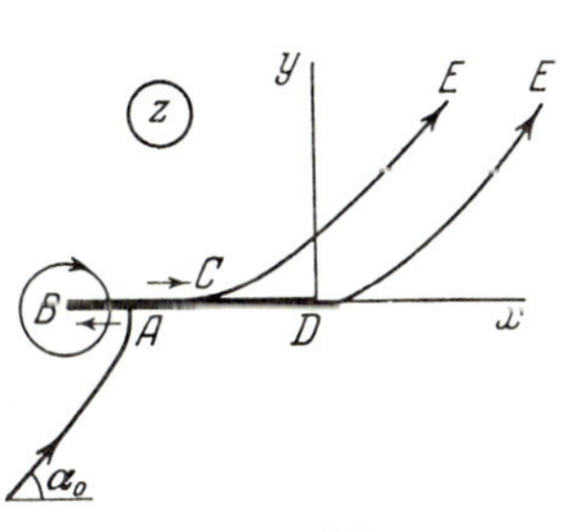

Fig. 46

a wing profile. A new analysis and solutions were given to the same problem by Sekerzh-Zenkovich [33] a year later. We shall discuss Chaplygin's and Lavrentiev's solution below.

We begin by mapping the regions of change of the complex potential w and the complex velocity dw/dz to the upper right quadrant of the auxiliary variable $u = \xi + i\eta$ (Fig. 47). We make the critical point A correspond to a point $u = \alpha$ in the u-plane, the front edge B of the plate to $u = \beta$, and the point E at infinity to $u = i$. As usual, we assume that $w = 0$ at A, where the flow bifurcates. Now, $w(u)$ has a second-order zero at A (see Chapter I, Section F.4). At $E(u = i)$, $w(u)$ has a second-order pole (Chapter I, Section F.1). The region of change of the complex potential w is a plane with a cut along the real axis (see, e.g., Fig. 2), exactly as in the previous problem or in those problems of flow past a plate or a wedge.

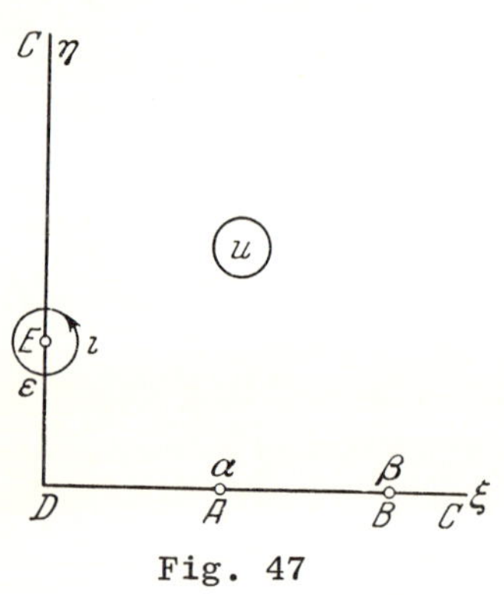

Fig. 47

Along the boundary CBADC, $\text{Im}\, w = 0$. By extending $w(u)$ to the entire u-plane in accordance with the symmetry principle, we show that $w(u)$ must have a second-order zero at the point $u = -\alpha$, symmetric to A relative to the imaginary axis, and a second-order pole at the point $u = -i$, symmetric to E relative to the real axis. From knowledge of the zeros and poles of $w(u)$, it is easy to construct

$$w = N\left(\frac{u^2 - \alpha^2}{u^2 + 1}\right)^2 , \tag{3.26}$$

where N is a real constant. From Eq. (3.26) we obtain

$$\frac{dw}{du} = v_o a \frac{u(u^2 - \alpha^2)}{(u^2 + 1)^3} , \tag{3.27}$$

where $v_o a = 4N(1 + \alpha^2)$.

Now we examine $dw/v_o dz$. This function has a first-order zero at the critical point A, as is shown by a comparison of the change of the arguments of $dw/v_o dz = (v/v_o) \exp[-i\theta]$ and $u - \alpha$ under a corresponding passage around A in the z- and u-planes. Of course, the velocity $v = |dw/dz|$ becomes infinite at the sharp front edge B. As we pass around B in the z-plane along an infinitesimal contour from the lower to the upper side of the plate, the angle θ between the velocity vector and the x-axis decreases by π, whereas the argument of $dw/v_o dz$, which is equal to $-\theta$, increases by π. On the other hand, in passing around B from AB to BC along an infinitesimal contour in a clockwise direction, we observe that the argument of $(u - \beta)^{-1}$ also increases by π. Thus, we conclude that $dw/v_o dz = O(u - \beta)^{-1}$, i.e., $dw/v_o dz$ has a first-order pole at B.

Along the positive real axis, $\mathrm{Im}\,[dw/v_o dz] = 0$ and $dw/v_o dz$ can be extended to the lower right quadrant in accordance with the symmetry principle. There will be no new singularities in the lower quadrant because the only zero and pole of the complex velocity are located on the real axis.

The upper imaginary axis of u corresponds to the free jets. Therefore along this semi-axis and, after the above extension, along the entire imaginary axis, $|dw/v_o dz| = 1$. It follows then that $dw/v_o dz$ can be extended through the imaginary axis. However, now the symmetry principle indicates that, at point B', symmetric to B, there is a zero; at point A', symmetric to A, there is a first-order pole.

Because the complex velocity is unity at $u = \infty$, we find that construction of $dw/v_o dz$ by its zeros and poles leads to

$$\frac{dw}{v_o dz} = \frac{(u - \alpha)(u + \beta)}{(u + \alpha)(u - \beta)} . \tag{3.28}$$

That Eqs. (3.26) and (3.28) give expressions for w and $dw/v_o dz$ which satisfy all appropriate boundary conditions may be verified directly. The angle α_o between the velocity at infinity and the plate is found in terms of α and β if we set $u = i$ in Eq. (3.28). We then obtain

$$\exp\left[-i\alpha_o\right] = \frac{(i - \alpha)(i + \beta)}{(i + \alpha)(i - \beta)} ,$$

from which we conclude that

$$k = \tan\frac{\alpha_o}{2} = \frac{\beta - \alpha}{1 + \alpha\beta} . \tag{3.29}$$

In addition to α_o, the problem is defined by certain other geometric elements, namely, the plate length ℓ and the distance c from the jet separation point at C to the trailing edge D of the plate. It is, however, too complicated to find a, α, and β given α_o, ℓ, and c. It is much more convenient (as we have done before) to prescribe values of the nonphysical parameters a, α, and β and then to determine the corresponding α_o, ℓ, and c. We may calculate α_o directly from Eq. (3.29).

We shall now proceed to determine ℓ and c. From Eqs. (3.27) and (3.28) we have

$$\frac{dz}{du} = a\,\frac{u(u + \alpha)^2\,(u - \beta)}{(u + \beta)\,(u^2 + 1)^3} .$$

By using this equation and the fact that $u = 0$ when $z = 0$, we can expand dz/du in partial fractions and obtain

$$\frac{z}{a} = \frac{Cu - B}{4(u^2 + 1)^2} + \frac{(3C + 4E)u - 4D}{8(u^2 + 1)} + \left(\frac{3C}{8} + \frac{E}{2} + H\right) \arctan u$$
$$+ \frac{F}{2} \ln \frac{\beta^2(u^2 + 1)}{(u + \beta)^2} + \frac{B}{4} + \frac{D}{2}, \tag{3.30}$$

where B, C, D, E, F, and H are:

$$B = -\frac{(1 - k^2)(1 + \beta^2)}{(1 + k\beta)^2} \qquad C = \frac{2k(1 + \beta^2)}{(1 + k\beta)^2}$$

$$D = \frac{1 + 2k\beta - k^2\beta^2}{(1 + k\beta)^2} \qquad E = -\frac{2k(1 + k\beta + \beta^2)}{(1 + k\beta)^2}$$

$$F = -\frac{2k^2\beta^2}{(1 + \beta^2)(1 + k\beta)^2} \qquad H = \frac{2k^2\beta^3}{(1 + \beta^2)(1 + k\beta)^2}.$$

When $u = \beta$, $z = -l$; when $u = \infty$, $z = -c$. Thus, Eq. (3.30) must give

$$-\frac{\ell}{a} = \frac{C\beta - B}{4(1 + \beta^2)^2} + \frac{(3C + 4E)\beta - 4D}{8(1 + \beta^2)} + \left(\frac{3C}{8} + \frac{E}{2} + H\right) \arctan \beta$$
$$+ \frac{F}{2} \ln \frac{1 + \beta^2}{4} + \frac{B}{4} + \frac{D}{2}, \tag{3.31}$$

$$-\frac{c}{a} = \left(\frac{3C}{8} + \frac{E}{2} + H\right) \frac{\pi}{2} + F \ln \beta + \frac{B}{4} + \frac{D}{2}. \tag{3.32}$$

When using Eqs. (3.31) and (3.32), it is convenient to recall that a, α, and β are real and positive, and that $\alpha < \beta$ and $\beta > k$. From Eq. (3.30) it is possible to determine the location of point B [32] by setting $u = \alpha$.

The resultant force $X + iY$ acting on the plate is determined next. In Section B a general formula [Eq. (3.22)] was derived for the resultant force acting on an obstacle in a separated flow. Equation (3.23) was a simplification of (3.22) derived under the following restrictions: 1) the jet surface is mapped on a sector of a straight line; 2) on the jet surface $\operatorname{Im} dw = 0$; and 3) on the jet surface $|dw/v_o dz| = 1$. The present problem meets all of these restrictions. Therefore, we may apply Eq. (3.23) here. However, note that, whereas in the previous problem the point at infinity in the parametric variable plane corresponded to the origin in the physical plane, in the present problem the point E at infinity of the physical z-plane corresponds to the point $u = i$ in the parametric u-plane. Thus, we have

$$X + iY = -\frac{i\rho v_o^2}{2} \oint dz \quad ,$$

where the contour integration is made counterclockwise over an infinitesimal circle ϵ with center at $u = i$. Consider now Eq. (3.30) for $z(u)$. Obviously, integration of the rational fractions will be simple. The logarithmic term can be given in the form

$$\frac{F}{2}\left[\ell n\ (u - i) + \ell n\ (u + i) + \ell n\ \frac{\beta^2}{(u + \beta)^2}\right] .$$

Obviously, as we pass around $u = i$ a jump is produced only in the first of the logarithms enclosed in the square brackets. Thus, in passing counterclockwise around ϵ we observe that the logarithmic term of Eq. (3.30) increases by $F\pi i$.

We are now left to discuss the term containing arctan u. We have

$$\frac{d}{du}(\arctan u) = \frac{1}{1 + u^2} = \frac{1}{2i}\left(\frac{1}{u - i} - \frac{1}{u + i}\right) .$$

Clearly, passage around $u = i$ along ϵ produces a jump of π in $\arctan u$ just as in $(1/2i)\, \ell n\, (u - i)$.* From the above, it follows that

$$\oint dz = a\pi \left[\frac{3C}{8} + \frac{E}{2} + H + iF\right] ,$$

and, consequently,

$$X + iY = \frac{\rho v_o^2 \pi a}{2}\left[F - i\left(\frac{3C}{8} + \frac{E}{2} + H\right)\right] . \qquad (3.33)$$

Equation (3.33) appears to be different from the corresponding equation in [32], but their equivalence is easily established by a few algebraic operations. From the expression given above for F, it can be seen that $X \leqq 0$. In mathematical wing theory X is the point suction force that appears at the leading edge of the wing B. When $\beta = \infty$, point C moves to the leading edge B of the plate and the flow becomes a Rayleigh flow, which was discussed in Section A. Then, the velocity at the leading edge becomes finite and the point suction force disappears $(X = 0)$. The computed values of lift, drag, c/ℓ, and AD/ℓ for various β are given in [32]. In addition, we present here some of the numerical data from Sekerzh-Zenkovich's report [33]. For each angle of attack α_o, Sekerzh-Zenkovich picked the location of the separation point C so that the theoretical lift P equals the experimentally determined lift $\bar{P}$ on the plate.

*This result could have been obtained from the well-known logarithmic representation of arctan u [4,34].

If the theoretical drag is Q, then P and Q are related to X and Y by $Q + Pi = \exp[-i\theta_o](X + iY)$ (Fig. 48). If, then, the experimental drag is $\overline{Q}$, we can construct Table 15 [33].

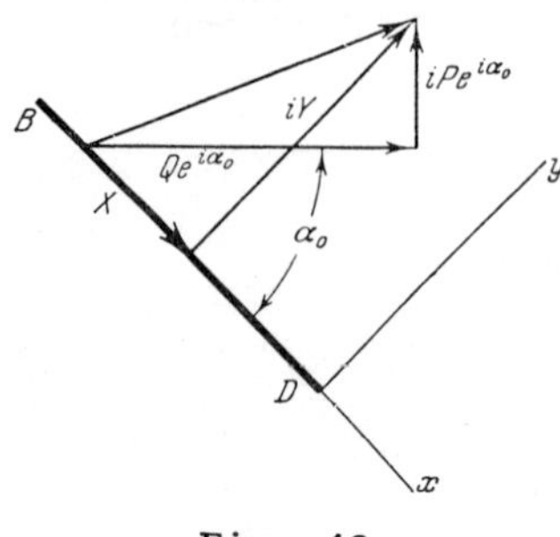

Fig. 48

Chaplygin and Lavrentiev computed the lift and drag for α_o equal to 5, 10, and 15 deg for several locations of the separation point C (Table 16). It is interesting to note that, when the separation point C coincides with the trailing edge (Fig. 49), the lift P is only slightly different from the lift P_Γ of a plane wing in the usual circulatory flow. The results of Chaplygin's and Lavrentiev's computations are shown in Table 16.

TABLE 15

α_o (deg)	$\frac{\overline{C}_p}{2} = \frac{C_p}{2} = \frac{P}{\rho \ell v_o^2}$	$\frac{\overline{C}_Q}{2} = \frac{\overline{Q}}{\rho \ell v_o^2}$	$\frac{C_Q}{2} = \frac{Q}{\rho \ell v_o^2}$	$\frac{c}{\ell}$
3	0.154	0.025	--	0.115
6	0.289	0.042	--	0.23
10	0.38	0.072	0.0132	0.53
20	0.392	0.144	0.0268	0.865
30	0.397	0.240	0.0723	0.943
40	0.372	0.320	0.131	0.97
50	0.323	0.405	0.206	0.983
70	0.19	0.536	0.303	0.99
80	0.1	0.580	0.340	1.0
88	0.016	0.597	0.410	1.0
90	0.000	0.600	0.440	1.0

TABLE 16

α_o (deg)	$P/\pi\rho v_o^2 \ell$	$P_\Gamma/\pi\rho v_o^2 \ell$
5	0.0874	0.0878
10	0.1759	0.1736
15	0.2665	0.2588

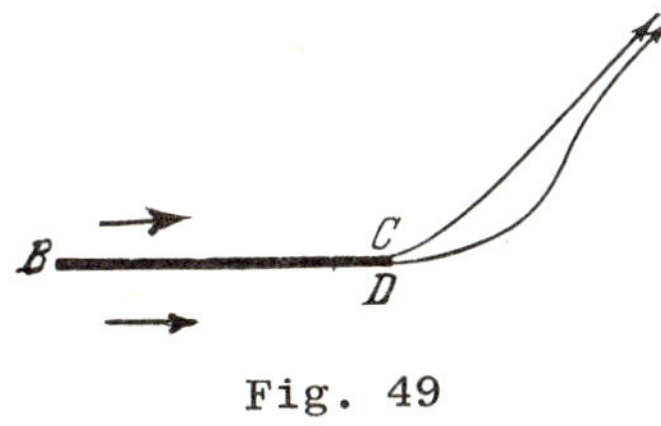

Fig. 49

They also made a detailed analysis of the shape of the free surfaces behind the plate. We shall now present the results of this analysis, at least to the extent to which they are required for our future work.

We first prove that the angle θ between the velocity vector and the x-axis takes a maximum on one of the free surfaces. From Eq. (3.28) it follows that, on the jet surfaces, where u has a purely imaginary value $i\eta$ and the velocity is v_o,

$$\ell n\left(\frac{dw}{v_o dz}\right) = -i\theta = \ell n \frac{(i\eta - \alpha)(i\eta + \beta)}{(i\eta + \alpha)(i\eta - \beta)} .$$

Thus,

$$\frac{d\theta}{d\eta} = \frac{-1}{i\eta - \alpha} - \frac{1}{i\eta + \beta} + \frac{1}{i\eta + \alpha} + \frac{1}{i\eta - \beta} ,$$

or

$$\frac{d\theta}{d\eta} = -\frac{2(\beta - \alpha)(\eta^2 - \alpha\beta)}{(\eta^2 + \beta^2)(\eta^2 + \alpha^2)} . \qquad (3.34)$$

A study of the sign of $d\theta/d\eta$ in the neighborhood of point $H[\eta_H = (\alpha\beta)^{1/2}]$, where $d\theta/d\eta$ becomes 0, shows that at

H, θ has a maximum—i.e., point H is an inflection point on the jet surface. If $\eta_H = (\alpha\beta)^{1/2} > 1$, then H is on CE (Fig. 50). If $\eta_H < 1$, then H is on DE (Fig. 51). If $\eta_H = 1$, then H goes to infinity and coincides with point E (Fig. 46).

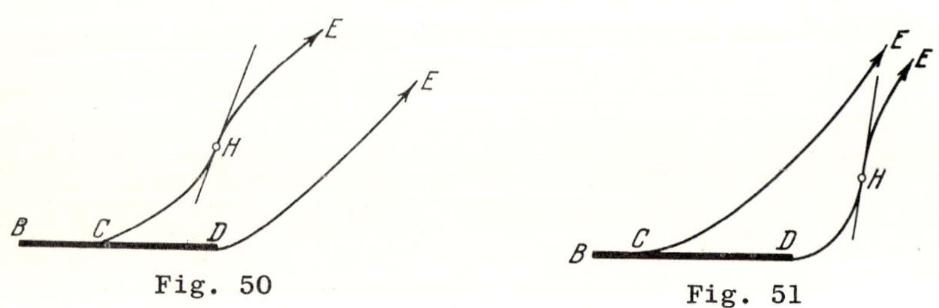

Fig. 50

Fig. 51

D. CRITICISM OF JET THEORY

In classical literature jet theory was exposed to various criticisms (see, e.g., Lamb [2] or Kelvin [35]). Briefly these objections were as follows:

1. The flows described in jet theory are not physically realistic because:
   a. The moving body carries along with it an unlimited "dead-water" mass with an infinite kinetic energy. Such flows cannot be formed in a finite time from fluid initially at rest.
   b. The separation line (surface of discontinuity) between the flow and "dead water" is equivalent to a thin, unstable vortex sheet. Thus, the motion can no longer be strictly irrotational and diffusion of the vorticity away from the separation line must eventually fill the "dead water" with vorticity.
   c. In a real flow the presence of vortices behind a body gives rise to a pressure defect or suction, which adds to the drag force. Thus, real-flow drag

is considerably larger than that drag predicted by jet theory. For example, the theoretical drag coefficient for a plane plate was found to be [see Eq. (1.34)]

$$C_x = \frac{2P}{\rho v_o^2 \ell} = \frac{2\pi}{4 + \pi} \approx 0.88 \quad ,$$

which is approximately one-half of the experimentally determined value of $C_x = 1.95$. Lamb asserts [2, Section 370], therefore, that the practical value of the Helmholtz, Kirchhoff, and Rayleigh jet theory lies in its application to free surface flows, such as jet flow from vessels, but not in application to drag determination problems.

2. The flows calculated according to jet theory may not be uniquely determined. In addition to the above discussed solutions obtained by Chaplygin, Lavrentiev and Sekerzh-Zenkovich, there are the analogous, but different, problem solutions of Tirri and Villat [36, where additional literature is mentioned], Belenkii and Zelenskii [37], Abramov [38], Ketchum [25], and others. An original view of non-uniqueness from the mechanical point of view appears in a technique developed by Zarantonello [39]. In addition to the cases discussed herein of non-unique solutions to jet problems, there are others with a less artificial appearance. In fact, in the flow past a curvilinear obstacle (see, e.g., Fig. 65), the separation points of the jet can be prescribed arbitrarily.

In Section B above we mentioned that the problem of which flow model should be chosen will be discussed in Chapter V on cavitation. This same problem, obviously, can be said to face us in all the flows that we consider and is a consideration whenever we use one of the techniques or models discussed above. Clearly, the non-uniqueness associated with the "washing away" of the critical point and stagnation region in our Section B flows has led to the multiplicity of solutions to jet-theory problems; a precisely analogous situation exists in wing theory.

The important criticism of jet theory--that it does not produce physically realistic flows--is evidenced by discrepancies between theoretical and experimental drag values for many flows. However, there are several flow regimes for flow about a body, and some practical and important regimes are very well represented by jet theory. The question of varying flow regimes is treated in Chapter V's discussion on cavitation. Furthermore, the criteria on which the type of flow regime depends will be designated. Then it will be clear why jet theory was found to agree first of all with experiments for flow from vessels.

In concluding this chapter, we must refute the objection (Point 1.a) to an infinite kinetic energy in the fluid for flow past a body. If the flow is steady relative to the uniform rectilinear motion of the body, then we cannot, in general, assume that the flow was formed in a finite time. If during its motion the body produces a finite drag, then in an infinite time the body would transfer infinite energy to the fluid. If the fluid is ideal, incompressible, and weightless, then its energy can only be kinetic. Thus, the infinite-energy concept cannot truly be considered an objection to jet theory. Note that, even if the fluid velocity at infinity (exterior to the "dead water") were zero, the kinetic energy of the fluid, exterior to the body and "dead water," is still infinite.

CHAPTER IV. FLOW AROUND CURVILINEAR OBSTACLES

A. LEVI-CIVITA'S METHOD

Consider an unlimited jet flow past a contour ACB as shown in Fig. 52. Along CA and CB the tangent to the contour turns continuously. At point C the angle between the tangents is $2\pi\kappa$, where $0 < \kappa < 1$. The velocity at infinity is parallel to and in the direction of the positive x-axis. The flow bifurcates at point C; the velocity at the stagnation point C is 0. We shall map the regions of change of the complex potential, $w = \varphi + i\psi$, and $\omega = i \ln (dw/v_0 dz) = \theta + i \ln (v/v_0)$, where v_0 is the velocity on the surface of the jet,* onto a unit semicircle in an auxiliary ζ-plane ($|\zeta| \leq 1$, $\text{Im}\ \zeta \geq 0$). The point D at infinity in the flow plane will be mapped to the coordinate origin in the ζ-plane (Fig. 53). The free surface is mapped onto the diameter ADB, and the contour ACB is mapped onto the semicircle ACB. For C we have $\zeta_C = \exp [i\sigma_0]$.

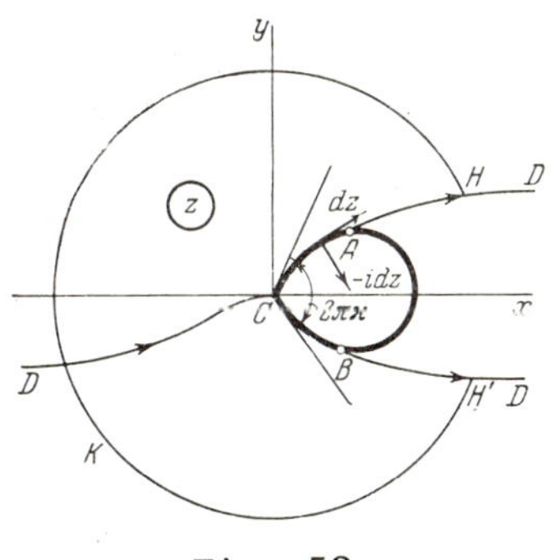

Fig. 52

Since w is determined only up to a constant term, it is possible to assume that, at C, w = 0. Several methods

*Levi-Civita's ω differs from Zhukovskii's only by the constant multiplier i [cf. Eq. (1.36)]. We use both forms of ω in this book.

can be used to determine w—in particular, that used by Chaplygin—and the final result is (we verify this below)

$$w = a^2 \left[\cos \sigma_o - \frac{1}{2}\left(\zeta + \frac{1}{\zeta}\right)\right]^2 , \tag{4.1}$$

where a is a real constant.

Now at $D(\zeta_D = 0)$, w has a second-order pole; at C $(\zeta_C = \exp[i\sigma_o])$, w has a second-order zero (Chapter I, Section F.1 and F.4). Also, on the upper semicircle ($\zeta = e^{i\sigma}$, $0 \leqq \sigma \leqq \pi$) and on the diameter AB($\text{Im}\ \zeta = 0$, $-1 \leqq \zeta \leqq 1$), $\text{Im}\ w = \psi = 0$. Thus, $w(\zeta)$ as given by Eq. (4.1), satisfies the boundary conditions and possesses the necessary singularities and zeros. Since ω is also analytic inside the region of change of ζ, it follows that the given result in Eq. (4.1) is the proper one.

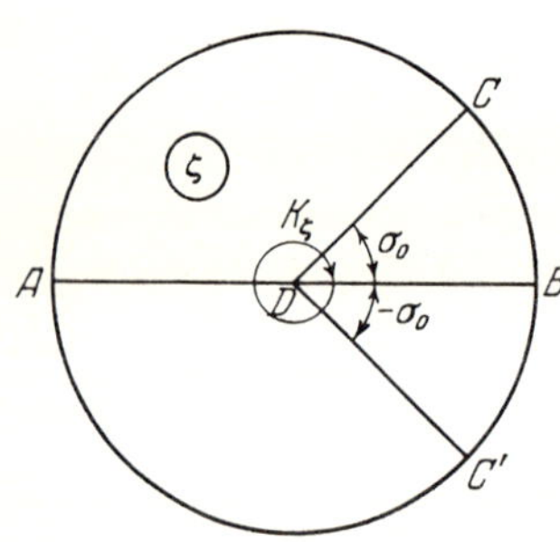

Fig. 53

The presentation given here of Levi-Civita's method [31] incorporates some additions contributed by Villat [40]. First we assume that, on the contour ACB, the relationship between the inclination angle of the velocity to the x-axis and σ is known—i.e., we know $\text{Re}\ \omega = \theta(\sigma)$. Now, since on the diameter ADB, $\text{Im}\ \omega = \ln(v/v_o) = \ln(v_o/v_o) = 0$, ω can be extended to the entire circle $|\zeta| \leqq 1$ in accordance with the symmetry principle. Consequently, at points symmetric to the real (x-) axis, the values of $\text{Re}\ \omega = \theta$ will be equal. Thus, we know $\text{Re}\ \omega = \theta$ on the entire circle $|\zeta| = 1$, and it is convenient to put $\theta(\sigma) = \theta(-\sigma)$. But, if $\text{Re}\ \omega$ is known on $|\zeta| = 1$, we can determine ω everywhere inside the circle from the Schwarz formula [4]

$$\omega = \frac{1}{2\pi} \int_{-\pi}^{\pi} \theta(\sigma) \frac{e^{i\sigma} + \zeta}{e^{i\sigma} - \zeta} d\sigma + iC \quad , \tag{4.2}$$

where C is an arbitrary constant. Because $\operatorname{Im} \omega = 0$ at $\zeta = 0$, $C = 0$. Equation (4.2) can be rewritten as

$$\omega = \frac{1}{2\pi} \int_{-\pi}^{0} \theta(\sigma) \frac{e^{i\sigma} + \zeta}{e^{i\sigma} - \zeta} d\sigma + \frac{1}{2\pi} \int_{0}^{\pi} \theta(\sigma) \frac{e^{i\sigma} + \zeta}{e^{i\sigma} - \zeta} d\sigma$$

or

$$\omega = \frac{1}{2\pi} \int_{0}^{\pi} \theta(-\sigma) \frac{e^{-i\sigma} + \zeta}{e^{-i\sigma} - \zeta} d\sigma + \frac{1}{2\pi} \int_{0}^{\pi} \theta(\sigma) \frac{e^{i\sigma} + \zeta}{e^{i\sigma} - \zeta} d\sigma \quad .$$

Finally, we have

$$\omega(\zeta) = \frac{1 - \zeta^2}{\pi} \int_{0}^{\pi} \theta(\sigma) \frac{d\sigma}{1 - 2\zeta \cos \sigma + \zeta^2} \quad . \tag{4.3}$$

With $\theta(\sigma)$ given, Eq. (4.3) together with (4.1) give the general solution to the problem.

In particular, we solve the problem of separated flow past a wedge (cf. Chapter III). Let the side CB (Fig. 54) form an angle $-\pi\nu$ with the x-axis, and the side CA an angle $\pi(2\kappa - \nu)$. Then Eq. (4.3) gives

$$\omega_{\text{wed}}(\zeta) = - \nu(1 - \zeta^2) \int_{0}^{\sigma_o} \frac{d\sigma}{1 - 2\zeta \cos \sigma + \zeta^2}$$

$$+ (2\kappa - \nu)(1 - \zeta^2) \int_{\sigma_o}^{\pi} \frac{d\sigma}{1 - 2\zeta \cos \sigma + \zeta^2} \quad ,$$

where $\omega_{wed}(\zeta)$ represents $\omega(\zeta)$ for the wedge. After evaluating the integrals we obtain

$$\omega_{wed}(\zeta) = -\pi\nu + 2i\kappa \, \ln \frac{\zeta - \exp[i\sigma_o]}{1 - \zeta \exp[i\sigma_o]} \quad . \qquad (4.4)$$

This equation can be easily and directly verified. Inside the upper unit semicircle in the ζ-plane, $\omega_{wed}(\zeta)$ is analytic. On the arc BC—i.e., with $\zeta = e^{i\sigma}$, $(0 \leq \sigma \leq \sigma_o)$—

$$\omega_{wed}(e^{i\sigma}) = -\pi\nu + 2i\kappa \, \ln \frac{\exp[i\sigma] - \exp[i\sigma_o]}{1 - \exp[i\sigma]\exp[i\sigma_o]}$$

$$= -\pi\nu + 2i\kappa \, \ln \frac{\sin[(\sigma_o - \sigma)/2]}{\sin[(\sigma_o + \sigma)/2]} \quad .$$

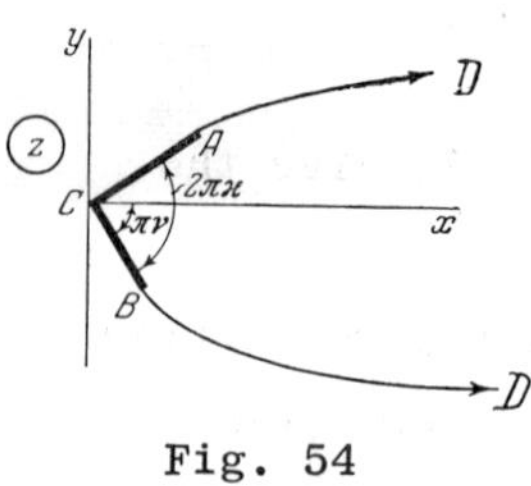

Fig. 54

Thus, ω_{wed} satisfies the boundary condition $\mathrm{Re}\,\omega_{wed} = -\pi\nu$ on BC. Also, $\mathrm{Im}\,\omega_{wed} = \ln(v/v_o)$ varies between the necessary limits (from 0 to $-\infty$).

As we pass clockwise around C along an infinitesimal semicircle, the argument of the vector $(\zeta - \exp[i\sigma_o])$ decreases by π, and so on the arc AC, $\omega_{wed}(\zeta)$ is given by

$$\omega_{wed}(\zeta) = -\pi\nu + 2i\kappa \, \ln \frac{\exp[-i\pi](\exp[i\sigma_o] - \zeta)}{1 - \exp[i\sigma_o]\,\zeta}$$

or

$$\omega_{wed}(\zeta) = \pi(2\kappa - \nu) + 2i\kappa \ell n \frac{\exp[i\sigma_o] - \zeta}{1 - \exp[i\sigma_o]\zeta} . \quad (4.5)$$

From Eq. (4.5) with $\zeta = e^{i\sigma}$ $(\sigma_o < \sigma \leq \pi)$ it is easy to obtain on the arc AC

$$\omega_{wed}(e^{i\sigma}) = \pi(2\kappa - \nu) + 2i\kappa \ell n \frac{\sin[(\sigma - \sigma_o)/2]}{\sin[(\sigma + \sigma_o)/2]} \quad (4.6)$$

and on AC, $\omega_{wed}(\zeta)$ also satisfies the appropriate boundary condition. On the diameter ADB (corresponding to the free surface) $\text{Im}\,\zeta = 0$, and from Eq. (4.5)

$$\omega_{wed}(\zeta) = \pi(2\kappa - \nu) + 2\kappa\sigma_o + 2i\kappa \ell n \frac{\exp[i\sigma_o] - \zeta}{\exp[-i\sigma_o] - \zeta} . \quad (4.7)$$

Since, with $\text{Im}\,\zeta = 0$,

$$\left| \frac{\exp[i\sigma_o] - \zeta}{\exp[-i\sigma_o] - \zeta} \right| = 1 ,$$

on ADB the last boundary condition $\text{Im}\,\omega_{wed}(\zeta) = 0$ is also satisfied. Recall that, according to our assumption, the velocity of the approaching flow is directed along the x-axis; thus, $\omega_{wed}(0) = 0$ and from Eq. (4.7) the equation relating the constants 2κ, ν, and σ_o is

$$\omega_{wed}(0) = \pi(2\kappa - \nu) - 2\kappa\sigma_o = 0 .$$

By choosing various physically significant $\theta(\sigma)$ for substitution in Eq. (4.3), we can generate an unlimited number of solutions for jet flows about curvilinear contours. As Birkhoff [5] points out, Levi-Civita can be said to have solved the inverse problem of describing all jets divided by curved barriers. However, it is much more difficult to obtain the solution to a problem when the actual contour shape is specified in advance. This latter problem will be touched upon in Section C of this chapter.

Levi-Civita did not use Eq. (4.3); instead, he gave ω as $\omega = \omega_{wed} + \Omega$, where

$$\Omega = \sum_{0}^{\infty} c_n \zeta^n ,$$

and the c_n are real constants. Clearly, since the c_n are real, ω is real when ζ is real. On the semicircle ACB ($\zeta = e^{i\sigma}$), the angle

$$\theta = \mathrm{Re}\ \omega = \mathrm{Re}\ \omega_{wed} + \sum_{0}^{\infty} c_n \cos n\sigma$$

is of variable magnitude. Different contours are obtained from different sets of c_n. The contour shape is easily determined. From Eq. (4.1) we obtain

$$dw = -\frac{a^2}{2}\left[2\cos\sigma_o - \left(\zeta + \frac{1}{\zeta}\right)\right]\left(\zeta - \frac{1}{\zeta}\right)\frac{d\zeta}{\zeta} , \qquad (4.8)$$

but $v_o dz = e^{i\omega}\, dw$, so

$$z = \frac{a^2}{2v_o}\int e^{i\omega}\left[-2\cos\sigma_o + \left(\zeta + \frac{1}{\zeta}\right)\right]\left(\zeta - \frac{1}{\zeta}\right)\frac{d\zeta}{\zeta} . \qquad (4.9)$$

Then on the contour we have $\zeta = e^{i\sigma}$, and

$$z = -2\,\frac{a^2}{v_0}\int e^{i\omega}\,[\cos\sigma - \cos\sigma_0]\,\sin\sigma\,d\sigma \quad . \qquad (4.10)$$

By separating the real and imaginary parts in the last equation, we find the contour equation in its parametric form:

$$\left.\begin{aligned} x &= -\,\frac{2a^2}{v_0}\int(\cos\sigma - \cos\sigma_0)\,e^{-\tau}\cos\theta\,\sin\sigma\,d\sigma \;, \\ y &= -\,\frac{2a^2}{v_0}\int(\cos\sigma - \cos\sigma_0)\,e^{-\tau}\sin\theta\,\sin\sigma\,d\sigma \;, \end{aligned}\right\} \qquad (4.11)$$

where $\tau = \ell n\,(v/v_0)$.

Now we derive Levi-Civita's formulas for the resultant force vector and the resultant moment acting on the contour. We shall obtain them by using Eq. (3.22).

Let $ds = |dz|$ be the differential arc distance along the contour BCA (Fig. 52). The difference between the pressure forces acting on both sides of the infinitesimal element ds is $(p - p_0)ds$. This pressure force is directed along the normal to the contour; if $p > p_0$, this normal will be the exterior normal, which points out of the region occupied by the fluid. Since the vector dz is tangent to the contour, the vector $-idz$ will be directed along the indicated normal (Fig. 52). The vector of the pressure-force difference acting on ds will then be

$$dX + idY = -idz(p - p_0) \quad ,$$

from which, by using the Bernoulli integral, we obtain

$$dX + idY = -idz\,\frac{\rho}{2}\left(v_o^2 - v^2\right) .$$

But $v^2 = \overline{(dw/dz)}(dw/dz)$; since we are moving along a streamline, $dw = \overline{dw}$ (because $d\psi = 0$). Therefore, we are led to

$$dX + idY = -\frac{i\rho}{2}\left(v_o^2\,dz - \overline{\frac{dw}{dz}\,dw}\right) . \qquad (4.12)$$

To obtain the resultant force vector $X + iY$ on the contour, it is sufficient to integrate $dX + idY$ along the contour BCA. But on the free surfaces $p = p_o$ and $dX + idY = 0$; therefore the integration can be carried from an arbitrary point H' on the free surface BD to a similar point H on AD (Fig. 52), and

$$X + iY = -\frac{i\rho}{2}\left(\int_{H'BCAH} v_o^2 dz - \int_{H'BCAH} \overline{\frac{dw}{dz}\,dw}\right) . \qquad (4.13)$$

Since both integrals on the right side of Eq. (4.13) depend only on the coordinates of the initial and final points of the integration path and not on the shape of the path, the present integration contour can be replaced by the contour K (Fig. 52) that is obtained by a continuous deformation of the original path H'BCAH. Inversion of the path of integration so that we move along K in the counterclockwise direction again leads us directly to the previously derived* Eq. (3.22)—i.e.,

$$X + iY = \frac{i\rho}{2}\left[v_o^2 \int_K dz - \int_K \overline{\frac{dw}{dz}\,dw}\right] . \qquad (4.14)$$

---

*In Eq. (3.22) a circle of infinitesimal radius was chosen as a contour for convenience of presentation and not out of necessity.

The moment (relative to the coordinate origin) of the pressure forces acting on the arc element ds on the contour BCA, is $dM = x\,dY - y\,dX = -\text{Re}\; i\bar{z}(dX + i\,dY)$. Introduction of Eq. (4.12) into this equation produces

$$dM = -\frac{\rho}{2}\,\text{Re}\left[\bar{z}\left(v_o^2 dz - \overline{\frac{dw}{dz}\,dw}\right)\right] . \qquad (4.15)$$

As before, integration can be performed along either contour K or contour BCA over which the fluid is flowing. In contrast to the computation of $X + iY$, the integration along the contour K for the computation of the moment has no particular advantage because of the difficulty of applying the residue theorem. Finally, since $\text{Re}\;\bar{z}\,dz = (1/2)d(x^2 + y^2) = (1/2)d(z\bar{z})$, we have, from Eq. (4.15),

$$M = -\frac{\rho}{2}\left[\frac{v_o^2}{2}\int_{BCA} d(z\bar{z}) - \int_{BCA} \overline{z\,\frac{dw}{dz}\,dw}\right] \qquad (4.16)$$

and

$$M = \frac{\rho}{2}\,\text{Re}\left[\frac{v_o^2}{2}\int_{K} d(z\bar{z}) - \int_{K} \overline{z\,\frac{dw}{dz}\,dw}\right] . \qquad (4.17)$$

The integrals in Eq. (4.14) can be evaluated in a general form by the same technique used in Section III.B [cf. Eq. (3.25)]. If in the flow plane the points H, H' and the entire contour K are moved to infinity, then in the ζ-plane the corresponding contour, which we designate as K_ζ, is an infinitesimal semicircle passing around $\zeta = 0$ in a clockwise direction (see Figs. 52 and 53). Furthermore,

$$dz = \frac{1}{v_o}\,\frac{v_o dz}{dw}\,dw = \frac{1}{v_o}\,e^{i\omega}\,dw . \qquad (4.18)$$

Now $\omega = \theta + i \ln (v/v_o)$ and dw is real when ζ is real. Thus, ω and dw take conjugate values at points symmetrically located with respect to the real axis in the ζ-plane. In other words, ω and dw on K_ζ are equal to $\bar{\omega}$ and $\overline{dw}$ at the corresponding points on the contour $K_{\bar{\zeta}}$ that is symmetric to K_ζ with respect to the diameter ADB. Thus, passage around D along K_ζ in a clockwise direction is equivalent to passage around D along $K_{\bar{\zeta}}$ in a counterclockwise direction, and

$$X + iY = \frac{i\rho}{2}\left[v_o \int_{K_\zeta} e^{i\omega}\, dw - v_o \overline{\int_{K_\zeta} e^{-i\omega}\, dw}\right] .$$

Since $i\bar{\omega} = -i\bar{\omega}$,

$$X + iY = \frac{i\rho v_o}{2}\left[\overline{\int_{K_\zeta} e^{-i\omega}\, dw} - \overline{\int_{K_\zeta} e^{-i\omega}\, dw}\right] .$$

By combining the contours into a common, infinitesimal, closed contour passing around D in a counterclockwise direction, we obtain

$$X + iY = \frac{i\rho v_o}{2} \oint \overline{e^{-i\omega}\, dw} . \tag{4.19}$$

From Eq. (4.8),

$$dw = -\frac{a^2}{2}\left[\frac{1}{\zeta^3} - \frac{2\cos\sigma_o}{\zeta^2} + 2\cos\sigma_o - \zeta\right] d\zeta . \tag{4.20}$$

Assume now that $i\omega$ can be expanded in a series of positive powers of ζ about $\zeta = 0$ and that $\omega(0) = 0$ because at D, $\theta = 0$ and $v = v_o$. Then,

$$\omega(\zeta) = \omega'(0)\,\zeta + \frac{\omega''(0)}{2}\,\zeta^2 + \ldots \qquad (4.21)$$

All the coefficients $\omega'(0)$, $[\omega''(0)]/2$, ... are real because on the real axis $\operatorname{Im}\omega(\zeta) = \ln v/v_o = 0$. From Eq. (4.21) it follows that

$$\exp\,[-i\omega(\zeta)] = 1 - i\omega'(0)\,\zeta - \frac{\omega'^2(0) + i\omega''(0)}{2}\,\zeta^2 + O(\zeta^3) \quad ;$$

hence, from Eqs. (4.19) and (4.20) we find

$$X + iY = \frac{i\rho v_o}{2}\left(-\frac{a^2}{2}\right)\int\overline{\left(\frac{1}{\zeta^3} - \frac{2\cos\sigma_o}{\zeta^2} + 2\cos\sigma_o - \zeta\right)}$$

$$\cdot\,\overline{\left(1 - i\omega'(0)\,\zeta - \frac{\omega'^2(0) + i\omega''(0)}{2}\,\zeta^2 \ldots\right)}\,d\zeta \;.$$

By evaluating the contour integral in terms of the residue at $\zeta = 0$, we obtain

$$X + iY = -\frac{a^2}{2}\,\frac{i\rho v_o}{2}\,2\pi i\,\overline{\left[-\frac{\omega'^2(0) + i\omega''(0)}{2} + i2\cos\sigma_o\omega'(0)\right]} \quad ,$$

or finally,

$$X + iY = \frac{v_o\pi\rho a^2}{4}\left\{\omega'^2(0) + i[\omega'(0)\,4\cos\sigma_o - \omega''(0)]\right\} \;. \qquad (4.22)$$

Equation (4.22) is Levi-Civita's important result; its acquisition concludes our discussion of his method. Two additional remarks can be appropriately added here:

1. From Eqs. (4.9) and (4.21) we obtain the expansion of of $z(\zeta)$ in the vicinity of $\zeta = 0$, i.e.,

$$z = -\frac{a^2}{2v_o} \int [1 + i\omega'(0)\,\zeta + O(\zeta^2)]\Big[1 - 2\,\zeta \cos\sigma_o + O(\zeta^2)\Big] \frac{d\zeta}{\zeta^3} \; ,$$

from which we get

$$z = -\frac{a^2}{2v_o} \left[-\frac{1}{2\zeta^2} - \frac{i\omega'(0)}{\zeta} + \frac{2\cos\sigma_o}{\zeta} + O(\ell n\ \zeta) \right] . \quad (4.23)$$

On the jet surfaces, ζ is real. By separating the real and imaginary parts in Eq. (4.23), we determine that the asymptotic shape of these surfaces at infinity is

$$x \approx \frac{a^2}{4v_o\zeta^2} \; , \qquad y \approx \frac{a^2\omega'(0)}{2v_o\zeta} \; .$$

Thus, we conclude that at infinity the jet surfaces asymptotically approach the parabola

$$y^2 = \frac{a^2\omega'^2(0)}{v_o}\, x \; . \quad (4.24)$$

In comparing Eqs. (4.24) and (4.22), we discover that the drag X is given in terms of the parabolic parameter $p = a^2\omega'^2(0)/(2v_o)$ as

$$X = \frac{\pi\rho a^2\omega'^2(0)\ v_o}{4} = \frac{\pi\rho v_o^2 p}{2} \; . \quad (4.25)$$

This original result was obtained by Chaplygin in 1910 [41].

2. Golubev [42] gave the following interesting expansion for z near infinity:

$$z = \frac{1}{v_o}\left[w + 2im\, w^{1/2} + \frac{in - m^2}{2}\ln w + O\left(\frac{1}{w^{1/2}}\right)\right], \quad (4.26)$$

where m and n are real constants. Equation (4.26) can, in particular, be obtained from Eqs. (4.1) and (4.23), if in the latter each expansion term is written out in detail. Furthermore, a new concept of a correct contour is introduced: the contour K (Fig. 52) is called correct if the abscissas of the contour ends H and H' are equal. It is possible to prove that, when H and H' of the correct contour move to infinity, the circulation Γ along K approaches πn. From Eqs. (4.26) and (4.14), we obtain Eq. (4.25) for the drag and also

$$Y = -\rho v_o \Gamma \quad (4.27)$$

for the force, normal to the approaching flow. Equation (4.27) formally represents the Zhukovskii theorem for wings. This result, as Golubev indicates, was obtained first by Taylor [43] by the momentum theorem.

B. FLOW AROUND A CIRCULAR CYLINDER

Physically it is obvious that the flow past a given contour will separate at some well defined points A and D (Fig. 52). However, as we saw in the example of the plane plate (Section III.C), the separation points can be chosen quite arbitrarily from the mathematical point of view. To select the location of the separation points on an arbitrary contour, it is necessary to study the behavior of the contour curvature κ_K and the jet curvature κ_c in the neighborhood of points A and B.

We begin our study by establishing appropriate notation and sign conventions. We consider that the arc differential distance ds on the contour and on the jets is positive with movement along DBCAD. Therefore, since φ increases with travel from point C to both points A and B, we have $d\varphi = v\,ds$ along CAD and $d\varphi = -v\,ds$ along CBD. We denote the angle formed by a tangent to DBCAD and the x-axis as β. Then, for movement along DBCAD, $dz = e^{i\beta}\,ds$ and the curvature $\kappa = d\beta/ds$. If the curve at the point under consideration is convex with respect to the fluid, then $\kappa < 0$. Finally, we note that, according to Fig. 52,

$$\beta = \theta \quad \text{on} \quad CA\,, \qquad \beta = \pi + \theta \quad \text{on} \quad CB\,.$$

Thus, $\kappa = d\theta/ds$ on DBCAD.

We now determine the location of point A (Fig. 52). Since $d\psi = 0$ and $v = v_o$ along the free surface, $d\omega = d\theta$ and $d\varphi = dw$; therefore, the curvature κ_c of the jet AD is

$$\kappa_c = \frac{d\theta}{ds} = v\,\frac{d\theta}{d\varphi} = v_o\,\frac{d\omega}{dw}\,. \tag{4.28}$$

The curvature of the jet at its separation from the contour at point A is

$$(\kappa_c)_A = \lim_{\zeta\to -1} v_o\,\frac{d\omega}{dw}\,, \tag{4.29}$$

where the limit is evaluated by passing into A along the jet—i.e., in the parametric plane, by passing along the real axis of ζ to -1.

On the contour BCA, $dw = d\varphi$, but $d\omega \neq d\theta$ because v is not constant. Thus, the relation for the curvature of the contour is

$$\kappa_K = \frac{d\theta}{ds} = \pm v \frac{d\theta}{d\varphi} = \pm v \operatorname{Re} \frac{d\omega}{dw} = \pm v \left[\frac{d\omega}{dw} - i \frac{d \ln (v/v_0)}{dw} \right] . \tag{4.30}$$

The plus sign is taken on CA and the minus sign on CB.

Since $v = v_0$ at A, we have there

$$(\kappa_K)_A = v_0 \lim_{\sigma \to \pi} \left[\frac{d\omega}{dw} - i \frac{d \ln (v/v_0)}{dw} \right] , \tag{4.31}$$

where the limit is evaluated from motion along the contour—i.e., along the circle $\zeta = e^{i\sigma}$. We must now analyze the behavior of $\omega(w)$ in the neighborhood of $A(w = w_A)$.

Along the free surface $\operatorname{Im} \omega = 0$, so the free surfaces AD and BD correspond to segments of the real axis in the ω-plane (hence, point D obviously corresponds to the coordinate origin $\omega = 0$). In general the real and imaginary parts of ω vary along the contour BCD. Thus, the contour BCD corresponds in the ω-plane to some curve which goes to infinity (because at C, $v = 0$ and $\operatorname{Im} \omega = -\infty$). The curves representing the contour and the free surfaces in the ω-plane either can have a common tangent or form an angle, different from π, at A. To clarify this point we shall discuss several examples.

Figure 55 shows the region of change of ω for the jet flow around a wedge (Fig. 54). Along the wedge sides CA and CB, $\operatorname{Re} \omega = \theta$ takes the constant values $\pi(2\kappa - \nu)$ and $-\pi\nu$, respectively, and $\operatorname{Im} \omega = \ln (v/v_0)$ varies from 0 at A and B to $-\infty$ at C. On the jets BD and AD, $\operatorname{Im} \omega = 0$ and the angle θ increases monotonically along BDA from $-\pi\nu$ to $\pi(2\kappa - \nu)$. As we move along CADBC,

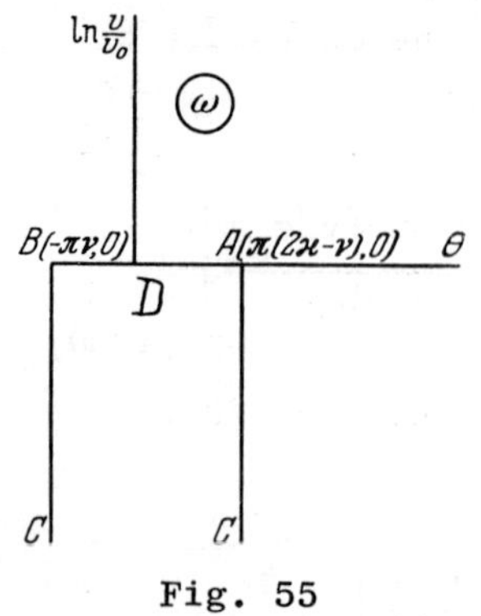

Fig. 55

the flow region in Fig. 54 lies to the left. Thus, it follows that the corresponding region in Fig. 55 is the interior of the figure traced out as we move along the contour CADBC— i.e., the region on the left.

We shall now consider the flow around a concave, curvilinear arc (Fig. 56). Assume that the flow is such that the velocity increases monotonically from C to A and B and that the jets AD and BD are everywhere concave to the liquid region. Since along contour BCA the angle θ changes continuously, the region of change of ω (Fig. 57)

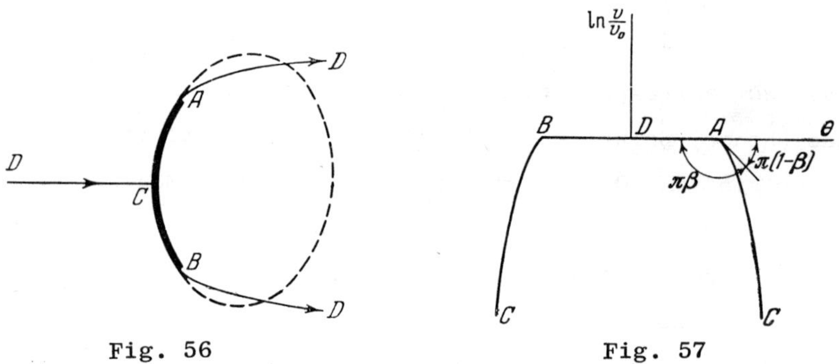

Fig. 56

Fig. 57

will differ from that for the case of the wedge (Fig. 55) in that AC and BC will be curved. Let the tangent to the curve AC at A in the ω-plane form an angle $-\pi(1 - \beta)$ with the θ-axis; then,

$$- \tan \pi (1 - \beta) = \lim_{\sigma \to \pi} \frac{d \ln (v/v_o)}{d\theta} .$$

The region of change of w is represented by a plane with a cut along the real positive semiaxis $\psi = 0$ and is the same as the region of change of w for flow around a plane plate (Fig. 2). Under a counterclockwise passage around A along an infinitesimal semicircle, the argument of $(w - w_A)$ increases by π (Fig. 2). A corresponding passage around A in the ω-plane increases the argument of $(\omega - \theta_A)$ only by $\pi\beta$. Therefore, $\omega - \theta_A = O(w - w_A)^{\beta}$. In other words, asymptotic expressions for $\omega(w)$ in the neighborhood of A have the form

$$\omega - \theta_A \approx N(w - w_A)^{\beta} \quad , \tag{4.32}$$

where N is a real coefficient, because $w > w_A$ and $\operatorname{Im} \omega = \ell n\ (v/v_o) = 0$ on AD.

With $0 < \beta < 1$, it follows from Eqs. (4.29) and (4.32) that the jet curvature at A is infinite. The contour curvature can be anything in this case. If we have a contour whose curvature is everywhere finite (for example, a circle or ellipse—dotted line on Fig. 56), then with the present scheme the assumed flow around the contour is impossible because the jet intersects the contour. However, the present scheme is useful for flows around an arc behind which we place any body that does not intersect the jet surface.

Of particular interest is the special case $\beta = 1$ or $d\ [\ell n\ (v/v_o)]/d\theta = 0$, when the angle between AD and AC in the ω-plane is π. In this case $\omega - \theta_A \approx N(w - w_A)$ and $(d\omega/dw)_A$ is finite, real, and determinable. From Eq. (4.29) it follows that $d\omega/dw$ at A is real, and then, according to Eq. (4.31),

$$\lim_{\sigma \to \pi} \frac{d\ \ell n\ (v/v_o)}{dw} = 0 \quad . \tag{4.33}$$

It follows that $(\kappa_K)_A = (\kappa_c)_A$ or, in summary, the jet curvature at the separation point either is equal to the curvature of the obstacle or is infinite. This conclusion was first obtained by Villat.

Equation (4.33) represents a condition that must be satisfied at the separation point of the jet if there is to be flow around a contour with a finite curvature (Fig. 58). Clearly, the analogous equation must hold at B—i.e.,

$$\lim_{\sigma\to 0} \frac{d\,\ell n\,(v/v_o)}{dw} = 0 \quad . \tag{4.34}$$

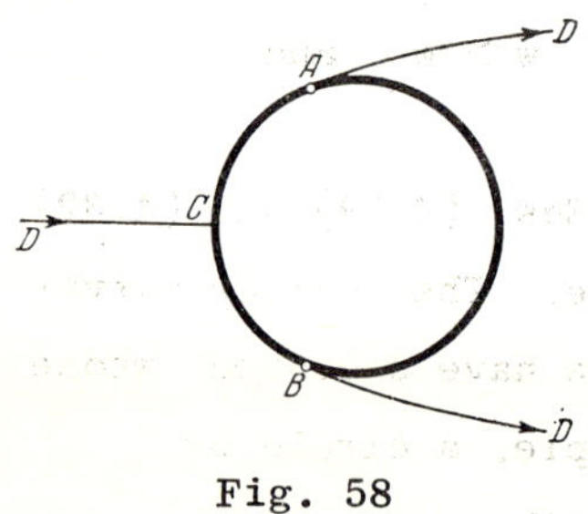

Fig. 58

For the flow around a concave contour (for instance, a circle), other flow configurations are possible. One of these is shown in Fig. 59a. We assume that between C and points A and B the velocity v first increases to a value greater than v_o and then decreases to v_o at A and B. Furthermore, we let segments AE and BH be convex with respect to the fluid and points E and H be the inflection points in the jet surface. It is not difficult to show that the region of change of ω

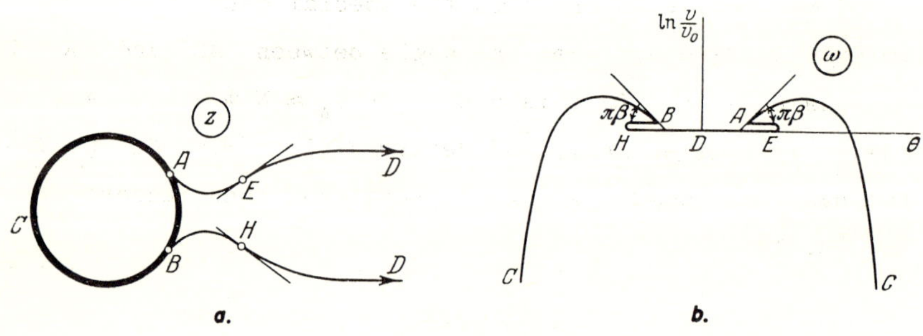

Fig. 59

then has the form presented in Fig. 59b. From the geometric point of view, the flow around a circular cylinder is possible, in accordance with the flow proposed in Fig. 59a, whether the curvatures at A and B are finite or infinite, since in passing through these points the signs of the curvatures change and the free surfaces do not intersect the circle. A particular flow case in Fig. 59a is the flow around a cylinder such that points E and H are at infinity and the jet surfaces are everywhere concave with respect to the fluid (Fig. 60).

A flow in which the constant-pressure region is of finite size is also a possibility (Fig. 61). Brillouin [44] argued

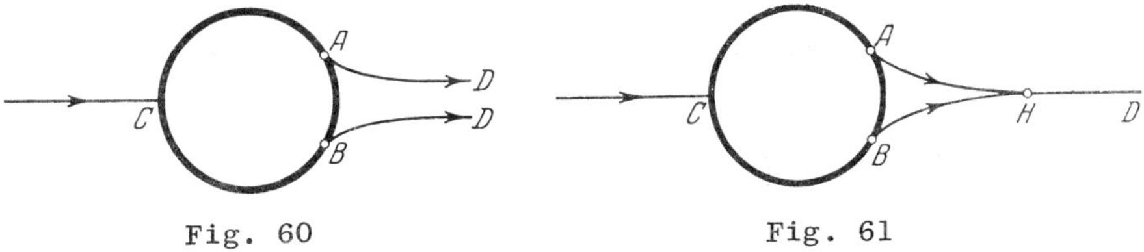

Fig. 60

Fig. 61

in favor of such a flow pattern under the condition that everywhere on the solid contour $v \leq v_o$. This condition is called Brillouin's first condition. His second condition requires that the jet boundaries do not intersect each other or the obstacle. However, he gave examples of geometrically contradictory solutions where his second condition was not satisfied. In the following chapter on cavitation we will see that, by cutting off the crossing or overlapping parts of the flow region, we can make good use of some solutions in which Brillouin's second condition is not satisfied.

It is easy to prove that if Brillouin's first condition is satisfied on the surface of the jet and the contour, then it is satisfied everywhere inside the fluid. Actually, since $\ln (v/v_o)$ is a harmonic function of the variables x and y, it takes a maximum only on the boundaries of the region. But

Brillouin's first condition holds on the contour and the free surfaces of the jets and $\ln (v/v_o) \leqq 0$ there; thus $\ln (v/v_o) < 0$ and $v < v_o$ everywhere inside the fluid. For the cylinder, Brillouin's conditions are satisfied in the flow shown in Fig. 58 and conditions (4.33) and (4.34) hold. Villat [45] studied the conditions to be imposed on contours when Brillouin's conditions were to be satisfied. Many of Villat's theorems were later generalized by Jacob [46].

The physical significance of Brillouin's conditions will be established in Chapter V, but for now we shall proceed to determine the flow around a cylinder in which conditions (4.33) and (4.34) are satisfied.

According to Eq. (4.30),

$$\kappa_K = \pm v \frac{d\theta}{d\varphi} = \pm v_o \exp\left[\ln \frac{v}{v_o}\right]\frac{d\theta}{d\sigma}\frac{d\sigma}{d\varphi} , \tag{4.35}$$

where, according to Eq. (4.9),

$$\frac{d\sigma}{d\varphi} = - \frac{1}{2a^2 (\cos\sigma - \cos\sigma_o) \sin\sigma} . \tag{4.36}$$

In order to write out a more detailed expression for $d\theta/d\sigma$ and $\ln (v/v_o)$, we first note that this flow around a cylinder is symmetric with respect to the x-axis. Then in the ζ-plane, $\omega(\zeta) = \theta + i \ln (v/v_o) = \omega_{wed}(\zeta) + \Omega(\zeta)$ is symmetric with respect to the imaginary axis (see Figs. 52 and 53). Therefore, at any two points symmetrically located with respect to the imaginary axis, the values of the angle $\theta = \mathrm{Re}\,\omega$ differ only in their sign and the values of $\ln (v/v_o) = \mathrm{Im}\,\omega$ are identical. Hence, $\omega(\zeta)$ is an odd function of ζ. Since for the circular cylinder the angle between the tangents at C (Fig. 52) is $2\pi\kappa = \pi$, $\kappa = 1/2$. Furthermore, the symmetry allows us to set $\nu = 1/2$ and $\sigma_o = \pi/2$.

Under these conditions it is easy to transform the wedge Eq. (4.7) to

$$\omega_{wed}(\zeta) = i \ln \frac{1 + i\zeta}{1 - i\zeta} , \qquad (4.37)$$

from which it is clear that $\omega_{wed}(\zeta) = -\omega_{wed}(-\zeta)$. Obviously, if $\omega = \omega_{wed} + \Omega$ is to be an odd function of ζ, it is sufficient to demand that $\Omega(\zeta)$ be an odd function of ζ. To accomplish this it is necessary to set $c_n = 0$ for all even values of n. Then

$$\Omega = \sum_{m=0}^{\infty} c_{2m+1} \zeta^{2m+1} , \qquad (4.38)$$

and on the solid contour

$$\Omega = \sum_{0}^{\infty} c_{2m+1} \exp [i(2m + 1)\sigma] . \qquad (4.39)$$

The problem will be solved if we select c_{2m+1}, v_o, and a^2 so that conditions (4.33) and (4.34) are satisfied and everywhere on the solid contour BCA

$$|\kappa_K| = \frac{1}{R} , \qquad (4.40)$$

where R is the radius of the circle. It is sufficient to satisfy the finite-curvature condition (4.34) at B and the constant-curvature condition (4.40) in the range $0 \leqq \sigma \leqq \pi/2$. Then, as a result of the symmetry of the solution, conditions (4.33) at A and (4.40) in $\pi/2 \leqq \sigma \leqq \pi$ are automatically satisfied.

From Eq. (4.6), by taking into account the value of the constants, we have

$$\omega_{\text{wed}}(e^{i\sigma}) = -\frac{\pi}{2} + i\,\ell n\,\frac{\sin[(\pi/4) - (\sigma/2)]}{\sin[(\pi/4) + (\sigma/2)]}\,. \tag{4.41}$$

Now the basic Eq. (4.40) is changed—with the help of Eqs. (4.41), (4.36) (with $\sigma_o = \pi/2$), (4.35), and (4.29)—to

$$\frac{1}{R} = \frac{v_o \sin[(\pi/4) - (\sigma/2)] \sum_{m=0}^{\infty} (2m+1)\, c_{2m+1} \sin(2m+1)\sigma}{a^2 \sin[(\pi/4) + (\sigma/2)] \sin 2\sigma}$$

$$\cdot \exp\left[\sum_{m=0}^{\infty} c_{2m+1} \sin(2m+1)\sigma\right]\,. \tag{4.42}$$

Condition (4.34) of finite jet curvature at B takes the form

$$\sum_{m=0}^{\infty} (2m+1)\, c_{2m+1} + \left[\frac{d}{d\sigma}\,\ell n\,\frac{\sin[(\pi/4) - (\sigma/2)]}{\sin[(\pi/4) + (\sigma/2)]}\right]_{\sigma=0} = 0$$

or*

$$\sum_{m=0}^{\infty} (2m+1)\, c_{2m+1} = 1\,. \tag{4.43}$$

*Condition (4.43) is easily obtained in a straightforward manner. In calculating the jet curvature κ_c, we find

After all the coefficients are determined, it is easy to find the drag X of the cylinder and the location of the flow separation points. Obviously the lift force Y is 0. From the general Eq. (4.22) we obtain, after differentiating Eqs. (4.37) and (4.38),

$$X = \frac{v_o \pi\rho a^2}{4} \omega'^2(0) = \frac{v_o \pi\rho a^2}{4} (-2 + c_1)^2 \quad . \qquad (4.44)$$

The coefficient a^2 in Eq. (4.44) can be expressed in terms of R and the Ω-series coefficients. From Eq. (4.42) with $\sigma = 0$ we have

$$\frac{1}{R} = \frac{v_o}{2a^2} \sum_0^\infty (2m + 1)^2 c_{2m+1} \quad . \qquad (4.45)$$

By introducing Eq. (4.45) into (4.44) we obtain

$$X = \frac{\pi\rho v_o^2 R}{8} (2 - c_1)^2 \sum_0^\infty (2m + 1)^2 c_{2m+1} \quad . \qquad (4.46)$$

The nondimensional drag coefficient, defined as X divided by the product of the density ρ, the square of the velocity v^2 and the cylinder radius R, is

---

$$\kappa_c = \frac{2v_o}{a^2} \frac{-2 + (1 + \zeta^2) \sum_{m=0}^\infty (2m + 1) c_{2m+1} \zeta^{2m}}{(\zeta^2 - 1)(\zeta^2 + 1)^2} \zeta^3 \quad .$$

For κ_c to be finite at B, the numerator of this equation must be 0 when $\zeta = 1$. Condition (4.43) follows immediately.

$$C_x = \frac{X}{\rho v_o^2 R} = \frac{\pi}{8}(2 - c_1)^2 \sum_0^\infty (2m+1)^2 c_{2m+1} \quad . \quad (4.47)$$

The location of the separation points A and B is determined in terms of the angle 2γ, formed by the radii drawn between A and B and the center of the cylinder. It is obvious that $\omega(1) = \theta_B = -(\pi/2) + \gamma$, and from Eqs. (4.41) and (4.38) we see that

$$\gamma = \sum_{m=1}^\infty c_{2m+1} \quad . \quad (4.48)$$

Brodetsky [47] constructed an approximate solution to the circular-cylinder problem. The solution is approximate because Eq. (4.42) is satisfied at a finite number of discrete points rather than everywhere on the solid contour. In fact, Brodetsky equated the curvature at B Eq. (4.45) with the curvature at C as a first approximation—i.e., the curvature with $\sigma = 0$ is equated to the curvature with $\sigma = \pi/2$ so that

$$\frac{1}{R} = \frac{v_o}{4a^2} \sum_{m=0}^\infty (2m+1)\, c_{2m+1} \sin \frac{2m+1}{2}\pi$$

$$\cdot \exp\left\{ \sum_{m=0}^\infty c_{2m+1} \sin\left[(2m+1)/2\right]\pi \right\} \quad (4.49)$$

From the above equation and condition (4.43), the two coefficients c_1 and c_3 were obtained numerically. The other coefficients were taken to be 0. Brodetsky* obtained the following results:

$$c_1 = 0.9426 \qquad c_3 = 0.0191$$

$$\gamma = 55°6' \qquad C_x = 0.493 \quad .$$

Brodetsky's solution is exact for a flow around some contour, nearly a circle. To determine how close to a circle this contour is, he computed the contour's curvature at different points and concluded that the deviation of the radius of curvature from the fixed value at A, B, and C did not exceed 3.5 percent at any point. He then made the solution of his problem more precise by choosing c_1, c_3, and c_5 so that: 1) condition (4.43) is satisfied where $\sigma = 0$, $\sigma = \pi/2$, $\sigma = \pi/4$; 2) the contour's curvature is the same at the points where $\sigma = 0$, $\sigma = \pi/2$, $\sigma = \pi/4$; and 3) all the values c_{2m+1} with $m > 2$ are 0. He obtained the following results: $c_1 = 0.9415$; $c_3 = 0.0167$; $c_5 = 0.00166$; $\gamma = 55$ deg; and $C_x = 0.5$. In this second approximation, when the first three coefficients c_1, c_3, and c_5 are not 0, the deviation of the radius of curvature from the constant value does not exceed one percent.

Schmieden [48] also studied approximate calculations of jet flow around a cylinder. He worked out in detail an approximate method for determining the coefficients c_{2m+1} and found for Ω an approximate expression, with the first five coefficients not equal to 0,

---

*Brodetsky's notation is quite different from that used herein; his region of change of the parametric variable is rotated by $\pi/2$ compared to ours.

$$\Omega = 0.94270\zeta + 0.01641\zeta^3 + 0.00121\zeta^5 + 0.00020\zeta^7 + 0.00006\zeta^9 . \qquad (4.50)$$

Schmeiden found that the separation angle $\gamma = 55$ deg 2 min 15 sec.

When the cylinder's drag coefficient is computed by Eqs. (4.47) and (4.50), C_x is found to be about the same in both cases; thus $C_x = 0.5$, as in Brodetsky's second approximation.

In fluids with a low viscosity, such as water, viscous effects are important only in thin boundary layers close to the body, provided that these layers do not separate from the body. In Section I.C, it was noted that, in a nonseparated or fully wetted flow past a cylinder, the boundary layer separates at an angle considerably larger than the γ calculated for separated jet flow past a cylinder. We can now, of course, substantiate this statement with numerical data. For a jet flow, we just determined that the angle γ, which located the separation points, is 55 deg. On the other hand, the corresponding angle γ, which determines the separation points of the laminar boundary layer, is 82 deg [49, Part II, Section 34]. We conclude then that in a jet flow around a cylinder the viscosity of the water has an important effect on the tangent forces at the surface of the cylinder. Thus, the viscous effect should be taken into account as an additional set of forces after solution of the inviscid jet problem for flow around a cylinder.

Besides the circular-cylinder problem, Brodetsky used the same method on a flow about an elliptic cylinder. His numerical results are presented in Table 17, in which b/a is the ratio of the vertical semi-axis b of the ellipse to the horizontal semi-axis a; $C_x(\pi + 4)/2\pi$ is the ratio of the drag of the ellipse to the drag of a flat plate with the same width $2b$. The angle 2γ is the angle between lines

TABLE 17

b/a	$\frac{C_x(\pi + 4)}{2\pi}$	γ (deg	min)
0.712	0.487	59	51
0.858	0.531	56	38
1.0	0.568	55	--
1.68	0.673	47	22

drawn from the center of the elipse to the separation points of the jet.

Brodetsky's work is closely related to that of Rosenhead [50]. The latter calculated the forces acting on curvilinear arcs, both convex $(2\gamma < 0)$ and concave $(2\gamma > 0)$ with respect to the flow, where 2γ is the central angle of the arc BA (Fig. 62). At the separation points A and B the jet-surface curvature is infinite, but this condition does not lead to geometrically inadmissible solutions because the arc is infinitely thin and A and B are its ends. The pressure-force vectors on small elements of a circular arc are normal to the elements and, consequently, pass through the center of the circle, a part of which represents the arc. The resultant pressure force, whose projections on the coordinate axis are denoted by X and Y, passes through this center, which is the origin of the cartesian coordinate system. The velocity is parallel to the x-axis at infinity. The angle of attack α_o is taken to be that angle with the smallest absolute value between tho chord of the arc BA and the x-axis (Fig. 62). Rosenhead's numerical data [50] is given in Table 18. His notation has been changed to conform with ours. In particular, Rosenhead

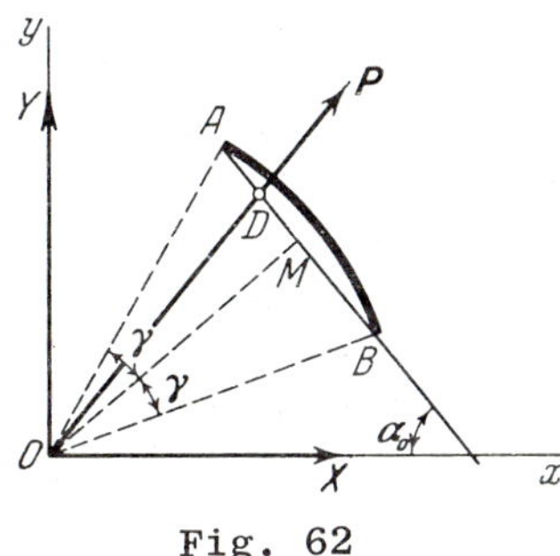

Fig. 62

TABLE 18

2γ (deg)	α_o (deg	min)	$c_x/2$	$c_y/2$	MD/BA
-10	12	55	0.0280	0.0995	0.2778
-20	24	47	0.0883	0.1532	0.2564
-30	35	19	0.1523	0.1661	0.2357
-30	50	19	0.2633	0.1860	0.1447
10	5	00	0.0085	0.1142	0.0682
20	10	00	0.0320	0.2031	0.0519
20	27	00	0.1377	0.2869	0.0668
20	30	00	0.1599	0.2924	0.0660
20	50	00	0.3055	0.2653	0.0479
20	70	00	0.4082	0.1527	0.0247
20	90	00	0.4522	0	0
30	15	00	0.0667	0.2702	0.0369
40	20	00	0.1101	0.3197	0.0240
40	30	00	0.1789	0.3253	0.0288
40	40	00	0.2523	0.3132	0.0276
40	60	00	0.3791	0.2256	0.0184
40	90	00	0.4645	0	0
60	30	00	0.2019	0.3521	0.0028
60	40	00	0.2742	0.3310	0.0055
60	50	00	0.3398	0.2892	0.0060
60	70	00	0.4370	0.1613	0.0038
60	90	00	0.4719	0	0
90	45	00	0.3357	0.3191	-0.0126
90	50	00	0.3636	0.2920	-0.0112
90	60	00	0.4113	0.2292	-0.0076
90	75	00	0.4632	0.1207	-0.0035
90	90	00	0.4797	0	0

related the drag and lift coefficients to the product of the length of chord AB, fluid density ρ, and the square of the velocity v_∞. Thus, his coefficients are: $X/(\rho ABv_\infty^2) = c_x/2$ and $Y/(\rho ABv_\infty^2) = c_y/2$—i.e., they are half of the corresponding lift and drag coefficients adopted for our use. The angles 2γ and α_o are given in degrees and minutes. The location of the resultant force P (with projections X and Y) is determined by the ratio MD/BA (Fig. 62). Values of MD/BA are also given in the table.

C. VILLAT'S INTEGRO-DIFFERENTIAL EQUATION AND THE EXISTENCE AND UNIQUENESS OF THE SOLUTION

From the discussion in Section A it is noted that the jet problem of flow around some arc BCA (Fig. 52) is solved if the following function can be found:

$$\omega(\zeta) = i\,\ell n \frac{dw}{v_o dz} = \theta + i\,\ell n \frac{v}{v_o} = \theta + i\tau \ .$$

Now, when using the Schwarz transformation, Eq. (4.3) to determine $\omega(\zeta)$, it is sufficient to know its real part $\theta(\sigma)$ on the semicircle BCA (Fig. 53). By prescribing $\theta(\sigma)$ it is possible to obtain the solution to a problem of flow around an arbitrary arc, whose form is not known at the outset. To determine the flow around an arc whose form is prescribed, Villat [40] derived an integro-differential equation for the real part of $\omega(\zeta)$.

By first removing from ω its known singularity, we may obtain a holomorphic function Ω from which ω may be determined. Thus, we may now derive Villat's integro-differential equation for the real part of Ω. Our derivation is essentially the same as that given by Cisotti [51]. However, we must precede our derivation of Villat's equation by some preliminary remarks.

We shall assume that the arcs BC and CA (Fig. 52) have a continuous tangent and curvature. Let $\omega_{wed}(\zeta)$ be that function determined by Eq. (4.4) with the further condition that $\omega_{wed}(0) = 0$. As was shown in Section A, the condition $\omega_{wed}(0) = 0$ is equivalent to

$$\pi\nu + 2\kappa\sigma_o = 2\pi\kappa \ . \qquad (4.51)$$

Thus, as in Section B, $\omega(\zeta)$ takes the form

$$\omega(\zeta) = \omega_{wed}(\zeta) + \Omega(\zeta) \quad . \tag{4.52}$$

Now $\omega(\zeta)$ is regular inside the semicircle ADBC (Fig. 53) and has a jump, equal to $2\pi\kappa$, at C, where the flow bifurcates. Since $\omega_{wed}(\zeta)$ possesses the same properties, $\Omega(\zeta) = \omega(\zeta) - \omega_{wed}(\zeta)$ is regular inside the semicircle and continuous on its boundary arc BCA. If $\Omega(\zeta) = \vartheta + iT$, then according to Eqs. (4.4) and (4.6)

$$\left.\begin{aligned}
&\vartheta = \theta + \pi\nu && \text{(on BC)} \\
&\vartheta = \theta + \pi\nu - 2\pi\kappa && \text{(on AC)} \\
&T = \tau - 2\kappa \,\ell n \frac{\sin\,[(\sigma_o - \sigma)/2]}{\sin\,[(\sigma_o + \sigma)/2]} && \text{(on BC)} \\
&T = \tau - 2\kappa \,\ell n \frac{\sin\,[(\sigma_o + \sigma)/2]}{\sin\,[(\sigma_o + \sigma)/2]} && \text{(on AC)}
\end{aligned}\right\} \quad . \tag{4.53}$$

It follows that, on BCA,

$$\left.\begin{aligned}
&T = \tau - 2\kappa \,\ell n \frac{\sin\,|(\sigma_o - \sigma)/2|}{\sin\,[(\sigma_o - \sigma)/2]} && \text{(on BCA)} \\
&\vartheta = \beta - 2\pi\kappa + \pi\nu && \text{(on AC)} \\
&\vartheta = \beta - \pi + \pi\nu && \text{(on BC)}
\end{aligned}\right\} \quad , \tag{4.54}$$

where, as in Section B, β is the angle between the x-axis and the tangent at a point on the contour. On the real diameter of the semicircle ADBC, $\operatorname{Im}\omega = \operatorname{Im}\omega_{wed} = 0$; thus, on this diameter, $\operatorname{Im}\Omega = \vartheta = 0$. Hence, $\Omega(\zeta)$ can be extended to the entire circle $|\zeta| < 1$ in accordance with the symmetry principle. Then, a conjugate value of ζ corresponds to a congugate value of $\Omega(\zeta)$, and $\Omega(0) = \omega(0) - \omega_{wed}(0) = 0$. From the symmetry principle it follows that, on the circle $|\zeta| = 1$, $\vartheta(\sigma) = \vartheta(2\pi - \sigma)$ and $T(\sigma) = -T(2\pi - \sigma)$. By using Schwarz's Eq. (4.2) or (4.3), $\Omega(\zeta)$ can be determined by its real or imaginary parts as given on the circle $|\zeta| = 1$.

From Eq. (4.53) it follows that knowledge of $\vartheta(\sigma)$ is equivalent to knowledge of $\theta(\sigma)$ and, furthermore, that $\theta'(\sigma) = \vartheta'(\sigma)$. Naturally, if we prescribe the derivative $\vartheta'(\sigma) = \theta'(\sigma)$ instead of $\vartheta(\sigma)$, $\Omega(\zeta)$ can be determined by the Schwarz integral only up to the constant term. From here, following a passage to the limit from the interior of the circle $|\zeta| \leqq 1$ to the circle $|\zeta| = 1$, it is possible to obtain the required Dini relation*

$$T = B - \frac{1}{2\pi}\int_0^{2\pi} \vartheta'(\epsilon)\,\ell n\,\frac{1}{4\sin^2[(\epsilon - \sigma)/2]}\,d\epsilon \quad ,$$

where B is a constant. This integral is first broken into two parts—one from 0 to π and the other from π to 2π. Then, by introducing in the second integral a new variable $2\pi - \epsilon_1$ and taking into consideration the fact that $\vartheta'(2\pi - \epsilon_1) = -\vartheta'(\epsilon_1)$, we obtain

$$T(\sigma) = B + \frac{1}{\pi}\int_0^{\pi} \vartheta'(\epsilon)\,\ell n\,\frac{\sin|(\epsilon - \sigma)/2|}{\sin[(\epsilon + \sigma)/2]}\,d\epsilon \quad .$$

*Dini's relation is derived in a different manner by Cisotti [51].

Since $T = 0$ on the real axis in the ζ-plane, $T(0) = 0$; therefore, $B = 0$, and we finally obtain

$$T(\sigma) = \frac{1}{\pi}\int_0^{\pi} \vartheta'(\epsilon)\, \ln \frac{\sin |(\epsilon - \sigma)/2|}{\sin [(\epsilon + \sigma)/2]}\, d\epsilon \quad . \tag{4.55}$$

We may now directly derive Villat's equation with $2\kappa = 1$. According to Eq. (4.54) the curvature of the solid contour is

$$\kappa_K = \frac{d\beta}{ds} = \frac{d\beta}{d\sigma}\frac{d\sigma}{ds} = \frac{d\vartheta}{d\sigma}\frac{d\sigma}{ds} \quad . \tag{4.56}$$

But $ds = |dz|$ and, by using Eqs. (4.10) and (4.54) with $d\sigma > 0$, we have

$$ds = |dz| = \frac{2a^2}{v_o} e^{-\tau} |\cos \sigma - \cos \sigma_o| \sin \sigma\, d\sigma$$

or

$$ds = \frac{2a^2}{v_o} \frac{\sin |(\sigma_o + \sigma)/2|}{\sin |(\sigma_o - \sigma)/2|} e^{-T(\sigma)} |\cos \sigma - \cos \sigma_o| \sin \sigma\, d\sigma$$

$$= \frac{2a^2}{v_o} e^{-T(\sigma)}\, 2 \sin^2 \left(\frac{\sigma_o + \sigma}{2}\right) \sin \sigma\, d\sigma \quad . \tag{4.57}$$

From Eqs. (4.56) and (4.57)

$$\frac{d\vartheta}{d\sigma} = \kappa_K \frac{2a^2}{v_o} e^{-T(\sigma)}\, 2 \sin^2 \left(\frac{\sigma_o + \sigma}{2}\right) \sin \sigma \quad . \tag{4.58}$$

If the shape of the solid contour is known, then its curvature will also be known as a function of the angle β. Therefore, $\kappa_K(\beta)$ is, according to Eq. (4.54), a known function of ϑ.

Now, in order to obtain Villat's integro-differential equation, it remains only to express $T(\sigma)$ in terms of $\vartheta'(\sigma)$ by using Eq. (4.55) so that Eq. (4.58) becomes

$$\vartheta'(\sigma) = \kappa_K \frac{2a^2}{v_o} 2 \sin^2\left(\frac{\sigma_o + \sigma}{2}\right) \sin\sigma \exp\left[-\frac{1}{\pi}\int_0^\pi \vartheta'(\epsilon) \cdot \ln \frac{\sin|(\epsilon - \sigma)/2|}{\sin|(\epsilon + \sigma)/2|} d\epsilon\right] \quad (4.59)$$

By using Eq. (4.56), we eliminate $\vartheta'(\sigma)$ from Eq. (4.55) but retain $T(\sigma)$. Thus we obtain Nekrasov's equation [52], which is equivalent to Villat's equation,

$$T(\sigma) = \frac{2a^2}{\pi v_o}\int_0^\pi \kappa_K \vartheta[\epsilon + \pi(1 - \delta)]\, e^{-T(\epsilon)}\, 2\sin^2\left(\frac{\sigma_o + \epsilon}{2}\right) \cdot \sin\epsilon \ln \frac{\sin|(\epsilon - \sigma)/2|}{\sin|(\epsilon + \sigma)/2|} d\epsilon \quad . \quad (4.60)$$

Here $\vartheta(\sigma)$ is expressed in terms of T' through Dini's second relation,

$$\vartheta(\sigma) = -\frac{1}{\pi}\int_0^\pi T'(\epsilon) \ln|\cos\sigma - \cos\epsilon|\, dc \quad .$$

This is obtained in a manner analogous to that leading to his first relation. Villat's equation, with or without Nekrasov's modification, forms the basis of a significant number of papers in which exact solutions to jet problems were sought or the existence of these exact solutions was proved.

As Brillouin [44] did, we consider two kinds of problems concerned with separated flow about an obstacle herein:

1. Flow around a contour, or flow around a closed contour with continuous curvature (except at point C), is that flow in which the jet curvature at the separation points A and B is finite—i.e., conditions (4.33) and (4.34) are satisfied.
2. Flow around an arc is that flow in which the curvature of the jet is infinite at one of the separation points A or B—i.e., one of the conditions (4.33) or (4.34) is not satisfied.

In case 1., the wetted surface arc can be closed with a contour having a continuous curvature (particularly at points A and B) such that Brillouin's second condition is satisfied and the solid body does not intersect the jet surfaces (Fig. 52). In case 2., if the solid contour and jet surfaces are convex with respect to the fluid, then it is impossible to close the arc AB with a continuously curving contour (Fig. 56).*

Nekrasov [52] found the first solution for flow about a circular arc. He solved his equation (4.60) by successive approximation, proved the uniqueness of the solution and the convergence of the process for small values of a parameter proportional to the central angle subtended by the arc, and computed the first approximation to all quantities characterizing the flow. Similar problems were studied also by Carleri and Weinstein. Under Nekrasov's influence the problems of jet flow about curved arcs were studied at Moscow by hydrodynamicists Arzhanikov, Mesnikov, Slezkin, Kalinin, and

*Remember, however, that if the curvature changes sign at A and B, then flow around a closed contour with continuous curvature (except at point C) is possible (see Figs. 59, 60, and 61).

Sekerzh-Zenkovich [53] and at Tomsk by mathematician Kufavrev [54]. Here, we briefly consider the method of Ref. 53.

Sekerzh-Zenkovich gave the arc curvature $\kappa_K(\beta)$ in the form $\kappa_K(\beta) = kK(\beta) = -\lambda/2a^2\ K(\beta)$ with $v_o = 1$. For each arc, λ has a particular value. He studied not only a single arc but also a family of arcs whose curvature satisfies the Cauchy-Lipschitz conditions and depends on the arbitrary parameter λ. He solved Villat's equation by successive approximations for such a family of arcs and proved the uniqueness and existence of the solution for small values of λ. For an arc whose curvature is an analytic function of β, Sekerzh-Zenkovich showed that a more effective method for solving problems was to expand the solution in powers of λ. In order to find the value of λ corresponding to a certain family of curves, it is necessary to solve a transcendental equation which, according to the theory of implicit functions, has a unique solution for sufficiently small λ.

It is valuable, of course, to increase (by using analytic continuation) the size of the parameter λ for which the above process will converge. In 1933, Weinstein [55] was the first to apply analytic continuation, in particular, to a straight or normal jet flow against a circular arc. Later, Sekerzh-Zenkovich [56] applied the method to problems concerned with oblique flow of jets against arcs with analytic curvatures.

Along with Weinstein's work [57,58], a series of investigations was carried out on the existence and uniqueness of solutions for jet flows from a symmetric nozzle. For the interested reader, the proceedings of a 1949 symposium [59] on free surface flow are recommended; an extensive list of references is given there. We note only that the method of continuity for curved boundaries, wherein the existence of a jet flow from a channel is inferred from a continuous deformation beginning with a known solution, is based on the first works on polygonal boundaries. Thus, curvilinear nozzles were approximated by piecewise straight walls—i.e., connected rectilinear segments; continuous curvature was approached by the limiting process of letting the segment length approach 0. Finn's paper [60] is representative of recent analysis with a similar orientation.

From those papers considered by Weinstein's proceedings [59], it is important to mention that of Friedrichs [61], in which he proved, in particular, that the problem of jet flow from a channel or nozzle can be reduced to determination of the minimum of some integral expression. The application of variational principles* to the solution of jet-flow problems is very fruitful, and the possibilities of successful applications are far from exhausted at the present time.

The two basic works in the field of the existence and uniqueness of solutions to infinite jet flow past an arc or contour are by Leray [63] and Lavrentiev [64]. Unfortunately, the great volume of these works prevents an extensive review of their content in this book.

By using the methods of functional analysis, Leray, together with Schauder [65], thoroughly studied the question of the existence and uniqueness of solutions to the infinite jet flow around an obstacle. However, their proofs are not constructive, since the problem of providing an effective solution is not examined.

Leray considered two types of obstacles. Obstacles of the first type have a finite curvature everywhere, and if the

*Apparently Riabouchinsky [62] was the first to indicate the possibilities in applying variational principles to studies of jet flow.

curvature is taken to be a function of arc length, then it satisfies a Hölder condition with $1/2 < \mu < 1$ [66]. In Fig. 63, an obstacle B_oC_o of the second type is shown. Leray called such obstacles "accolades." In particular, we see that arcs B_oB_1 and C_1C_o are convex with respect to the flow, while arcs B_1A and AC_1 are concave. With movement along the arcs B_oB_1 and C_1C_o from B_1 to B_o and C_1 to C_o respectively, the absolute values of the curvatures are nondecreasing functions. Furthermore, arcs B_1A and AC_1 can contain straight sections, while at point A the arc can have an angle, a cusp, or a continuously turning tangent. Except in the latter case, the approaching streamline that lies along the solid obstacle bifurcates at point A. Obstacles that are concave to the fluid flow, or circular obstacles, are both particular cases of the accolade.

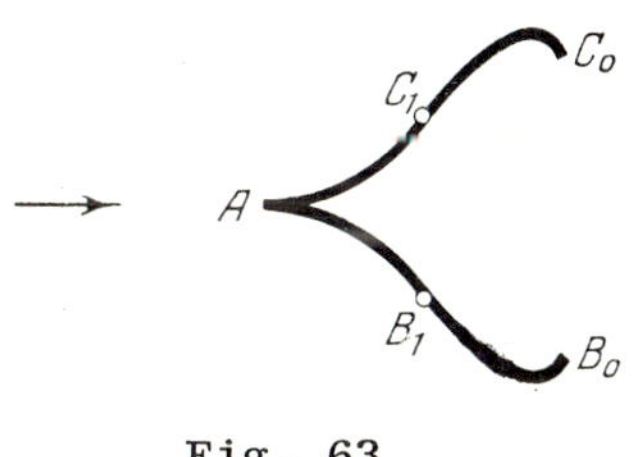

Fig. 63

Leray's basic functional equation can be obtained from Eq. (4.57) and from an integral relation that expresses T in terms of $\beta(s)$. The class of obstacles considered by Leray was characterized by the fact that any straight line parallel to the flow velocity at infinity (which points along the x-axis) intersects an obstacle in no more than one point. For these obstacles, he proved that problems of jet flows around a contour or an arc always have at least one solution that satisfies the Brillouin conditions. Furthermore, Leray proved that the following problems have a unique solution:

1. Flow around a convex arc
2. Flow around a symmetric arc
3. Flow around a convex circular contour
4. Symmetric flow around an accolade.

He also showed that symmetric convex contours exist for which flows are not uniquely determined and therefore several flow solutions exist.

The basic works of Kravtchenko [69] and Oudart [68] were further developments of Leray's ideas. Kravtchenko generalized Leray's results to the case of an obstacle located in a rectilinear channel,* and Oudart studied the questions of the existence and uniqueness of solutions to flow past an obstacle in a channel with curved walls. Subsequently, Kravtchenko provided more general results [69] by studying conditions for the existence (but not uniqueness) of solutions to the problems of flow in a channel around an arc having angle points and an arc without tangents.

We go now to Lavrentiev's original work [64] based on his developments in variational principles [70].** The first part of Ref. [64] discusses the functions that accomplish a conformal mapping of the half-plane onto a region with one limiting point at infinity. The second part is concerned with the applications of these mathematical results to jet theory. In this paper Lavrentiev demonstrates the existence and uniqueness of the solution to the infinite jet flow around an

---

*Of particular interest is Kravtchenko's analysis of the case when the distances between the obstacles and the walls of the channel are small.

**Lavrentiev's variational principle has the following simple hydrodynamic interpretation: if we take the velocity at infinity to be unity, then a deformation of a region of the contour around which the fluid flows causes the flow velocity in the undeformed region of the contour to decrease or increase depending upon whether the deformed region of the contour is located respectively inside or outside the region originally occupied by the fluid.

arc symmetrically located with respect to the x-axis. It is, of course, necessary to consider only one half of the flow. The flow with separation of the jet from a semi-infinite obstacle (Fig. 64) was also investigated. This new problem is a natural generalization of the symmetric infinite-jet problem mentioned above. This latter problem differs from the symmetric flow around a circle in that it is no longer

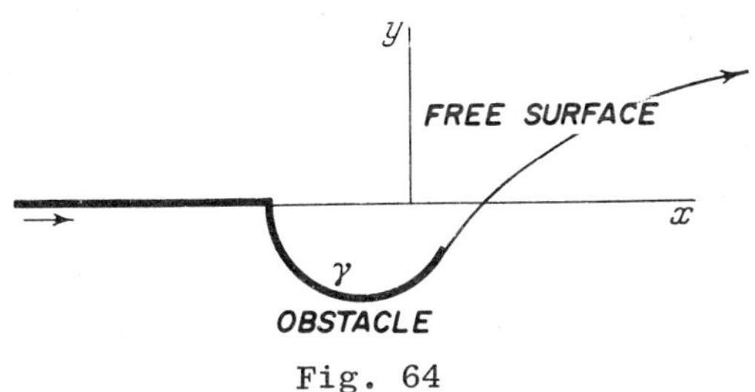

Fig. 64

required that the jet remain within the half-plane—i.e., the jet may penetrate the upper half-plane. Furthermore, two cases are considered for the symmetric flow around the arc. In the first the jets go to infinity; in the second they join together a finite distance behind the arc. Lavrentiev prescribed the conditions sufficient to guarantee the existence of finite and infinite jets.* In contrast to Leray, Lavrentiev does not make any hypotheses with respect to the number of points of intersection between the arc γ and straight lines parallel to the velocity vector at infinity (the x-axis), but requires that every perpendicular to the x-axis intersect the arc γ in no more than two points (or lie along a segment). As for the arc around which the flow passes, it is required only that γ be formed by a finite number of arcs of bounded curvature.

*In the literature the free surfaces of the jets are often called jets. In such cases, when this terminology cannot lead to a misunderstanding, we will use "jet" in this sense.

Lavrentiev proved that, if the above conditions are fulfilled, the solution to the problem of flow around an arc exists and is unique. In addition to investigating the questions of the existence and uniqueness of jet-flow solutions, Lavrentiev obtained a series of interesting qualitative results. In particular, he examined flow past convex contours that are symmetric about the x-axis. He considered this problem in a manner somewhat different from that used by Leray, in which the questions of whether or not the curvature of the jet is finite at separation and whether or not Brillouin's first condition is fulfilled are studied. Lavrentiev was interested only in determining whether or not the jet, after separation from the contour, intersects it. Accordingly, the following theorems were proved:

1. Among all possible points of jet separation from the convex contour Γ (for a symmetric flow around Γ), there exist the points A, A' (the ends of an arc Γ_o) that are located forward or to the left of the points of Γ with maximum ordinates (Fig. 65).
2. The free jets that correspond to two different flows around the same convex contour have no common points.
3. For two different flows around the same contour Γ with jet separation, the fluid-pressure force on Γ will be greater for that flow with earlier (more forward) separation.

Finally, we note the presentation in Ref. [64] of the solution to an interesting variational problem, namely, the determination of the arc Γ, contained within a given rectangle, that has the minimum drag. It is found that Γ consists of three parts AB, BC, and CD (Fig. 66). The segment BC is a straight line of such a length that the jet surfaces of a Kirchhoff flow springing from points B

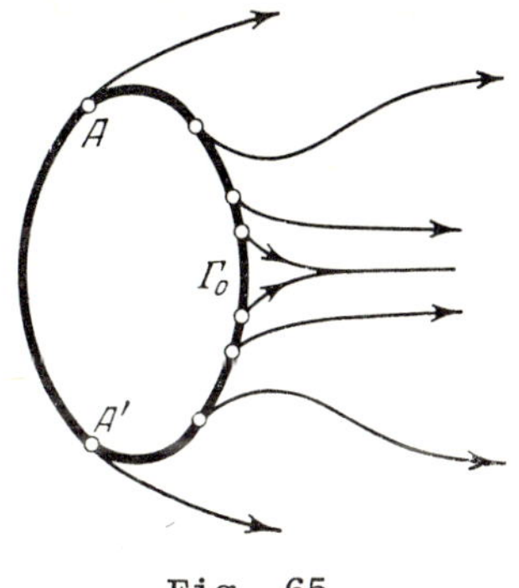

Fig. 65

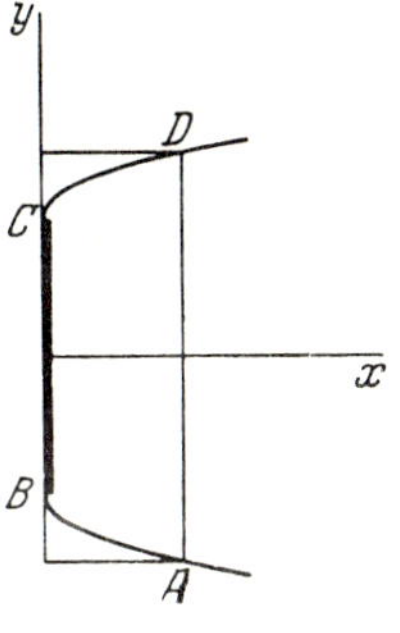

Fig. 66

and C pass through A and D. Then, of course, the arcs AB and CD of the minimum-drag flow are taken to coincide with the sections of the Kirchhoff jets within the given rectangle.

D. SEDOV'S METHOD

Until now only the flow around single curvilinear obstacles has been considered. A general method for the solution to flows around several curvilinear arcs was given by Sedov [24,71].

Consider the separated jet flow about n curvilinear arcs (Fig. 67). The velocity at infinity and on the jets equals v_0. The x-axis is oriented parallel to the velocity of the approaching flow at infinity. The direction of the jets at infinity is also chosen parallel to the x-axis, since they would otherwise intersect the free surface of the basic flow.

We conformally map the region occupied by the moving fluid onto the upper half-plane of the complex variable $u = u_1 + iu_2$ so that the points at infinity on the extreme upper and lower free-jet surfaces correspond to $u_1 = \infty$ and points A_1 and B_1 correspond to $u = 0$ and $u = 1$

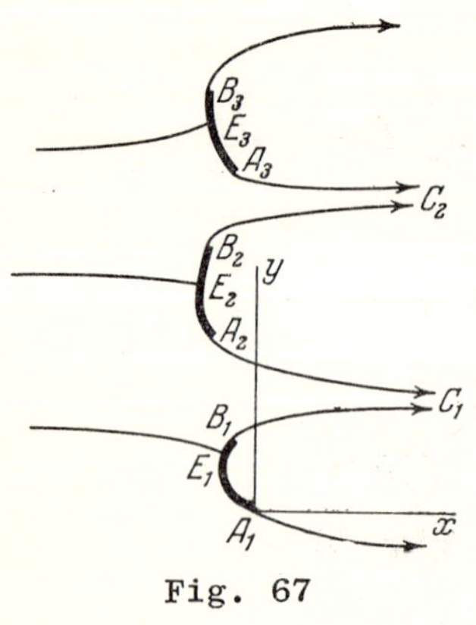

Fig. 67

respectively (Fig. 68). The contours A_kB_k beome the segments a_kb_k in the u-plane, while the stagnation or critical points E_1, E_2, ..., E_n correspond to the points e_1, e_2, ..., e_n on the segments a_1b_1, a_2b_2, ..., a_nb_n. The points at infinity of the jets C_1, C_2, ..., C_{n-1} correspond to to some points c_1, c_2, ..., c_{n-1} that lie in the intervals b_1a_2, b_2a_3, ..., $b_{n-1}a_n$. The region of change of $w = \varphi + i\psi$ is an entire plane that is cut along semi-infinite straight lines parallel to the real axis (Fig. 69). These cuts, where ψ = const., correspond to the jets and arcs. The cuts begin

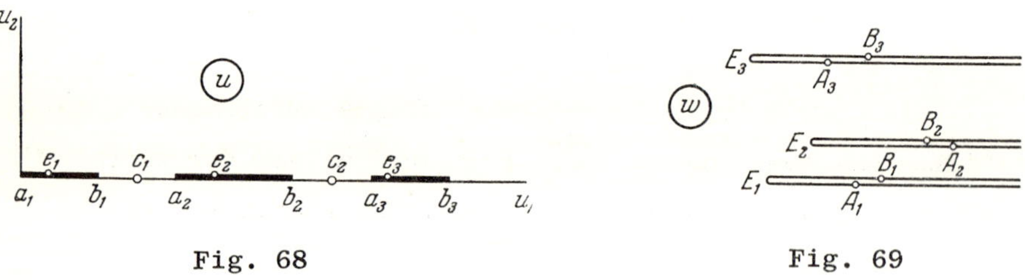

Fig. 68

Fig. 69

at the points E_1, E_2, ..., E_n, corresponding to the critical points, where bifurcation of the stream lines occurs.

Along the real axis u_1, dw/du is real. In accordance with Sections I.F.1 and .2, w has a second-order pole at $u_1 = \infty$ and logarithmic singularities at C_1, C_2, ..., C_{n-1}. Furthermore (Section I.F.4), dw/du = 0 at e_1, e_2, ..., e_n. Thus, by using the singular-point method, it is possible to write

$$\frac{dw}{du} = C \prod_{k,s} \frac{u - e_k}{u - c_s}, \tag{4.61}$$

where C is a real constant; k takes the values $1, 2, \ldots, n-1, n$; and s takes the values $1, 2, \ldots, n-1$.

The same expression for dw/du may be obtained from the Schwarz-Christoffel Eq. (1.40). The function w is easily obtained from Eq. (4.61) by elementary integration. We now introduce $\omega = i\ \ell n\ (dw/v_o dz) = \theta + i\ \ell n\ (v/v_o)$, which is regular in the upper half-plane and vanishes at infinity. In the intervals $b_k a_k$, corresponding to the jets, the imaginary part of $\omega(u)$ is 0. On the segments $a_k b_k$ we have

$$\left.\begin{aligned} \theta &= \beta - \pi \qquad (\text{on } a_k e_k) \\ & \qquad\qquad\qquad\qquad (k = 1, 2, \ldots, n) \\ \theta &= \beta \qquad\quad\ \ (\text{on } e_k b_k) \end{aligned}\right\}, \tag{4.62}$$

where β is the angle formed between tangents to the solid arcs and the x-axis. At the edges a_k and b_k, $\omega(u)$ is finite. By using the Keldysh-Sedov equation [4], which gives the solution to the mixed-boundary-value problem for a semicircle, we are led to

$$\omega = \frac{1}{\pi}\left(\prod_{k=1}^{n} \frac{u - a_k}{u - b_k}\right)^{1/2} \left[\sum_{k=1}^{n} \int_{a_k}^{b_k} \frac{\beta(\xi)}{\xi - u}\left(\frac{b_k - \xi}{\xi - a_k} \prod \frac{\xi - b_s}{\xi - a_s}\right)^{1/2} d\xi \right.$$

$$\left. - \pi \sum_{k=1}^{n} \int_{a_k}^{e_k} \left(\frac{b_k - \xi}{\xi - a_k} \prod_{s \neq k} \frac{\xi - b_s}{\xi - a_s}\right)^{1/2} \frac{d\xi}{\xi - u}\right]. \tag{4.63}$$

Equation (4.63) can also be obtained from Schwarz's equation for the half-plane if, instead of $\omega(u)$, we consider the function

$$\omega(u)\left(\prod_{k=1}^{n} \frac{u - b_k}{u - a_k}\right)^{1/2} ,$$

the imaginary part of which is known on the real axis of the u-plane.

Equation (4.63) determines $\omega(u)$ with finite values at the points a_k. By employing the conditions that $\omega(u)$ have finite values at the points b_k, we obtain

$$\sum_{k=1}^{n} \int_{a_k}^{b_k} \frac{\beta(\xi)}{\xi - b_j} \left(\frac{b_k - \xi}{\xi - a_k} \prod_{n \neq k} \frac{\xi - b_s}{\xi - a_s}\right)^{1/2} d\xi$$

$$= \pi \sum_{k=1}^{n} \int_{a_k}^{e_k} \left(\frac{b_k - \xi}{\xi - a_k} \prod_{s \neq k} \frac{\xi - b_s}{\xi - a_s}\right)^{1/2} \frac{d\xi}{\xi - b_j}$$

$$(j = 1, 2, \ldots, n) \quad . \tag{4.64}$$

Condition (4.64) can be considered as n equations for the determination of the n constant cooredinates e_k that are images in the u-plane of the critical points.

By assumption, the velocity at infinity in the jets is parallel to the x-axis and is equal to v_o; consequently, the quantities $c_1, c_2, \ldots, c_{n-1}$ must be zeros of $\omega(u)$--i.e., the roots of the equation

$$\omega(u) = 0 \quad . \tag{4.65}$$

We can now form an integro-differential equation for determining $\beta(u)$; this equation is a generalization of Villat's equation, discussed earlier. From

$$\frac{dw}{dz} = v_o e^{-i\omega}, \qquad \frac{dw}{du} = C \prod_{s,k} \frac{u - e_k}{u - c_s} \tag{4.66}$$

we produce

$$\frac{dz}{du} = \frac{C}{v_o} \prod_{s,k} \frac{u - e_k}{u - c_s} e^{i\omega(u)} \quad . \tag{4.67}$$

On the segments $a_k e_k$

$$\omega(u) = \beta - \pi - \frac{i}{\pi|g(u)|}\left[\sum_{k=1}^{n} \text{V.P.} \int_{a_k}^{b_k} \frac{\beta|g(\xi)|}{\xi - u} d\xi - \pi \sum_{k=1}^{n} \text{V.P.} \int_{a_k}^{e_k} \frac{|g(\xi)|\, d\xi}{\xi - u}\right] . \tag{4.68}$$

On the segments $e_k b_k$,

$$\omega(u) = \beta - \frac{i}{\pi|g(u)|}\left[\sum_{k=1}^{n} \text{V.P.} \int_{a_k}^{b_k} \frac{\beta|g(\xi)|}{\xi - u} d\xi - \pi \sum_{k=1}^{n} \text{V.P.} \int_{a_k}^{e_k} \frac{|g(\xi)|\, d\xi}{\xi - u}\right] . \tag{4.69}$$

In Eqs. (4.68) and (4.69)

$$g(u) = \left(\prod_{k=1}^{n} \frac{u - b_k}{u - a_k}\right)^{1/2} \quad ;$$

the symbol V.P. indicates the Principal Value of the integral (the Cauchy Principal Value) obtained by a limiting process that excludes the region containing the poles of the function. Furthermore, we have

$$\frac{dz}{du} = e^{i\beta}\frac{ds}{du} = e^{i\beta}\frac{ds}{d\beta}\frac{d\beta}{du} = \frac{e^{i\beta}}{\kappa_k(\beta)}\frac{d\beta}{du} , \qquad (4.70)$$

where ds is the differential distance on the arc and $\kappa_k(\beta)$ is the curvature of the arcs A_kB_k around which the flow passes.

By using Eqs. (4.66) to (4.70) we find

$$\frac{d\beta}{du} = \pm C\frac{\kappa(\beta)}{v_o}\prod_{s,k}\frac{u-e_k}{u-e_s}\exp\left\{\frac{1}{\pi|g(u)|}\left[\sum_{k=1}^{n}\text{V.P.}\right.\right.$$

$$\left.\left.\cdot\int_{a_k}^{b_k}\frac{\beta(\xi)}{\xi-u}|g(\xi)|\,d\xi-\pi\sum_{k=1}^{n}\text{V.P.}\int_{a_k}^{e_k}\frac{|g(\xi)|\,d\xi}{\xi-u}\right]\right\}. \qquad (4.71)$$

If u lies in one of the intervals e_kb_k, then the plus sign is used; if it lies in one of the intervals a_ke_k, then the minus sign is used. Equation (4.71) can be considered the summation of the integro-differential equations for $\beta_k(u) = \beta(u)$ on the segments a_kb_k.

If $\beta(u)$ is determined from Eq. (4.71), then, after determination of the constants $e_1, e_2, \ldots, e_n, c_1, c_2, \ldots, c_{n-1}$ by using Eqs. (4.64) and (4.65), there will remain $2n-1$ undetermined parameters $a_2, a_3, \ldots, a_n, b_2, b_3, \ldots, b_n$, and C. To prescribe n arcs A_kB_k, $3n-2$ constants are required (the coordinate origin can be placed at one end of a solid arc). Clearly, with only $2n-1$ free parameters available, it is not possible to prescribe an arbitrary arrangement of arcs A_kB_k. In 1921, Tiri [24] was the first to establish these results for the case of two plane plates.

E. THE INVERSE PROBLEM

In lieu of a direct physical problem it is of great interest to pose the following inverse problem: given the velocity v on an arc as a function of the distance s along the arc, find the details of the jet flow about the arc and the arc shape. Pykhteev examined several such inverse problems. He studied separated jet flow about symmetric arcs in a channel and in an infinite fluid by the usual methods; he also considered a cavity flow (see Chapter V) past a symmetric arc by the Gilbarg-Efros method. In addition to a general statement of the inverse problem, Pykhteev obtained new, exact solutions for particular jet problems. Here we shall present only a short exposition of the basic concepts and a statement of the inverse problem. The computational details are found in Pykhteev's works [72 - 74].

Consider an arc BCA that is symmetric* to the x-axis (Fig. 70). In contrast to Section C, the arc distance s is measured from point C toward points A and B; hence, on arcs CA and CB, $s > 0$ and $d\varphi = v\,ds$. Assume then that the length of BCA is $2s_0$ and the velocity on BCA is given by

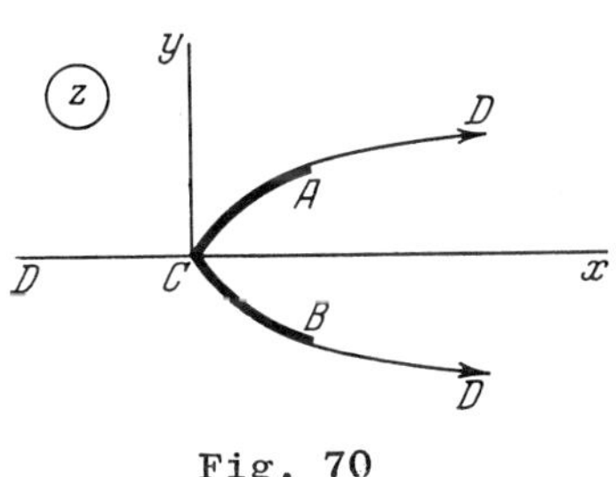

Fig. 70

$$v = v_0 f(s/s_0) \quad , \tag{4.72}$$

where $f(s/s_0)$ is a known function satisfying the conditions $f(0) = 0$ and $f(1) = 1$.

We map the region of change of z, the complex potential $w = \varphi + i\psi$, and $\omega = i\,\ell n\,(dw/v_0 dz)$ onto the upper half-plane

---

*The assumption of symmetry is not essential, being adopted here only for convenience and clarity.

of the parametric variable t. The point correspondence between the z- and t-planes is seen in Figs. 70 and 71.

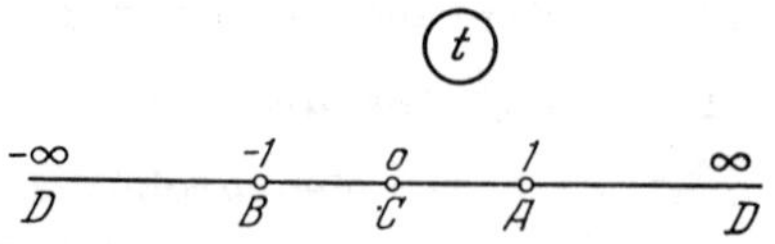

$-\infty$ D, -1 B, 0 C, 1 A, ∞ D

Fig. 71

The region of change of w is the same as that given in Fig. 2; thus, we have, obviously,

$$w = \varphi_o t^2 \quad , \tag{4.73}$$

where φ_o is the value of φ at points A and B. Since $w = \int_o^s v ds$ on ACB, the relationship between t and s on ACB is given by

$$\varphi_o t^2 = v_o s_o \int_0^{s/s_o} f(u)\, du \quad . \tag{4.74}$$

If we know s as a function of t, we must also know the velocity $v = v_o f$ as a function of t. It is then easy to find ω as a function of t. In fact, $\omega = \theta + i\,\ell n\,(v/v_o) = 0$ at infinity, $\text{Im}\,\omega = \ell n\,(v/v_o) = 0$ on the free surfaces, and $\text{Im}\,\omega$ is a known function of t on the solid arc BCA. Thus, we may use Schwarz's formula for the half-plane to determine $\omega(t)$ [4] as

$$\omega(t) = \frac{1}{\pi} \int_{-1}^{1} \ell n\, f \,\frac{d\xi}{\xi - t} \quad . \tag{4.75}$$

Therefore, the problem can be considered solved. The shapes of the arc BCA and the jets are obtained from

$$z = \frac{2\varphi_o}{v_o} \int e^{i\omega}\, t\, dt \quad , \tag{4.76}$$

where the real and imaginary parts are separated after substitution of limits in the integral.

According to Pykhteev [72], the drag of the contour calculated either by summing the projections of the pressure on the arc or by using an equation analogous to Levi-Civita's Eq. (4.22). In Ref. [72] an example is examined wherein $v = v_o f\,(s/s_o) = v_o\,(s/s_o)^{\lambda}$, for $\lambda > 1$, while in Ref. [74] one finds exact solutions to problems of jet flow around some two-parameter, symmetric contours.

CHAPTER V. FLOW AROUND A BODY AT SMALL CAVITATION NUMBER

A. CAVITATION

A fluid is said to cavitate when bubbles appear within the flow region. The bubbles generally contain fluid vapor or gases, previously dissolved in the fluid, but released by low pressure.

From physics it is known that fluids generally have a low resistance to tensile stresses (opposite to pressures); however, in certain special experiments it has been possible to subject the fluid to large negative pressure (tensile stresses) without "rupturing" the fluid. Some fluids, found in nature and used in engineering, contain both solid particles in suspension and dissolved gases; such fluids are even less capable of supporting tensile stresses than those cleansed of this mixture of solids and gases.*

It is reasonable, then, to require that fluid pressures cannot fall below some limiting value p_o and that, if the pressure in some fluid filled region seeks to fall below p_o, then the fluid must "rupture." Thus, a region, called a cavity, will be formed that is full of fluid vapor or gases— i.e., cavitation will occur. It follows that the flow form

---

*Common tap water contains a great number of small particles and dissolved gases; when flowing in a thin tube under pressure, it can resist large negative pressures for short periods of time. Such flows are unstable, however [75].

must change. Inside the entire flow region the pressure is greater than p_o, except where cavities exist. As a result of the small density of the gases and vapors in these cavities, the pressure is essentially constant and equal to p_o.

Frequently p_o is equal to p_d, the saturated-vapor pressure of the fluid at a given temperature. Then, the cavitation appears as boiling fluid which, it is known, can be produced not only by an increase in temperature but also by pressure reduction. In general p_o depends on:

1. The quantity of gases dissolved in the fluid
2. The quantity, sizes, and shapes of suspended particles
3. The length of time during which the fluid is subject to the reduced pressures
4. The capillary forces.

For practical purposes, p_o is generally very small compared to atmospheric pressure.

The cavities in the fluid may have widely varied dimensions—some microscopically small bubbles (in the initial stages of cavitation) or some many times larger than the body around which fluid is flowing and cavitation is occurring. We shall confine our attention to the case in which a single continuous cavity is formed behind a given solid body that is considerably smaller than the trailing cavity. This flow regime is called a regime of fully developed cavitation or separated cavitational flow.*

In this chapter, as before, we consider only steady flow of a weightless, incompressible fluid. The pressure than is determined from Bernoulli's integral

$$p - p_o = \frac{\rho}{2}\left(v_o^2 - v^2\right) \quad , \tag{5.1}$$

*Sometimes called supercavitating flow.

where p_o is the pressure in the cavity. It follows that, with $p = p_o$, we have $v = v_o$—i.e., at the surface of the jet bounding the cavity the velocity is constant and equal to v_o. Since the minimum pressure is reached on the boundary of the cavity, v_o will be the maximum velocity in the fluid. Thus, the first condition of Brillouin [44] for fully developed cavity flow must be satisfied (cf. Chapter IV.B).

Let a flow approach a body with a fluid velocity v_∞ at infinity. The flow regime around the body depends on the nondimensional number

$$Q = \frac{2(p_\infty - p_o)}{\rho v_\infty^2} = \frac{v_o^2}{v_\infty^2} - 1 \quad , \tag{5.2}$$

where p_∞ is the static pressure in the approaching flow—i.e., the pressure at infinity. The number Q is called the cavitation number and is the most important parameter for characterizing a cavity flow. In the initial stages of cavitation, Q is large and v_∞ is relatively small. In fully developed cavity flows, the opposite is true. In engineering practice the appearance of cavitation coincided with development of high-velocity propellers, turbine blades, pumps, and other movable parts of hydraulic machines.

In 1910 when Brillouin wrote Ref. [44], engineers were already acquainted with cavitation [76]. It appears that Brillouin was also acquainted with the technical problems associated with cavitation. In particular, he introduced his condition that the velocity on the free surface of a jet must be a maximum for the flow. He concluded that otherwise the pressures in some other part of the fluid would be less than the free-stream pressure and hence bubbles of vapor and gases could be produced in the fluid region—i.e., the fluid continuity would be destroyed [44, p. 151].

Cavity flows possess two important features. First, cavity-boundary streamlines must always be concave with respect to the center of the cavity. In fact, the pressure must increase as we pass into the fluid away from the cavity streamline. Thus, the resultant pressure force acting on a fluid particle moving along the boundary streamline, as well as the acceleration of that particle, is directed from the fluid into the cavity. Clearly, the center of curvature of the boundary streamline is located within the cavity—i.e., jet (cavity) surfaces must be convex with respect to the fluid (or concave to the cavity) [44]. Second, the density ρ of the main fluid must be much larger than the density ρ' of the mixture of vapor and gases in the cavity—i.e., $\rho'/\rho \ll 1$. The ratio ρ'/ρ was introduced by Betz and Petersohn [77]. At the end of Chapter III it was noted that, when the dead zone behind a body is filled with the same fluid as that which is flowing around the body, the boundaries between the flow region and the dead zone are unstable and are washed away as the dead zone becomes filled with vorticity. Some elementary considerations lead to a confirmation of this instability of the flow at separation boundaries [see, e.g., Lamb's *Hydrodynamics*]. Practically speaking, the free surface of a dense fluid bounding a region filled with vapor and gases is stable and will not be washed away. The flow over a weir, the flow of water jets in air, and flow around supercavitating propellers—all these are examples containing these more or less stable free surfaces.

We may now make a new interpretation of the jet flow around a contour—i.e., Kirchhoff's flow (see Section I.D). We assume that the dead zone behind the body is filled with gases or fluid vapor—i.e., that behind the contour there is a cavity of infinite length. In the case of a cavity flow, only the basic Kirchhoff flow is suitable (as described in Chapter I, Figs. 1 and 15 or in Chapter III, Figs. 33, 37, and 38). The flow shown in Fig. 36 cannot be considered a cavity flow because the velocity is infinite at H. Also, it is not possible to consider the flow in Fig. 41 (Section III.B) as a cavity flow because the boundaries of the dead region are concave to the fluid flow and the dead-region pressure is not the required minimum. Similarly, the flow around a plate (Section III.C) is discarded as a possible cavity flow because in all the variants of the flow (Figs. 46 and 49 - 51) some parts of the boundary are concave to the flowing fluid, and the velocity is infinite at the first edge B.

Kirchhoff's flow represents only the limiting case of a cavity flow with $Q = (v_o^2/v^2) - 1 = 0$. In this flow the cavity extends to infinity and the velocity v_∞ of the approaching flow equals the velocity v_o on the cavity boundaries. The models for an established cavity flow with $Q > 0$ are described later in this chapter. In comparing Kirchhoff's flow with experiments it is necessary first to carry out the experiments under conditions of fully developed cavitation and, second, to remember that flow with an infinite cavity is not actually possible and can be considered only as the limiting case $(Q \rightarrow 0)$ of a real flow. The literature about cavitation mentions the existence of a great number of experiments concerned with cavity flow about various profiles. However, the amount of published data is small. Thus, we carry out an analysis of Walchner's old experiments [78] which were run in Gottingen's cavitation tunnel early in the 1930's. The physical picture of cavity flow is shown quite clearly in Walchner's experiments, irrespective of their degree of completeness or perfection. The experimental body was placed in the water jet. By using a special force balnace it was possible to measure the forces acting on the body. The flow of water around the body was photographed through a glass window. The experiments consisted of the measurement of the lift and drag of circular-segment profiles (Fig. 72). The lift coefficient C_y and drag coefficient C_x of the segment profile are plotted vs. Q in Fig. 73 ($f/\ell = 0.0385$, $\alpha_o = 6$ deg, $C_y = 2Y/\rho\ell v_\infty^2$, $C_x = 2X/\rho\ell v_\infty^2$, where f is the thickness of the segment, ℓ is the chord length, α_o is the angle between the chord of the profile and the direction of the approaching flow, Y is the lift force, and X is the drag).

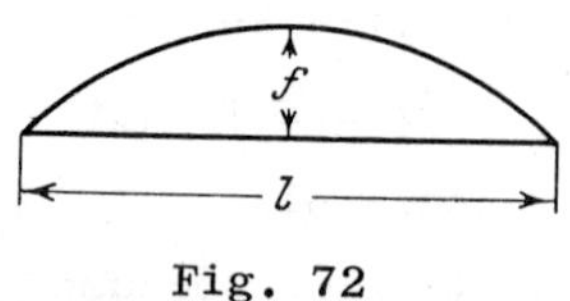

Fig. 72

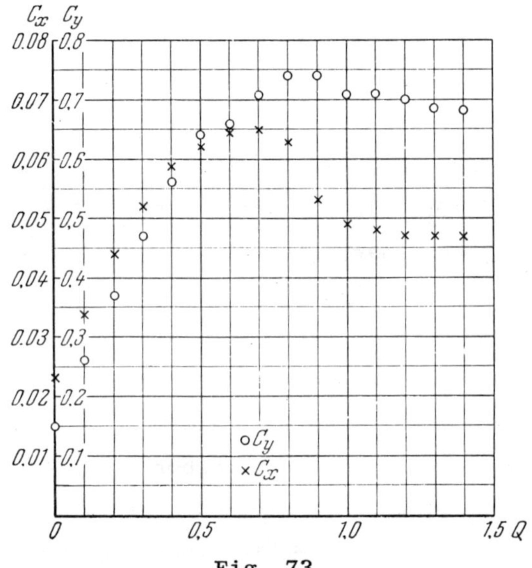

Fig. 73

For small cavitation numbers a cavity exists behind the profile and is filled with air and water vapor. Figure 74 shows a flow around a wing AB in the cavitation tunnel. The cavitation zone D (free from water) is distinctly seen behind the wing; on the other hand, zone E is filled with

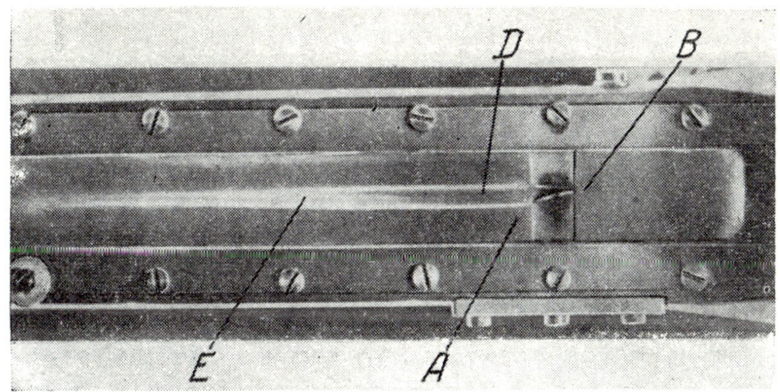

Fig. 74

bubbles and foam. In the present case the flow past the profile does not differ from flow past a flat plate because the curved, back side of the profile is not wetted by the fluid.

If the water were completely inviscid, then the drag X of the plate would be given in terms of the lift force Y by $X = Y \tan \alpha_o$. At small angles of attack, viscosity has practically no effect on the lift force, but it does increase the drag considerably. Thus, when the back of the profile is not wetted, X/Y is larger than $\tan \alpha_o \approx 0.105$ (for $\alpha_o = 6$ deg). According to the data of Fig. 73, $X/Y > 0.105$ when $Q < 0.4$. With further increases in Q, the back of the profile is first partially and then totally wetted by the water and foam. Finally, this process leads to a maximum and then to a decrease in the magnitudes of C_y and C_x. As a result the ratio X/Y may become considerably less than $\tan \alpha_o$ in the end.

Clearly, comparisons between experimental and theoretical results should be made in terms of C_y, because while the drag depends strongly on viscosity, lift does not. Accordingly, we obtain

$$C_y = \frac{\pi \sin 2\alpha_o}{4 + \pi \sin \alpha_o} \tag{5.3}$$

from the projection of the normal force on the y-axis in Rayleigh's equation [13]. For $\alpha = 6$ deg, $C_y = 0.151$, which we see agrees well with the corresponding point in Fig. 73. Walchner ran additional experiments for $\alpha_o = 2, 3, 4,$ and 5 deg. His experimental results also agree with values obtained from Eq. (5.3).

When Q is large, the flow picture corresponds to one in which a Karman vortex street forms behind the profile. From Fig. 73 we see that, when Q is large, the resultant pressure force on the body is considerably larger than when $Q = 0$. Thus in years past, the hydrodynamicists were greatly concerned with the lack of agreement between jet theory and experiments. It was only after a detailed study of the appearance of cavitation was made that the disagreement was found to be a result of comparing jet-theory data for $Q = 0$ with experimental data for cases where Q was large. The evolution in hydrodynamic thought on this problem can be clearly traced in the classical aero- and hydrodynamics of Prandtl [79,80]. In his 1931 work [80], Prandtl remarked about the dissatisfaction with jet-theory results. However, in his 1944 book [79], he pointed out that "Good agreement between theoretical calculations and experiments exists when, in a water flow around a plate, the region behind the plate is filed with air (or fluid vapor, as happens when the flow velocity is very large). In this case the surfaces of separation remain almost completely intact and as a result the basic assumptions of the theory are well satisfied." (Chapter III, Section 14)

It is easy to see why for many years it was believed that jet theory gave good results for jet flow from vessels but was inapplicable to flow about bodies. Characteristically, in problems concerning jet flow from vessels, water was flowing into air or, more generally, a liquid into a gas where ρ'/ρ is small. In problems concerning bodies, when the velocities were high, the fluid was usually air; when the fluid was water, most cases exhibited large cavitation numbers. The following elementary calculation [81] shows that cavity flow around bodies in air that is assumed incompressible cannot be realized in practice.*

We consider a perfect gas. The mach number $\mathbf{M}$ at infinity in the flow approaching the body in an adiabatic process is

$$\mathbf{M}_\infty^2 = \frac{v_\infty^2 \rho_\infty}{\gamma p_\infty} , \tag{5.4}$$

where $\gamma = c_p/c_v$ is the ratio of the specific heat at constant pressure to the specific heat at constant volume, and p_∞ and ρ_∞ are the pressure and density of the gas in the approaching flow. On the other hand, if p_o/p_∞ is negligibly small in comparison to unity, then the cavitation number is

$$Q \approx \frac{2p_\infty}{\rho_\infty v_\infty^2} . \tag{5.5}$$

We let $\gamma = 1.4$ for the air and obtain

$$\mathbf{M}_\infty^2 \approx \frac{1.43}{Q} \approx \frac{1.5}{Q} . \tag{5.6}$$

As we pointed out above, in the case of the plate inclined at $\alpha_o = 6$ deg, separated cavity flow takes place for $Q < 0.4 - 0.5$. As we shall see later, separated cavity flow around a circular cylinder occurs at approximately the same

*We are not, of course, speaking of any specially designed experiments for this purpose which now exist or could be invented.

order of magnitude of Q. For the cylinder, the permissible values of Q for a developed cavity regime should not exceed 1.5. From Eq. (5.6) it follows that, for $Q < 1.5$, $\mathbf{M}_\infty > 1$. Thus, in the above cases, as the velocity of the air flowing around the body increases, the effects of compressibility become dominant before separated cavity flow occurs. Therefore, the incompressibility hypothesis must be rejected and, in particular, the appearance of shock waves must be considered.

In water, where the velocity of sound is 1435 m/sec, fully developed cavity flow is easily achieved with $\mathbf{M}_\infty$ considerably less than unity. We have now answered practically all the questions (criticisms) raised in Section III.D. We can return now to our logical development.

For incompressible flow around bodies, there exist real flow regimes that correspond to the basic premises of jet theory. One such regime* is the separated-cavity-flow regime. In separated cavity flows the cavity-free surfaces do not break down in the vicinity of the body, and jet theory gives quite accurate values for the normal fluid force on the body. In a fully developed cavity, its surfaces are convex with respect to the fluid; thus, it is possible to select from the infinite number of mathematically permissible solutions a unique solution, corresponding to the real physical situation. We should now consider models for a cavity flow around a body with $Q > 0$ and a cavity of finite dimensions. Before

---

*Without further discussion of jet flow from vessels, we shall see that jet theory is directly applicable to the study of planing (Chapter VII) and to some problems of jet collision (Chapter VIII). Even practical applications of jet theory to flows with free surfaces that are concave with respect to the fluid are not excluded [82].

proceeding to this problem, we note one of the known difficulties that arises when establishing such a model. Kolschev's model [83] shows a zone of constant pressure behind the plate (Fig. 75). This model is useless for representing a cavity flow around a plate because not only is the zone behind the plate bounded by concave streamlines, but also the net force on the plate is equal to 0, according to the d'Alembert paradox. Later in this chapter we will show how the d'Alembert paradox is overcome for the case of a cavity with finite dimensions.

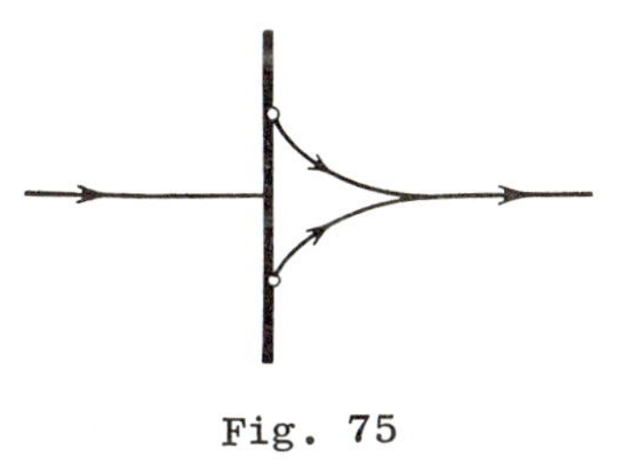

Fig. 75

B. CAVITATING FLOW AROUND A FLAT PLATE

The jet surfaces that separate from the solid contour to form a cavity are stable in the neighborhood of the contour. The jets collide chaotically at the end of the cavity, where visible eddies and great quantities of foam are produced. Periodic filling and emptying of the eddies and foam are observed. Despite the periodic character of the motion at the end of the cavity, the flow is characteristically steady near the solid body. Thus, for sufficiently small Q, it appears reasonable to alter the flow picture radically at the end of the cavity without producing any noticeable change in the flow near and the pressure distribution on the body.

If we accept the above hypothesis then we may forego the necessity of giving an accurate physical representation of the flow at the end of the cavity. It is possible now to consider a model of cavitating flow around a body as a model of a steady flow. The various hypotheses regarding the form of the flow at the end of the cavity (while physically plausible for various reasons) have no direct physical meaning. The appropriate choice for cavity termination or closure then is dictated purely by the necessity for mathematical convenience.

One of the most successful cavity models for flow around a body is the Efros re-entrant jet model [84] which was also studied independently by Gilbarg and Rock [5,85]. This model is shown in Fig. 76 for flow past a flat plate placed normal

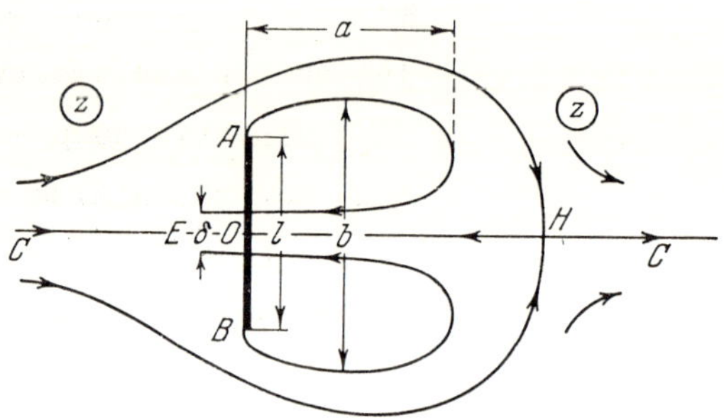

Fig. 76

to the approaching flow. The fluid jets collide behind the plate and form a re-entrant jet. This jet, which in reality is broken up and periodically washed away by the mean flow, continues to infinity to the left in the Efros model and at some point goes onto a second Riemann sheet. Thus, the flow plane is two-sheeted in the re-entrant jet model.* It must be noted again that this flow model is intended only to give a correct representation of the flow in front of (generally near) the flat plate. The introduction of the re-entrant jet is a mathematical device that permits computation of the plate form-drag. The basic assumption thus remains that the flow picture at the end of the cavity has a small influence on the velocity field in the vicinity of the body.

---

*This means that Brillouin's second condition is not satisfied in the re-entrant-jet-model flow.

We shall solve the flow problem represented by the re-entrant jet model in Fig. 76. The functions dw/dz and $dw/d\zeta$ are found as functions of a parametric variable ζ that varies over the upper half of the unit circle in the ζ-plane ($|\zeta| \leq 1$, $\text{Im}\,\zeta \geq 0$) (Fig. 77). We require that:

1. The plate BOA corresponds to the arc of the circle $\zeta = \sigma^{i\sigma}$ $(0 \leq \sigma \leq \pi)$
2. The critical (stagnation) point O corresponds to $\zeta = 1$
3. The point E at infinity on the re-entrant jet corresponds to $\zeta = 0$.

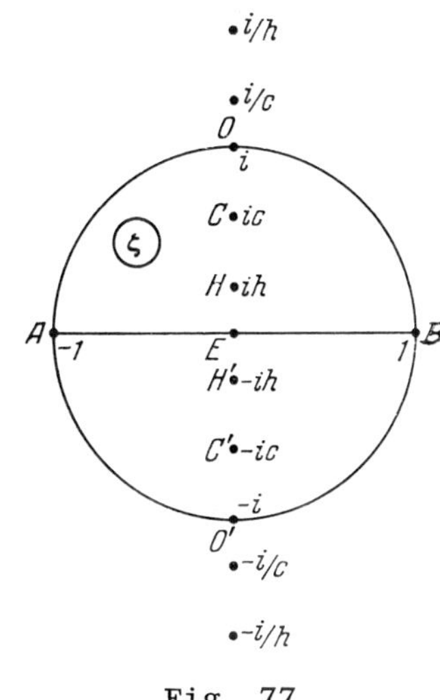

Fig. 77

Accordingly, the stagnation point H inside the fluid and point C at infinity are mapped to the ζ-plane points ih and ic respectively (h and c are real, and obviously $0 \leq h \leq c$).

Consider the complex potential $w(\zeta)$; it has a logarithmic singularity at $E(\zeta = 0)$ that corresponds to the re-entrant jet with finite discharge. At C, $w(\zeta)$ has both a logarithmic singularity (for the jet flow) and a pole (for the source or infinite flow). Since on the cavity-bounding streamline (i.e., on the semicircle AOB) and on the real diameter AEB of the circle the stream function $\psi = \text{Im}\, w = 0$, $w(\zeta)$ can be extended by the symmetry principle to the entire ζ-plane. Thus, a logarithmic singularity must be placed at $\zeta = \infty$, and logarithmic singularities and poles must be placed at $\zeta = -ic$ and $\zeta = \pm\, i/c$, that are symmetric to $C(\zeta = ic)$ with respect to the real axis $(\zeta = -ic)$ and the circle $|\zeta| = 1$, $(\zeta = \pm i/c)$. The logarithmic singularities make $w(\zeta)$ multiple-valued. It can be made single-valued if a cut is made along the streamline EHC in the z-plane, so that $\psi = 0$ along the streamlines OAE and OBE, $\psi = q/2$ along the upper side of the cut EHC, and $\psi = -q/2$ along the lower side of the cut EHC. Here q is the fluid flowrate in the re-entrant jet. A corresponding cut would be made in the ζ-plane. However, $w(\zeta)$ is not required hereafter; only its derivative $dw/d\zeta$ is needed, and it has only simple poles at $\zeta = 0$ and $\zeta = \infty$ and second-order poles at $\zeta = \pm ic$ and $\zeta = \pm i/c$. Thus, $dw/d\zeta$ has no logarithmic singularities and is single-valued without any cuts.

Now consider the function $\zeta\, dw/d\zeta$. This function has second-order poles at $\zeta = \pm ic$ and $\zeta = \pm i/c$, is real on that real axis, and is purely imaginary on the semicircle AOB (on which $\zeta = e^{i\sigma}$, $d\zeta = ie^{i\sigma}\, d\sigma$, $\text{Im}\, dw = 0$). Thus $\zeta\, dw/d\zeta$ may be extended from the semicircle AEBO to the entire ζ-plane by the symmetry or reflection principle. On the semicircle AEBO, $\zeta\, dw/d\zeta$ has zeros at the critical points $O(\zeta = i)$ and $H(\zeta = ih)$ and at points A and B, where the mapping is not conformal.* Therefore, $\zeta\, dw/d\zeta$ has zeros at $\zeta = \pm 1$, $\zeta = \pm ih$, $\zeta = \pm i/h$, and $\zeta = \pm i$. We now know all the zeros and singular points of the single-valued functions $\zeta\, dw/d\zeta$ and $dw/d\zeta$. Since the ratio

$$\frac{dw}{d\zeta} \Bigg/ \frac{(\zeta^4 - 1)(\zeta^2 + h^2)(h^2\zeta^2 + 1)}{\zeta(\zeta^2 + c^2)^2\,(c^2\zeta^2 + 1)^2}$$

*Now, as later, we shall not carry out a detailed analysis of the zeros and singular points; this type of analysis was done several times for analogous cases in Chapter I.

is bounded everywhere, according to Liouville's theorem [3,4] the ratio must be equal to a constant designated by Nv_o. It follows that

$$\frac{dw}{d\zeta} = Nv_o \frac{(\zeta^4 - 1)(\zeta^2 + h^2)(h^2\zeta^2 + 1)}{\zeta(\zeta^2 + c^2)^2 (c^2\zeta^2 + 1)^2} . \tag{5.7}$$

We shall now determine the complex velocity dw/dz. It has zeros at $\zeta = i$ and $\zeta = ih$ and is bounded everywhere in the flow region. If v_o is the constant velocity on the cavity boundaries, then on this boundary $|(1/v_o)(dw/dz)| = 1$. On the other hand, on the plate the argument of $dw/v_o dz$ is $\pm \pi/2$. Thus, under a mirror (reflection) mapping of dw/dz through the real ζ-axis, the zeros become poles; under extension through the circle $|\zeta| = 1$, the zeros remain zeros and poles remain poles. Construction of a single-valued function $dw/v_o dz$ from the zeros and poles (in a manner analogous to that used for $dw/d\zeta$) gives

$$\frac{dw}{v_o dz} = \frac{(\zeta - ih)(h\zeta - i)(\zeta - i)}{(\zeta + ih)(h\zeta + i)(\zeta + i)} . \tag{5.8}$$

The validity of Eqs. (5.7) and (5.8) can be verified directly because, for $h = 0$ and $c = 0$, they must give the solution to Kirchhoff's problem (Section I.D).

With the help of Eqs. (5.7) and (5.8), all the flow characteristics can be computed. The approaching flow velocity is determined by setting $\zeta = ic$ in Eq. (5.8) and

$$\frac{v_\infty}{v_o} = \frac{(c - h)(1 - hc)(1 - c)}{(c + h)(1 + hc)(1 + c)} . \tag{5.9}$$

From Eqs. (5.9) and (5.2) it is easy to find the cavitation number Q. The streamline shapes and dimensions are computed from the integral of the expression for $dz/d\zeta$, which is obtained from Eqs. (5.7) and (5.8)—i.e.,

$$\frac{dz}{d\zeta} = N\,\frac{(\zeta + ih)^2(h\zeta + i)^2(\zeta + i)^2(\zeta^2 - 1)}{\zeta(\zeta^2 + c^2)^2(c^2\zeta^2 + 1)^2} \quad . \tag{5.10}$$

If no additional conditions are imposed on h and c, then $z(\zeta)$ as obtained from Eq. (5.10) will be multi-valued in the flow region. For $z(\zeta)$ to return to its previous value after a passage around $\zeta = ci$ in the ζ-plane, $dz/d\zeta$ must equal 0 at $\zeta = ci$. After appropriate computations, the single-valuedness condition on z is reduced to [86]

$$h = \frac{2}{R + (R^2 - 4)^{1/2}} \quad , \tag{5.11}$$

where $R = [c + (1/c)]^2 - [(c + (1/c)] - 4 \geqq 2$. Note that, since $h \leqq c$, it follows that

$$c \leqq \frac{1 + (5)^{1/2} - [2 + 2(5)^{1/2}]^{1/2}}{2} \approx 0.346 \quad .$$

After expansion in terms of partial fractions and integration in the corresponding intervals, Eq. (5.10) becomes

$$\frac{\ell}{N} = \frac{h^2}{c^4}\left[\pi + \frac{v_\infty}{v_o}(\pi - 4 \arctan c)\right] + \frac{(c + h)^2(1 + ch)^2}{c^2(1 + c^2)^2(1 - c)^2}\left(1 - \frac{v_\infty^2}{v_o^2}\right) \tag{5.12}$$

for the determination of the plate length [86]. Also, from Eq. (5.10) integration along an infinitesimal semicircle around $\zeta = 0$ gives the thickness of the jet δ as

$$\frac{\delta}{\ell} = \pi \frac{N}{\ell}\frac{h^2}{c^4} \quad . \tag{5.13}$$

The resultant of the difference between the pressures on either side of the plate (i.e., the drag X) is determined by an artificial method employing the momentum principle We study the plate when it is symmetrically located between two parallel walls that are separated by 2L. The flow around the plate is assumed to conform to the Efros model (Fig. 78) with the re-entrant jet leaving the flow region on a second Riemann sheet. Let p_C and p_D and v_C and v_D be the pressures and velocities at infinity to the left and right respectively of the plate BA. They are related by the Bernoulli integral

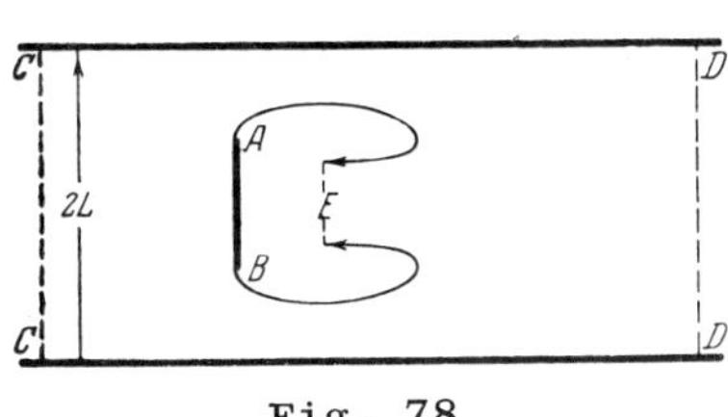

Fig. 78

$$p_C - p_D = \frac{\rho}{2}\left(v_D^2 - v_C^2\right) \quad . \qquad (5.14)$$

Obviously, the fluid flowrate in the re-entrant jet is

$$q\rho = \rho \cdot 2L(v_C - v_D) \quad . \qquad (5.15)$$

We apply the momentum theorem to the flow mass bounded by parallel walls, the plate, the free surfaces, and the rectilinear sections, drawn parallel to the plate at infinity to the left and right and, at infinity to the left, the perpendicular on the re-entrant jet. Equating the resultant pressure forces to the momentum increase produces

$$-X + (p_C - p_D) \cdot 2L = -v_C^2\rho \cdot 2L + v_D^2\rho \cdot 2L - v_o q\rho \quad ,$$

where v_o is the velocity on the cavity walls. Thus, $X = (p_X - p_D) \cdot 2L + v_C^2\rho \cdot 2L - v_D^2\rho \cdot 2L + v_o q\rho$. By using Eq. (5.14), we then obtain $X = \rho L(v_D^2 - v_D^2) + v_o q\rho$ or, according to Eq. (5.15)

$$X = q\rho\left(v_o + \frac{v_C + v_D}{2}\right) . \tag{5.16}$$

In an unbounded flow $2L \to \infty$, and as the walls move away to infinity, $v_C \to v_D$. If we denote $v_C = v_D$ by v_∞, we obtain

$$X = q\rho(v_o + v_\infty) . \tag{5.17}$$

From Eq. (5.17) the drag coefficient of the plate is found to be

$$C_x = \frac{2X}{\rho v_\infty^2 \ell} = \frac{2q}{v_\infty \ell}\left(1 + \frac{v_o}{v_\infty}\right) .$$

But $q/v_o = \delta$, and by using Eq. (5.13) we obtain

$$C_x = 2\pi \frac{N}{\ell} \frac{h^2}{c^4}\left(1 + \frac{v_o}{v_\infty}\right)\frac{v_o}{v_\infty} . \tag{5.18}$$

Since, according to Eqs. (5.12) and (5.9), the quantities N/ℓ and v_o/v_∞ are functions of h and c, which are joined by the Eq. (5.11), then C_x is a function of only one parameter, say for example, c. By using c and Eqs. (5.9) and (5.2), it is also possible to compute the cavitation number Q. Thus, the relation between C_x and Q is established in terms of the common parameter c. Figure 79 (Curve 3) shows the results of computations presented in Ref. [86]. It is interesting to note that, as $Q \to 0$ and we approach Kirchhoff's flow configuration, the re-entrant jet does not vanish, but the base of the jet moves away to infinity. The thickness of the re-entrant jet can be obtained by a limiting process with $h \to 0$ in Eqs. (5.11), (5.9), (5.12), and (5.13):

$$\lim_{h \to 0} \frac{\delta}{\ell} = \frac{\pi}{2(\pi + 4)} \approx 0.22 \quad .$$

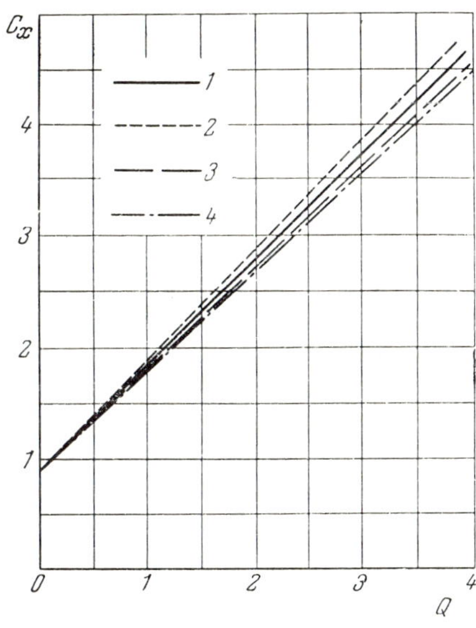

Fig. 79

By using this limiting relation, Eq. (5.17), and $q = \delta v_o = \delta v_\infty$, we obtain for the drag of the plate the usual Kirchhoff equation

$$X = \rho v_\infty^2 \ell \frac{\pi}{\pi + 4} \quad .$$

Of course, if in the limiting process we study the flow only up to the vertical plane that passes through the maximum section of the cavity, then in the limit we obtain the usual Kirchhoff cavity shape. In [87] a comparison was made between the various cavity-flow models for flow normal to a flat plate. From the results shown in Fig. 79* we see that the models give equivalent results for C_X as a function of Q.

Of the various models employed above, the simplest was developed by Betz [88]. He assumed that the pressure on the front side of the plate was that obtained from solution of the Kirchhoff flow, while the pressure p_o behind the plate was that corresponding to the finite cavitation number. Thus, the

*In Fig. 79, Curve 1 arises from calculations using a model with variable velocity on the jets, Curve 2 from Betz's model, Curve 3 from Efros's model, and Curve 4 from Riabouchinsky's model.

pressure was discontinuous across the free surface, and the hydrodynamic problem could not be considered solved. However, for a plate placed perpendicular to the approaching flow, the dependence of the computed drag on Q (Curve 2, Fig. 79) is quite close to that subsequently obtained from the Efros and other equivalent models. As we shall see subsequently, the Betz model gives less accurate results for a circular cylinder and a wedge. According to Betz's model, the drag coefficient of the plate, normal to the flow, is

$$C_x = \frac{2\pi}{\pi + 4} + \frac{2(p_\infty - p_0)}{\rho v_\infty^2} = \frac{2\pi}{\pi + 4} + Q \quad . \tag{5.19}$$

Excellent agreement with the various theoretical models is given by the approximate equation [81,89]

$$c_x(Q) = (1 + Q)c_x(0) \quad , \tag{5.20}$$

where $c_x(0)$ is the drag coefficient of the contour in the Kirchhoff flow.

It was under Sedov's direction that much of the work directed toward finding and developing cavity-flow models for flow around a plate was accomplished. This work led, for example, to the Efros re-entrant jet model. Many other such models were tried and discarded for various reasons, but one hydrodynamically correct model was proposed by Sedov [87]. It gave a drag coefficient for the plate placed normal to the flow close to the actual drag coefficient.* Sedov proposed to

*Analogous methods employing the idea of a certain special law for the velocity distribution on the surface of the cavity behind the body were studied by Woods [90] and Mimura [91].

use the general flow picture given in the Kirchhoff model (see Fig. 1), but to allow the velocity on the surface of the jets to vary from the velocity v_o at the separation points A and B to the velocity v_∞ at infinity for the corresponding cavitation number Q. The velocity-variation law was prescribed in the following manner. It was assumed that the region of change of $v_\infty\, dz/dw$ was represented in the half-plane by a region bounded by an ellipse with semi-axes v_o and v_∞. The surfaces of the jets correspond to the elliptical contour. When $v_\infty = v_o$, then the flow corresponds to the usual Kirchhoff flow. The drag coefficient obtained by the Sedov method [87] is

$$C_x = 1 + Q + \frac{4}{4(1+Q)^{1/2} + \pi(1+Q)} \left\{ \frac{\pi}{4}(1 - Q) - (1+Q)^{1/2} + Q^{1/2} \ln\left[(1+Q)^{1/2} + Q^{1/2}\right] \right\} . \tag{5.21}$$

The Riabouchinsky "mirror-image" model is shown in Fig. 80. This model, as does the re-entrant jet, allows calculation of not only the drag forces acting on the body, but also the order of magnitude of the cavity dimensions [92]. It was Riabouchinsky's idea to introduce at the end of the cavity an

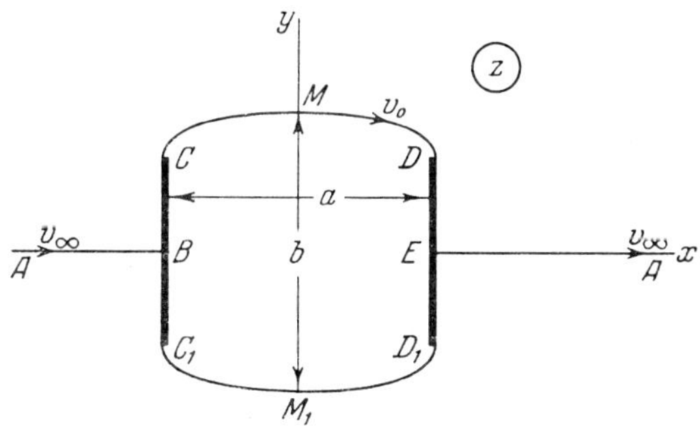

Fig. 80

image plate that prevents the periodic formation and disintegration of the re-entrant jet and transforms the flow into a steady one. When the cavities are sufficiently large, the flow in the region of the first or front plate changes very little as a result of the "image plate." Weinig [93] proposed application of the Riabouchinsky model to the problem of cavity flow around a plate. The flow picture as represented in Fig. 80 is symmetric with respect to both the x- and y-axes.*

We shall consider that portion of the region of change of $dw/v_o dz$ where v_o is the velocity on the free surfaces CMD and $C_1M_1D_1$, that corresponds to the upper half of the flow. We map this region of change onto the upper half-plane (Fig. 81) of the parametric variable t in such a way that

1. The critical points B and E go to $t = \pm 1/k$.
2. The points C and D go to $t = \pm 1$.

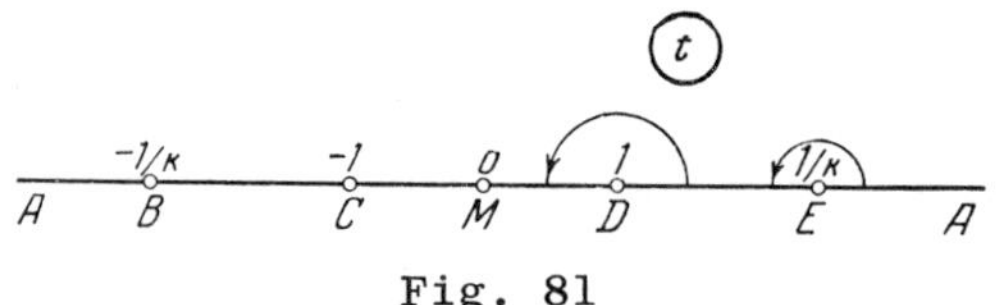

Fig. 81

This mapping is given by

$$\frac{dw}{v_o dz} = \frac{(k^2t^2 - 1)^{1/2}}{(t^2 - 1)^{1/2} + t(1 - k^2)^{1/2}} = \frac{(t^2 - 1)^{1/2} - t(1 - k^2)^{1/2}}{(k^2t^2 - 1)^{1/2}} . \tag{5.22}$$

Equation (5.22) can be obtained also by the Zhukovskii method and its validity can be easily checked directly. Now, in the

*Demtchenko [94] showed that, for a flow symmetric with respect to the x-axis, an image flow of the type shown in Fig. 80 cannot exist with plates of different lengths.

section from $t = \infty$ to $t = 1/k$, dw/v_0dz is real and varies from $v_\infty/v_0 = k[1 + (1 - k^2)^{1/2}]^{-1}$ to 0. After passage around $E(t = 1/k)$, dw/v_0dz takes the form on the section $1 < t < 1/k$

$$\frac{dw}{v_0 dz} = \frac{i(1 - k^2t^2)^{1/2}}{(t^2 - 1)^{1/2} + t(1 - k^2)^{1/2}} = \frac{(t^2 - 1)^{1/2} - t(1 - k^2)^{1/2}}{i(1 - k^2t^2)^{1/2}} . \tag{5.23}$$

It is seen from Eq. (5.23) that on ED the velocity is vertical and varies from 0 at E to $v_y = -v_0$ at D $(t = 1)$. After passage around D,

$$\frac{dw}{v_0 dz} = \frac{i(1 - k^2t^2)^{1/2}}{i(1 - t^2)^{1/2} + t(1 - k^2)^{1/2}} = \frac{i(1 - t^2)^{1/2} - t(1 - k^2)^{1/2}}{i(1 - k^2t^2)^{1/2}} .$$

By multiplying together these two expressions for dw/v_0dz, we obtain

$$\left(\frac{dw}{v_0 dz}\right)^2 = \frac{i(1 - t^2)^{1/2} - t(1 - k^2)^{1/2}}{i(1 - t^2)^{1/2} + t(1 - k^2)^{1/2}} . \tag{5.24}$$

Thus, it is easy to see that on CMD $(-1 < t < 1)$, $|dw/v_0dz| = 1$. Analogously, it is possible to determine the behavior of dw/v_0dz on the other sections along the real axis of t. Since $dw(t)/v_0dz$, which has been determined above, satisfies the boundary conditions and is holomorphic at any point in the upper half-plane, Eq. (5.22) gives the conformal mapping of dw/v_0dz onto the upper half of the t-plane. The region of change of the complex potential w for the upper half of the flow is the upper half-plane. Point A corresponds to the point at infinity in the w-plane, and the streamline ABCMDEA corresponds to the real axis of w (where $\psi = 0$). Thus, we have

$$w = \varphi_D t \quad , \tag{5.25}$$

where φ_D is the value of the velocity potential at D. Equations (5.22) and (5.25) give the general solution to the problem. By using these equations in the usual way, it is possible to obtain the following:

1. The cavitation number

$$Q = \frac{2(1 - k^2)^{1/2}}{k^2} [1 + (1 - k^2)^{1/2}] \quad ; \tag{5.26}$$

thus, knowledge of the parameter k is equivalent to knowledge of the cavitation number.

2. The length of the cavitation region (the distance between the plates)

$$a = \frac{2\varphi_o}{v_o} \left[\frac{1}{k^2} E - \frac{1 - k^2}{k^2} K \right] \quad . \tag{5.27}$$

3. The width of the cavitation region

$$b = \ell + \frac{2\varphi_D}{v_o} \frac{(1 - k^2)^{1/2}}{1 + (1 - k^2)^{1/2}} \quad . \tag{5.28}$$

4. The length of the plate

$$\ell = \frac{2\varphi_D}{v_o} \left(\frac{1 - k^2}{k^2} + \frac{1}{k^2} E' - K' \right) \quad . \tag{5.29}$$

In the above Eqs. (5.27) - (5.29), K and E are the complete elliptic integrals of the first and second kind with modulus k; K' and E' are the equivalent integrals with modulus $k' = (1 - k^2)^{1/2}$.

Using the Bernoulli equation to compute the pressures on the front plate and integrating these pressures over the plate leads, after division by $\rho v_\infty^2 \ell/2$, to the drag coefficient of the plate

$$C_x = 2\left[1 - 2\frac{\varphi_D}{v_o \ell}\frac{1 - k^2}{k^2}\right](Q + 1) \quad . \tag{5.30}$$

It is important to remember that the quantity $\varphi_D/v_o\ell$ in Eq. (5.30) is expressed through Eq. (5.29) in terms of k, while k and Q are related according to Eq. (5.26). Therefore, C_x can be determined as a function of Q. As was pointed out before, a comparison of the plate drag coefficients computed by the different methods and models is given in Fig. 79. Figures 82 and 83 show a comparison of the cavity dimensions obtained from the "mirror-image" (Riabouchinsky-Weinig)(Curve 2) and the re-entrant jet (Efros-Gilbarg)(Curve 1) models.

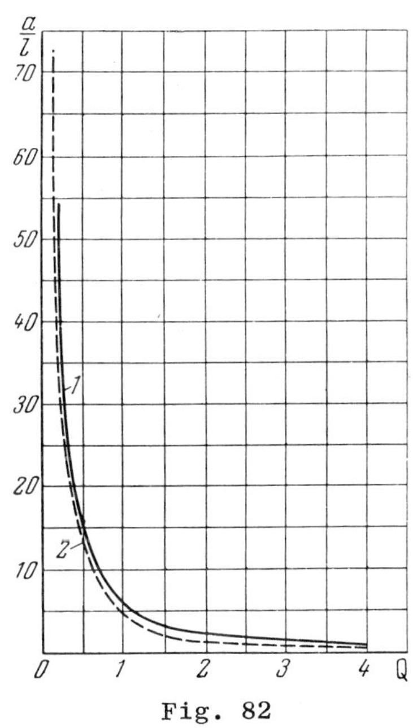

Fig. 82

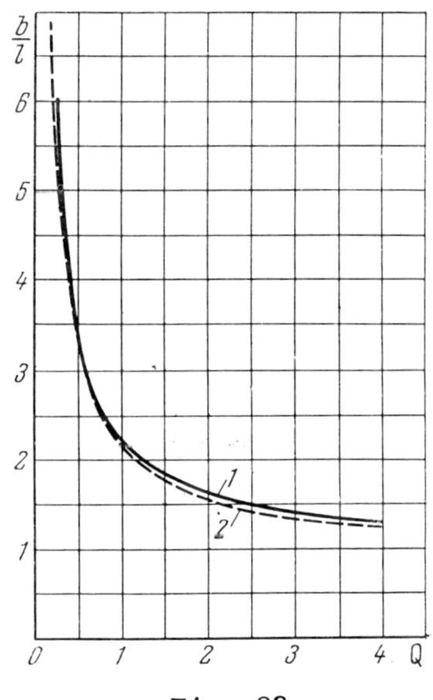

Fig. 83

For the re-entrant jet (see Fig. 76) the dimensions of the cavity region are determined as follows: the cavity length a is the distance from the plate to that point of the cavity surface with a vertical tangent; the cavity width b is the distance between the points of the free surface with horizontal tangents. Figures 79, 82, and 83 show that the flow elements computed from the Efros and Riabouchinsky models are in close agreement, thus confirming, to a certain extent, the hypothesis that the influence of the cavity back-flow (re-entrant jet) on the flow close to the body is small.

In attempting to extend the "mirror-image" and the re-entrant jet models to the case of flow around an inclined plate, we encounter a serious difficulty. It is clear that for such a flow passing around the inclined plate and the cavity, there could exist a circulation Γ in the mean flow. In wing theory the Kutta-Zhukovskii hypothesis is used to determine the circulation around the wing. However, in cavity theory for flow around a profile, a rational hypothesis for determination of Γ does not exist; as a result one superfluous parameter is obtained in the analysis [84,95].*

In the 1950's, several scientists (Roshko, Plesset and Perry) studied another new model for cavity flow around a profile. In addition, Eppler [82] tried to use the same model for calculating fluid flows with small viscosity and laminar or turbulent boundary layer separation. Reference to these efforts appears in Birkhoff and Zarantonello's monograph [5].**

---

*Gilbarg and Serrin [95] applied the Schwarz-Christoffel transformation to the problem of the re-entrant jet flow around a contour. The formula was generalized by Gilbarg [96] to apply to the case of multi-valued functions (or polygons appearing on several Riemann sheets).

**See also [97].

We note that the model examined by the above authors was completely studied by Zhukovskii in 1890 [10] (Section IV.B) for the case of a plate placed normal to the approaching flow. Of course, he did not consider the flow as a cavity flow but solved the problem as a purely mathematical one. Henceforth, we shall call this model the Zhukovskii-Roshko (or parallel-wall) model.

As we shall see in Section E, the parallel-wall model is naturally suited to computation of the cavity flow around an inclined plate. Although this model does not permit us to calculate the cavity dimensions effectively, calculation of the pressure forces is simpler by the method employing parallel walls than by that employing the re-entrant jet or the "mirror image." In addition, the parallel-wall model permits use of direct methods for calculation of the forces acting on an inclined plate in a cavity flow (Section E).

To illustrate the method, we now utilize the Zhukovskii-Roshko parallel-wall model to solve the problem of symmetric cavity flow around a wedge.

C. SYMMETRIC CAVITATING FLOW AROUND A WEDGE

We shall consider a symmetric wedge B'AB with an included angle of $2\pi\kappa$. Jets separate from the base of the wedge and pass onto infinitely long parallel plates CH and C'H', which prevent closure of the jet-bounded cavity (Fig. 84). The velocity on the jets is v_0. Along the walls CH and C'H' the velocity decreases monotonically from v_0 to the velocity v_∞ of the flow at infinity. Zhukovskii gave complete calculations for the particular case when $\kappa = 1/2$—i.e., when the wedge becomes a flat plate.

We map the upper half of the flow region z and the corresponding regions of change of dw/v_0dz and w onto the

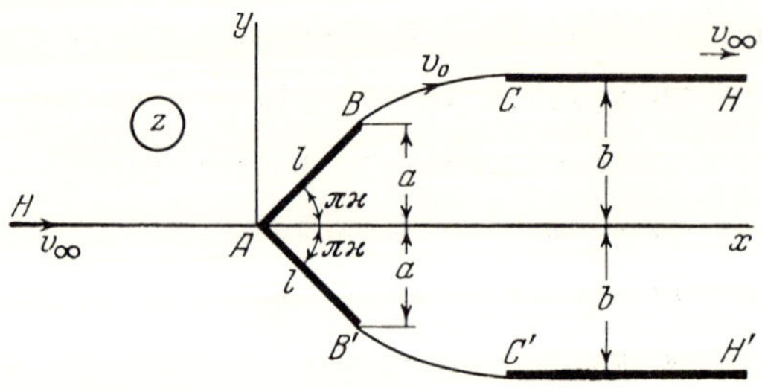

Fig. 84

lower right quadrant of the plane of a parametric variable t (Fig. 85). By using the singular points method, we immediately find

$$\frac{dw}{v_o dz} = \left(\frac{t-1}{t+1}\right)^{\kappa} , \tag{5.31}$$

$$w = N\frac{t^2-1}{t^2-h^2} , \tag{5.32}$$

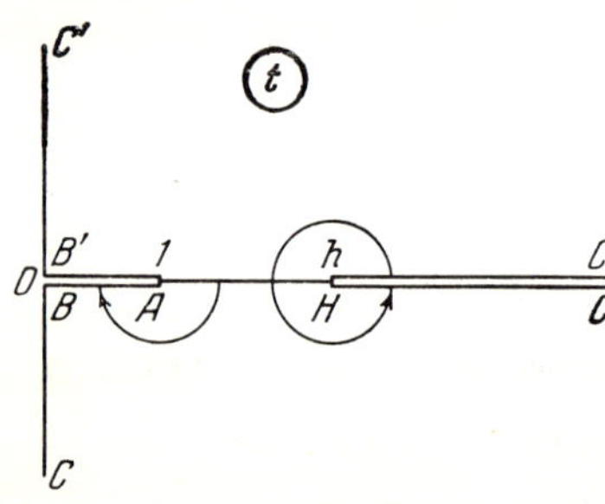

Fig. 85

where N is a real constant. We study Eq. (5.31) first. As $t \to +\infty$, we have $dw/v_o dz = 1$. Along $HC(h < t < \infty)$ and $AH(1 < t < h)$ the complex velocity is real and varies from unity to 0. In passing clockwise around $A(t = 1)$ along an infinitesimal semicircle, the argument of $(t - 1)$ decreases by π and $dw/v_o dz$ takes the form

$$\frac{v}{v_o} e^{-i\theta} = \frac{dw}{v_o dz} = \left(\frac{1-t}{1+t}\right)^{\kappa} e^{-\pi i\kappa} . \tag{5.33}$$

It follows that θ, which is the angle formed by the velocity vector and the x-axis, is now equal to $\pi\kappa$. At $B(t = 0)$ we have $|dw/v_o dz| = 1$. Furthermore, the free surface BC corresponds to the lower imaginary semi-axis of the t-plane. If we put $t = -i\eta$, where $0 \leqq \eta < \infty$, then on BC we have

$$\frac{dw}{v_o dz} = \left(\frac{1 - i\eta}{1 + i\eta}\right)^{\kappa} e^{-\pi i\kappa} \quad ;$$

hence, on BC $|dw/v_o dz| = 1$ and the velocity's argument varies from $-\pi\kappa$ to 0.

It is even easier to determine the behavior of Eq. (5.32). Obviously, $w(t)$ has a pole at $t = h$ and is real along CBAHC. When $N > 0$, $w(t)$ decreases from ∞ to N as t varies over HC; it continues to decrease from N to $-\infty$ as t varies over CBAH. At A the complex potential is 0.

We shall now determine expressions for the geometrical elements in terms of the parameters appearing in Eqs. (5.31) and (5.32), from which we have

$$\frac{dw}{dt} = -\frac{N(h^2 - 1)2t}{(t^2 - h^2)^2} \tag{5.34}$$

and

$$\frac{dz}{dt} = -\frac{N(h^2 - 1)2t}{v_o(t^2 - h^2)^2}\left(\frac{t + 1}{t - 1}\right)^{\kappa} \quad . \tag{5.35}$$

The latter expression can be used to find the distance 2b between the walls. Clearly, dz/dt can be extended to the upper right quadrant that corresponds to the lower half of the flow. Then it is convenient to make cuts in the t-plane along the real axis from $t = 0$ to $t = 1$ and from $t = h$

to $t = \infty$. The upper side of the first cut corresponds to the lower side of the wedge AB', and the upper side of the second cut corresponds to the lower wall HC'. Now it remains only to compute the integral along a closed contour surrounding the point H—i.e.,

$$\int \frac{dz}{dt}\, dt = 2bi \quad , \tag{5.36}$$

where the integration is carried out in a counterclockwise direction. From Eqs. (5.35) and (5.36) it follows that

$$2bi = -\frac{2N(h^2 - 1)}{v_o} \int \frac{t(t+1)^{\kappa}\, dt}{(t-h)^2(t+h)^2(t-1)^{\kappa}}$$

$$= -\frac{2N(h^2 - 1)}{v_o}\, 2\pi i \left(\frac{dU}{dt}\right)_{t=h} \quad ,$$

where $U(t) = t(t+h)^{-2}(t+1)^{\kappa}(t-1)^{-\kappa}$. In carrying out the differentiation, we easily find

$$b = \frac{N\pi\kappa H^{\kappa}}{v_o h} \quad , \tag{5.37}$$

where for brevity, we set $H = (h+1)/(h-1)$. It is also possible to find the length ℓ of the wedge sides by using Eq. (5.35). Thus,

$$\ell = -\frac{2N(h^2 - 1)}{v_o} \int_1^0 \left(\frac{1+t}{1-t}\right)^{\kappa} \frac{t\, dt}{(t^2 - h^2)^2} \quad . \tag{5.38}$$

If $\kappa = 1/n$, where n is an integer, the integral appearing in Eq. (5.38) may be evaluated in terms of elementary functions. Actually, following the change of variable

$t = (1 - s^n)/(1 + s^n)$, this integral is reduced to one of a rational ratio so that

$$\ell = \frac{4Nn}{v_o(h^2 - 1)} \int_0^1 \frac{s^{n-2}(1 - s^{2n})\, ds}{\left(s^n + \frac{1}{H}\right)^2 (s^n + H)^2} \quad . \tag{5.39}$$

However, even if the integral in Eq. (5.38) can be computed exactly, it is simpler to compute it numerically.

Next it is convenient to eliminate the unknown constant N from Eqs. (5.37) and (5.39). Thus,

$$\frac{\ell}{b} = \frac{4n^2 h}{(h^2 - 1)H^{1/n}\pi} \int_0^1 \frac{s^{n-2}(1 - s^{2n})\, ds}{\left(s^n + \frac{1}{H}\right)^2 (s^n + H)^2} \quad . \tag{5.40}$$

Furthermore, it will later be necessary to know the magnitude $2a$ of the projection of the wedge on the vertical axis and, from Fig. 84, it follows that

$$\frac{a}{b} = \frac{\ell}{b} \sin \pi\kappa = \frac{\ell}{b} \sin \frac{\pi}{n} \quad . \tag{5.41}$$

Now, having expressed all the geometrical elements in terms of the parameter h and the angle $\pi\kappa = \pi/n$, we are able to express the cavitation number Q as a function of h and κ and find the drag X of the wedge.

Since at H, $v = v_\infty$, setting $t = h$ in Eq. (5.31) gives

$$\frac{v_\infty}{v_o} = \left(\frac{h - 1}{h + 1}\right)^{\kappa} = H^{-\kappa} \quad ; \tag{5.42}$$

hence

$$Q = \frac{v_o^2}{v_\infty^2} - 1 = H^{2\kappa} - 1 \quad . \tag{5.43}$$

The drag of the wedge is

$$X = \int (p - p_o)\, dy \quad , \tag{5.44}$$

where the integration is made over the wedge surface. However, the integration can also be accomplished over an infinite contour H'C'B'ABCH because along the free streamlines $p - p_o = 0$, and along the walls CH and C'H', $dy = 0$. On the other hand, if the surfaces of the jets BC and B'C' are replaced by solid walls and the resultant pressure on the halfbody H'C'B'ABCH of finite width is calculated, then, as is well known [80] the drag of this halfbody is

$$\int (p - p_\infty)\, dy = 0 \quad . \tag{5.45}$$

Here the integration is carried out along the entire surface of the halfbody. If we subtract Eq. (5.45) from Eq. (5.44), we obtain a simple formula for the drag [82]

$$X = \int (p_\infty - p_o)\, dy = (p_\infty - p_o)\, 2b \quad . \tag{5.46}$$

This equation can be transformed, by using the Bernoulli integrals to

$$X = \frac{\rho}{2}\left(v_o^2 - v_\infty^2\right) 2b = \rho v_\infty^2 a \frac{b}{a} Q \quad . \tag{5.47}$$

Finally, the drag coefficient of the wedge, related to its base width $2a$, is

$$C_x = \frac{2X}{\rho 2av_\infty^2} = \frac{b}{a} Q \quad . \tag{5.48}$$

Thus, the result for the drag coefficient with the parallel wall model is exactly the same as Reichardt's approximate equation [5].

Equations (5.40), (5.41), (5.43), and (5.48) permit computation of C_x and Q as functions of h and n and finally of the relationship of C_x to Q for a given included angle of the wedge. Figure 86 shows the surves of C_x vs. Q computed by the Zhukovskii-Roshko method for

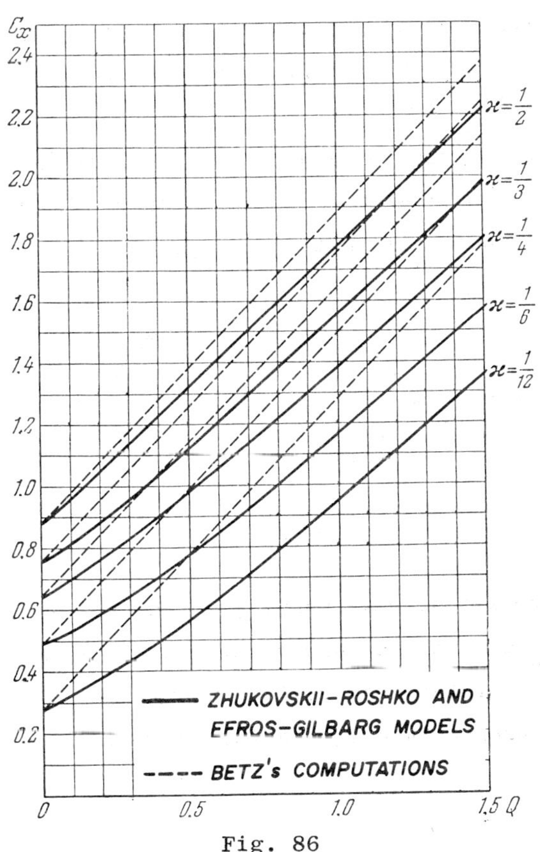

Fig. 86

$\kappa = 1/2, 1/3, 1/4$—i.e., for an included angle of the wedge of 180 deg (flat plate), 120, and 90 deg. For all practical purposes, these curves coincide with the corresponding curves computed for a re-entrant jet model.

In addition, in Fig. 86 the curves of $C_x(Q)$ for $\kappa = 1/6$ and $\kappa = 1/12$ are plotted—i.e., for the wedges with included angles of 60 and 30 deg. However, these curves were obtained from the theory for a re-entrant jet [98]. This method of solution will be presented in Chapter VI, when the more general problem of flow around a wedge located between parallel walls is considered. In Fig. 86 the straight lines represent the $C_x(Q)$ relation of Betz's approximate theory ([88], cf. with Section B). There is, obviously, a significant difference between Betz's approximate scheme and the more exact methods.

The mirror-image or Riabouchinsky model (Fig. 87) of the wedge flow was considered by several authors [5, Chapter V, Section 9]. It is not difficult to change Eqs. (5.22) and (5.25) so

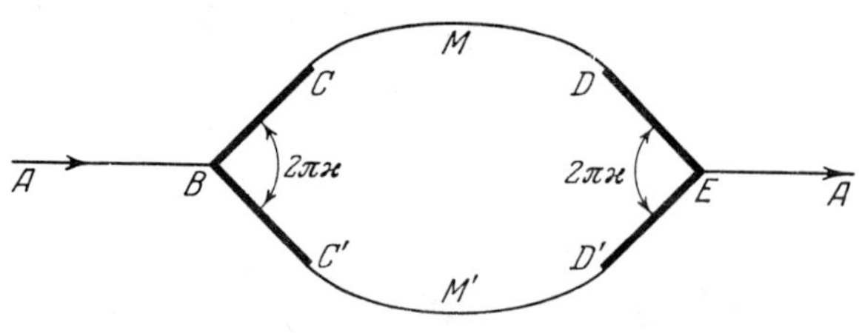

Fig. 87

that they give a conformal mapping of the regions of change of w and dw/v_0dz onto the upper half t-plane (Fig. 81) for the upper half of the flow region in Fig. 87. Actually, Eq. (5.25) is unchanged, and Eq. (5.22) becomes

$$\frac{dw}{v_o dz} = \left[\frac{(k^2t^2 - 1)^{1/2}}{(t^2 - 1)^{1/2} + t(1 - k^2)^{1/2}}\right]^{2\kappa}$$

$$= \left[\frac{(t^2 - 1)^{1/2} - t(1 - k^2)^{1/2}}{(k^2t^2 - 1)^{1/2}}\right]^{2\kappa} \qquad (5.49)$$

where $2\pi\kappa$ is the included angle of the wedge (Fig. 87). This result can be easily verified directly in the same way as was Eq. (5.22). On AB and EA $(t^2 > 1/k^2)$, $dw/v_o dz$ is real and positive. Similarly on CMD $(t^2 < 1)$, we have $|dw/v_o dz| = 1$, but on BC $(-1/k < t < -1)$ and DE $(1 < t < 1/k)$ the argument of $dw/v_o dz$ is $-\pi\kappa$ and $\pi\kappa$ respectively. Equations (5.49) and (5.25) give the general solution to the problem; by using them it is possible to compute the cavitation number Q, all the geometrical dimensions, and the drag on the front wedge. However, the integrals, through which the drag and the wedge and cavity dimensions are expressed, are no longer elliptical and can be computed only by numerical methods. Such work was carried out by Plesset and Shaffer [99]. The wedge drag depends, obviously, on two physical parameters: 1) the cavitation number Q and 2) the angle of the wedge $\beta = 180\kappa$ deg. In Eq. (5.49) we introduced an auxiliary parameter k instead of Q; of course, it is possible to express Q in terms of κ and k. Plesset and Shaffer made use of another auxiliary parameter γ. The relationship between γ, Q, and the angle β is shown in Table 19. Plesset and Shaffer also determined the drag coefficient C_x (Table 20) as a function of the parameters γ and β. By comparing the coefficients C_x, given in the table, with the curves of Fig. 86, we see that the drag of Riabouchinsky's model is a little less than that of Zhukovskii's model. In addition to

TABLE 19

γ (deg)	Values of the Cavitation number $Q\ (\pi\kappa,\gamma)$ $\beta = 180$ deg κ (deg)										
	15	30	45	60	75	90	105	120	135	150	165
0	0.0000	0.0000	0.0000	0.0000	0.0000	0.0000	0.0000	0.0000	0.0000	0.0000	0.0000
5	0.0296	0.0600	0.0913	0.1236	0.1568	0.9100	0.2262	0.2624	0.2997	0.3381	0.3777
10	0.0602	0.1241	0.1918	0.2635	0.3396	0.4203	0.5058	0.5965	0.6926	0.7945	0.9026
15	0.0923	0.1931	0.3032	0.4235	0.5549	0.6984	0.8551	1.0264	1.2154	1.4177	1.6408
20	0.1261	0.2682	0.4281	0.6083	0.8112	1.0396	1.2969	1.5866	1.9126	2.2803	2.6940
25	0.1622	0.3506	0.5697	0.8242	1.1201	1.4639	1.8635	2.3279	2.8676	3.4948	4.2237
30	0.2009	0.4423	0.7321	1.0801	1.4981	2.0000	2.6028	3.3267	5.1962		
35	0.2431	0.5453	0.9210	1.3880	1.9685	2.6902	3.5873				
40	0.2896	0.6630	1.1445	1.7655	2.5663	3.5989					
45	0.3415	0.7996	1.4142	2.2387	3.3447						

TABLE 20

γ (deg)	Value of the Drag Coefficient C_x $(\pi\kappa, \gamma)$ β = 180 deg κ (deg)										
	15	30	45	60	75	90	105	120	135	150	165
0	0.2838	0.4885	0.6370	0.7448	0.8230	0.8798	0.9207	0.9498	0.9703	0.9845	0.9939
5	0.2927	0.5185	0.6959	0.8375	0.9528	1.6482	1.1293	1.1993	1.2613	1.3176	1.3694
10	0.3029	0.5521	0.7624	0.9943	1.1057	1.2522	1.3885	1.5180	1.6436	1.7674	1.8914
15	0.3146	0.5901	0.8385	1.0688	1.2880	1.5016	1.7142	1.9297	2.1514	2.3825	2.6259
20	0.3281	0.6330	0.9258	1.2148	1.5073	1.8097	2.1279	2.4676	2.8346	3.2346	3.6741
25	0.3436	0.6826	1.0278	1.3889	1.7754	2.1966	2.6621	3.1825	3.7695	4.4364	5.1975
30	0.3618	0.7401	1.1481	1.5993	2.1080	2.6898	3.3634	4.1497	5.0738		
35	0.3829	0.8076	1.2922	1.8574	2.5274	3.3308	4.3031				
40	0.4080	0.8880	1.4676	2.1803	3.0676	4.1830					
45	0.4378	0.9853	1.6852	2.5927	3.7806						

calculating C_x, Plesset and Shaffer found the cavity dimensions for the same range of cavitation numbers [99].

In the conclusion of this section we briefly touch upon the problem of an asymmetric cavity flow past a wedge. Cox and Clayden's recent and very interesting paper [100] dealt with this particular problem.

Consider the flow around a symmetric wedge with a cavitation number equal to 0. From the results of Meshcherskii's work (see Section III.A) it follows that a separated flow around a symmetric wedge is possible only when the angle α between the axis of symmetry of the wedge and the velocity vector at infinity is zero (Fig. 88). Actually, the flow shown in Fig. 88b is not physically possible because at C

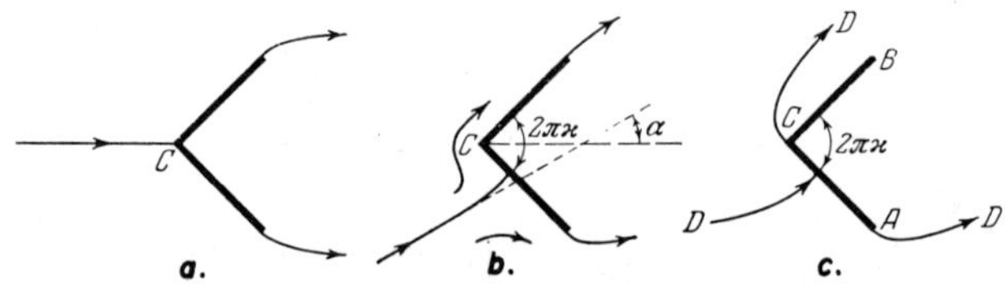

Fig. 88

the velocity is infinite. Thus, in the vicinity of C, there are unbounded negative pressures. It is obvious that the jet must separate from the wedge, not at B, but at C (Fig. 88c). For some values of the angles $2\pi\kappa$ and α the free surface CD will not intersect the side CB of the wedge, and we will have, in fact, the usual Kirchhoff flow around the plane plate AC. For other combinations of α and $\pi\kappa$, the streamline CD will intersect CB, and it was for this case that Cox and Clayden proposed their model of the flow around a wedge,*

*We propose the following elementary geometric method of determining the angles α and $\pi\kappa$, for which the Cox and

shown in Fig. 90. As a result of the collision of the upper jet with the side CB, a critical (stagnation) point H is formed on CB. The main flow separates at the edge B, and a re-entrant jet goes forward and leaves, as in the Efros-Gilbarg model, on a second sheet of the Riemann surface. Cox and Clayden solved the problem by mapping the region of change of the complex potential and the logarithm of the complex velocity onto a rectangle. The method can, of course, be used for the case of an asymmetric wedge.

In their work, Cox and Clayden present not only the results of numerical calculations using their theory but also data from water-tunnel cavitation experiments. The agreement between the theoretical and experimental results is good.

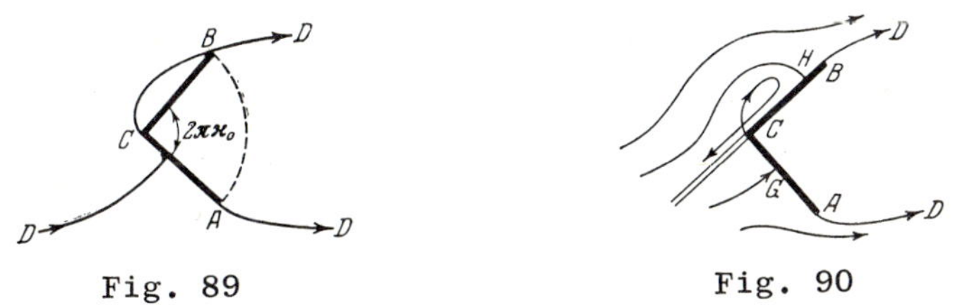

Fig. 89　　　Fig. 90

Clayden model is appropriate. We first construct the free surface for the known solution of the Kirchhoff flow around a plate at a given angle of attack. Then a circular arc with radius CA is drawn until it intersects the free surface CBD (Fig. 89) at B. The resulting angle $2\pi\kappa_0$ between the radii CA and CB is the critical angle. With a given angle of attack for the lower side of a wedge with an included angle of $2\pi\kappa < 2\pi\kappa_0$, the upper side of the wedge has no influence on the flow around it; but with $2\pi\kappa > 2\pi\kappa_0$ a Kirchhoff flow around the lower side of the wedge is not possible, and the Cox and Clayden model is appropriate. This technique can, obviously, be extended to an asymmetric-wedge flow.

D. CAVITATING FLOW AROUND A CIRCULAR CYLINDER

We now use the re-entrant jet [98] flow model to study the flow around a circular cylinder (Fig. 91). The region of

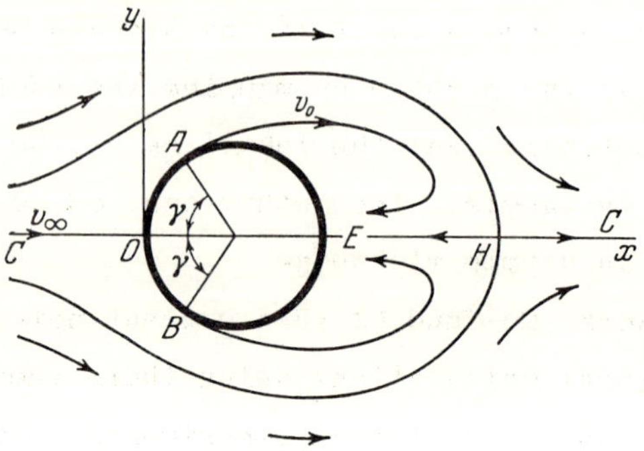

Fig. 91

change of the parametric variable ζ is taken as a unit-radius semicircle (Fig. 77), and the regions of change of $dw/d\zeta$ and $dw/v_o dz$, where v_o is the velocity on the surface of the cavity, are mapped onto this semicircle. In the present problem $w(\zeta)$ is identical to the $w(\zeta)$ for a flow around a flat plate (Fig. 76). Thus, we can use Eq. (5.7), which for convenience is rewritten as

$$\frac{dw}{d\zeta} = Nv_o \frac{(\zeta^4 - 1)(\zeta^2 + h^2)(h^2\zeta^2 + 1)}{\zeta(\zeta^2 + c^2)^2\,(c^2\zeta^2 + 1)^2} . \qquad (5.50)$$

For the circular-cylinder problem, Eq. (5.8) for the complex velocity of the flow is altered to conform to Levi-Civita's method for a curvilinear contour. Thus, we have $dw/v_o dz$ in the form

$$\frac{dw}{v_o dz} = \frac{(\zeta - ih)(h\zeta - i)(\zeta - i)}{(\zeta + ih)(h\zeta + i)(\zeta + i)}\, e^{F(\zeta)} , \qquad (5.51)$$

where

$$F(\zeta) = iA_1\zeta - \frac{iA_3}{3}\zeta^3 + \frac{iA_5}{5}\zeta^5 - \dots , \quad (5.52)$$

and A_1, A_3, ... are real constants. Here $F(\zeta)$ is completely analogous to Ω in Section IV.B. As a result of the flow symmetry, $F(\zeta)$ contains, as did Ω, only odd powers of ζ. It is obvious that dw/v_0dz, as determined in accordance with Eq. (5.51), has modulus of unity on the free surface, and the contour, where $F(\zeta) \neq 0$, is curvilinear.

From Eqs. (5.50) and (5.51) we find

$$\frac{dz}{d\zeta} = N \frac{(\zeta^2 - 1)(\zeta + ih)^2(h\zeta + i)^2(\zeta + i)^2}{\zeta(\zeta^2 + c^2)^2 (c^2\zeta^2 + 1)^2} e^{-F(\zeta)}. \quad (5.53)$$

As in Section B, we require that $z(\zeta)$ return to its original value after a passage around the point $\zeta = ic$—i.e., z is single-valued. It follows that the residue of $dz/d\zeta$ must be 0 at $\zeta = ic$. This condition can be reduced to the following equality:

$$i\left\{\frac{d}{d\zeta}\left[\ln \frac{dz}{N\,d\zeta}(\zeta - ic)^2\right]\right\}_{\zeta=ic} = \frac{2}{1 - c^2} + \frac{2h}{1 + hc} - \frac{2h}{c(c + h)}$$

$$+ A_1 + A_3c^2 + A_5c^4 + \dots = 0 . \quad (5.54)$$

The problem can be considered completely solved when all the constants in Eqs. (5.50) - (5.53) are determined. The constant N is a scale coefficient and, as we shall see later, each value of N gives a particular radius R for the cylinder. More precisely, considering the value of R as known, we shall eliminate N from the final equations. Equation (5.54) permits determination of one parameter, which by convention is h.

One more parameter (for instance, c) can be determined by specifying the cavitation number $Q = (v_\infty/v_o)^2 - 1$. For this purpose, the ratio v_∞/v_o is found from Eq. (5.51). By setting $\zeta = ic$ in Eq. (5.51) we obtain

$$\frac{v_\infty}{v_o} = \frac{(c - h)(1 - hc)(1 - c)}{(c + h)(1 + hc)(1 + c)} \exp\left[-\left(A_1 c + \frac{A_3 c^3}{3} + \frac{A_5 c^5}{5} + \cdots\right)\right] . \tag{5.55}$$

It is very difficult to determine explicitly the value of c from Eq. (5.55); thus it is more convenient to prescribe c and then to determine v_∞/v_o, and subsequently Q, by using Eq. (5.55).

Now, we need only to determine the coefficients A_1, A_3, A_5, ...; we shall therefore make use of Brodetsky's method (see Section IV.B). We begin with an approximation by assuming that the coefficients A_{2m+1}, for m greater than some arbitrary number, are 0. Then, for determination of the nonzero coefficients A_1, A_3, ... the curvature at a corresponding number of isolated, arbitrarily selected points of the contour must be equal to $-1/R$.

In addition, we apply the well known condition that the curvature of the jet at its separation point from the cylinder must be finite and equal to the curvature of the cylinder. To formulate this condition we compute the curvature of the free surface. It is easy to see that

$$\frac{d}{d\zeta}\left(\ln \frac{dw}{v_o dz}\right) = \frac{1}{\zeta - ih} - \frac{1}{\zeta + ih} + \frac{h}{h\zeta - i} - \frac{h}{h\zeta + i}$$
$$+ \frac{1}{\zeta - i} - \frac{1}{\zeta + i} + \frac{dF}{d\zeta} .$$

But ζ is real along the free surface, so

$$\mathrm{Re}\left[i \frac{d}{d\zeta} \ln \frac{dw}{v_o dz}\right] = \frac{d\theta}{d\zeta} = -\frac{2h}{\zeta^2 + h^2} - \frac{2h}{\zeta^2 h^2 + 1} - \frac{1}{\zeta^2 + 1}$$

$$- A_1 + A_3\zeta^2 - A_5\zeta^4 + \ldots \quad (5.56)$$

On the other hand, the arc differential on the free surface is given by

$$ds = \left| N \frac{(\zeta^2 - 1)(\zeta + ih)^2(h\zeta + i)^2(\zeta + i)^2}{\zeta(\zeta^2 + c^2)^2 (c^2\zeta^2 + 1)^2} e^{-F(\zeta)} d\zeta \right| . \quad (5.57)$$

From Eqs. (5.56) and (5.57) one can see that, at the separation points $(\zeta = \mp 1)$, the curvature of the free surface is infinite if $(d\theta/d\zeta)_{\zeta=\pm 1} \neq 0$. As a result, in order to have finite curvature of the free surface at B and A, we set $(d\theta/d\zeta)_{\zeta=\pm 1} = 0$ and ultimately obtain

$$\frac{4h}{h^2 + 1} + 1 + A_1 - A_3 + A_5 - A_7 + \ldots = 0 . \quad (5.58)$$

Now we find the curvature of the cylinder. We consider only the upper half of the flow, taking into account the symmetry with respect to the x-axis. On the upper half of the cylinder OA $(\pi/2 \leq \sigma \leq \pi)$ the angle between the velocity vector and the x-axis is

$$\theta = \frac{\pi}{2} - A_1 \cos \sigma + \frac{A_3}{3} \cos 3\sigma - \frac{A_5}{5} \cos 5\sigma + \ldots \quad (5.59)$$

From Eq. (5.53) the arc differential on the contour is found to be

$$ds = |dz|$$

$$= N \left| \frac{(e^{2i\sigma} - 1)(e^{i\sigma} + ih)^2(he^{i\sigma} + i)^2(e^{i\sigma} + i)^2}{e^{i\sigma}(e^{2i\sigma} + c^2)^2(c^2 e^{2i\sigma} + 1)^2} \right|$$

$$\times \exp\,[-\mathrm{Re}\; F(e^{i\sigma})]\; d\sigma$$

$$= N \frac{2 \sin\sigma \cos^2[(\sigma/2) - (\pi/4)]\,(1 + h^2 + 2h \sin\sigma)^2}{(1 + c^4 + 2c^2 \cos 2\sigma)^2}$$

$$\times \exp\left[A_1 \sin\sigma - \frac{A_3}{3}\sin 3\sigma + \frac{A_5}{5}\sin 5\sigma \ldots\right] d\sigma \quad .$$

By combining this result with that of Eq. (5.56) and denoting by $R > 0$ the local radius of the contour, we obtain for the arc OA

$$\frac{1}{R} = -\frac{d\theta}{ds}$$

$$= -\frac{(A_1 \sin\sigma - A_3 \sin 3\sigma + A_5 \sin 5\sigma - + \ldots)(1 + c^4 + 2c^2 \cos 2\sigma)}{8N \sin\sigma \cos^2 [(\sigma/2) - (\pi/4)](1 + h^4 + 2h \sin\sigma)^2}$$

$$\times \exp\left[-A_1 \sin\sigma + \frac{A_3}{3}\sin 3\sigma \ldots\right] \quad . \tag{5.60}$$

In particular, with $\sigma = \pi/2$

$$\left(\frac{N}{R}\right)_{\pi/2} = -\frac{(A_1 + A_3 + A_5 + \ldots)(1 - c^2)\exp\left[-A_1 - \frac{A_3}{3} - \frac{A_5}{5} \ldots\right]}{8(1 + h)^4} , \tag{5.61}$$

with $\sigma = \pi$

$$\left(\frac{N}{R}\right)_{\pi} = -\frac{(A_1 - 3A_3 + 5A_5 \ldots)(1 + c^2)^4}{4(1 + h^2)^2}, \tag{5.62}$$

or with $\sigma = 3\pi/4$

$$\left(\frac{N}{R}\right)_{3\pi/4} = -\frac{(A_1 - A_3 - A_5 - \ldots)(1 - c^4)\exp\left\{-(2^{1/2}/2)[A_1(A_3/3) - (A_5/5) - \ldots]\right\}}{2(2 + 2^{1/2})(1 + h^2 + h2^{1/2})^2}. \tag{5.63}$$

In [98] computations were made with two approximations. In the first it was assumed that $A_{2m+1} \equiv 0$ when $m \geqq 2$. Then A_1 and A_3 were determined through Eqs. (5.54), (5.58), (5.61), and (5.62). In the second approximation, Eq. (5.63) was added to the above four equations, and it was assumed that coefficient A_5 was not equal to 0 *a priori*. The jet separation angle $\gamma = (\pi/2) - \theta_A$ (Fig. 91) is determined by using the following equation, obtained from Eq. (5.59) under the condition that $\sigma = \pi$,

$$\gamma = -A_1 + \frac{A_3}{3} - \frac{A_5}{5} + \ldots \tag{5.64}$$

It was found that within the accuracy of the calculations, the values obtained by the two approximations were nearly equal.

For computing X it is possible to take advantage of Eq. (5.17), where $X = \rho q\,(v_0 + v_\infty)$. The discharge of the re-entrant jet is $q = \delta v_0$ and δ is the thickness of the re-entrant jet. From Eq. (5.53) after integrating $(dz/d\zeta)\,d\zeta$ along an infinitesimal semicircle around the point $\zeta = 0$, we obtain

$$\delta = \frac{\pi N h^2}{c^4}. \tag{5.65}$$

The drag coefficient is then

$$C_x = \frac{X}{\rho v_\infty^2 R} = \frac{\pi N}{R} \frac{v_o}{v_\infty}\left(\frac{v_o}{v_\infty} + 1\right)\frac{h^2}{c^4} \quad . \tag{5.66}$$

The numerical results are given in Table 21 and Fig. 92. The jet separation angles are given in degrees in this table.

TABLE 21

Q	γ (deg)	First Approximation C_x	Second Approximation C_x
0	55.1	0.493	0.5
0.5	56.7	0.758	0.774
0.77	58.4	0.915	---
0.98	60.3	1.05	---
1.44	63.3	1.34	1.36
1.73	65.0	1.53	---
2.37	71.7	2.02	2.06

Also shown in Fig. 92 are the values of C_x obtained by Efros [101] by a method employing a finite-difference representation of the fluid-motion differential equation and boundary conditions, as well as results from Betz's approximate method [88]. Finally, Fig. 92 shows some experimental data collected by (and in part obtained by) Efros for $Q < 1.5$. It is reasonable to assume that separated jet flow occurred for these cavitation numbers. Clearly, Fig. 92 shows the applicability of the re-entrant jet model for flow past a cylinder and the inaccuracy of Betz's method for this case.

This problem of cavity flow around a cylinder can also be solved by using a Riabouchinsky model. The results of such computations for the drag and separation angle agree well with the results given for the Efros model. Table 22, adopted from Birkhoff and Zarantonello [5], gives values computed by a three-point approximation for Riabouchinsky flows.

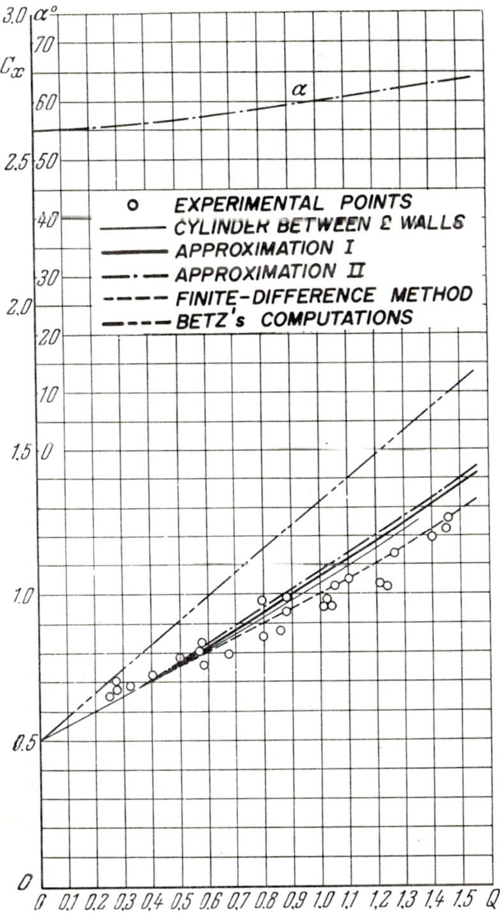

Fig. 92

TABLE 22

γ (deg)	Q	C_x
54.988	0	0.499
56.143	0.135	0.568
55.431	0.235	0.621

Certain other aspects of the cylinder-type problem have also been studied. Pykhteev [73] considered the inverse problem for cavity flow about a symmetric arc with a re-entrant jet model. Then, Serrin [102] examined the question of the existence of solutions to problems employing jet and "mirror-image" models. The cylinder flow was studied by Eppler [82] by using the parallel-wall, wake model. Setting aside most of the mathematical details, we shall discuss only Eppler's method of solution and some of his ideas relative to new applications of jet theory.

Figure 93 shows an arc A_2SA_1 that is symmetric about the x-axis and passes through the stagnation point S. The jets separate at points A_1 and A_2 and pass smoothly onto symmetrically located parallel walls B_1D and B_2D. The velocity of the approaching flow at infinity is unity. The fluid velocity on the free surfaces is $v_1 > 1$. The variables w and $\ln(dz/dw)$ are obtained as functions of the parametric variable τ, which varies over the unit semicircle

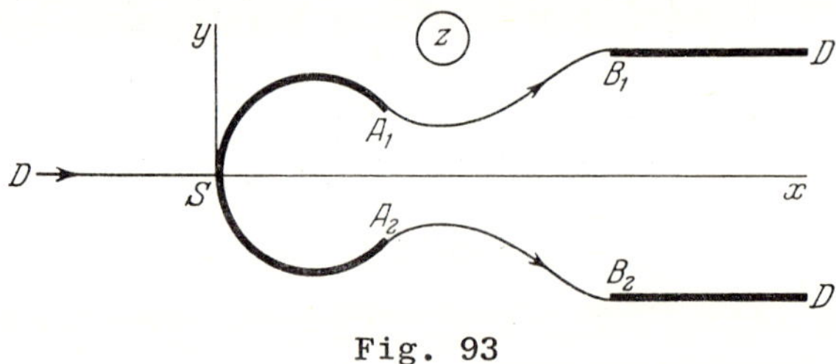

Fig. 93

(Fig. 94). The relationship between the planes τ and z is seen from Figs. 93 and 94. In particular, point D at infinity in the z-plane corresponds to point $\tau = ir$ in the τ-plane, where r is a real constant $(0 \leq r < 1)$. Then the walls B_1D and B_2D become a cut along the imaginary axis in the τ-plane. If we set $w(i) = 0$, then through the singular-point method the following equation for $w(\tau)$ is easily obtained:

$$\varphi + i\psi = w = C \frac{(1 + \tau^2)^2}{(\tau^2 + r^2)(r^2\tau^2 + 1)} , \qquad (5.67)$$

where C is a real constant. Eppler found $\ln (dz/dw)$ in the form

$$T + i\theta = \ln \frac{dz}{dw} = \ln \frac{i + \tau}{i - \tau} + i \sum_{n=0}^{\infty} a_{2n+1} \tau^{2n+1} - \ln v_1 ; \qquad (5.68)$$

it follows that on the arc A_2SA_1

$$\theta = \pm \frac{\pi}{2} + \sum_{n=0}^{\infty} a_{2n+1} \cos (2n + 1) \sigma . \qquad (5.69)$$

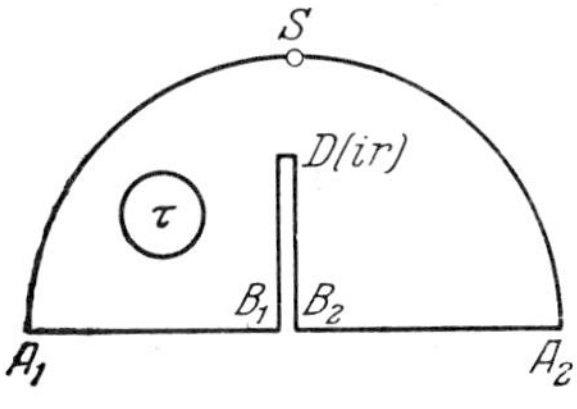

Fig. 94

The arc curvature is taken as a known continuous function of θ. On the other hand, the curvature can also be determined by using Eqs. (5.67) - (5.69) because along the arc A_2SA_1 $\tau = e^{i\sigma}$, where σ is real, and we have on SA_1

$$\kappa_k(\theta) = \frac{d\theta}{d\sigma} \frac{d\sigma}{d\varphi} e^{-T} . \qquad (5.70)$$

Equation (5.70) was used by Eppler to determine the coefficients a_{2n+1}. He employed the same finite-difference method used by Schmieden [48] to solve the problem of Kirchhoff flow around a circular cylinder.

As in the Kirchhoff flow with the Zhukovskii flow model, it is possible to obtain free surfaces possessing varying geometric properties. Refer to Fig. 95, in which several possible cases are shown. Flow I (separation at A_1) represents the flow around an arc that ends at point A_1; the free surface is convex with respect to the fluid and the curvature of the jet at A_1 is infinite. The other cases II, III, IV represent, on the other hand, contour flows with a continuous curvature. In Case II the free surface is convex; in Case III it has an inflection point; and in Case IV it is concave with respect to the fluid.

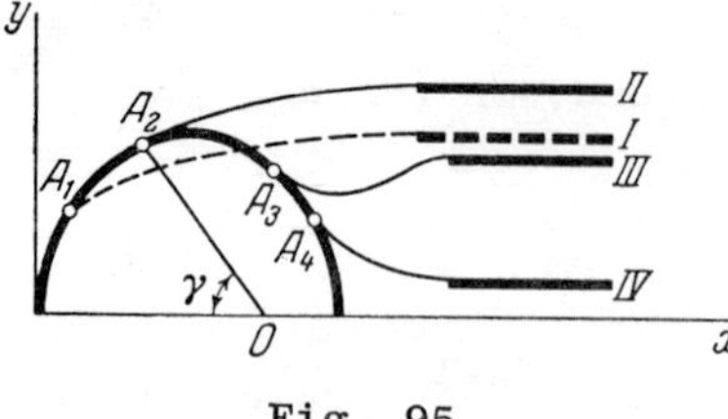

Fig. 95

From the mathematical point of view it is possible to prescribe independently two parameters in these flows around contours. The first is the pressure in the stationary region or, equivalently, the velocity v_1. The second is the location of the point of jet separation from the contour (given by the angle γ in Fig. 95). In Fig. 95 point 0 on the x-axis is some fixed point, which, for a circle, is conveniently taken as its center.

For a cavitation flow around a contour it is always convenient to consider Case II, for then the location of the separation points of the jet are determined. But Eppler was not concerned only with cavity flows. His above-mentioned idea was to choose the pressure in the stagnation region and the angle γ so that they agree with the pressure and angle γ for boundary-layer separation with fluids of low viscosity. Thus, through jet theory, one can find the pressure distribution on the front side of the contour up to the separation point. Now, for a laminar boundary layer the location of the separation point has been well-determined theoretically. We note that for a given pressure in the stagnation zone, it is possible to select the separation-point location so that the distance between the downstream parallel walls is a minimum. Then the drag is also a minimum. Eppler used the flow with a minimum drag to describe a flow with small viscosity and a turbulent boundary layer.

In [82], flows around a flat plate and a circular cylinder are considered as examples. In particular, for the circular cylinder with $v_1 = 1.41421$, Eppler found that $C_x = 1.16420$ when $\gamma = 62.566$ deg (cavity flow) and $C_x = 1.03583$ when $\gamma = 81.502$ deg (laminar boundary layer). By comparing $C_x = 1.16420$ with Fig. 92, we see that the cylinder's drag for a cavity flow as determined by the Zhukovskii model exceeds that obtained with the re-entrant jet model. Eppler did not give any exact method for determining the parameters for the minimum-drag (turbulent-boundary-layer) case; however, by means of his finite-difference calculations, he seems to come sufficiently close to this limiting case [82].

E. CAVITATING FLOW AROUND A THIN PROFILE AT AN ARBITRARY ANGLE OF ATTACK

We have already noted that up to now we are unable to determine the appropriate magnitude of the circulation in a cavity flow about a wing. This problem arises for both the re-entrant jet and "mirror-image" flow models. However, if we begin with the parallel-wall model and make only one necessary assumption—i.e., the walls are parallel to the flow velocity at infinity—then the problem is solved uniquely. Furthermore, the results of the solution are in good agreement with experiments.

In 1956, Wu [103] presented a solution for fully developed cavity flow around slightly curved profiles. In that work he employed the parallel-wall model, and his work is taken as the basis for the present exposition.

The fluid flow is shown schematically in Fig. 96. The jets separate from the leading and trailing edges A and B

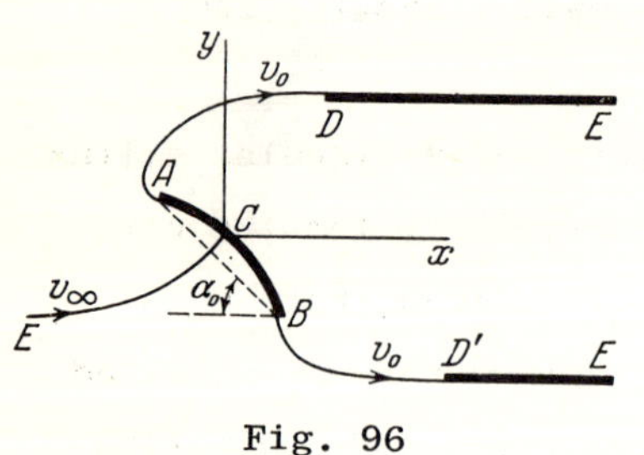

Fig. 96

of the profile. The flow bifurcates at the stagnation point C. As before, the walls DE and D'E' are parallel to each other, to the x-axis, and to the velocity at infinity. This velocity is $v_\infty = v_o/(1 + Q)^{1/2}$, where Q is the cavitation number. The angle between the profile's chord and the negative x-direction is denoted by α_o.

A solution is obtained by mapping the region of change of the complex potential w and $\omega = i \ln dw/v_o dz$ onto the upper unit semicircle in a parametric ζ-plane (Fig. 97). If the complex potential is taken as 0 at C, then it is easy to see that the region of change of w is a plane with a cut along the positive real axis (Fig. 98). Furthermore, we easily observe [Eq. (4.1), Chapter IV] that $w(\zeta)$ can be written as

$$w^{1/2} = -b\left[\cos\beta + \frac{1}{2}\left(\zeta + \frac{1}{\zeta}\right)\right] , \qquad (5.71)$$

where $\pi - \beta$ is the angle made by the vector $\overrightarrow{EC}$ with the real axis in the ζ-plane (Fig. 97). Thus

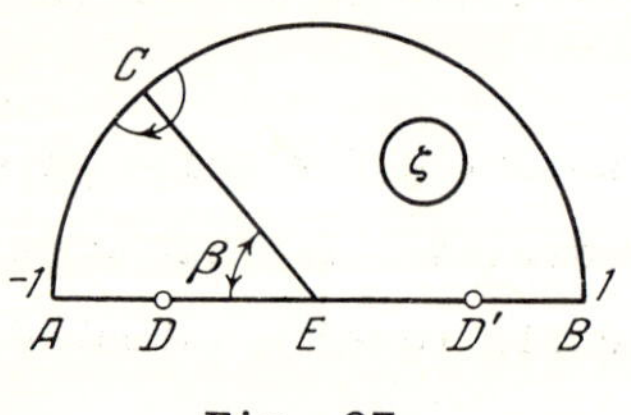

Fig. 97

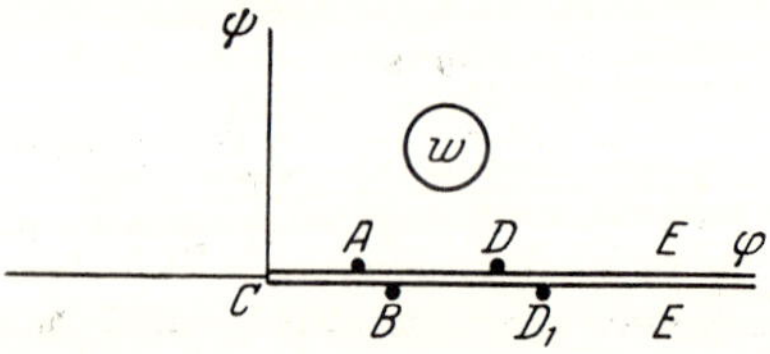

Fig. 98

$$\cos\beta = (b_2 - b_1)/(b_1 + b_2) \quad ; \qquad b = (b_1 + b_2)/2 \quad ,$$

where b_1 and b_2 are positive quantities, related to the values of w at A and B by $w_A = b_1^2$; $w_B = b_2^2\, e^{2\pi i}$.

The region of change of ω is represented in Fig. 99. To study it in more detail, we separate ω into its real and imaginary parts so

$$\omega = \theta + i\tau = \theta + i\,\ell n\,\frac{v}{v_o} \quad ,$$

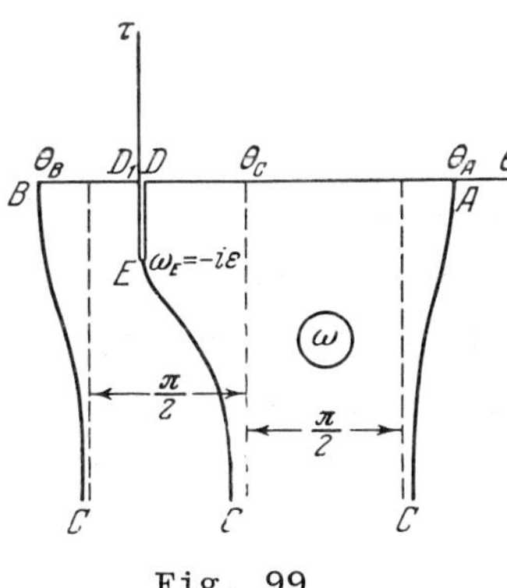

Fig. 99

where v is the velocity magnitude. At D we have $\theta = 0$ and $v = v_o$; therefore, $\ell n\,(v/v_o) = 0$ and $\omega = 0$. With motion along DA the angle increases to the value θ_A, but the imaginary part of ω remains 0. With motion along DE, however, θ remains equal to 0, and $\operatorname{Im}\omega = \ell n\,(v/v_o)$ decreases from 0 to some negative value

$$-\epsilon = \ell n\,\frac{v_\infty}{v_o} \quad . \tag{5.72}$$

Furthermore, with motion along ED' the velocity again increases to v_o, and at D' $\omega = 0$ again. In the ω-plane a vertical cut along the negative part of the imaginary axis corresponds to the walls DE and D'E. Along D_1B the angle decreases from 0 to a value θ_B, and $\operatorname{Im}\omega = \ell n\,(v_o/v_o) = 0$.

Since $v \leq v_o$, the region of change of ω is located in the lower half plane. If the profile DCA were a flat plate, then AC and BC would be vertical straight lines in the ω-plane. These lines would be separated from one another by $\Delta\theta = \pi$, since along CA and CB the angle θ has a constant value but, with passage around C, undergoes a jump of π. In the general case of an arbitrary profile with a continuous curvature, the lines BC and AC (Fig. 99) are curves with vertical asymptotes that are separated by $\Delta\theta = \pi$. The shapes of these curves depend on the profile shape, and to obtain the general solution to the problem we must solve an integro-differential equation, analogous to Villat's equation, or expand $\omega(\zeta)$ in a series. When $\epsilon = 0$ we have the common Kirchhoff flow around a profile. Wu's idea for solving the problem was to study the new function

$$\Omega = -(\omega^2 + \epsilon^2)^{1/2} , \qquad (5.73)$$

in lieu of ω. Under the transformation Eq. (5.73) the lower half-plane (Fig. 99) is mapped onto the upper half-plane (Fig. 100). The real axis of the ω-plane and the cut D_1ED pass onto the real axis of the Ω-plane, while E is at the coordinate origin in the Ω-plane. The lines BC and AC in the Ω-plane, as in the ω-plane, have a vertical asymptote, separated by a distance π.

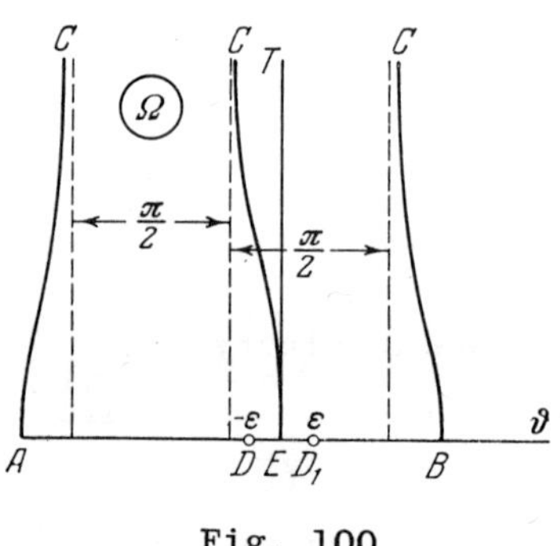

Fig. 100

Examination of Figs. 57 and 100 shows that the region Ω for the flow with the parallel walls is the same as the region of change of $-\omega$ for a Kirchhoff flow around some obstacle different from the initial obstacle ACB. This is clear from the fact that the cut in the ω-plane (Fig. 99) becomes a segment of the real axis of the Ω-plane. Finding Ω for an arbitrary obstacle by using the Levi-Cevita method is no more difficult than finding ω for a Kirchhoff flow about an arbitrary obstacle. However, for flow around a flat plate with the trailing parallel walls (Zhukovskii model) the straight lines BC and AC (Fig. 99) pass onto the Ω-plane as curves in Fig. 100. Thus, Wu's method for determination of flow around a flat plate with Zhukovskii's model is equivalent to finding the Kirchhoff flow around some curvilinear arc.

Obviously, as in the case of a curvilinear arc or a rectilinear plate, Ω can be represented by using the Levi-Civita expansion in the form

$$\Omega(\zeta) = i\,\ln \frac{1 + \zeta e^{-i\beta}}{1 + \zeta e^{i\beta}} + \sum_{n=r}^{\infty} A_n \zeta^n \quad , \tag{5.74}$$

where A_n are real, constant coefficients that are determined in principle from the given shape of the arc ACB. It is easily seen that on the real axis in the ζ-plane (i.e., on $ADED_1B$), we have $|(1 + \zeta e^{-i\beta})/(1 + \zeta e^{i\beta})| = 1$, so that $\operatorname{Im}\Omega = 0$. Clearly, on the semicircle ACB, $\zeta = e^{i\sigma}$. Therefore, on BC $(\sigma < \pi - \beta)$ the argument of $(1+\zeta e^{-i\beta})/(1+\zeta e^{i\beta})$ is $-\beta$. It is readily noted that the argument of

$$\frac{1 + \zeta e^{-i\beta}}{1 + \zeta e^{i\beta}} = e^{-2i\beta}\left\{\frac{\zeta - \exp\,[i(\pi + \beta)]}{\zeta - \exp\,[i(\pi - \beta)]}\right\}$$

becomes $\pi - \beta$ after passage around C $(\zeta = \exp\,[i(\pi - \beta)]$, along an infinitesimal semicircle (Fig. 97). On the other hand, on the semicircle ACB, we have

$$\left|\frac{1 + \zeta e^{-i\beta}}{1 + \zeta e^{i\beta}}\right| = \frac{[1 + \cos\,(\zeta - \beta)]^{1/2}}{[1 + \cos\,(\zeta + \beta)]^{1/2}} \quad .$$

Hence, in separating the real and imaginary parts in Eq. (5.74), we find that on the semicircle ACB $(\zeta = e^{i\sigma})$

$$\text{Im}\ \Omega = T(\sigma) = \frac{1}{2}\ \ell n\ \frac{1 + \cos(\sigma - \beta)}{1 + \cos(\sigma + \beta)} + \sum_{n=1}^{\infty} A_n \sin n\sigma\ , \tag{5.75}$$

and

$$\text{Re}\ \Omega = \vartheta(\sigma) = \beta + \beta_o + \sum_{n=1}^{\infty} A_n \cos \sigma\ , \tag{5.76}$$

where $\beta_o = 0$ for $0 \leqq \sigma < \pi - \beta$ and $\beta_o = -\pi$ for $\pi - \beta < \sigma \leqq \pi$. Thus, on BC and AC the real and imaginary parts of Ω vary continuously, while in passing through C from the line AC to BC the real part of Ω undergoes a jump of π.

When β and all A_n are determined, the problem can be considered solved. Then we are able 1) to find the location of points D and D_1 by using Bernoulli's integral and 2) to perform an integration to compute the axis projections of the resultant pressure force on the arc ACB and the moment of this resultant relative to a chosen point. To determine β and A_n we must first compute the curvature of the arc ACB. From Eqs. (5.71) and (5.73) we have

$$dz = \frac{e^{i\omega}}{v_o}\ dw$$

$$= \frac{b^2}{2v_o}\left[2 \cos \beta + \left(\zeta + \frac{1}{\zeta}\right)\right]\left(\zeta - \frac{1}{\zeta}\right) \exp\ [-i(\Omega^2 - \epsilon^2)^{1/2}]\ \frac{d\zeta}{\zeta}\ . \tag{5.77}$$

Now the arc differential on BCA is easily found to be

$$ds = |dz| = \frac{2b^2}{v_o}\ |\cos \sigma + \cos \beta|\ \sin \sigma\ \exp\ [-\tau(\sigma)]\ d\sigma\ , \tag{5.78}$$

where $\tau = \text{Im}\,\omega = -\text{Im}\,(\Omega^2 - \epsilon^2)^{1/2}$. From Eq. (5.78) it follows that the length of BCA is

$$S = 2b^2 \int_0^{\pi} \exp\,[-\tau(\sigma)]\, |\cos\sigma + \cos\beta|\, \sin\sigma\, d\sigma\,. \quad (5.79)$$

Wu's sample computations were for a flat plate and a circular arc with small central angle 2γ (Fig. 101). Wu retained only A_1, A_2, and A_3 in Eq. (5.74) and set the other coefficients A_n $(n > 3)$ equal to 0. The role of the scale coefficient b is equivalent to that of the arc length. Similarly, according to Eq. (5.72), the role of ϵ is equivalent to that of $Q = (v_0^2/v_\infty^2) - 1$. Actually, from Eq. (5.72) it follows that $Q = e^{2\epsilon} - 1$. For $0 < Q < 1$, $0 < \epsilon^2 < 0.123$.

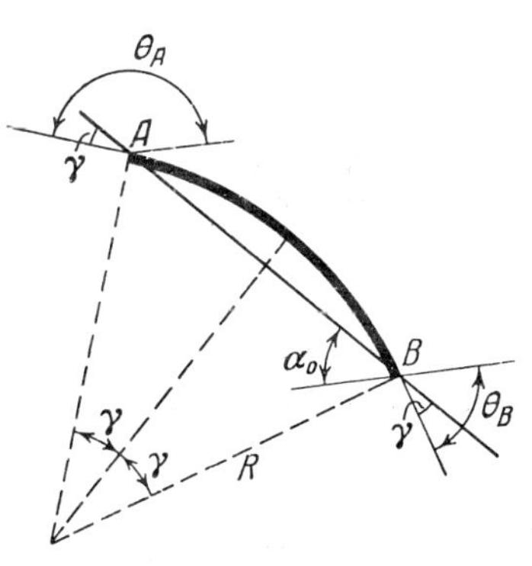

Fig. 101

Wu determines the coefficients β, A_1, A_2, and A_3 from the following conditions: at A, $\theta_A = \pi - \alpha_0 + \gamma$; at B, $\theta_B = -\alpha_0 - \gamma$; the radii of curvature at A and B are equal to $R = S/2\gamma$, where S is determined by using Eq. (5.79), together with the assumption that ϵ^2 is small compared with unity.

The resultant force projections X and Y on the coordinate axes and the moment M of these forces with respect to the stagnation point C are expressed by*

*In Eqs. (5.80) and (5.81), $v_0 = 1$.

$$X + iY = -\frac{i\rho}{2}\oint e^{i\omega}\frac{dw}{d\zeta}\,d\zeta$$

$$= -\frac{i\rho b^2}{4}\oint \exp\left[-i(\Omega^2 - \epsilon^2)^{1/2}\right]\left(\zeta + \frac{1}{\zeta} + 2\cos\beta\right)$$

$$\times\left(\zeta - \frac{1}{\zeta}\right)\frac{d\zeta}{\zeta}\ , \qquad (5.80)$$

where the integration is carried out over the entire circle $|\zeta| = 1$, and

$$M = \frac{\rho}{2}\,\mathrm{Re}\int_{(BCA)}\left\{\exp\left[-i\omega(\zeta)\right] - \exp\left[-i\omega(\overline{\zeta})\right]\right\}z\,\frac{dw}{d\zeta}\,d\zeta . \quad (5.81)$$

In Eq. (5.81) the contour of integration is the upper semicircle $|\zeta| = 1$, $\mathrm{Im}\,\zeta \geqq 0$, and z is obtained by integration of Eq. (5.77).

Figures 102 and 103 are adopted from Wu's work [103]. Some of his numerical results for flow past a flat plat are presented in these figures. The drag coefficient C_x and the lift coefficient C_y have the form

$$C_x = \frac{2X}{\rho v_\infty^2 \ell}\ ; \qquad C_y = \frac{2Y}{\rho v_\infty^2 \ell}\ ,$$

where ℓ is the chord length of the profile. The basic results of Wu's theory are represented by the solid lines, while the dotted lines represent the results of the approximate computations based on [cf. Eq. (5.20)]

$$\left.\begin{aligned} C_x(Q, \alpha_0) &= (1 + Q)C_x(0, \alpha_0)\ , \\ C_y(Q, \alpha_0) &= (1 + Q)C_y(0, \alpha_0)\ . \end{aligned}\right\} \qquad (5.82)$$

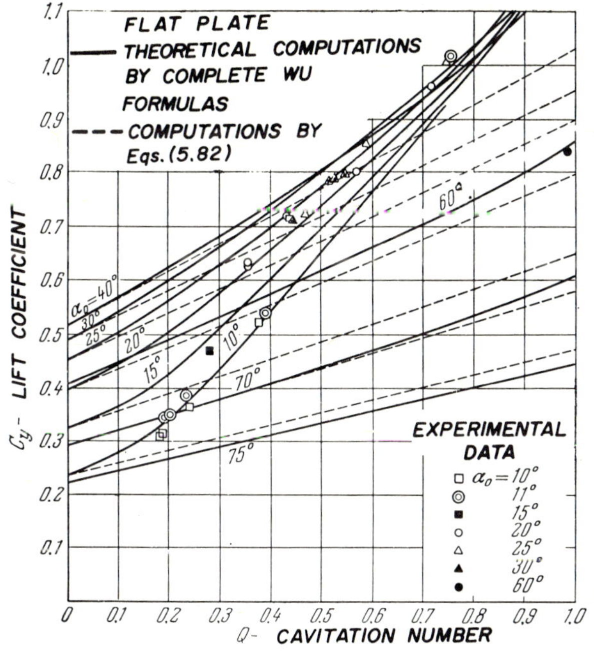

Fig. 102

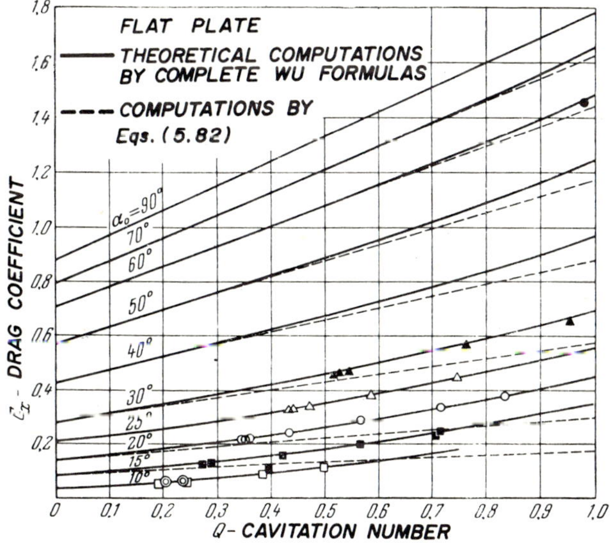

Fig. 103

The experimental data, represented by the discrete points, were obtained in the Hydrodynamic Laboratory at the California Institute of Technology.

Study of Figs. 102 and 103 leads to several conclusions. First, the experimental points coincide well with the theoretical results. Second, the approximate Eqs. (5.82) are considerably less accurate for small α in the present case than for the case of a plate placed normal to the approaching flow.

Wu gave a series of asymptotic formulas for small Q and γ, with $\alpha_o \to 0$ and with $\alpha_o \to \pi/2$. Only one of those formulas is given here for small γ and Q and for $\alpha_o = \pi/2$.

$$C_x = \frac{2\pi}{4+\pi}(1+Q)\left[1 + \frac{4\gamma}{3(4+\pi)}\right] .$$

Obviously, when $\alpha_o = \pi/2$, $C_y = 0$.

The exact solution to the problem of the flow around an inclined plate with a parallel wall model was obtained in 1958 by Mimura [91,104], who also made numerical computations and compared them with the experiments of Fage and Johansen [105]. They tested a plate in a wind tunnel. The agreement between the theory and experiments was satisfactory.

In the present chapter it has been noted many times that, to use jet theory properly, the free surfaces must be distinctly bounded and the pressure on them must remain constant. Therefore, the fully developed, cavitating flow is very well suited to study by jet theory, while air flow around bodies is not very appropriate for such an investigation. However, Eppler's [82] and Mimura's [104] results show that, in certain cases, this limitation on jet theory can be relaxed. Of course, jet theory cannot give a full picture of air flow around a plate and a cylinder because the theory does not permit calculation of the pressure distribution behind the body. But if the pressure behind the body is chosen in accordance with experimental data and, without insisting that Brillouin's first condition be satisfied, the separation points of the jet are matched with the real separation points of the boundary layer, then jet theory permits satisfactory computation of the pressure distribution on the front side of the contour around which the fluid flows.

CHAPTER VI. FLOW OF LIMITED JETS AROUND OBSTACLES

A. FLOW AROUND A WEDGE IN A JET OF FINITE WIDTH

In Chapter II various cases of flow from a vessel were considered. For these flows Fig. 17 represented a universal model, which included all the various problems discussed in Chapter II as special cases. We shall now see that it is possible to give one additional, new interpretation to the flow in Fig. 17.

We reflect the flow in Fig. 17 about the upper horizontal wall and shift the coordinate origin for future convenience (Fig. 104). Finally, we replace the wall HC by a streamline that is located within the fluid. Thus, in Fig. 104 we see symmetric jet flow around a wedge with an included angle $2\pi\kappa$. The fluid jet comes from a channel that is bounded by plane walls, and, without solving the problem again, we can take advantage of the results of Chapter II. To facilitate the discussion we shall repeat briefly those results that are needed here.

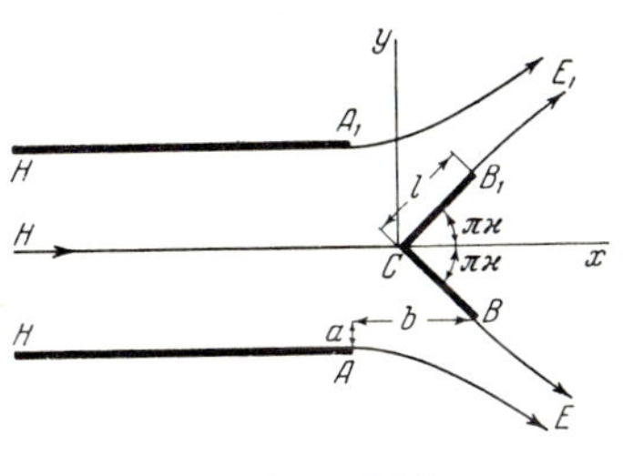

Fig. 104

The problem is solved by mapping the regions of change of $dw/v_o dz$ and w for the lower half of the flow in Fig. 104 onto a unit semicircle in the parametric t-plane (Fig. 18). We recall Eqs. (2.1) and (2.2) which were

$$\frac{dw}{v_o dz} = t^{\kappa} , \qquad (6.1)$$

and

$$w = \frac{q}{\pi}\,\ell n\,(t - h) + \frac{q}{\pi}\,\ell n\left(\frac{1}{h} - t\right) - \frac{q}{\pi}\,\ell n\,(t - e^{i\beta}) - \frac{q}{\pi}\,\ell n\,(t - e^{-i\beta})\,. \tag{6.2}$$

Here, in accordance with the notation of Chapter II, $2q$ is the flow rate between the walls HA_1 and HA.

In Eq. (6.1) v_o represents the magnitude of the velocity on the free surface; h and β are parameters (see Fig. 17). From Eqs. (6.1) and (6.2) we find [see Eq. (2.6)]:

$$z(t) = \frac{q}{\pi v_o}\int \frac{dt}{t^{\kappa}}\left[\frac{1}{t - h} + \frac{1}{t - (1/h)} - \frac{1}{t - e^{i\beta}} - \frac{1}{t - e^{-i\beta}}\right]\,. \tag{6.3}$$

If the distance between the walls is $2L$ and the velocity at upstream infinity between walls is $v_\infty = v_H$, then Eqs. (2.4) and (2.5) can be rewritten as

$$2L = \frac{2q}{v_o h^{\kappa}}\,, \qquad \frac{v_\infty}{v_o} = h^{\kappa}\,. \tag{6.4}$$

The ratios ℓ/L (or a/L) and b/L (Fig. 104), and the included angle of the wedge $2\pi\kappa$ are geometric elements that are completely determined for a family of geometrically similar flows. However, in the numerical computation it is more convenient to prescribe the mathematical parameters β and h rather than ℓ/L or b/L and to determine ℓ/L, b/L, a/L from Eqs. (2.11) through (2.13), that are obtained from Eq. (6.3) and (6.4) or from the corresponding equations of Chapter II, Section A.

While in Chapter II our main interest lay in determining the contraction coefficient of the jet, now we are interested primarily in obtaining the drag X of the wedge or, equivalently, the wedge drag coefficient

$$C_x - \frac{X}{\rho \ell \sin \pi \kappa v_\infty^2} \tag{6.5}$$

An equation for C_x is obtained by applying the momentum theorem to the fluid mass M that is originally bounded by the parallel walls, the wedge, the free surfaces, and plane sections that are located at infinity to the left and to the right and are perpendicular to the flow plane and to the local streamlines.

If the pressure and velocity are p_∞ and v_∞ at infinity to the left (point H) and p_o and v_o on the free surface, then the resultant force, acting on the fluid mass M, is $(p_\infty - p_o)2L - X$, where X is the wedge drag. If the angle formed between the flow velocity and the x-axis at infinity on the jet $A_1E_1B_1$ (Fig. 104) is θ_o, then the momentum increase in the fluid mass M in a unit of time is

$$2q\rho v_o \cos \theta_o - 2q\rho v_\infty \quad .$$

Thus, the momentum theorem for M gives

$$(p_\infty - p_o)2L - X = 2q\rho v_o \cos \theta_o - 2q\rho v_\infty \quad .$$

From this equation, by using the Bernoulli integral and replacing $2q$ by $2Lv_\infty$, we obtain

$$X = \frac{\rho}{2}\left(v_o^2 - v_\infty^2\right) 2L + \rho\ 2L\left(v_\infty^2 - v_\infty v_o \cos \theta_o\right)$$

or*

$$X = \rho L v_\infty^2 \left(\frac{v_o^2}{v_\infty^2} - 2 \frac{v_o}{v_\infty} \cos \theta_o + 1 \right) . \tag{6.6}$$

Finally, from Eqs. (6.5) and (6.6) we find

$$C_x = \frac{L}{\ell \sin \pi\kappa} \left(\frac{v_o^2}{v_\infty^2} - 2 \frac{v_o}{v_\infty} \cos \theta_o + 1 \right) . \tag{6.7}$$

To determine the angle θ_o it is sufficient to set $t = e^{i\beta}$ (point E) in Eq. (6.1) because at E we have $dw/v_o dz = \exp(-i\theta_E) = \exp(i\alpha_o)$ so that

$$\theta_o = \beta\kappa . \tag{6.8}$$

We may now study some particular cases.

First we let points A_1 and A coincide with E_1 and E—i.e., flow past a wedge that is symmetrically located between two parallel walls [$b = -\infty$, $\theta_o = 0$, $\beta = 0$, and ℓ/L can be determined from Eq. (2.30)]. In Chapter II the corresponding flow is that from a symmetric vessel with a funnel-shaped bottom (see Section D and Fig. 22).

It is interesting to note that, in this case, C_x can be expressed in terms of the jet's coefficient of contraction k_a and a/L. Indeed, by equating the expressions for the flow rate at infinity to the right and the left, we find that $v_\infty L = v_o k_a a$ and $v_o/v_\infty = L/ak_a$. Considering, in addition,

*Equation (6.6) and its derivation are not altered when the wedge is replaced by any symmetric contour.

that $\ell \sin \pi\kappa = L - a$ and $\theta_o = 0$, we find that, from Eq. (6.7),

$$C_x = \frac{1}{1 - (a/L)} \left(\frac{L}{ak_a} - 1 \right)^2 . \qquad (6.9)$$

Values of C_x can be computed by taking advantage of the numerical results in Chapter II, Section D as long as too large values of a/L are not used.

Birkhoff, Plesset, and Simmons [106] showed that, for flow around an obstacle located between two walls, the cavitation number cannot be zero but must be greater than some limiting value. From Eq. (6.7), with $\theta_o = 0$, by expressing v_o/v_∞ in terms of the cavitation number $Q = \left(v_o^2/v_\infty^2\right) - 1$, we have

$$C_x = \frac{L}{\ell \sin \pi\kappa} \left[(1 + Q)^{1/2} - 1\right]^2 < \frac{L}{\ell \sin \pi\kappa} \frac{Q^2}{4} ,$$

from which we obtain

$$Q > 2 \left(\frac{C_x \, \ell \sin \pi\kappa}{L} \right)^{1/2} . \qquad (6.10)$$

As another particular case, consider a wedge in a free jet (Fig. 105). Here points A and H coincide, $b = -\infty$, and it is convenient to set $h = 1$. Clearly, Eq. (6.1) is unchanged, and Eq. (6.2), after a passage to the limit,* takes the form

---

*In addition, an imaginary constant is added to the right part of Eq. (6.11) [as compared to Eq. (6.1)] so that $\psi = 0$ on the streamline HCE.

$$w = \frac{2q}{\pi} \ln (1 - t) - \frac{q}{\pi} \ln (t^2 + 1 - 2t \cos \beta) . \quad (6.11)$$

By combining this equation and Eq. (6.1) we have

$$z = \frac{2q}{\pi v_o} \int t^{-\kappa} \left[\frac{1}{t - 1} + \frac{\cos \beta - t}{t^2 + 1 - 2t \cos \beta} \right] dt . \quad (6.12)$$

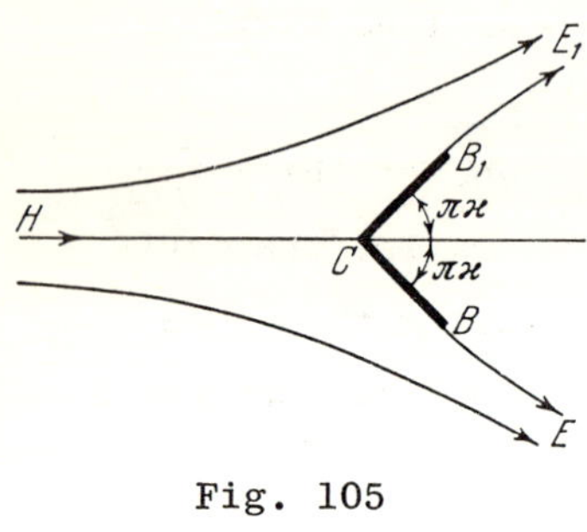

Fig. 105

Equation (6.12) gives the mapping of the lower half of the flow onto the semicircle in Fig. 106. The drag coefficient is computed from Eq. (6.7), in which we set $v_o/v_\infty = 1$, so that

$$C_x = \frac{2L}{\ell \sin \pi\kappa} (1 - \cos \theta_o) . \quad (6.13)$$

The value ℓ/L, determined from Eq. (2.11) with $h = 1$, is

$$\frac{\ell}{L} = \frac{2}{\pi} \int_0^1 \frac{d\xi}{\xi^\kappa} \left[\frac{1}{\xi + 1} - \frac{\xi + \cos \beta}{\xi^2 + 2\xi \cos \beta + 1} \right] . \quad (6.14)$$

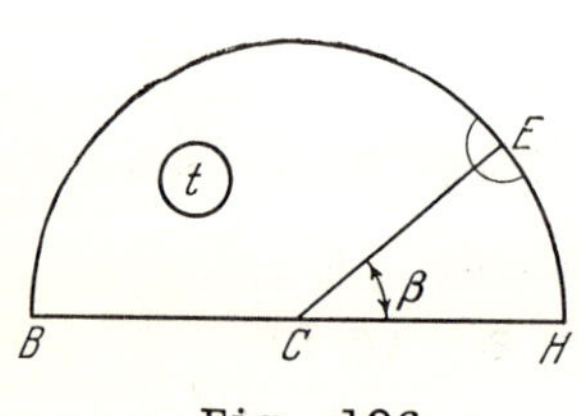

Fig. 106

Equation (6.14) can also be obtained from Eq. (6.12). Interesting calculations were carried out by Birkhoff, Plesset, and Simmons [106] for a flat plate in a free jet and in a channel as shown in Fig. 107, from which it is seen that the width of the free jet has a small influence on the drag coefficient C_x, while the wall of the channel has an appreciable influence on C_x, even when the distance between the walls is quite large in comparison

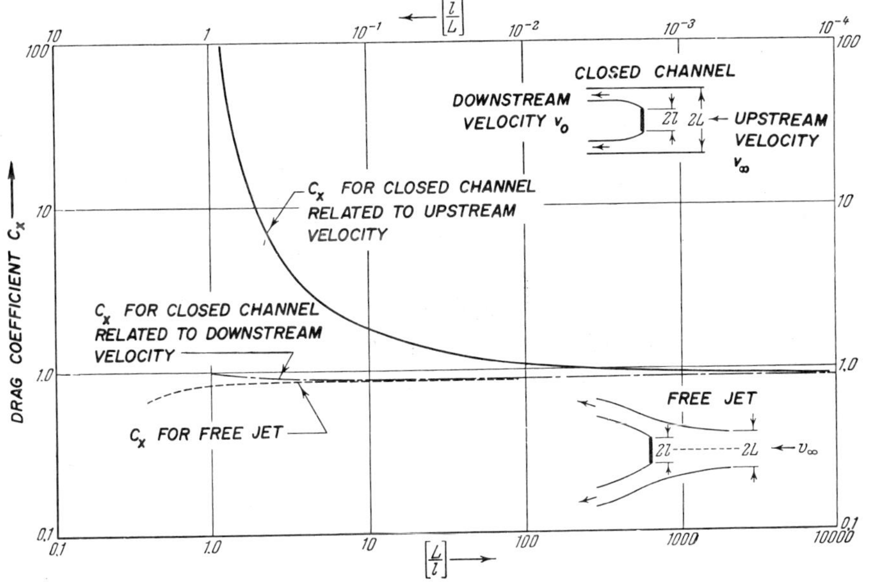

Fig. 107

with the dimension of the plate. However, if we relate the drag to the velocity of the jet v_o instead of the approaching flow velocity v_∞, then the coefficient C_{xo} is practically constant and agrees with the approximate Eq. (5.20)—i.e., we examine $C_{xo} = C_x\left(v_\infty^2/v_o^2\right) = C_x/(Q + 1)$. (Of course, for a plate in a free jet these velocities are equal.) In Figs. 108 through 111 are presented the results of calculations for the drag coefficient of a flat plate in a jet issuing from a semi-infinite channel for several plate positions [106].

The problem of a finite-width jet flow around an asymmetric wedge was studied for the first time by Kotelnikov*

*Actually Kotelnikov solved only the case when the stream is divided by the wedge into two jets with equal flow rates.

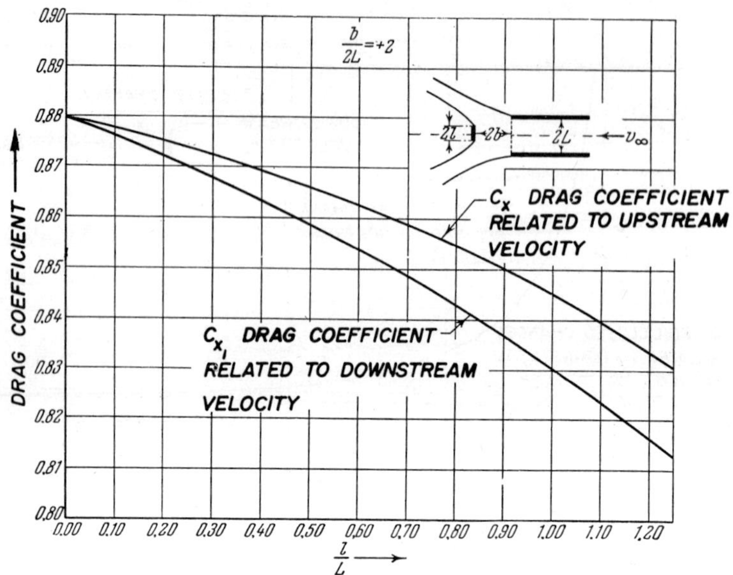

Fig. 108

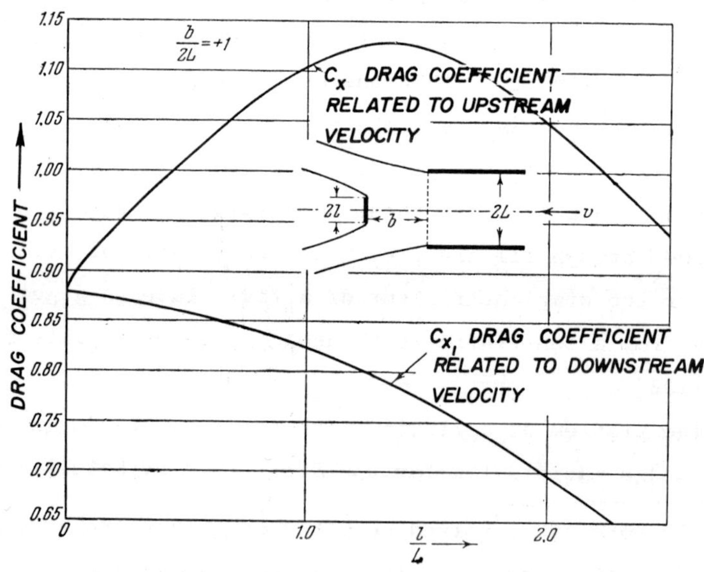

Fig. 109

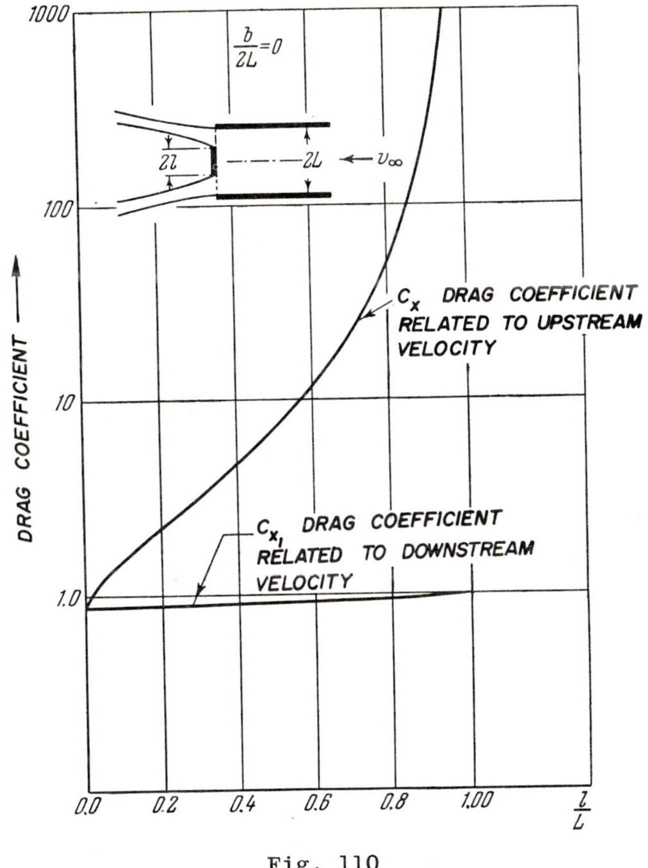

Fig. 110

[107 and 10]. Such a flow is shown in Fig. 112a. Let $q = q_1 + q_2$ be the flow rate of fluid in the approaching jet while q_1 and q_2 are the flow rates in the jets G and H respectively. The velocity on the free surfaces is v_o, the angles $2\pi\alpha$ and $2\pi\beta$, that are formed by the jets with the x-axis, are also shown in Fig. 112a. Finally, $2\pi\kappa$ is the included angle of the wedge. The streamline $\psi = 0$ is required to approach the vertex O of the wedge. This streamline CO divides at O into the streamlines OBG and OAH.

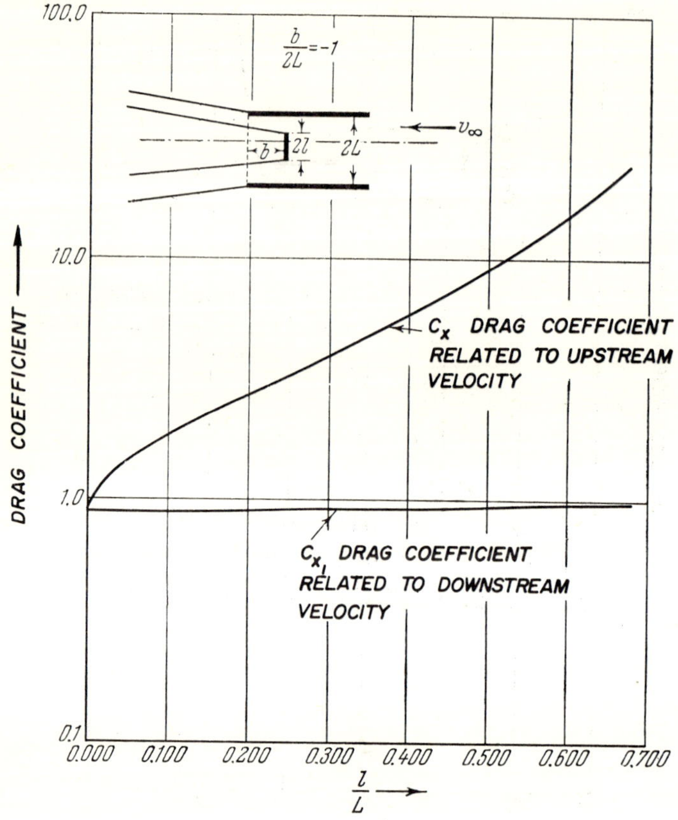

Fig. 111

We select the right upper quadrant as the region of change of the parametric variable u (Fig. 113) and will obtain $v_o dz/dw$ and dw/du, where $w = \varphi + i\psi$ is the complex potential of the flow, as functions of u. On the free surfaces $|v_o dz/dw| = 1$, on the wedge side OB the argument of $v_o dz/dw$ is 0, and on the wedge side OA the argument of $v_o dz/dw$ is $-2\pi\kappa$. Obviously, $v_o dz/dw$, when considered as a function of u, has a singularity of the form $(u-i)^{-2\kappa}$ at $O(u = i)$. By extending $v_o dz/dw$ to the entire u-plane by the symmetry principle, we find that, because $|v_o dz/dw| = 1$ everywhere on the real axis of u, $v_o dz/dw$ has a

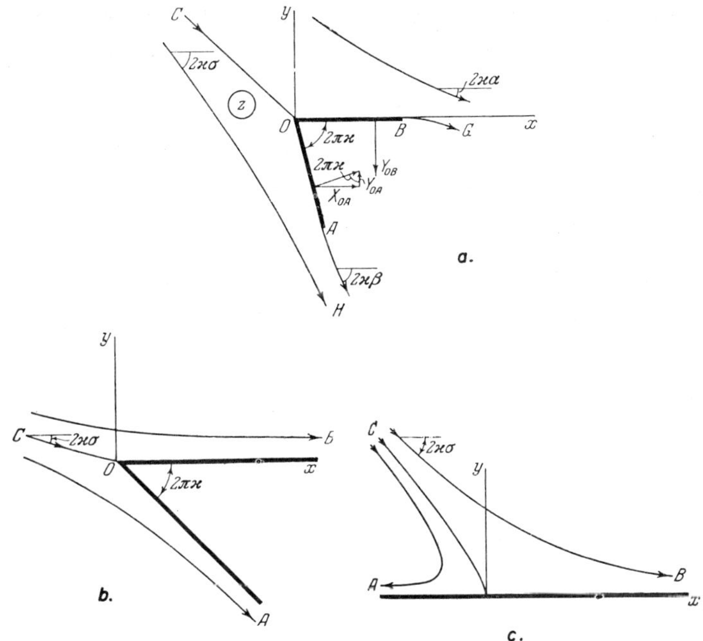

Fig. 112

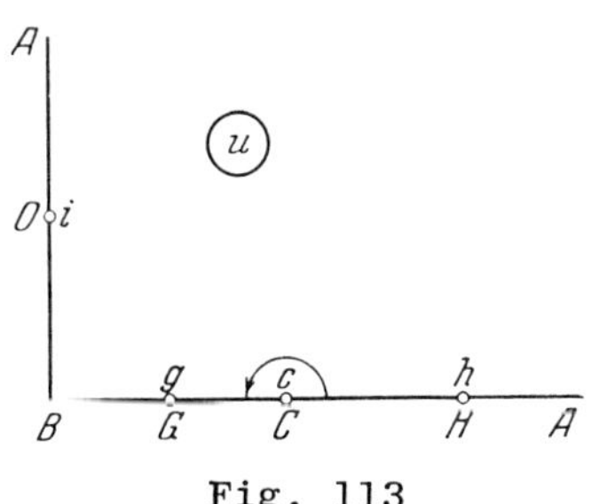

Fig. 113

singularity of the form $(u+i)^{2\kappa}$ at $u = -i$. The function $v_o dz/dw$ has no other signularities or zeros in the u-plane. After constructing $v_o dz/dw$ in terms of its singularities and taking advantage of the condition that $v_o dz/dw = 1$ at $B(u = 0)$, we find

$$\frac{v_o dz}{dw} = \left(\frac{i + u}{i - u}\right)^{2\kappa} = \left(\frac{1 - iu}{1 + iu}\right)^{2\kappa} . \qquad (6.15)$$

The function $w(u)$ is real on the streamlines CBG and CAH—i.e., on the sides of the quadrant in Fig. 113. Also, dw/du has real values on the real axis of u and imaginary values on its imaginary axis. The function $w(u)$

has logarithmic singularities at the points of infinity on the jet $C(u = c)$, $G(u = g)$, and $H(u = h)$; thus dw/du has poles (Chapter I, Section F) at these points. In addition, dw/du has zeros at points O (at this point the streamline divides—Chapter I, Section F) and $B(u = 0)$ (at B the conformality of the mapping of w onto u is violated). By extending dw/du to the entire u-plane with the help of the symmetry principle, we see that dw/du also has poles at $u = -c$, $u = -g$, $u = -h$, and a zero at $u = -i$. Now it is easy to construct dw/du from its zeros and poles as

$$\frac{dw}{du} = \frac{Nu\,(u^2 + 1)}{(u^2 - g^2)(u^2 - c^2)(u^2 - h^2)} \quad . \tag{6.16}$$

The constant N is determined from a condition on $\operatorname{Im} w = \psi$ at C. In a clockwise passage around C on an infinitesimal semicircle in the u-plane* it is required that ψ increase by q—i.e.,

$$\operatorname{Im} \int \frac{dw}{du}\, du = qi \quad ,$$

so that

$$qi = \frac{N\,(c^2 + 1)\,\pi i}{2(c^2 - g^2)(c^2 - h^2)} \quad ,$$

and

$$N = -\frac{2q(c^2 - g^2)(h^2 - c^2)}{\pi\,(c^2 + 1)} \quad . \tag{6.17}$$

*Such a passage corresponds to moving from the streamline CH to the streamline CG.

By an analogous method it is possible to find the flowrates q_1 and q_2 in the jets G and H:

$$\left.\begin{aligned} q_1 &= -\frac{N(g^2+1)\pi}{2(c^2-g^2)(h^2-g^2)} \\ q_2 &= -\frac{N(h^2+1)\pi}{2(h^2-g^2)(h^2-c^2)} \end{aligned}\right\} . \qquad (6.18)$$

Equations (6.15) and (6.16) give the general solution for a finite-width jet flow around a wedge. We can find, in terms of the parameters in these equations, not only the flowrates in the jets but also all the geometric and hydrodynamic characteristics of the problem. We shall find, for example, the angle that the jet at infinity forms with the x-axis. By designating θ as the angle between the velocity and the x-axis, we find from Eq. (6.15) that, on the free surface,

$$\theta = -4\kappa \arctan u \quad . \qquad (6.19)$$

Since at points G, C, and H the angle θ is equal to $-2\kappa\alpha$, $-2\kappa\sigma$, and $-2\kappa\beta$, respectively, then, by setting u equal to g, c, and h in Eq. (6.19), we find

$$g = \tan\frac{\alpha}{2}, \qquad c = \tan\frac{\sigma}{2}, \qquad h = \tan\frac{\beta}{2} \quad . \qquad (6.20)$$

All the geometric quantities—in particular the length of the wedge's sides—are determined with the help of the integral

$$z = \frac{1}{v_o}\int_i^u \frac{v_o\,dz}{dw}\frac{dw}{du}\,du \quad . \qquad (6.21)$$

The pressure at each point in the flow is, as always, computed by application of the Bernoulli integral; however, the resultant force (but not the moment) acting on the wedge can be computed without an integration. By using the momentum theorem, we easily obtain

$$\left.\begin{aligned} \rho v_o(-q\cos 2\kappa\sigma + q_1\cos 2\kappa\alpha + q_2\cos 2\kappa\beta) &= -X \\ \rho v_o(q\sin 2\kappa\sigma - q_1\sin 2\kappa\alpha - q_2\sin 2\kappa\beta) &= -Y \end{aligned}\right\}, \quad (6.22)$$

where X and Y are projections on the coordinate axes of the resultant hydrodynamic force acting on the wedge. Equations (6.22) can be replaced by the single, complex equation

$$X + iY = \rho v_o(qe^{-2i\kappa\sigma} - q_1e^{-2i\kappa\alpha} - q_2e^{-2i\kappa\beta}). \quad (6.23)$$

If X and Y are known, it is easy to find the individual forces X_{OA}, X_{OB}, Y_{OA}, and Y_{OB} that act on the sides of the wedge. Since these forces are normal to the sides, $X_{OB} = 0$, and we have $X_{OA} = X$. Now knowing X_{OA}, we easily find Y_{OA}. From Fig. 112a, it follows that $Y_{OA} = X\cot 2\pi\kappa$, and, finally,

$$Y_{OB} = Y - Y_{OA} = Y - X\cos 2\pi\kappa \ .$$

In the particular case when the sides of the wedge are infinitely long (Fig. 112b) and the flowrates q_1 and q_2 are given, Eq. (6.23) gives the resultant force acting on a wedge without our having to solve the corresponding hydrodynamic problem. Actually, in this case $\beta = \pi$, $\alpha = 0$, and we have, from Eq. (6.23),

$$X + iY = \rho v_o\left[q_1(e^{-2i\kappa\sigma} - 1) + q_2(e^{-2i\kappa\alpha} - e^{-2\pi i\kappa})\right] \ . \quad (6.24)$$

When the wedge becomes a flat plate, $\kappa = 1/2$ (Fig. 112c). But then $X = 0$, and this condition, together with Eq. (6.24), allows determination of a relation between the flowrates, which, in contrast to a flow around a wedge, are not arbitrary—i.e.,

$$q_1(1 - \cos\sigma) = q_2(1 + \cos\sigma) \quad .$$

Simultaneously, from Eq. (6.24), with $\kappa = 1/2$, we obtain

$$Y = -\rho v_o q \sin\sigma \quad . \tag{6.25}$$

It is important now to examine the case where the flowrate q_2, together with $q = q_1 + q_2$, is infinite, while q_1 is finite (Fig. 114). This particular problem was studied in

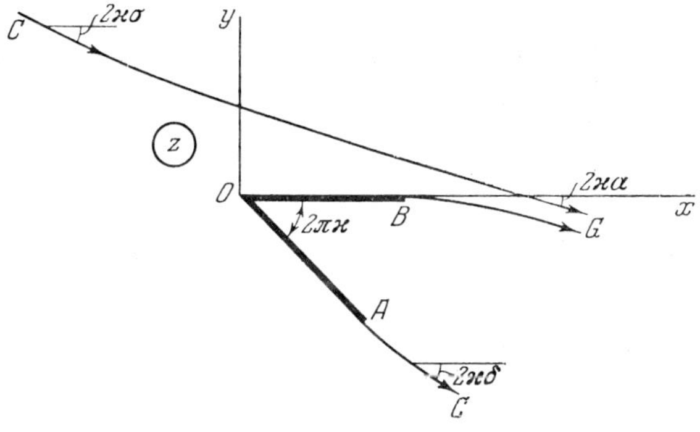

Fig. 114

detail by Tseitlin and Fedorov, who presented it to a computing-center seminar at the USSR Academy of Sciences. For this case $h = c$ and we have, instead of Eq. (6.15),

$$\frac{dw}{du} = \frac{Nu\,(u^2 + 1)}{(u^2 - g^2)(u^2 - c^2)^2} \quad . \tag{6.26}$$

The region of change of u is shown in Fig. 115. Equations (6.15) and (6.20) are unchanged except that in the latter $h = c$ and $\beta = \sigma$. Because, as we pass to the necessary limit on the right side of Eq. (6.17), it becomes indeterminate, we find it more convenient to use the first of Eqs. (6.18) to determine N. Thus, with $h = c$, we obtain

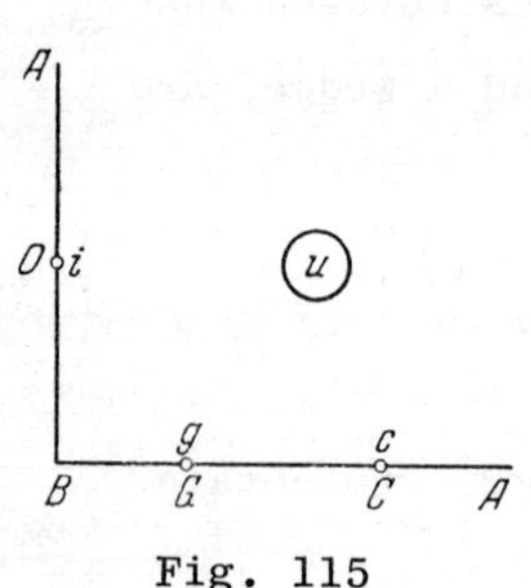

Fig. 115

$$N = - \frac{2q_1(c^2 - g^2)^2}{\pi(1 + g^2)} \quad . \tag{6.27}$$

Passing to the limit in Eq. (6.23) to obtain the forces acting on the wedge is a little more difficult. We first write Eq. (6.23) in the form

$$X + iY = \rho v_o q_1 \left[e^{-2i\kappa\sigma} - e^{-2i\kappa\alpha} + \frac{q_2}{q_1} (e^{-2i\kappa\sigma} - e^{-2i\kappa\beta}) \right] . \tag{6.28}$$

Then we set $\beta = \sigma + \epsilon$, where $\epsilon \to 0$ and we have

$$e^{-2i\kappa\sigma} - e^{-2i\kappa\beta} \approx e^{-2i\kappa\sigma} - e^{-2i\kappa\sigma}(1 - 2i\kappa\epsilon) = 2i\kappa\epsilon e^{-2i\kappa\sigma} . \tag{6.29}$$

On the other hand, Eq. (6.20) gives

$$h - c = \tan\frac{\beta}{2} - \tan\frac{\sigma}{2} = \frac{\sin[(\beta - \sigma)/2]}{\cos(\beta/2)\cos(\sigma/2)} \approx \frac{\epsilon}{2\cos^2(\sigma/2)}$$

$$= \frac{\epsilon}{2}\left[1 + \tan^2\left(\frac{\sigma}{2}\right)\right] = \frac{\epsilon}{2}(1 + c^2) \quad ,$$

so that

$$\epsilon = \frac{2(h - c)}{1 + c^2} \quad . \tag{6.30}$$

Dividing the first of Eqs. (6.18) into the second produces

$$\frac{q_2}{q_1} \approx \frac{(c^2 + 1)(c^2 - g^2)}{2c(h - c)(1 + g^2)} \quad ,$$

or, in accordance with Eq. (6.30),

$$\frac{q_2}{q_1} \epsilon \approx \frac{c^2 - g^2}{c(1 + g^2)} \quad . \tag{6.31}$$

Substituting Eqs. (6.29) and (6.31) in Eq. (6.28) and recalling that, in the limit, approximate equalities become exact, leads finally to

$$X + iY = \rho v_o q_1 \left[e^{-2i\kappa\sigma} - e^{-2i\kappa\alpha} + \frac{2i\kappa(c^2 - g^2)}{c(1 + g^2)} e^{-2i\kappa\sigma} \right] . \tag{6.32}$$

The lengths ℓ_{OB} and ℓ_{OA} of the sides of the wedge are expressed in terms of the following integrals [see Eqs. (6.15), (6.16), (6.18), (6.20), and (6.21)]:

$$\ell_{OA} = \frac{4q_1}{\pi v_o} \frac{(\cos\alpha - \cos\sigma)^2}{(1 + \cos\alpha)(1 + \cos\sigma)^2}$$

$$\cdot \int_0^1 \left(\frac{1 + \xi}{1 - \xi}\right)^{2\kappa} \frac{(1 - \xi^2)\, \xi \, d\xi}{\left[1 + \xi^2 \tan^2\left(\frac{\alpha}{2}\right)\right]\left[1 + \xi^2 \tan^2\left(\frac{\sigma}{2}\right)\right]} \tag{6.33a}$$

$$\ell_{OB} = \frac{4q_1}{\pi v_o} \frac{(\cos \alpha - \cos \sigma)^2}{(1 + \cos \alpha)(1 + \cos \sigma)^2}$$

$$\cdot \int_0^1 \left(\frac{1 + \xi}{1 - \xi}\right)^{2\kappa} \frac{(1 - \xi^2)\, \xi\, d\xi}{\left[\xi^2 + \tan^2\left(\frac{\alpha}{2}\right)\right]\left[\xi^2 + \tan^2\left(\frac{\sigma}{2}\right)\right]} . \tag{6.33b}$$

Tseitlin and Fedorov carried out detailed computation for the forces acting on the wedge. Some of their results are given in Fig. 116. Also of interest are their asymptotic formulas obtained for a wedge with a small κ—i.e.,

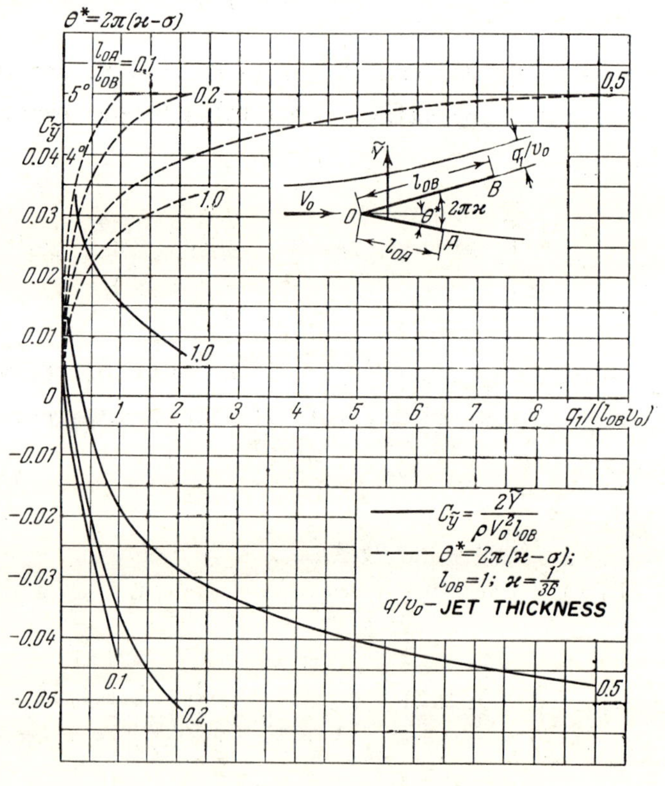

Fig. 116

$$\ell_{OB} \approx \frac{q_1}{\pi v_o}\left\{\ell n\,\frac{1 - \cos\sigma}{1 - \cos\alpha} - 1 + \frac{1 - \cos\alpha}{1 - \cos\sigma}\right.$$

$$\left. + 2\kappa\left[\frac{(\pi - \alpha)^2}{2} - \frac{(\pi - \sigma)^2}{2} - \frac{\cos\alpha - \cos\sigma}{\sin\sigma}(\pi - \sigma)\right]\right\}, \tag{6.34}$$

$$\ell_{OA} \approx \frac{q_1}{\pi v_o}\left\{\ell n\,\frac{1 + \cos\sigma}{1 + \cos\alpha} - 1 + \frac{1 + \cos\alpha}{1 + \cos\sigma}\right.$$

$$\left. + 2\kappa\left[\frac{\alpha^2}{2} - \frac{\sigma^2}{2} + \frac{\cos\alpha - \cos\sigma}{\sin\sigma}\sigma\right]\right\}. \tag{6.35}$$

B. FLOW AROUND A FLAT PLATE IN THE PRESENCE OF A WALL

Here we consider the jet flow around a plate AB, which is perpendicular to an infinite wall EG (Fig. 117), and study the influence of the distance h from the plate's end A to the wall on the plate's drag. Bonder [108] was the first to study this problem; however, we will also take advantage of the solution obtained by Tseitlin.

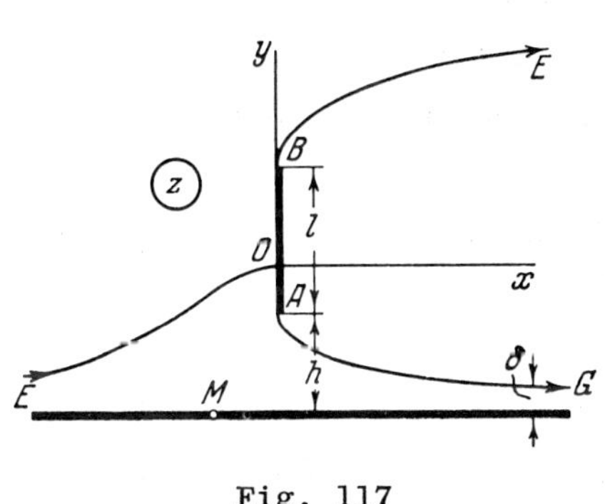

Fig. 117

We shall consider that, along the branches of the streamline OBE and OAG, the stream function $\psi = 0$. If δ is the jet width and v_o is the velocity at infinity, then along the horizontal wall EMG, $\psi = -\delta v_o$. Thus the region of change of w (Fig. 118) is the half-plane $\psi \geqq -\delta v_o$ with a cut corresponding to the streamline (OBE, OAG) along the positive real axis.

The region of change of the complex velocity (Fig. 119) $\zeta = dw/v_o dz = ve^{-i\theta}/v_o$ is a notched, unit semicircle, bounded by the vertical diameter BOA, that corresponds to the plate. The horizontal notch or cut GME corresponds to the wall EMG, along which the velocity is horizontal. There, the velocity varies from v_o at E to some value $v_M < v_o$ at M, and then increases again to v_o at G.

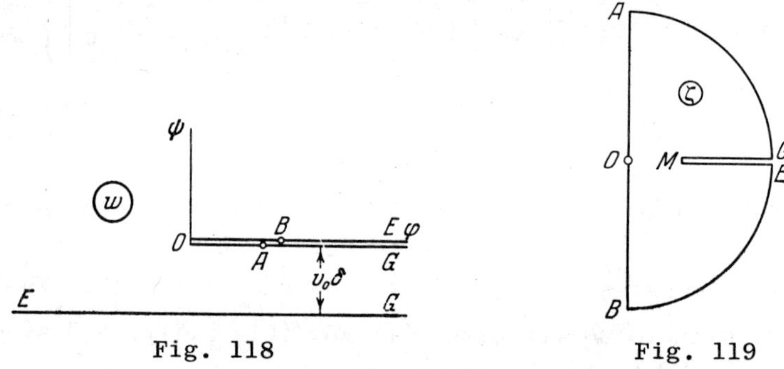

Fig. 118

Fig. 119

We now map the regions of change of ζ and w onto the upper half-plane u (Fig. 120a). The singular-point method is easily employed to map w. It has a logarithmic singularity at G and both a logarithmic singularity and a pole at E. Accordingly, at these points dw/du has first- and second-order poles. In addition, the conformality of the mapping is violated at O. Hence, at this point dw/du = 0 and so

$$\frac{dw}{du} = C \frac{u}{(u + 1)(u - 1)^2} . \tag{6.36}$$

The constant C can be expressed in terms of the jet width δ at infinity. Actually, in integrating Eq. (6.36) along an infinitesimal semicircle around G in the u-plane (Fig. 120a), we find that

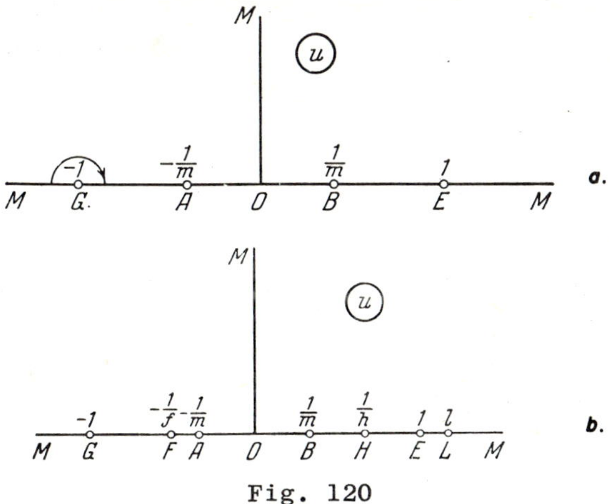

Fig. 120

$$v_o \delta i = \int \frac{dw}{du} du = -\frac{C}{4}(-\pi i)$$

or

$$C = \frac{4v_o\delta}{\pi} .$$

It follows that Eq. (6.36) becomes

$$\frac{dw}{du} = \frac{4v_o\delta u}{\pi(u+1)(u-1)^2} . \tag{6.37}$$

Unfortunately, the singular-point method is not useful for a direct determination of $dw/v_o dz$, and application of Zhukovskii's method leads to long computations. On the other hand, a solution is obtained with relative ease if we first extend the lower half of the ζ-plane—i.e., a quarter-circle—to a half-circle and then map the result onto a half-plane. Finally, the half-plane is folded onto the upper-right quarter of the u-plane (Fig. 120a). In consequence of the symmetry principle, the resulting $\zeta(u)$ gives the mapping of the entire ζ-plane onto the upper half of the u-plane. We shall not carry out these steps here, but shall be content to use directly the formula for $\zeta(u)$, obtained by Tseitlin, and to verify it. Thus, we have

$$\frac{dw}{v_o dz} = \zeta = -\frac{iu(m^2 - 1)^{1/2}}{(1 - u^2)^{1/2} + (1 - m^2u^2)^{1/2}} . \qquad (6.38)$$

Since $\zeta(u)$ has no singularities in the upper half-plane, it is sufficient to check only the behavior of $\zeta(u)$ on the real axis. Under a motion from $u = 0$ to

$$u = \frac{1}{m}, \qquad \zeta = \frac{ve^{-i\theta}}{v_o} ,$$

while remaining purely imaginary, changes monotonically from 0 to $-i$ at B, where $v = v_o$ and $\theta = \pi/2$. On the segment BE and after passage around point B, ζ is written in the form

$$\zeta = \frac{-iu(m^2 - 1)^{1/2}}{(1 - u^2)^{1/2} - i(m^2u^2 - 1)^{1/2}} . \qquad (6.39)$$

When $|\zeta|$ is computed by Eq. (6.39), we see that, on the BE, $|\zeta| = 1$. The argument of ζ changes from $\pi/2$ at B to 0 at $E(u = 1)$. After passage around E, $\zeta(u)$ takes the form

$$\zeta = \frac{u(m^2 - 1)^{1/2}}{(u^2 - 1)^{1/2} + (m^2u^2 - 1)^{1/2}} . \qquad (6.40)$$

As u varies from 1 to ∞, ζ is, according to Eq. (6.40), real and varies from 1 to

$$\frac{v_M}{v_o} = \frac{(m - 1)^{1/2}}{(m + 1)^{1/2}} ,$$

from which we observe that

$$m = \frac{v_o^2 + v_M^2}{v_o^2 - v_M^2} , \tag{6.41}$$

where v_M is the minimum velocity that occurs at point M. Finally we observe that $\zeta(u)$ has the correct behavior on the negative real axis MGAO. Since $\operatorname{Im} \zeta = 0$ from Eq. (6.38) when u is purely imaginary, the symmetry principle requires that, at points on the real u-axis equidistant from the coordinate origin, the real parts of ζ be equal while the imaginary parts differ only in sign.

To determine h and ℓ we first find, from Eqs. (6.36) and (6.38), the function $z(u)$:

$$z(u) = \frac{4\delta i}{\pi(m^2 - 1)^{1/2}} \int_0^u \frac{(1 - u^2)^{1/2} + (1 - m^2u^2)^{1/2}}{(u + 1)(u - 1)^2}\, du . \tag{6.42}$$

This becomes, after evaluation of the integral,

$$z(u) = \frac{4\delta i}{\pi(m^2 - 1)^{1/2}} \left[\left(\frac{1 + u}{1 - u}\right)^{1/2} - \frac{(m^2 - 1)^{1/2}}{2} \arcsin\, (m^2 - 1)^{1/2} \frac{u}{(1 - u^2)^{1/2}} \right.$$
$$\left. + \frac{(1 - m^2u^2)^{1/2}}{2(1 - u)} - \frac{m^2}{2(m^2 - 1)^{1/2}} \arcsin \frac{1 - m^2u^2}{m(1 - u)}\right]_0^u . \tag{6.43}$$

Obviously, $\ell = (z_B - z_A)/i$. The values z_B and z_A are computed by substituting the values i/m and $-i/m$ in Eq. (6.43). As a result, we obtain

$$\ell = \frac{2\delta}{\pi(m^2 - 1)} (4 + \pi) \quad . \tag{6.44}$$

From Fig. 117,

$$h = \text{Im}\,(z_A - z_G) + \delta \quad , \tag{6.45}$$

where, according to Eq. (6.42),

$$\text{Im}\,(z_A - z_G) = \text{Im}\,\frac{4\delta i}{\pi(m^2 - 1)^{1/2}}$$

$$\cdot \int_{-1}^{-1/m} \frac{(1 - u^2)^{1/2} + i(m^2u^2 - 1)^{1/2}}{(u + 1)(u - 1)^2}\,du \ ;$$

it follows that

$$\text{Im}\,(z_A - z_G) = \frac{4\delta}{\pi(m^2 - 1)^{1/2}} \int_{-1}^{-1/m} \frac{(1 - u^2)^{1/2}\,du}{(u + 1)(u - 1)^2}$$

$$= \frac{4\delta}{\pi(m^2 - 1)^{1/2}} \left(\frac{1 + u}{1 - u}\right)^{1/2} \Bigg|_{-1}^{-1/m} = \frac{4\delta}{\pi(m + 1)} \quad . \tag{6.46}$$

From Eqs.(6.44) - (6.46) we easily find

$$\frac{h}{\ell} = \frac{[4 + \pi(m + 1)](m - 1)}{2(4 + \pi)} \quad . \tag{6.47}$$

As m varies from 1 to ∞, the ratio h/ℓ varies from 0 to ∞.

The normal force X that acts on the plate AB is found next. This computation is carried out by a direct integration of the pressure acting on the plate. By using Bernoulli's integral, we obtain

$$X = \int_{AB} (p - p_o) \, |dz| = \frac{\rho v_o^2}{2} \int_{AB} (1 - |\zeta|^2) \, |dz| \quad ,$$

where $p - p_o$ is the difference between the pressure on the plate front and that on the back at the point under consideration. Then, by making use of Eqs. (6.38) and (6.42), we find

$$X = \frac{qv_o^2}{2} \int_{-1/m}^{1/m} \left\{ 1 - \frac{u^2 (m^2 - 1)}{\left[(1 - u^2)^{1/2} + (1 - m^2u^2)^{1/2}\right]^2} \right\}$$

$$\cdot \frac{4\delta}{\pi(m^2 - 1)^{1/2}} \frac{(1 - u^2)^{1/2} + (1 - m^2u^2)^{1/2}}{(u + 1)(u - 1)^2} \, du$$

or

$$X = \frac{4\rho v_o^2 \delta}{\pi(m^2 - 1)^{1/2}} \int_{-1/m}^{1/m} \frac{(1 - m^2u^2)^{1/2}}{(u + 1)(1 - u)^2} \, du \quad . \qquad (6.48)$$

The integral appearing in Eq. (6.46) is easily evaluated [cf. Eqs. (6.42) and (6.43)] as

$$\frac{4\delta}{\pi(m^2 - 1)^{1/2}} \int_{-1/m}^{1/m} \frac{(1 - m^2u^2)^{1/2}}{(u + 1)(1 - u)^2} \, du = \frac{2\delta}{m^2 - 1} \quad . \qquad (6.49)$$

From Eqs. (6.48) and (6.49) it follows that

$$X = \frac{4\delta}{m^2 - 1} \frac{\rho v_o^2}{2} \quad . \qquad (6.50)$$

By comparing Eqs. (6.44) and (6.50), we can obtain the drag coefficient of the plate in the presence of the wall,

$$C_x = \frac{2X}{\rho \ell v_0^2} = \frac{2\pi}{4 + \pi} . \tag{6.51}$$

This is a remarkable result. The drag coefficient of a plate, placed normal to a wall and in a jet flow, doesn't depend on the plate's distance from the wall [108].

Tseitlin has obtained a more general result, which he presented to a seminar at the USSR Academy of Sciences computing center. Consider a symmetric extension of the flow in Fig. 117 to the lower half-plane (Fig. 121). The result is a symmetric jet flow about two equal plates, placed normal to the approaching flow. Tseitlin proved that, if a flow impinges on any two parallel plates at any angle such that the trailing jet at downstream infinity is parallel to the velocity of the approaching flow, then the total normal pressure on both plates is the same as if the plates were joined together. In other words, the pressure on these two plates is determined by Rayleigh's Eq. (3.11), where the length ℓ is taken as the sum of the plate lengths.

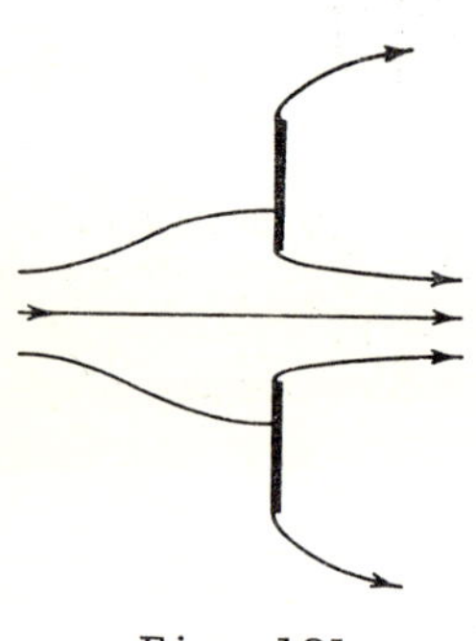

Fig. 121

Other generalizations of Fig. 117 are possible, too. In Fig. 122, we show a flow around a plate set perpendicular to the channel walls between which the jet flows.* This problem's solution is given by Birkhoff and Zarantonello [5]. Their

*Of course, it is possible to consider even more general problems. For example, there is the symmetric problem wherein a

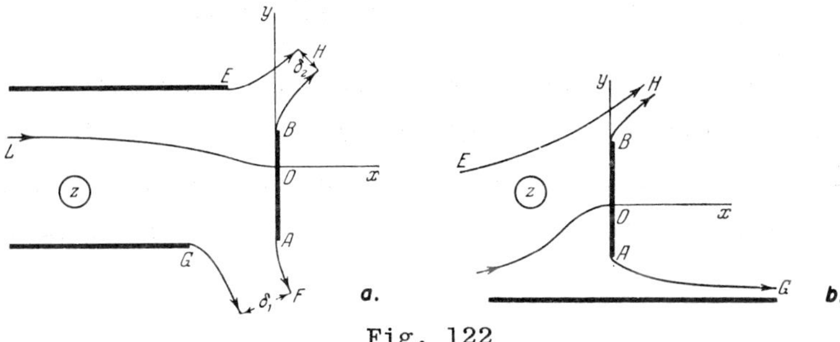

Fig. 122

presentation is based on the use of elliptic functions, which is not absolutely necessary. Tseitlin's somewhat different method also leads easily to a solution and is presented here.

Clearly, the region of change of the nondimensional velocity (Fig. 119) is the same for the general case (Fig. 122a) as for the particular problem solved above. Thus, the ζ-plane mapping to the upper half of the u-plane (Figs. 120a and 120b) is given by Eq. (6.38) or its variations, Eqs. (6.39) and (6.40). Therefore, we need only to find dw/du such that it has simple poles at the infinitely distant points $F(u = -1/f)$, $H(u = 1/h)$, and $L(u = \ell)$ and a first-order zero at the critical point $O(u = 0)$, where the streamlines bifurcate. On extending dw/du to the entire u-plane, we do not obtain any new zeros or poles, and accordingly we can then write

---

jet approaches a rectangular vessel that is located perpendicular to the flow; or the problem wherein the jet flows from a channel with parallel walls and approaches an inclined plate or even an asymmetric wedge (see, e.g., [106]). However, in the present section, as the reader may have noticed, we are interested only in these problems with a general solution that can be obtained in a simple final form.

$$\frac{dw}{du} = \frac{Nu}{[u + (1/f)][u - (1/h)](u - \ell)} , \tag{6.52}$$

where N is a real constant, which can be determined if the width δ_1 of the jet F is given. Integrating Eq. (6.52) along an infinitesimal semicircle around F in the u-plane and considering that the flowrate in the jet F in equal to $v_o\delta_1$, leads us to

$$N = \frac{v_o\delta_1(h + f)(1 - f\ell)}{\pi f h} . \tag{6.53}$$

We shall consider now several particular cases. If we set $f = 1$, then points G and F coincide and the wall LG becomes the bottom of a flow that extends to infinity in both directions. We shall also set $\ell = 1$; then points E and L coincide and the entire upper wall disappears (Fig. 122b)—i.e., we have a finite-width jet flow around a plate, where the jet is bounded on the lower side by the bottom wall. For this problem we obtain, from Eqs. (6.52) and (6.53),

$$\frac{dw}{du} = \frac{2v_o\delta_1(1 + h)u}{\pi h(u^2 - 1)[u - (1/h)]} . \tag{6.54}$$

By integrating along an infinitesimal semicircle around the point $u = 1/h$, we now easily find that the width of the upper jet H is

$$\delta_2 = \frac{2\delta_1}{h - 1} . \tag{6.55}$$

When $h = 1$ the jet width δ_2 becomes infinite and we return to the solution of the problem studied at the beginning of this section [see Eq. (6.37)].

From Eqs. (6.38) and (6.54) we find by an integration that ℓ, which is the length of the plate AB, is

$$\ell = \frac{2\delta_1(1 + h)}{\pi(m^2 - 1)^{1/2} h} \int_{-1/m}^{1/m} \frac{(1 - u^2)^{1/2} + (1 - m^2u^2)^{1/2}}{(u^2 - 1)[u - (1/h)]} du . \tag{6.56}$$

The above integral, evaluated by well-known procedures, becomes

$$\ell = \frac{2\delta_1(1 + h)}{\pi(m^2 - 1)^{1/2} h} \left\{ \frac{\pi(m^2 - 1)^{1/2}}{h^2 - 1} + \frac{\pi h^2}{1 - h^2}\left(\frac{m^2}{h^2} - 1\right)^{1/2} - \frac{h}{(h^2 - 1)^{1/2}} \ln \frac{(m^2 - 1)^{1/2} - (h^2 - 1)^{1/2}}{(m^2 - 1)^{1/2} + (h^2 - 1)^{1/2}} \right\} . \tag{6.57}$$

If θ_o denotes the angle formed at infinity by the jet H and the x-axis, then, from Eq. (6.44), after some simple transformations, we have (with $u = 1/h$)

$$\exp\left[-i\theta_o\right] = \frac{(m^2 - h^2)^{1/2}}{(m^2 - 1)^{1/2}} - i\,\frac{(h^2 - 1)^{1/2}}{(m^2 - 1)^{1/2}} ,$$

from which it follows that

$$\cos\theta_o = \frac{(m^2 - h^2)^{1/2}}{(m^2 - 1)^{1/2}} ; \qquad \sin\theta_o = \frac{(h^2 - 1)^{1/2}}{(m^2 - 1)^{1/2}} ;$$

$$\tan\theta_o = \frac{(h^2 - 1)^{1/2}}{(m^2 - h^2)^{1/2}} . \tag{6.58}$$

By using Eqs. (6.55) and (6.58), we find from Eq. (6.57)

$$\ell = 2\delta_2 \sin^2\left(\frac{\theta_o}{2}\right)\left[1 + \frac{2}{\pi}\cot\left(\frac{\theta_o}{2}\right)\ln\tan\left(\frac{\pi}{4} + \frac{\theta_o}{2}\right)\right] . \tag{6.59}$$

By employing the momentum theorem, we find (cf., Section A of this chapter) that the drag X is completely determined by the flow rate $v_o\delta_2$ and the inclination of the upper jet; hence,

$$X = \rho v_o^2\delta_2(1 - \cos\theta_o) ,$$

and the drag coefficient is

$$C_x = \frac{2X}{\rho v_o^2\ell} = \frac{2\delta_2}{\ell}(1 - \cos\theta_o) . \tag{6.60}$$

From Eqs. (6.59) and (6.60) we have finally

$$C_x = \frac{2}{1 + (2/\pi)\cot(\theta_o/2)\ln\tan[(\pi/4) + (\theta_o/2)]} . \tag{6.61}$$

When θ_o approaches 0, Eq. (6.61) transforms, as it should, into Eq. (6.51).

Another simple limiting case is obtained when $f = h = 1$. Then we have a plate that is perpendicular to and asymmetrically located with respect to a pair of channel walls. In Ref. [5] an interesting result is presented—namely, that the drag coefficient of the plate depends only on the ratio v_∞/v_o, where v_∞ is the velocity of the approaching flow at infinity, so that

$$C_x = \frac{1 - (v_\infty/v_0)}{(v_\infty/v_0)^2 \left[1 - 2\{[1 + (v_\infty/v_0)]/\pi\} \arctan (v_\infty/v_0)\right]} \quad . (6.62)$$

C. CASCADE FLOW

We consider now a separated flow about a cascade consisting of equal and parallel flat plates (Fig. 123). The velocity of the approaching flow at infinity is v_∞, and it forms an angle α_0 with the plates. The velocity on the free surfaces of the jets is v_0, and it forms an angle $\alpha_0 - \beta$ with the x-axis at ∞ on the right. The distance between adjacent plates and their relative displacement is completely determined if the vector $\vec{B_1B} = a \exp \{i[(\pi/2) + \alpha_0 - \beta]\}$ (called the period of the cascade) is known.

A particular case of the cascade problem—i.e., when the approaching flow velocity is perpendicular to the cascade

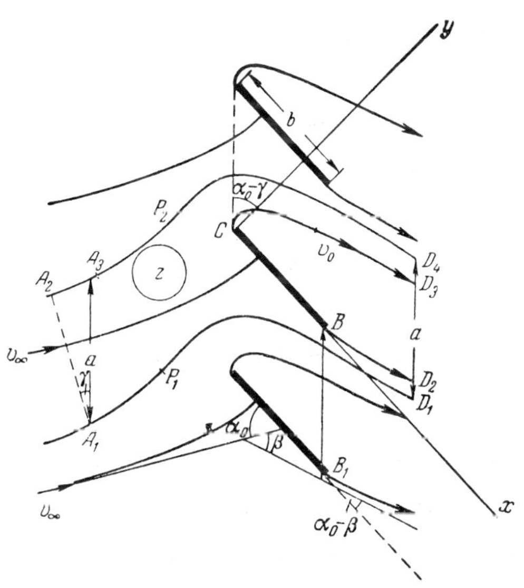

Fig. 123

period—was studied by Zhukovskii [10] in relation to turbine theory. The complete solution to the general problem has been given by Chaplygin and Minakov [109]. However, below we present a simpler solution to the same problem, obtained by Betz and Petersohn [77]. In addition, Betz and Petersohn did not limit themselves to obtaining only theoretical formulas, but also made numerical computations and experimentally confirmed the theory.

To solve the general problem we first introduce

$$\zeta = \frac{dw}{v_o dz} = \frac{v}{v_o} e^{-i\theta} \quad .$$

Now, consider the flow of a fluid between two similar streamlines A_3D_4 and A_1D_1 and the infinitely distant rectilinear sections A_1A_3 and D_1D_4, where $A_1A_3 = D_1D_4 = B_1B$. The appropriate region of change of ζ is the lower half of a unit circle (Fig. 124). On OB, the angle $\theta = 0$; on OC, $\theta = \pi$ and the argument of ζ is $-\pi$. On the lower semicircle BDC, $|\zeta| = 1$ and the argument of ζ changes monotonically from 0 at B to $-\pi$ at C. Some line L* (which joins points A and D) corresponds to the streamlines A_3D_4 and A_1D_1 in Fig. 124. Note that, at those points separated by a period, the velocities are the same, but the complex potentials w are different. Because of this, it is necessary to make a cut along L in the ζ-plane in order to determine w. Thus, for two points located at the same ζ value but on

*The shape of the line L depends on which streamline is chosen as A_1D_1. However, while L can be found after completion of the general solution, there is no necessity to find the shape of L.

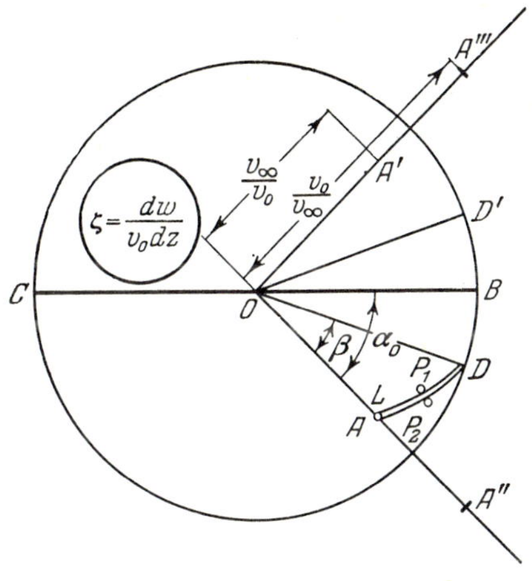

Fig. 124

opposite sides of the cut there are two corresponding points P_1 and P_2 on the streamlines A_3D_4 and A_1D_1, respectively, in the z-plane (Figs. 123 and 124). Clearly, P_1 and P_2 are separated by the distance of a period. The difference in ψ values between P_1 and P_2 is equal to the flowrate q between the streamlines A_3D_4 and A_1D_1—i.e., $q = \psi(P_2) - \psi(P_1) = a\ v_\infty \cos\gamma$ where γ is as indicated in Fig. 123. The difference Γ between the velocity potentials at any points P_1 and P_2 is a constant and is equal to $\Gamma = \varphi(P_2) - \varphi(P_1) = a\ v_\infty \sin\gamma$. Actually, at infinity to the left, the equipotential line is the straight-line segment that is perpendicular to the streamlines. Thus,

$$\Gamma = \varphi(A_3) - \varphi(A_1) = \varphi(A_3) - \varphi(A_2) = a\ v_\infty \sin\gamma \quad .$$

Also, because of the equality of the velocities at P_1 and P_2, it follows that at these points $d\varphi$ is also equal. Finally, then, $\varphi(P_2) - \varphi(P_1)$ is both unknown and equal to $\varphi(A_3) - \varphi(A_1)$. Therefore, under passage around point A in a counterclockwise direction, we go from the upper to the lower side of the cut L, and w increases by $q + i\Gamma$. This means that, at point A--$\zeta = v_\infty/v_o \exp[-i\alpha_o]$, there is a source with discharge q and a vortex with circulation Γ.

Since the semicircle BDC and its diameter COB represent a plate and jet surfaces along which $\psi = \text{const}$, $w(\zeta)$ can be extended by the symmetry principle to the entire

ζ-plane. Then, at

$$A''\left(\zeta = \frac{v_o}{v_\infty}\exp\,[-i\alpha_o]\right), \qquad A'\left(\zeta = \frac{v_\infty}{v_o}\exp\,[i\alpha_o]\right),$$

$$A'''\left(\zeta = \frac{v_o}{v_\infty}\exp\,[i\alpha_o]\right),$$

there are sources with discharge q; at A' and A'' there are also vortices with circulation $-\Gamma$; and at A''' there is a vortex with circulation Γ. The flow from the sources located at A and A'' is absorbed by a sink, located at $D\{\zeta = \exp\,[-i(\alpha_o - \beta)]\}$. Of course, the strength of the sink at D must be twice that of the sources at A and A''. At $D'\{\zeta = \exp\,[i(\alpha_o - \beta)]\}$, which is symmetric with respect to D, there must be a sink with the same strength as the one at D. Now it is easy to construct $w(\zeta)$ from the sources, sinks, and vortices—i.e., from its singularities:*

$$\begin{aligned} w = \frac{q}{2\pi}\,\ln &\left[(\zeta - v_1\exp\,[-i\alpha_o])\left(\zeta - \frac{\exp\,[-i\alpha_o]}{v_1}\right)\right.\\ &\left.\cdot\,(\zeta - v_1\exp\,[i\alpha_o])\left(\zeta - \frac{\exp\,[i\alpha_o]}{v_1}\right)\right]\\ &+ \frac{\Gamma}{2\pi i}\,\ln\frac{(\zeta - v_1\exp\,[-i\alpha_o])\,\{\zeta - (\exp\,[i\alpha_o]/v_1)\}}{\{\zeta - (\exp\,[-i\alpha_o]/v_1)\}\,(\zeta - v_1\exp\,[i\alpha_o])}\\ &- \frac{q}{\pi}\,\ln\left\{(\zeta - \exp\,[-i(\alpha_o - \beta)])\,(\zeta - \exp\,[i(\alpha_o - \beta)])\right\}, \end{aligned} \tag{6.63}$$

*Instead of seeking the unique function $w(\zeta)$, it is also possible to seek its unique derivative that has simple poles at A, A', A'', A''', D, and D' and zeros at B, O, and C, where the conformality of the mapping is violated.

where $q = a\,v_\infty \cos\gamma$, $\Gamma = a\,v_\infty \sin\gamma$, and, for brevity, $v_1 = v_\infty/v_o$ was used. Not all the parameters appearing in Eq. (6.63) are independent. In fact, a relation must exist between them because at 0, where the streamline bifurcates, we must have

$$\left(\frac{dw}{d\zeta}\right)_{\zeta=0} = 0$$

(cf., Chapter I, Section F.4). By differentiating $w(\zeta)$ we are led to

$$\frac{dw}{d\zeta} = \frac{q}{\pi}\left[\frac{\zeta - v_1 \cos\alpha_o}{\zeta^2 + v_1^2 - 2v_1\zeta\cos\alpha_o} + \frac{v_1(v_1\zeta - \cos\alpha_o)}{v_1^2\zeta^2 + 1 - 2v\cos\alpha_o} - \frac{2\zeta - 2\cos(\alpha_o - \beta)}{\zeta^2 + 1 - 2\zeta\cos(\alpha_o - \beta)}\right]$$

$$+ \frac{\Gamma v_1 \sin\alpha_o}{\pi}\left[-\frac{1}{\zeta^2 + v_1^2 - 2v_1\zeta\cos\alpha_o} + \frac{1}{v_1^2\zeta^2 + 1 - 2v_1\zeta\cos\alpha_o}\right]. \tag{6.64}$$

With $\zeta = 0$, $w(0) = 0$ so that

$$0 = \frac{q}{\pi}\left[-\frac{\cos\alpha_o}{v_1} - v_1\cos\alpha_o + 2\cos(\alpha_o - \beta)\right] + \frac{\Gamma v_1 \sin\alpha_o}{\pi}\left(-\frac{1}{v_1^2} + 1\right),$$

from which, by considering that $\Gamma/q = \tan\gamma$, we have

$$2\cos(\alpha_o - \beta) = \left(\frac{1}{v_1} + v_1\right)\cos\alpha_o + \left(\frac{1}{v_1} - v_1\right)\sin\alpha_o \tan\gamma . \tag{6.65}$$

To determine the plate length b, it is necessary to evaluate

$$b = \frac{1}{v_o}\int_{-1}^{1} \frac{v_o dz}{dw}\frac{dw}{d\zeta}\, d\zeta = \frac{1}{v_o}\int_{-1}^{1} \frac{dw}{d\zeta}\frac{d\zeta}{\zeta} , \tag{6.66}$$

where $dw/d\zeta$ is taken from Eq. (6.64). It follows, after many tedious but straightforward operations, that

$$\frac{b}{a} = \frac{1}{\pi}\frac{v_\infty}{v_o}\cos\gamma\left\{\cos(\alpha_o - \beta)\,\ell n\,\frac{1 + \cos(\alpha_o - \beta)}{1 - \cos(\alpha_o - \beta)}\right.$$

$$+ \frac{\cos\alpha_o}{2}\left(\frac{v_\infty}{v_o} + \frac{v_o}{v_\infty}\right)\ell n\,\frac{1 - 2(v_\infty/v_o)\cos\alpha_o + (v_\infty/v_o)^2}{1 + 2(v_\infty/v_o)\cos\alpha_o + (v_\infty/v_o)^2}$$

$$+ \pi\left[\frac{v_o}{v_\infty}\sin\alpha_o - \sin(\alpha_o - \beta)\right]$$

$$\left. + \left(\frac{v_\infty}{v_o} - \frac{v_o}{v_\infty}\right)\sin\alpha_o \arctan\left(2\frac{v_o v_\infty}{v_o^2 - v_\infty^2}\sin\alpha_o\right)\right\}$$

$$+ \frac{1}{\pi}\frac{v_\infty}{v_o}\sin\gamma\left\{\frac{\sin\alpha_o}{2}\left(\frac{v_\infty}{v_o} - \frac{v_o}{v_\infty}\right)\ell n\,\frac{1 + 2(v_\infty/v_o)\cos\alpha_o + (v_\infty/v_o)^2}{1 - 2(v_\infty/v_o)\cos\alpha_o + (v_\infty/v_o)^2}\right.$$

$$\left. + \left(\frac{v_\infty}{v_o} + \frac{v_o}{v_\infty}\right)\cos\alpha_o \arctan\left(\frac{2v_o v_\infty}{v_o^2 - v_\infty^2}\sin\alpha_o\right) - \frac{v_o}{v_\infty}\pi\cos\alpha_o\right\} .$$

With the help of Eq. (6.65) we obtain the simple form

$$\frac{b}{a} = \frac{1}{\pi}\frac{v_\infty}{v_o}\Bigg\{\cos\gamma\cos(\alpha_o - \beta)$$

$$\cdot\ \ell n\left[\frac{1+\cos(\alpha_o-\beta)}{1-\cos(\alpha_o-\beta)}\cdot\frac{1-2(v_\infty/v_o)\cos\alpha_o + (v_\infty/v_o)^2}{1+2(v_\infty/v_o)\cos\alpha_o+(v_\infty/v_o)^2}\right]$$

$$+\left[\frac{v_\infty}{v_o}\sin(\alpha_o+\gamma) - \frac{v_o}{v_\infty}\sin(\alpha_o-\gamma)\right]$$

$$\cdot\ \arctan\left(2\frac{v_\infty v_o}{v_o^2 - v_\infty^2}\sin\alpha_o\right)$$

$$+\ \pi\cos\gamma\left[\frac{v_o}{v_\infty}\sin\alpha_o - \sin(\alpha_o-\beta)\right]\Bigg\} - \cos\alpha_o\sin\gamma\ . \tag{6.67}$$

To determine the normal pressure force Y on the plate we simply apply the momentum theorem in the direction of the B_1B-axis. The mass of fluid considered is that bounded by the streamlines A_3D_4, A_1D_1, CD_3, and BD_2 and by the straight segments A_1A_3, D_1D_2, and D_3D_4. Because of the periodicity of the flow the pressures p on the streamlines A_3D_4 and A_1D_1 cancel each other. The pressures on sections A_1A_3, D_1D_2, and D_3D_4 have no components in the B_1D-direction. During a unit increment of time the fluid mass acquires in its B_1B-direction component an increase of momentum of

$$-\rho q[v_\infty \sin\gamma + v_o\sin(\beta-\gamma)] = -\rho a v_\infty\cos\gamma$$
$$\cdot\ [v_\infty\sin\gamma + v_o\sin(\beta-\gamma)]\ .$$

The projection of $-Y$ onto the B_1B-axis is

$$-Y \cos(\alpha_o - \gamma) \quad .$$

Therefore, according to the momentum theorem,

$$Y = \rho a v_\infty^2 \cos\gamma \, \frac{\sin\gamma + (v_o/v_\infty)\sin(\beta - \gamma)}{\cos(\alpha_o - \gamma)} \quad . \tag{6.68}$$

Application of the momentum theorem for some other axial direction—e.g., the x-axis—must produce a result that reduces to Eq. (6.68). It is apparent then that finding the complete solution to the hydrodynamical problem was necessary primarily for the determination of the ratio b/a [see Eq. (6.67)].

Betz and Petersohn wrote the normal force coefficient in the form

$$C_y = \frac{2Y}{\rho v_o^2 b} = \frac{2a}{b}\,\frac{v_\infty}{v_o}\,\frac{\cos\gamma}{\cos(\alpha_o - \gamma)}\left[\frac{v_\infty}{v_o}\sin\gamma + \sin(\beta - \gamma)\right] \quad . \tag{6.69}$$

Their results—obtained from Eqs. (6.65), (6.67), and (6.69)—are shown in Fig. 125.

The interesting limiting case, when the length of the cascade elements is infinite (Fig. 126), can be computed without solving the hydrodynamical problem. In this case $\beta = \alpha_o$. Now, from Eq. (6.65), by solving the quadratic equation with $v_o/v_\infty > 1$, $0 < \alpha_o < \pi/2$, and $0 < \alpha < \pi/2$, we find

$$\frac{v_o}{v_\infty} = \frac{\cos\gamma + \sin\alpha_o}{\cos(\alpha_o - \gamma)} \quad . \tag{6.70}$$

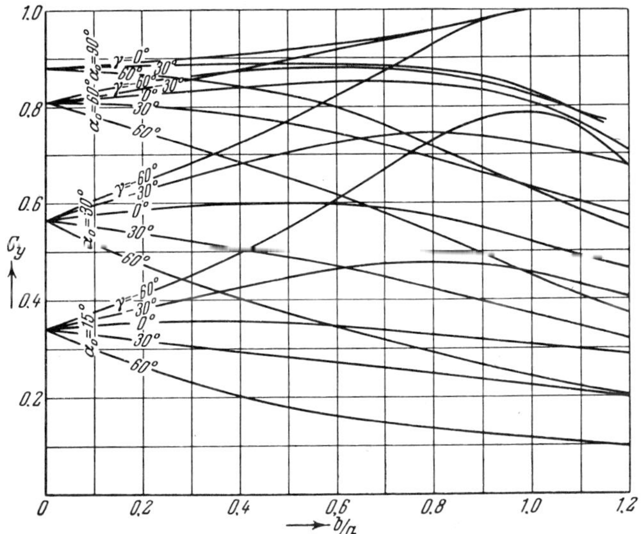

Fig. 125

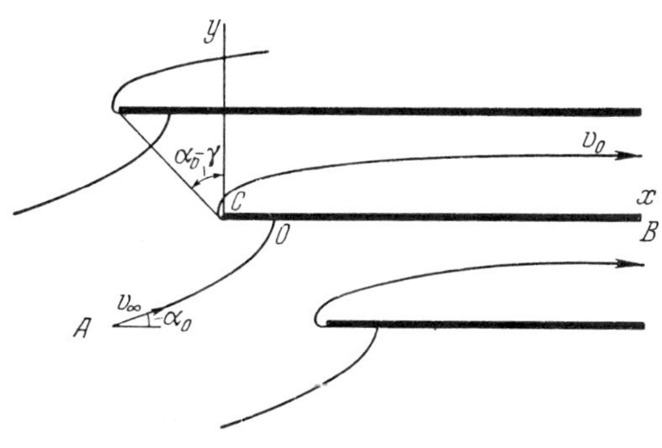

Fig. 126

From Eqs. (6.68) and (6.70) we obtain

$$Y = \rho a v_\infty^2 \left[1 + \sin(\alpha_o - \gamma)\right] \frac{\cos\gamma \sin\alpha_o}{\cos^2(\alpha_o - \gamma)} . \quad (6.71)$$

If α_0 and γ are small, then

$$Y \approx \rho a v_\infty^2 \alpha_0 \quad . \tag{6.72}$$

As noted above, Betz and Petersohn [77] carried out special experiments to verify their theoretical formulas. They measured v_∞/v_0 as a function of the other parameters, explained the physics, and showed experimentally that the jet-theory results agree well with real flow of water into air or with actual separated cavitational flows (see, e.g., Figs. 127a and 127b). In the case of an air flow around a

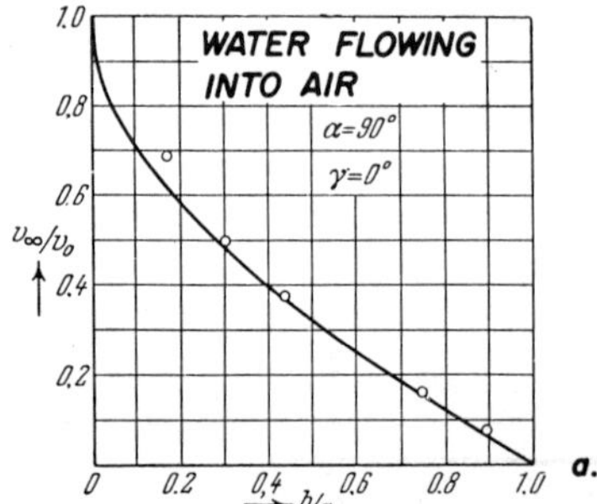

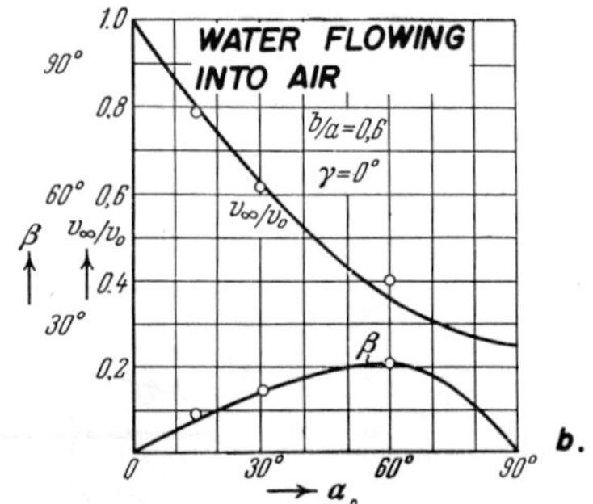

Fig. 127

cascade or a water flow without fully developed cavitation, the boundary conditions on the jet surfaces are not satisfied (along the jet surfaces a mixture of the uniform fluid masses occurs) and the results of the theory, as shown by the Betz and Petersohn experiments, are substantially different from those of the experiments. In Figs. 128 we show a sample of Betz's and Petersohn's graphs, to illustrate the above conclusions. Figure 129 demonstrates that, for the special case of an air flow (into air) around a cascade with $\gamma = 0$ and the flow normal to the cascade elements, the theory gives satisfactory results if the distance between the elements is small.

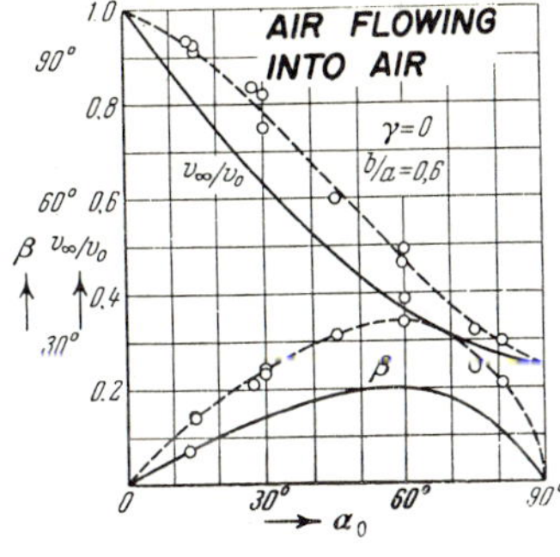

Fig. 128

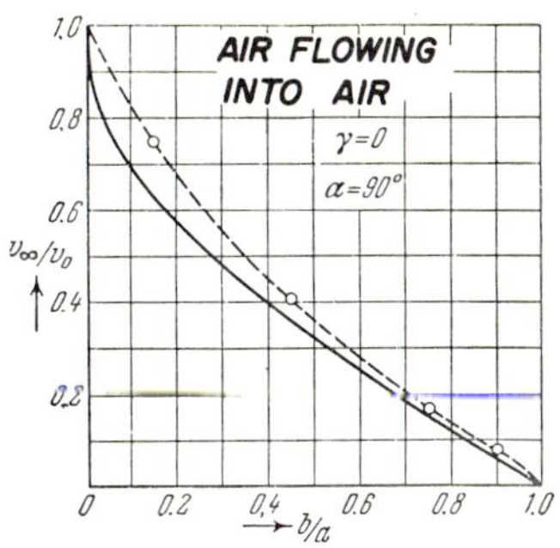

Fig. 129

The cascade analyses have direct application to the theory of water turbines and pumps (e.g., [110]), and extensions of the above problem have been made by many authors. Lambin [111] and Ernst [112] studied cascades formed by wedges in lieu of flat plates. The latter gave, in particular, an approximate equation for the forces acting on thick cascades formed by flat plates. A theory can also be developed for jet flow about curvilinear cascades; more will be said later about this problem.

Akhiezer [113] examined flow about flat-plate cascades under the assumption that the flow separates from one sharp edge but flows around the other and separates on the back side of the cascade plate (i.e., the Chaplygin and Lavrentiev scheme). The more general case of arbitrary separation of both jets from the back side of the cascade plate was the object of studies by Belenkii and Zelenskii [114].

Sedov's method (Chapter IV, Section D) can also be generalized to the case of a cascade formed by curvilinear plates. A complete explanation of the method is found in Sedov's monograph [24]. Here only the formulas that give the general solution of the problem are presented.

Assume that a cascade is formed by a translation of one element AB through a whole number of periods $L + iH$ (Fig. 130). The jets separate from the ends of the arc AB. The approaching flow has a velocity v_∞ that is parallel with the x-axis at $x = -\infty$. The velocity on the surface of the jets is constant, equal in magnitude to v_0, and at $x = \infty$ forms an angle θ_2 with the x-axis. The flow region is mapped on the upper half-plane of the parametric variable u. The critical point E corresponds to a value $u = \epsilon$ (Fig. 131); the element AB corresponds to the segment $0 \leqq u \leqq b$; and the surfaces of the jets BC and CA correspond to the segments $b \leqq u \leqq c$ and $c \leqq u \leqq \pi$. Point $D(x = -\infty)$ corresponds to $\operatorname{Im} u = +\infty$. The angle of inclination of the cascade element with the horizontal is β; the angle θ between the velocity and the x-axis on the segment $(0,\epsilon)$ is $\theta = \beta - \pi$ and on the segment (ϵ, b) is $\theta = \beta$.

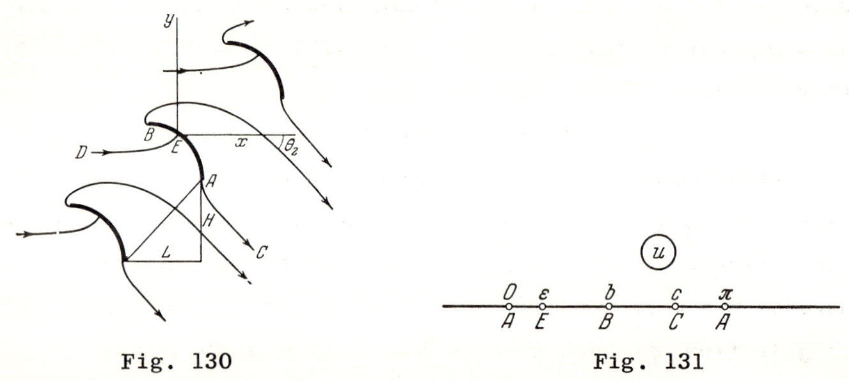

Fig. 130

Fig. 131

The complex potential $w(u)$ is given by

$$w(u) = -Nu \cos (c - \epsilon) + N \sin (\epsilon - c) \ln \sin (u - c) + \text{const.} \tag{6.73}$$

After application of the Sedov-Keldysh (or Hilbert inversion) formula [66] and evaluation of several integrals, dw/dz (the complex velocity) can be obtained in the form

$$\frac{dw}{dz} = v_o \frac{\{[\sin (b - \epsilon)]/\sin \epsilon\}^{1/2} - \{[\sin (\epsilon - u)]/\sin u\}^{1/2}}{\{[\sin (b - \epsilon)]/\sin \epsilon\}^{1/2} + \{[\sin (b - u)]/\sin u\}^{1/2}}$$

$$\cdot \exp \left[- \frac{[\sin u \sin (b - u)]^{1/2}}{\pi} \right.$$

$$\left. \cdot \int_0^b \frac{\beta (\xi) \, d\xi}{\sin n (\xi - u) \, [\sin \xi \sin (b - \xi)]^{1/2}} \right] . \qquad (6.74)$$

The magnitudes N and $\epsilon - c$ are determined from the relation

$$L + iH = -\pi \frac{N}{v_\infty} \exp [i(\epsilon - c)] \ .$$

The values of $\ell n(v_o/v_\infty)$, θ_2, and the thickness of the jet are determined through the mapping parameters.

To determine $\beta(\xi)$, when the radius of curvature R of an element is given as $R(\beta)$, Sedov gives a very complex integro-differential equation

$$R(\beta) \frac{d\beta}{du} = \frac{N}{v_o} \frac{\sin (u - \epsilon)}{\sin (c - u)}$$

$$\cdot \frac{\{[\sin (b - \epsilon)]/\sin \epsilon\}^{1/2} + \{[\sin (b - u)]/\sin u\}^{1/2}}{\{[\sin (b - \epsilon)]/\sin \epsilon\}^{1/2} - \{[\sin (b - u)]/\sin u\}^{1/2}}$$

$$\cdot \exp \left[\frac{[\sin u \sin (b - u)]^{1/2}}{\pi} \right.$$

$$\left. \cdot \text{V.P.} \int_0^b \frac{\beta (\xi) \, d\xi}{\sin (\xi - u) \, [\sin \xi \sin (b - \xi)]^{1/2}} \right] .$$

While to this point we have discussed only cascades formed by a series of repeated contours, it is possible to develop a problem for jet flow about a cascade formed by several series of profiles. For example, Stepanov [115] examined the jet flow around a cascade formed by two series of curvilinear profiles.

D. A CYLINDER BETWEEN TWO WALLS

Figure 132 shows a jet flow around a circular cylinder that is symmetrically placed between two parallel walls. We shall described Berman's solution [116] to this problem for determination of the cylinder's drag.

Because of the flow symmetry, we need to consider only the lower half of the flow, replacing the axis of symmetry x by a solid wall. The regions of change of dw/du, where w is an arbitrary complex potential, and $\omega = \ln\,[dw/v_o dz]$, where v_o is the velocity on the free surface, are mapped onto the upper right quadrant of the plane of the auxiliary variable u (Fig. 133). The function $w(u)$ has logarithmic singularities at $A(u = a)$ and $D(u = \infty)$. Setting $w = 0$ at B leads to $\operatorname{Im} w = 0$ everywhere on the boundary ABCD. Then, on the basis of the symmetry principle, $w(u)$ must also have a logarithmic infinity at $A'(u = -a)$. To make $w(u)$ single-valued in the u-plane, cuts have to be made along parts AD

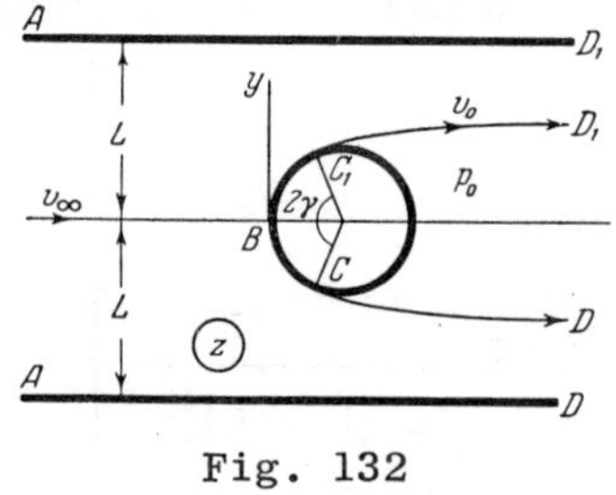

Fig. 132

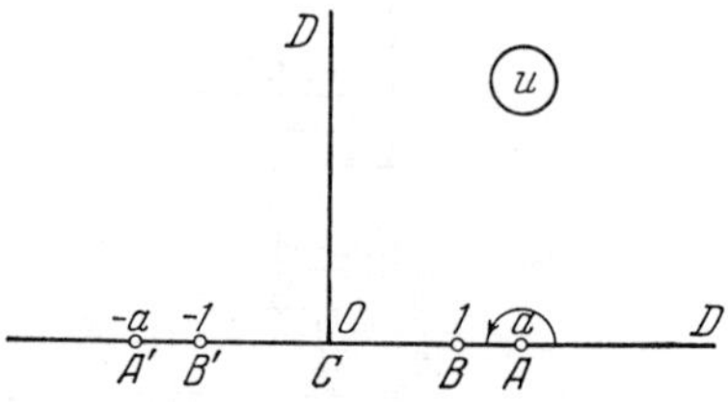

Fig. 133

and A'D of the real axis. However, it is not necessary for us to know $w(u)$, but only its derivative dw/du, which is already single-valued in u and has simple poles at A and A'. At infinity, dw/du is of the order of $1/u$. In addition, because the conformality of the mapping is violated at $C(u = 0)$, dw/du has a simple zero there. Now, knowing all the zeros and poles of dw/du, we may write

$$\frac{dw}{du} = N \frac{u}{u^2 - a^2} \quad . \tag{6.75}$$

The constant N can be determined from the condition that the jet's discharge is $q = Lv_\infty$, where v_∞ is the velocity of the approaching flow at infinity and $2L$ is the channel width (Fig. 132). Computing $\int (dw/du)du = iq$ with the help of Eq. (6.75), counterclockwise along an infinitesimal semicircle (Fig. 133), we find $iq = N\pi i/2$; thus,

$$\frac{dw}{du} = \frac{2q}{\pi} \frac{u}{u^2 - a^2} \quad . \tag{6.76}$$

On part BAD of the real axis, the angle $\theta = 0$. On the imaginary axis of u, corresponding to the free surface CD, $v = v_o$ and $\mathrm{Re}\, \omega = \mathrm{Re}\, [\ell n\, (v/v_o) - i\theta] = 0$. On extending $\omega(u)$ to the entire upper half-plane, we find that, on the real axis, θ is an even function of u. As a result, on DA'B' $\theta = 0$. If $\theta(u)$ were known in $-1 < u < 1$ also, then $\omega(u)$ could be determined in the upper half-plane by using the Schwarz formula,

$$\omega(u) = \frac{1}{\pi} \int_{-1}^{1} \frac{-\theta\ (\xi)\ d\xi}{\xi - u} \quad . \tag{6.77}$$

We now expand $\theta(\xi)$ on the segment $(-1,1)$ in the form

$$\theta(\xi) = -\left[\frac{\pi}{2} + (1 - \xi^2)^{1/2}\left(A_o + A_2\xi^2 + A_4\xi^4 + \ldots + A_{2n}\xi^{2n}\right)\right] , \tag{6.78}$$

where A_o, A_1, ..., A_{2n} are some constant coefficients. The shape of the contour is varied by changing the coefficients. Clearly, $\theta(1) = -\pi/2$. Introducing Eq. (6.78) into Eq. (6.77) and performing the indicated integration gives

$$\begin{aligned}\omega(u) = {} & \frac{1}{2}\,\ell n\,\frac{u - 1}{u = 1} + (u^2 - 1)^{1/2}\left(A_o + A_2u^2 + \ldots + A_{2n}u^{2n}\right) \\ & - (A_o\alpha_o + A_2\alpha_2 + \ldots + A_{2n}\alpha_{2n})u \\ & - (A_2\alpha_o + A_4\alpha_2 + \ldots + A_{2n}\alpha_{2n-2})u^3 - \ldots \\ & - (A_{2n-2}\alpha_o + A_{2n}\alpha_2)u^{2n-1} - A_{2n}\alpha_o u^{2n+1} ,\end{aligned} \tag{6.79}$$

where $\alpha_o = 1$ and

$$\alpha_{2k} = \frac{(-1)^k}{k!}\,\frac{1}{2}\left(\frac{1}{2} - 1\right)\ldots\left(\frac{1}{2} - k + 1\right) \qquad (k = 1,\ 2,\ \ldots,\ n) .$$

Clearly, Eq. (6.79) has the desired properties, since with $|u| > 1$, $\mathrm{Im}\ \omega = 0$, and with $|u| < 1$,

$$\mathrm{Im}\ \ \omega(u) = -\theta(u) = \frac{\pi}{2} + [1 - u^2]^{1/2}\left(A_o + A_2u^2 + \ldots + A_{2n}u^{2n}\right).$$

By expanding $(u^2 - 1)^{1/2}$ in powers of $1/u$, we may observe that $\omega(\infty) = 0$.

With $A_o = A_2 = \ldots = A_{2n} = 0$, Eqs. (6.76) and (6.79) give a solution for a symmetric flow around a flat plate located between two walls. But, just as in the problem of an infinite jet flow around a circular cylinder (Chapter IV, Section B), it is possible to choose the coefficients A_o, ..., A_{2n} so that the contour in the flow does not differ appreciably from a circle. For determination of the (n+1) coefficients $A_o, \ldots, A_{2n}$, n conditions are obtained by prescribing the curvature at n points on the circle in the flow.

One final condition must be satisfied: the curvature of the jet $|d\theta/ds|$ at the separation point $C(u = 0)$ must be finite. We may derive this condition. On CD, $\omega = -i\theta$ so $id\omega = d\theta$. At C, $id\omega = [\omega'(u)]_{u=0}\, du$ and

$$[\omega'(u)]_{u=0} = -1 - (A_o\alpha_o + A_2\alpha_2 + \ldots + A_{2n}\alpha_{2n}) \ . \quad (6.80)$$

On the other hand, on CD the differential distance along the arc is

$$ds = |dz| = \left|\frac{e^{-\omega}\,dw}{v_o}\right| = \left|\frac{dw}{v_o}\right| = \left|\frac{2q}{\pi v_o}\,\frac{u\,du}{u^2 - a^2}\right| \ ;$$

thus, with $u = 0$ we have $ds = 0$. In order to have $\lim |d\theta/ds| \neq \infty$ at point C (in passing to the limit we move along the upper imaginary semi-axis of u), it is necessary that at C, $d\omega = 0$—i.e., $[\omega'(u)]_{u=0} = 0$. This is the final condition we sought and in accordance with Eq. (6.80), can be written in the form

$$A_o\alpha_o + A_2\alpha_2 + \ldots + A_{2n}\alpha_{2n} = -1 \ . \quad (6.81)$$

To obtain the remainder of the conditions for determining the unknown coefficients, we find the radius of curvature $R = |ds/d\theta| = |dz/d\theta|$ at an arbitrary point of the arc BC. Using Eqs. (6.76), (6.78) and (6.79), we easily find

$$R(u) = \frac{2Lv_\infty}{\pi v_o}$$

$$\cdot \frac{u(1+u)\exp\left[u\sum_{k=0}^{n} A_{2k}\alpha_{2k} + u^3\sum_{k=1}^{n} A_{2k}\alpha_{2k-2} + \cdots + A_{2n}\alpha_o u^{2n+1}\right]}{(a^2-u^2)\left|(1-u^2)\left(-\sum_{k=1}^{n} A_{2k}u^{2k-1}\right) + u\sum_{k=0}^{2n} A_{2k}u^{2k}\right|} \tag{6.82}$$

where $0 \leqq u \leqq 1$.

If we had the exact solution to the problem of a flow around a circular cylinder, then the following equation would be satisfied

$$R(u) = R_o \qquad 0 \leqq u \leqq 1 \ . \tag{6.83}$$

where R_o is the radius of the circle. As noted above, in the approximate solution of the problem it is possible to satisfy Eq. (6.83) only at a finite number of points. Berman [116] studied the first two approximations. In the first approximation $(n = 1)$, Eq. (6.83) was replaced by

$$R(0) = R(1) \ , \tag{6.84}$$

and the coefficients A_o and A_2 were determined from Eqs. (6.81) and (6.84). In the second approximation $(n = 2)$, the condition

$$R(1) = R\left(\frac{1}{2}\right) \tag{6.85}$$

was added to Eq. (6.84), and the coefficients A_o, A_2, and A_4 were determined from Eqs. (6.81), (6.84), and (6.85).

In the first approximation $R(u)$ was within 4 percent of $R(1)$. In the second, $R(u)$ and $R(1)$ were equal to two significant figures.

Equation (6.6) (for the drag of a symmetric contour in a jet flow partly enclosed by a channel) may be used to calculate the contour drag X. Since the present contour (the cylinder) is completely surrounded by the channel, the downstream jets are parallel to the channel walls at infinity; thus, in Eq. (6.6), $\theta_o = 0$ for this case. As a result, we obtain

$$X = \rho L v_\infty^2 \left(\frac{v_o}{v_\infty} - 1 \right)^2 . \tag{6.86}$$

The drag coefficient is then

$$C_x = \frac{X}{\rho R_o v_\infty^2} = \frac{L}{R_o} \left(\frac{v_o}{v_\infty} - 1 \right)^2 . \tag{6.87}$$

To determine C_x, one must first find v_o/v_∞. This ratio is easily ascertained from Eq. (6.79), if we set $u = a$ and condition (6.81) is used; thus

$$\begin{aligned} \frac{v_o}{v_\infty} &= e^{-\omega(a)} \\ &= \left(\frac{a+1}{a-1} \right)^{1/2} \exp \left[-(a^2 - 1)^{1/2} \left(A_o + A_2 a^2 + \dots + A_{2n} a^{2n} \right) \right. \\ &\quad \left. - a + (A_2 \alpha_o + A_4 \alpha_2 + \dots + A_{2n} \alpha_{2n-2}) a^3 + \dots + A_{2n} \alpha_o a^{2n+1} \right] . \end{aligned} \tag{6.88}$$

From v_o/v_∞, we also obtain easily the cavitation number $Q = v_o^2/v_\infty^2 - 1$ [see Eq. (5.2)]. Finally, the central angle 2γ of the arc CBC, around which the flow passes (Fig. 132), is obtained from Eq. (6.78):

$$2\gamma = \pi + 2\theta(0) = -2A_o \quad . \tag{6.89}$$

The results of Berman's computations [116] are given in Table 23.*

TABLE 23

Q	First Approximation			Second Approximation
	γ (deg	min)	C_x	C_x
2.113	63	25	1.580	---
1.686	61	29	1.386	---
1.233	59	14	1.155	1.186
0.894	57	45	0.967	---
0.759	57	09	0.893	---
0.437	55	57	0.714	0.729
0.307	55	35	0.645	---
0.142	55	14	0.559	---
0.112	55	11	0.544	---
0	55	07	0.488	0.501

Comparison of the C_x results from the first and second approximations shows that there is very little difference between them. A graphical representation of the tabulated C_x results was given earlier in Fig. 92.

*In his dissertation, defended in 1949 at the Institute of Mechanics of the Academy of Sciences of USSR, Berman also included computations of the drag on an ellipse in a channel.

From Fig. 92 it follows that the dependence of C_x on Q, obtained in the Efros model, differs only slightly from the relation obtained by Berman for the cylinder between walls. Thus, the drag coefficient of the cylinder depends on the distance between walls only when this distance influences the cavitation number of the flow. In other words, if the flow cavitation numbers are equal, the drag coefficient C_x is virtually independent of the distance between walls, be it infinite or infinite. As we shall see later, the same result holds for cavitating flow about a flat plate that is normal to the flow. Finally, but to a lesser degree of accuracy, the same thing can be said for flow past a symmetric wedge.

Now, we consider a symmetric jet flow from a channel and about a curvilinear contour (Fig. 134). In particular, we shall examine a very convenient way of obtaining general solutions to jet-theory problems that has been presented in the Birkhoff and Zarantonello monograph [5]. As a region of change of a parametric variable t we use the upper half of the unit circle $|t| \leqq 1$--i.e., $\mathrm{Im}\ t \geqq 0$--and place a cut EHD along the segment $(0 \leqq \mathrm{Im}\ t \leqq h)$ of the imaginary axis (Fig. 135). This cut corresponds to the walls of the channel. The segment HC corresponds to the negative real (x-)axis in

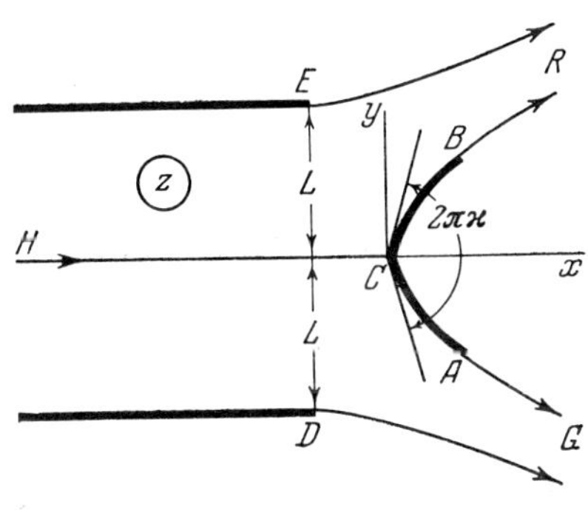

Fig. 134

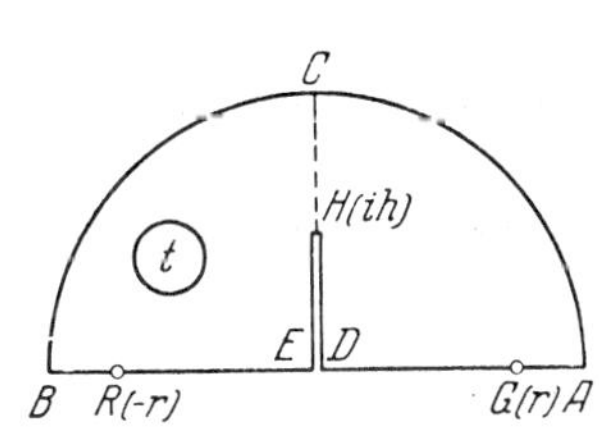

Fig. 135

the physical plane. The circumference of the t-plane semicircle corresponds to the obstacle ACB, and the free surfaces are mapped onto the diameter of the t-plane circle (real axis). The function $dw/v_o dz$, where v_o is the velocity on the free surface, can be given in the form

$$\frac{dw}{v_o dz} = \left(\frac{1 + it}{1 - it}\right)^{2\kappa} \exp\left[-i\Omega(t)\right] \quad , \tag{6.90}$$

where, because of the flow symmetry, $\Omega(t)$ has the form

$$\Omega(t) = c_1 t + c_3 t^3 + c_5 t^5 + \ldots \quad . \tag{6.91}$$

To determine the complex potential, Birkhoff and Zarantonello employ a quarter-circle BREHC (Fig. 135). They first map it onto the quadrant (Fig. 136) of a T-plane

$$T = -\frac{1}{2}\left(t + \frac{1}{t}\right) \quad , \tag{6.92}$$

and then onto the upper half of a τ-plane (Fig. 137)

$$T^2 = \tau \quad . \tag{6.93}$$

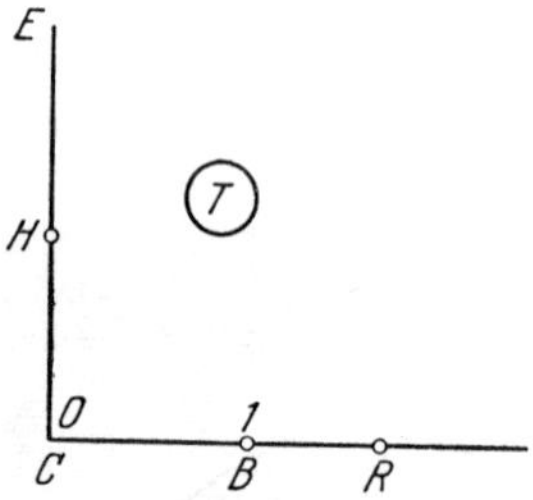

Fig. 136

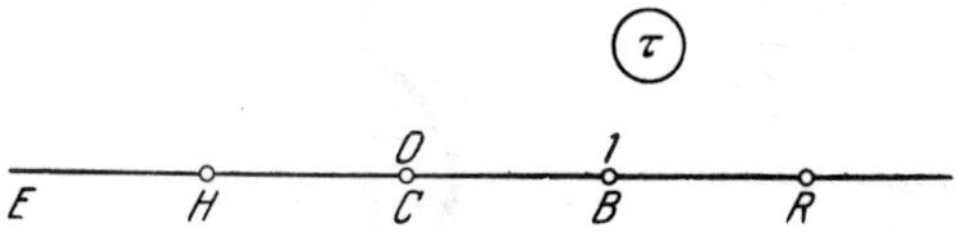

Fig. 137

The complex potential w has logarithmic singularities at points H and R in the upper half-plane. Accordingly,

$dw/d\tau$ has simple poles at these points. By extending $dw/d\tau$ to the entire τ-plane, we find

$$\frac{dw}{d\tau} = \frac{M}{2[1 - (\tau/\tau_H)][1 - (\tau/\tau_R)]} , \tag{6.94}$$

where M is a real constant. Then, we have

$$\frac{dw}{dT} = \frac{MT}{\left[1 - \left(T^2/T_H^2\right)\right]\left[1 - \left(T^2/T_R^2\right)\right]} , \tag{6.95}$$

where $\tau_H = T_H^2 < 0$ and $\tau_R = T_R^2 > 1$ are the values of τ at H and T. Equations (6.90) through (6.92) and (6.95) provide the general solution to the flow past a great class of curvilinear symmetric obstacles. When the cut EHD is reduced to a point $(h = 0)$, we have a free-jet flow around a curvilinear obstacle. When R coincides with E, and G with D $(r = 0$ or $T_R = \infty)$, then we have a solution to the flow past a curvilinear obstacle in a channel--i.e., the solution for a circular cylinder in a channel is obtained from Birkhoff and Zarantonello's method as a particular case. We also note that dw/dT is easily converted into dw/dt by using Eq. (6.92). Of course, dw/dt could also be obtained independently by the singular-point method. To accomplish this, it is sufficient to observe that dw/dt has simple poles at $\pm ih$, $\pm i/h$, $\pm r$, and $\pm 1/r$ and first order zeros at ± 1, $\pm i$, and 0 in the t-plane. Thus, the following expression is obtained

$$\frac{dw}{dt} = \frac{N\,(t^4 - 1)t}{\{t^4 + 1 - t^2[r^2 + (1/r^2)]\}\,\{t^4 + 1 + t^2[h^2 + (1/h^2)]\}} , \tag{6.96}$$

where N is a real constant.

Birkhoff and Zarantonello [5] present computed results for a cylinder in a channel, in a free jet, and in a jet flowing from a channel—see also [117]. Their results for a cylinder in a channel are very close to Berman's results. It is valuable to mention a singularly interesting observation of Birkhoff and Zarantonello. If the drag coefficient C_x of the cylinder is not defined relative to the velocity v_∞ of the approaching flow, but relative to the velocity v_o on the jet—i.e., instead of $C_x = X/\rho R_o v_\infty^2$ consider $C_x^* = C_x\left(v_\infty^2/v_o^2\right) = C_x/(Q + 1)$ than C_x^* has a practically constant value [cf., Eq. (5.20)]. According to their computations, as Q varies from 0 to 1.809, C_x changes from 0.499 to 1.495, while C_x^* varies from 0.499 to 0.532.*

Pykhteev [72] solved the problem of a separated flow around a symmetric contour located between parallel walls, when the flow velocity along the contour is known as a function of arc length. Other analyses of jet flows about arbitrary obstacles in channels are found in Cisotti's monograph [51], the works of Villat [40] and Oudart [68].

E. SYMMETRIC CAVITATING FLOW AROUND A WEDGE IN A CHANNEL

Consider a wedge [98],** defined symmetric to the x-axis, with side lengths ℓ and included angle $2\pi\kappa$, where $0 < \kappa < 1/2$ (Fig. 138). The flow is bounded by walls parallel to the x-axis, and the distance between the walls is $2L$. The velocity of the approaching flow at infinity is $v_\infty = v_o$. Behind the wedge there is a re-entrant jet, and the velocity on the free surfaces is v_o.

---

*Translator's note: See Birkhoff's outline [81] of the principle of stability of the pressure coefficient.

**The particular cases of a wedge and a plate normal to the walls are studied in [118].

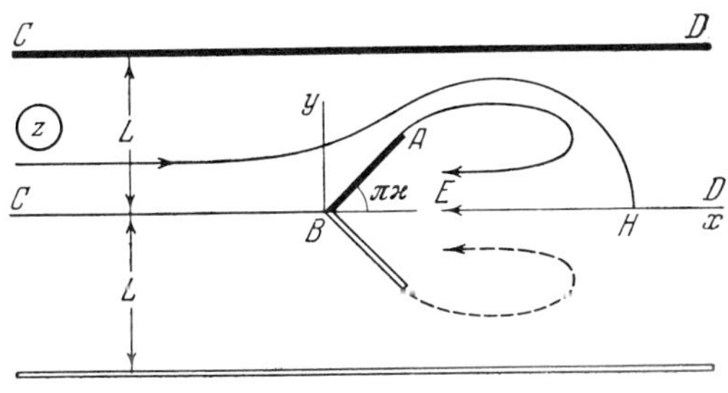

Fig. 138

Because of the symmetry of the flow, it is enough to consider only the upper half of the flow. We map the region of change of the dimensionless complex velocity dw/v_0dz and the derivative of the complex potential w with respect to the parametric variable u onto the upper right quadrant of the u-plane (Fig. 139). The function $w(u)$ has logarithmic singularities at points C, A, and E $(u = c,\ u = d,\ u = 0)$ and, consequently, dw/du has poles at these points. In addition, $dw/du = 0$ at that point $H(u = h)$ where the streamline divides. On the boundaries in the u-plane corresponding to the streamlines, dw/du has either real or purely imaginary values. Thus, dw/du can be extended by the image-mapping principle to the entire u-plane.

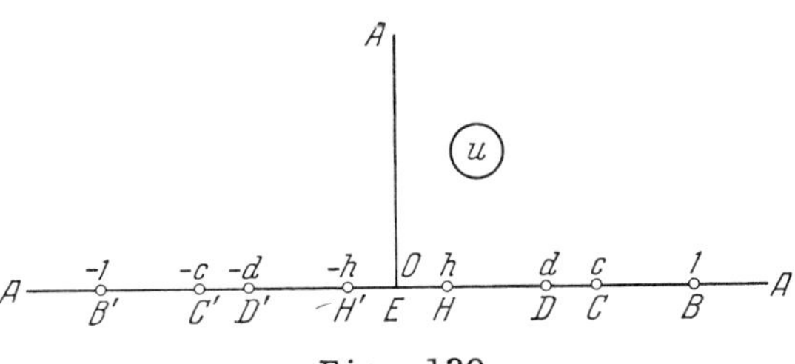

Fig. 139

It is then obvious that the analytically extended function dw/du has a zero at $u = -h$ and poles at $u = -d$ and $u = -c$. Constructing dw/du from knowledge of its zeros and poles, we are led to

$$\frac{dw}{du} = \frac{N\,(u^2 - h^2)}{u(u^2 - d^2)(u^2 - c^2)} \, , \tag{6.97}$$

where N is a real constant.

In the region of flow dw/dz is bounded everywhere, but it does have a simple zero at $H(u = h)$ and a singularity of the type $(u - 1)^{\kappa}$ at $B(u = 1)$. The region of change of $dw/v_o dz$ is bounded partly by straight lines (on BA, BCDH, and HE, the argument of $dw/v_o dz$ is $\pi\kappa$, 0, and π, respectively) and partly by a circular arc (on the free surface $|dw/v_o dz| = 1$). Therefore, by using the image-mapping principle, it is easy to see that $dw/v_o dz$ has a first-order pole at $u = -h$, and at $u = 1$ (the reflection of point B) $dw/v_o dz$ has a singularity of the type $(u + 1)^{-\kappa}$.

We now know all the zeros and singularities of $dw/v_o dz$ in the u-plane and can write

$$\frac{dw}{v_o dz} = \frac{u - h}{u + h}\left(\frac{1 - u}{1 + u}\right)^{\kappa} \, . \tag{6.98}$$

From Eqs. (6.97) and (6.98) it follows that

$$v_o \frac{dz}{du} = N \frac{(u + h)^2}{u(u^2 - d^2)(u^2 - c^2)} \left(\frac{1 + u}{1 - u}\right)^{\kappa} \, . \tag{6.99}$$

When $c = d$, the walls recede to infinity, and a cavity flow results around a wedge in an infinite fluid. When $d = h = 0$, the result is a Kirchhoff flow around a wedge in a channel (an infinite cavity) (see Section A).

The present flow is completely determined by the following parameters:

1. The velocity v_∞ of the approaching flow.
2. The velocity v_o on the jet surface (or the cavitation number Q).

3. The wedge side length ℓ.
4. The distance $2L$ between walls.
5. The included angle $2\pi\kappa$ of the wedge.

Observe then that at our disposal are six parameters appearing in Eqs. (6.97) and (6.98). An extra parameter is present in these equations because in reality they give a more general solution than that presented above. Equations (6.97) - (6.99) are not changed if the distances L_1 between the upper wall and the center line CB and L_2 between the upper wall and DHE are unequal (Fig. 140).

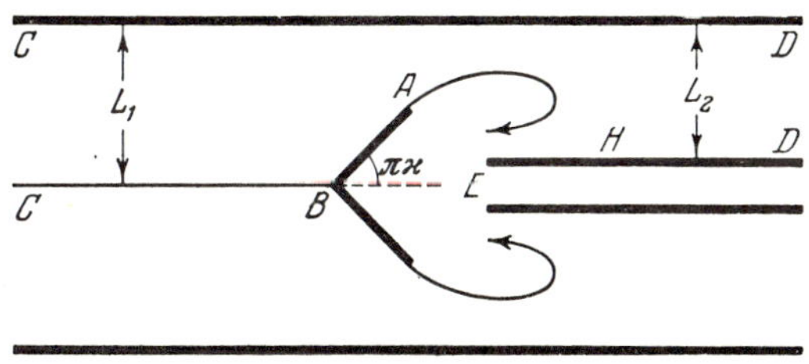

Fig. 140

The condition, expressing that the distances L_1 and L_2 are equal,* permits one to determine h in terms of c and d. Thus, we must require that

$$\operatorname{Im} \int_C \frac{dz}{du}\, du = -\operatorname{Im} \int_D \frac{dz}{du}\, du \quad , \qquad (6.100)$$

where the integrals are taken along infinitesimal semicircles around points C and D. On computing these integrals, we find

*This condition is the same as those uniqueness conditions of Eqs. (5.11) and (5.54) for an unlimited flow about a contour employing the Efros model.

$$\left(\frac{c + h}{c}\right)^2 \left(\frac{1 + c}{1 - c}\right)^\kappa = \frac{(h + d)^2}{d^2} \left(\frac{1 + d}{1 - d}\right)^\kappa \quad , \tag{6.101}$$

from which we easily obtain

$$\frac{c + h}{d + h} = \frac{c}{d}\gamma \; ; \qquad h = \frac{cd(1 - \gamma)}{c\gamma - d} \quad , \tag{6.102}$$

where

$$\left.\begin{aligned} \gamma &= \left(\frac{1 - c}{1 + c}\right)^{\kappa/2} \left(\frac{1 + d}{1 - d}\right)^{\kappa/2} = \left(\frac{\alpha}{\chi}\right)^\kappa \\ \alpha &= \left[\frac{1 - c}{1 + c}\right]^{1/2} , \qquad \chi = \left[\frac{1 - d}{1 + d}\right]^{1/2} \end{aligned}\right\} \quad . \tag{6.103}$$

The cavitation number Q is determined from

$$Q = \frac{v_o^2}{v_\infty^2} - 1 \quad , \tag{6.104}$$

after the introduction of v_o/v_∞ obtained by setting $u = a$ in Eq. (6.98)--i.e.,

$$\frac{v_o}{v_\infty} = \frac{c + h}{c - h}\alpha^{-2\kappa} \quad . \tag{6.105}$$

The half distance between walls L is found by integration of $-idz/du$ over an infinitesimal semicircle around the point $u = c$. Thus,

$$L = -i \int_C \frac{dz}{du}\, du = \frac{\pi N}{2v_o} \frac{(c + h)^2}{c^2(c^2 - d^2)} \alpha^{-2\kappa} \quad . \tag{6.106}$$

On the other hand, the length of the sides is

$$\ell = \exp\,[-\pi i \kappa] \int_1^{\infty} \frac{dz}{du}\,du = \frac{N}{v_o}\,I \quad , \tag{6.107}$$

where

$$I = \int_1^{\infty} \frac{(u+h)^2[(u+1)/(u-1)]^{\kappa}}{u(u^2-d^2)\,(u^2-c^2)}\,du \quad . \tag{6.108}$$

By determining N from Eqs. (6.106) and (6.107), we obtain

$$\frac{\ell}{L} = \frac{2c^2(c^2-d^2)\alpha^{2\kappa}}{\pi(c+h)^2}\,I \quad . \tag{6.109}$$

The integral I can be evaluated in closed form, when $\kappa = m/n$ and m and n are integers. Then, the change of variable $s = (u-1)^{1/n}(u+1)^{-1/n}$ reduces I to an integral of a rational fraction. However, when n is large, it is better to evaluate I numerically.

The wedge drag X can be computed from Eq. (5.16), taking into account the differences in notation between Section B of Chapter V and this section. By comparing Figs. 78 and 138, we see that Eq. (5.16) can conveniently be rewritten in the form

$$X = \rho q \left(v_o + \frac{v_\infty + v_D}{2} \right) \quad , \tag{6.110}$$

where the fluid discharge q in the re-entrant jet [see Eq. (5.15)] is

$$q = 2L(v_\infty - v_D) \quad , \tag{6.111}$$

and the velocity v_D at infinity to the right is easily computed, by using Eq. (6.98), as

$$\frac{v_D}{v_o} = \frac{d - h}{d + h} \chi^{2\kappa} \quad . \tag{6.112}$$

From Eq. (6.110) it is also possible to determine the drag coefficient C_x of the wedge in the channel as

$$C_x = \frac{X}{\rho \ell \sin \pi\kappa v_\infty^2}$$

$$= \frac{L}{\ell \sin \pi\kappa} \left(1 - \frac{v_D}{v_\infty}\right) \left(2 \frac{v_o}{v_\infty} + 1 + \frac{v_D}{v_\infty}\right) \quad . \tag{6.113}$$

The most convenient order of computation using the above results is as follows: 1) given κ, α, χ, find c, d, γ, and h from Eqs. (6.102) and (6.103); 2) determine ℓ/L from Eqs. (6.108) and (6.109); 3) from Eqs. (6.104), (6.105) and (6.112) obtain Q, v_D/v_o, and v_∞/v_o; and 4) from Eq. (6.113) obtain the drag coefficient C_x. The detailed computations for the plane problem were carried out in [118]. In particular, integration of Eq. (6.99) gave the width R and the length T of the cavity. These results of the author's work [118] are shown in Figs. 141a and 141b. For a given ℓ/L, there can be various cavitation numbers Q, the smallest of which is obtained when the base of the re-entrant jet moves off to infinity and the resulting flow is the classical Kirchhoff flow around a plate in a channel. In Fig. 142 the dependence of the smallest possible cavitation number Q_{min} on the ratio ℓ/L is shown. This figure also demonstrates how the distance between the walls influences the cavitation number. However, the results of [118] show that, as in the case of a cylinder (see Section D of this chapter), the distance between the walls influences the drag coefficient of the plate only through the cavitation number. Although the ratios ℓ/L are different in

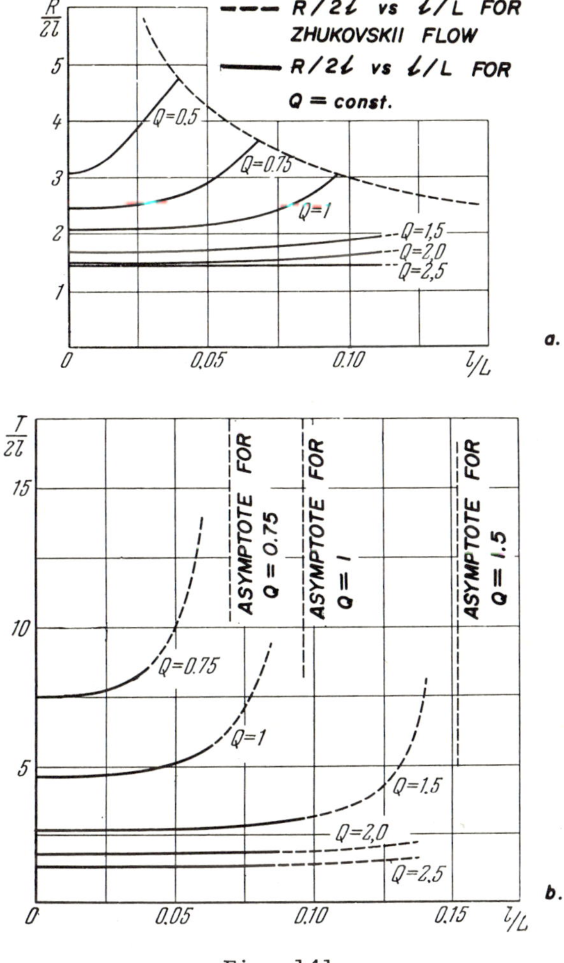

Fig. 141

two flows, C_x is the same if Q is the same. For a wedge, as κ decreases, the influence of the walls on C_x becomes more pronounced. In Fig. 143 are plotted the curves of C_x vs. Q for a wedge of 30 deg included angle, an unlimited flow with a reentrant jet, and a wedge located between parallel walls for the classical Kirchhoff flow (without re-entrant jet) [98]. The results are appreciably different.

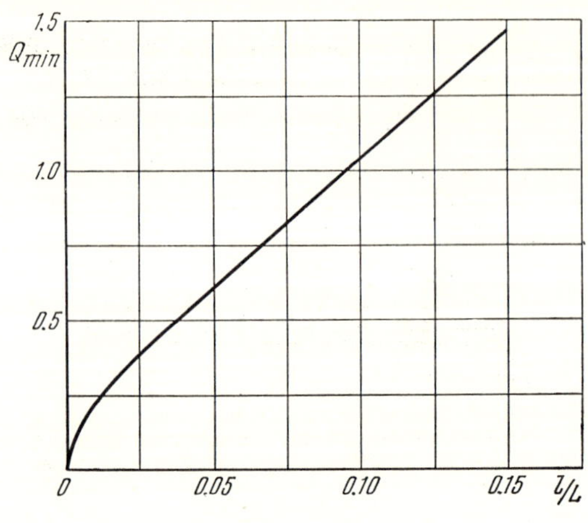

Fig. 142

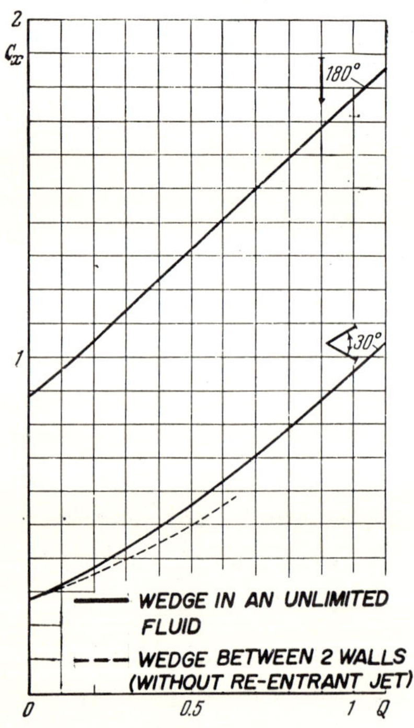

Fig. 143

First reference to the employment of the Riabouchinsky "mirror image" model for cavity flow in a channel is made in Cisotti's monograph [57]. A convenient form for solving such a flow is given by Birkhoff, Plesset, and Simmons [106]. As noted by Birkhoff [81], the Riabouchinsky flow past a wedge in a channel (Fig. 144) was studied by Caywood in 1946. Cavity flow past a plate in a channel, with downstream parallel walls bounding the cavity (Fig. 145), has apparently yet to be studied in detail, but a general solution to an equivalent flow is found in Rethy's old work [21].

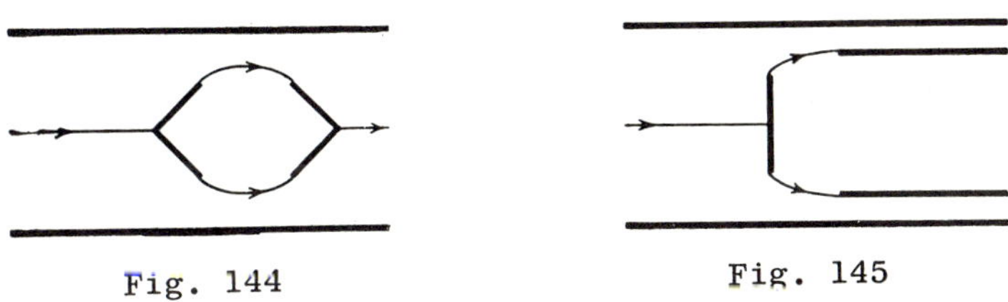

Fig. 144 Fig. 145

The authors of [106, Part II] gave a solution to a symmetric, free-jet flow past a flat plate, employing a "mirror image" flow model (Fig. 146). Their limiting formulas for very small cavitation numbers Q are

$$\left.\begin{aligned} \frac{2}{\delta} &= 1 - \cos\beta + \frac{1}{\pi}\sin\beta\,\ell n\,\frac{1+\sin\beta}{1-\sin\beta} \\ 1 &= \frac{\delta}{Q}\sin\beta \\ a &= \frac{\delta}{Q}(1-\cos\beta) \\ C_x &= \delta(1-\cos\beta) \end{aligned}\right\} . \qquad (6.114)$$

In Eqs. (6.114), β is an auxiliary parameter, the jet fluid discharge is δ, the plate length is 2, and the cavity width is 2a. To the first order in Q—i.e., neglecting higher-order terms—C_x can be equally related to the velocity either of the approaching flow or of the free surface of the cavity.

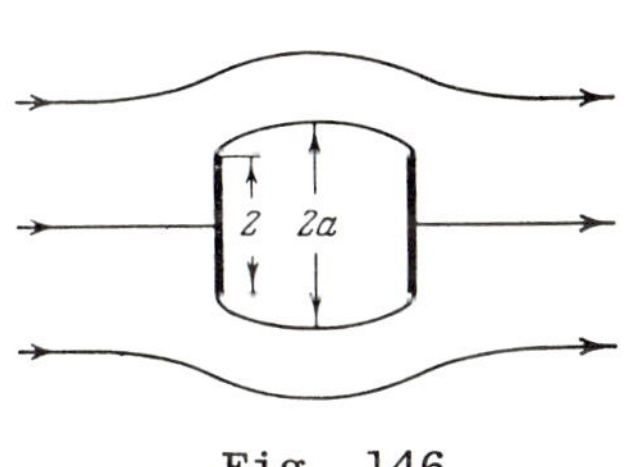

Fig. 146

The linearized theory of symmetric, cavity flow around a wedge with curvilinear sides in a channel is given by Cohen and Gilbert [119].* They employ, in effect, complex function theory and the Keldish-Sedov formula** for a strip to solve the linearized boundary-value problem for the flow.

F. CAVITATING CASCADE FLOW

We present here a general solution to a cavity flow about a cascade. The equations for determining the parameters will not be written in detail because of their complexity. Certain obvious operations have also been omitted.

In Chapter V, three basic cavity-flow models were introduced and examined: 1) the Efros-Gilbarg re-entrant jet model, 2) the Riabouchinsky mirror-image model, and 3) the Zhukovskii-Roshko parallel-wall cavity model. While for flow around a single profile it is possible to employ either the second or third model, they are apparently quite difficult to apply to a cascade flow. In fact, the author is not aware of such an attempt. In any case, use of the latter models requires special analysis.

It is suggested, then, to employ the re-entrant jet model for cascade flow. Figure 147 shows a cascade with period $R + iS$. The flow approaching element RCD of the cascade divides at point C. On FC and CD the profile and flow tangents turn continously. At the critical point C both parts of the contour meet at an angle $2\pi\kappa$. Let us mark in the z-plane a region bounded by two streamlines H'B' and HB that are shifted from one another by a period $R + iS$.

We assume first that the arcs FC and CD are rectilinear segments—i.e., that the cascade is formed by wedges.

*Translator's note: The extensive literature and theory of linearized flow are elegantly summarized by Tulin [120].

**Also known as the Hilbert inversion formula [66].

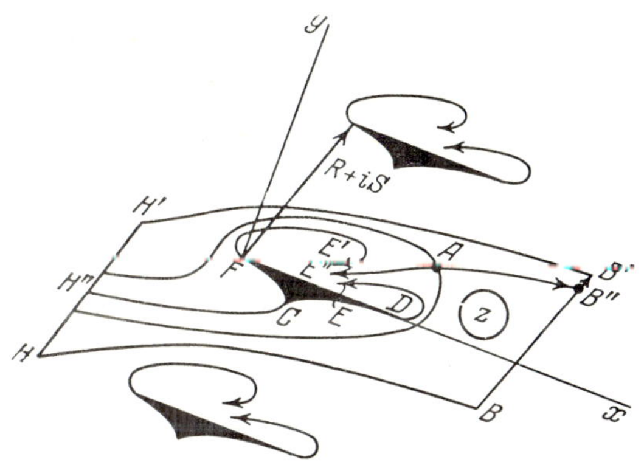

Fig. 147

We denote the complex potential of such a flow as w_{wed}. We shall map the region of change of the dimensionless complex velocity $dw_{wed}/v_0 dz$ onto the upper half of the unit circle in the plane of the parametric variable $\zeta(|\zeta| \leq 1;\ \operatorname{Im} \zeta \geq 0)$ (Fig. 148) so that the free surface of the cavity FED corresponds to the upper-half circumference. The points HH' and BB' at infinity map into the points $H\{\zeta = h \exp[i(\pi - \epsilon)]\}$ and $B\{\zeta = b \exp[i(\pi - \beta)]\}$ in the ζ-plane. At the arbitrary point M on the streamline HB and at the corresponding point M' (streamline H'B'), shifted relative to M by a period $R + iS$, the complex velocities are equal. The streamlines HB and H'B' are represented in the ζ-plane by the two sides

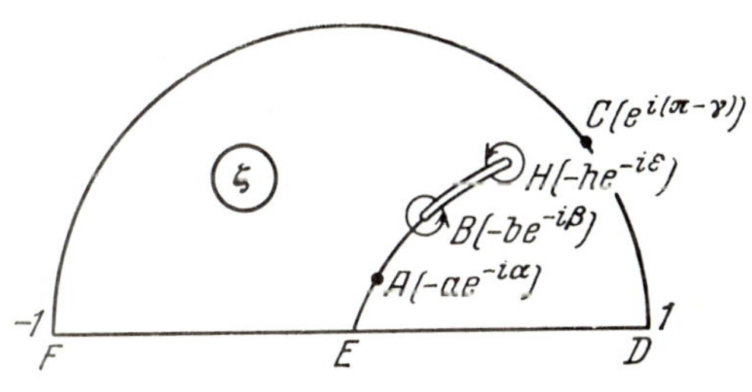

Fig. 148

of the cut joining points H and B.* The function $dw_{wed}/v_o dz$ is single-valued inside the semicircle and has a simple zero at the critical point $A\{\zeta = a \exp[i(\pi - \alpha)]\}$. At the critical point in the corner $C\{\zeta = \exp[i(\pi - \gamma)]\}$ the complex velocity has a singularity of the form $\{\zeta - \exp[i(\pi - \gamma)]\}^{2\kappa}$. On the free surface, FED $|dw_{wed}/v_o dz| = 1$, and on CD and CF the argument $dw_{wed}/v_o dz$ has constant values. Thus, upon extending $dw_{wed}/v_o dz$ analytically to the entire ζ-plane, we find that $dw_{wed}/v_o dz$ at $\zeta = (1/a)\exp[i(\pi - \alpha)]$ has a simple zero; while at $\zeta = (1/a)\exp[i(\pi + \alpha)]$ and $\zeta = a \exp[i(\pi + \alpha)]$ it has simple poles; and at $\zeta = \exp[i(\pi + \gamma)]$, it has a singularity of the form $\{\zeta - \exp[i(\pi + \gamma)]\}^{-2\kappa}$. From these known singularities and zeros of $dw_{wed}/v_o dz$, we can construct

$$\frac{dw_{wed}}{v_o dz} = \frac{(a + \zeta e^{i\alpha})(1 + \zeta a e^{i\alpha})}{(a\zeta + e^{i\alpha})(ae^{i\alpha} + \zeta)} \left(\frac{1 + \zeta e^{i\gamma}}{e^{i\gamma} + \zeta}\right)^{2\kappa} . \qquad (6.115)$$

To obtain the complex velocity $dw/v_o dz$ of the flow around a cascade formed by curvilinear wedges, $dw_{wed}/v_o dz$ can be modified by using the Levi-Civita method and

$$\begin{aligned}\frac{dw}{v_o dz} &= \frac{dw_{wed}}{v_o dz} \exp[i\Omega(\zeta)] \\ &= \frac{(a + \zeta e^{i\alpha})(1 + \zeta a e^{i\alpha})}{(a\zeta + e^{i\alpha})(ae^{i\alpha} + \zeta)} \left(\frac{1 + \zeta e^{i\gamma}}{e^{i\gamma} + \zeta}\right)^{2\kappa} \\ &\quad \cdot \exp\left[ic_1\zeta + ic_2\zeta^2 + ic_3\zeta^3 + \dots\right] , \qquad (6.116)\end{aligned}$$

*After solving the problem it is possible to determine the shape of this cut; however, this step is not necessary and is omitted.

where c_1, c_2, and c_3 are real constants. The function $\Omega(\zeta)$ can also be determined by using Schwarz's formula as Villat did (Chapter IV, Section A). Determination of the coefficients c_1, c_2, ... can be accomplished by the methods presented in Chapter IV.

The complex potential w has logarithmic singularities at $B\{\zeta = b \exp[i(\pi - \beta)]\}$, $H\{\zeta = h \exp[i(\pi - \epsilon)]\}$, and $E(\zeta = 0)$. If $w(\zeta)$ is extended to the entire ζ-plane and we recall that, along the boundaries of the semicircle, $\operatorname{Im} w(\zeta)$ is constant, then we see that $w(\zeta)$ has logarithmic singularities at $\zeta = \infty$, $b \exp[i(\pi + \beta)]$, $(1/b) \exp[i(\pi + \beta)]$, $h \exp[i(\pi + \epsilon)]$, $(1/h) \exp[i(\pi + \epsilon)]$. Therefore, $w(\zeta)$ is not single-valued in the semicircle (Chapter V, Section B). To make w single-valued it is necessary to make cuts along the streamlines AE" and AB" in addition to the cut corresponding to streamlines BB' and HH'.

As before, however, we need only $dw/d\zeta$, not $w(\zeta)$; $dw/d\zeta$ has simple poles at those points where w has logarithmic singularities and simple zeros at the critical points and their reflections:

$$\zeta = \exp[i(\pi \pm \gamma)], \qquad a \exp[i(\pi \pm \alpha)],$$

$$\zeta = \exp[i(\pi \pm \alpha)]/a$$

Furthermore, $dw/d\zeta$ has simple zeros at $\zeta = \pm 1$, where the conformality of the mapping is violated. From the character of the zeros and singular points of $dw/d\zeta$, it is seen that $dw/d\zeta$ is single-valued on the entire ζ-plane. Constructing $dw/d\zeta$ from its zeros and poles gives

$$\frac{dw}{d\zeta} = \frac{N(1-\zeta^2)(\zeta + e^{-i\gamma})(\zeta + e^{i\gamma})(\zeta + ae^{-i\alpha})(\zeta + ae^{i\alpha})(e^{i\alpha} + a\zeta)(e^{-i\alpha} + a\zeta)}{\zeta(be^{-i\beta} + \zeta)(be^{i\beta} + \zeta)(e^{i\beta} + \zeta b)(e^{-i\beta} + \zeta b)(he^{-i\epsilon} + \zeta)(he^{i\epsilon} + \zeta)(e^{i\epsilon} + \zeta h)(e^{-i\epsilon} + \zeta h)}, \quad (6.117)$$

where N is a real constant.

The solution to a flow around a cascade of flat plates, with the re-entrant jet model, was obtained by Veitsmanov under the guidance of Sedov [24]. If we set $a = b = 0$ in Eqs. (6.116) and (6.117), then we obtain the general solution to a Kirchhoff flow around a cascade formed from curvilinear wedges.

From Eqs. (6.116) and (6.117) $dz/d\zeta$ is easily obtained; then z is found by integration of

$$\frac{dz}{d\zeta} = \frac{dz}{dw}\frac{dw}{d\zeta}$$

$$= \frac{Ne^{-2i\alpha}(\zeta + e^{i\gamma})^{2\kappa}(1 - \zeta^2)\exp\left[-i(c_1\zeta + c_2\zeta^2 + c_3\zeta^3 + \dots)\right]}{v_o\zeta(1 + \zeta e^{i\gamma})^{2\kappa}}$$

$$\cdot \frac{(e^{i\alpha} + a\zeta)^2(ae^{i\alpha} + \zeta)^2(\zeta + e^{-i\gamma})(\zeta + e^{i\gamma})}{(be^{-i\beta} + \zeta)(be^{i\beta} + \zeta)(e^{i\beta} + b\zeta)(e^{-i\beta} + b\zeta)(he^{-i\epsilon} + \zeta)(he^{i\epsilon} + \zeta)(e^{i\epsilon} + \zeta h)(e^{-i\epsilon} + \zeta h)} . \tag{6.118}$$

Obviously, $z(\zeta)$ must be single-valued in the flow plane. Therefore, the parameters in Eq. (6.118) must be chosen so that z returns to the same value after ζ traverses around the cut BH along an arbitrary contour. The selected contour consists of two circles of infinitesimal radius and the two sides of the cut between B and H (Fig. 148). Since $dz/d\zeta$ is a single-valued function, the integrals along the sides of the cut cancel each other and all that remains is to evaluate the integrals over the small circles. These integrals are easily evaluated by using residues. The condition for single-valuedness is then

$$\oint_B \frac{dz}{d\zeta}\,d\zeta + \oint_H \frac{dz}{d\zeta}\,d\zeta = 0 \quad . \tag{6.119}$$

This complex equation (6.119) provides two conditions for determination of the unknown constants. All the basic characteristics of the flow can be expressed in terms of the constants in Eqs. (6.116) - (6.118).

The circulation Γ around an element of the cascade and the reentrant-jet discharge q (which is equal to the difference between the discharges at infinity to the right and left between the streamlines H'B' and HB) are determined from

$$-\Gamma + iq = \oint_B \frac{dw}{d\zeta}\, d\zeta + \oint_H \frac{dw}{d\zeta}\, d\zeta \quad . \tag{6.120}$$

Integration of this equation is accomplished along infinitesimal circles around B and H. Note that in Eq. (6.120), if the contour of integration is the same as that used in deducing Eq. (6.119), then the integrals along the sides of the cut BH will again cancel each other.

Let the complex velocities at infinity to the left and to the right be $v_H \exp[-i\theta_H] = v_\infty \exp[-i\theta_\infty]$ and $v_B \exp[-i\theta_B]$, respectively. These quantities can be obtained by setting $\zeta = -he^{-i\epsilon}$ and $\zeta = -be^{-i\beta}$ respectively in Eq. (6.116); then

$$\left.\begin{aligned} \frac{v_\infty}{v_o} \exp[-i\theta_\infty] &= \left(\frac{dw}{v_o dz}\right)_{\zeta=-he^{-i\epsilon}} \\ \frac{v_B}{v_o} \exp[-\theta_R] &= \left(\frac{dw}{v_o dz}\right)_{\zeta=-be^{-i\beta}} \end{aligned}\right\} \quad . \tag{6.121}$$

The period $R + iS$ is obtained by integrating Eq. (6.118) along an infinitesimal circle around the point $\zeta = -he^{-i\epsilon}$ so that

$$R + iS = \oint_H \frac{dz}{d\zeta}\, d\zeta \quad . \tag{6.122}$$

The contour's shape and dimensions are obtained by integrating Eq. (6.118) along the semicircle FED ($\zeta = e^{i\sigma}$), where $0 \leqq \sigma \leqq \pi$.

Let H'H be a segment—at infinity to the left (Fig. 147)—equal in magnitude to the magnitude of the vector $R + iS$, but directed in the opposite direction—i.e., $z_H - z_{H'} = -(R + iS')$. We consider also (Fig. 147) the segment BB' determined by the vector $z'_B - z_B = R + iS$. If $q_H = q_\infty$ and q_B are discharges through these segments and $\Gamma_\infty = \Gamma_H$ and Γ_B are the circulations along them, we have

$$\left.\begin{aligned} \Gamma_B + iq_B &= v_B(R + iS)\exp\,[-i\theta_B] \\ -\Gamma_B + iq_\infty &= v_\infty(R + iS)\exp\,[-i\theta_\infty] \\ q &= q_\infty - q_B \end{aligned}\right\} \quad . \tag{6.123}$$

By using the momentum theorem, we find the projections X and Y of the resultant pressure force acting on the contour FCD as

$$X + iY = (p_B - p_\infty)\, i(R + iS) + \rho q_\infty v_\infty \exp\,[i\theta_\infty] - \rho q_o v_B \exp\,[i\theta_B] - \rho q v_o \exp\,[i\theta_o], \tag{6.124}$$

where ρ is the fluid density and p_B and p_∞ are the pressures at infinity to the right and to the left respectively. The Bernoulli integral is now used to transform Eq. (6.124) into the form

$$\frac{X + iY}{\rho} = -\frac{i}{2}\left[v_B \exp\,[i\theta_B]\Gamma_B + v_\omega \Gamma_\omega \exp\,[i\theta_\infty]\right] + \frac{q_\infty v_\infty \exp\,[i\theta_\infty]}{2}$$
$$- \frac{q_B v_B \exp\,[i\theta_B]}{2} - (q_\infty - q_B)\, v_o \exp\,[i\theta_o] \quad . \qquad (6.125)$$

We now evaluate the number of parameters at our disposal. For simplicity we shall limit our attention to the case of a grid of flat plates. In this case $2\kappa = 1$, $c_1 = c_2 = c_3 = \ldots = 0$—i.e., $\exp\,[i\Omega(\zeta)] = 1$. In Eqs. (6.116) and (6.117) there are nine parameters: a, α, b, β, h, ϵ, γ, v_o, N. Two may be determined from the complex condition of single-valuedness in Eq. (6.119). Prescription of the scale coefficient N is equivalent to prescription of the plate length ℓ, which can be obtained by integrating Eq. (6.119) between the limits $\zeta = -1$ to $\zeta = 1$. Furthermore, we can prescribe the direction of the flow at infinity to the left—i.e., the angle θ_∞—the cavitation number $v_o^2/v_\infty^2 - 1$, and the pressure difference $p_\infty - p_B$ at infinity before and after the plate. Accordingly, we can determine three additional parameters. Finally, since we know the geometry of the grid, we know its period R + iS—i.e., another two parameters. Thus, we have eight conditions for determining nine parameters. Hence, in this cascade flow, as in the case of cavitating flow around an inclined plate in an unlimited fluid, we must prescribe one more parameter to completely determine the flow. It would be natural to select the circulation Γ as this parameter. But theory to determine Γ—i.e., a theory equivalent to the Chaplygin-Zhukovskii wing theory—has yet to be developed.

CHAPTER VII. PLANING SURFACES AND HYDROFOILS

A. PHENOMENON OF PLANING--THE PLANING FLAT PLATE

Planing or gliding is a motion of a body over a free water surface in which the basic supporting force is not the hydrostatic "Archimedes" bouyancy force, but the hydrodynamic lift produced by the displaced water. The planing or gliding principle is presently employed for the high-speed motion of comparatively small vessels and the take-off and landing of seaplanes.

During motion the wetted bottom of a planing vessel is represented by a smoothly curved surface inclined at a small angle to the horizontal. The planing surface throws a high-speed sheet of spray ahead and in part to the sides of the surface. Generally, the sides and trailing edge of a planing surface are sharp-edged, and viscosity plays a role only in the thin boundary layer on the surface. This layer is swept from the planing surface at the sharp edges without any noticeable deformation of the main flow. Thus, the planing problem can be separated into two parts: 1) studying planing on the surface of an ideal, incompressible fluid, and 2) accounting for the viscosity of the fluid and determining the fluid motion in the boundary layer.

The first (or planing problem for an ideal fluid) is solved independently from the second (or viscous) one. The first solution gives the velocity field outside the boundary layer and the normal pressure on the bottom of the planing body. The solution to the second problem is conveniently approached after the velocity field in the ideal fluid is found. From knowledge of the motion in the boundary layer, it is not difficult to compute the friction forces.

The problems of unsteady planing and the influence of gravity on the fluid motion were studied by Sedov [121, 122, 24], who used a linearized formulation. By using the analogy between thin wings and the planing flat plate (enunciated by Wagner [123]), together with a linearized formulation, one can also account for the effects of a finite span of the planing surface.

Here we shall be concerned only with application of jet theory to plane, nonlinear problems about a contour that is planing at a constant velocity over an ideal, weightless fluid, or equivalently, uniform flow past a fixed planing surface. The simplest problem of this kind is that of the planing flat plate, which was already considered in Chapter I, Section E. Now we give another, more general and useful solution to this problem based on Refs. [123] and [123a].

The flow around a planing plate is shown in Figs. 10 and 149a. Note that this problem is a typical one in which jet theory should give good agreement with experiments, since the jet free surfaces are stable boundaries between water and the comparatively very light air. Actually, following correction of theoretical results for the influence of the finite span and gravity, the theory and experiments agree very well [123a].

The planing plate is a particular type of flow around a wedge, shown in Figs. 112 and 113, where here $\kappa = 1/2$ while B and G coincide $(g = 0)$. The case when B and G do not coincide is also considered in this chapter. For convenience the coordinate axes are chosen in the same way as shown in Fig. 149a, not as in Fig. 112. Accordingly, minor rearrangements are required if the equations of Chapter V,

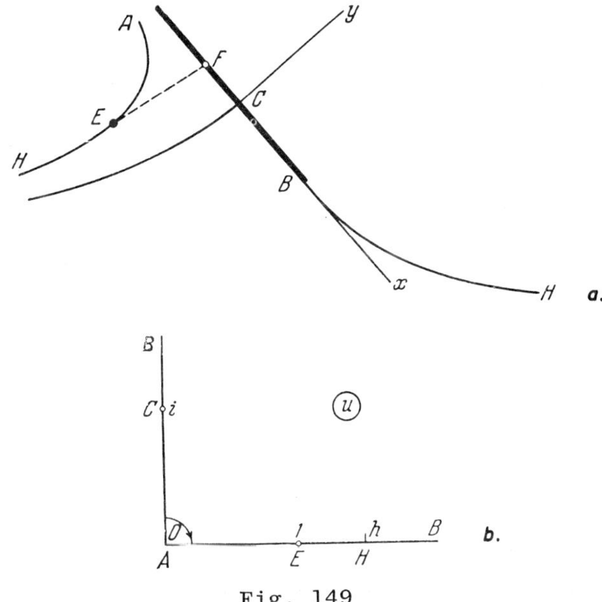

Fig. 149

Section A, are to be used. Also, in Fig. 149, h replaces the value c used previously.

We present a direct and short derivation of the general solution to our problem. The region of change of the dimensionless complex velocity for the model used in Fig. 149a is mapped onto the upper right quadrant of the plane of the parametric variable (Fig. 149b). Then, we have [cf., Eq. (6.15)]

$$\frac{dw}{v_o dz} = \frac{u - i}{u + i} \quad . \tag{7.1}$$

Clearly, $dw/v_o dz$ has a unique zero at the point $u = i$ in the upper right quadrant of the u-plane. Correspondingly, after the analytical extension to the entire plane, there will be a pole at the point $u = -i$. The validity of Eq. (7.1) is easily verified. On the real axis,

$$|dw/v_o dz| = |(u - i)/(u + i)| = 1$$

because the numerator and denominator are conjugates. Then, $(dw/v_o dz)_{u=0} = [(u - i)/(u + i)]_{u=0} = 1$ and finally, setting $u = i\eta$ in Eq. (7.1) shows that $dw/v_o dz = (\eta - 1)/(\eta + 1)$ is real on the imaginary axis.

The function dw/du has the form [cf., Eq. (6.23)]

$$\frac{dw}{du} = \frac{N(u^2 + 1)}{u(u^2 - h^2)^2}, \tag{7.2}$$

where N is a real constant. The singular-points method can be used to find dw/du if it is noted that dw/du has a zero at the critical point $u = i$, a first-order pole at $A(u = 0)$, and a second-order pole at $H(u = h)$, because the complex potential has a logarithmic singularity and a pole respectively at A and H. Along the surface of the jet (real positive semi-axis), dw/du is real. Along the plate, because du is imaginary, dw/du is purely imaginary. Thus, extending dw/du to the entire u-plane, we find that dw/du has another zero at $u = -i$ and a pole of the second order at $u = -h$.

It is easy to see that, according to Eq. (7.2), dw/du is real along the real axis and imaginary along the imaginary axis. If the fluid discharge in the spray sheet is q, then integration of Eq. (7.2) along a quarter of a circle with an infinitesimal radius (Fig. 149) gives $N = -2h^4 q/\pi$; now Eq. (7.2) can be rewritten as

$$\frac{dw}{du} = -\frac{2h^4 q(u^2 + 1)}{\pi u(u^2 - h^2)^2}. \tag{7.3}$$

Equations (7.1) and (7.2) give the general solution to the problem that was obtained in Russia by Chaplygin* with the help of Gurevich and Yanpolskii [123a] and in Germany by Wagner [123].

If α_o is the angle between the velocity at infinity and the x-axis and, obviously, also the attack angle of the plate, then from Eq. (7.1) we find

$$\exp\left[-i\alpha_o\right] = \frac{h - i}{h + i}$$

or

$$h = \cot\frac{\alpha_o}{2} \quad . \qquad (7.4)$$

In the present problem formulation, where the fluid is weightless, the wetted length of the plate is naturally infinite. Actually, because of gravity and friction between the jet and the plate, the wetted length is finite. Thus, Wagner suggested that the wetted length ℓ be defined in our problem as the distance FB between the trailing edge B of the plate and the intersection F of the plate and the normal EF (to the plate) that is tangent to the free surface (Fig. 149a). As a partial justification of this method, observe that, for the practical and most interesting small angles of attack, the spray sheet is thin and the pressure on the region washed by the spray sheet is small in comparison to the pressure on BF.

Next, ℓ is found. From Eqs. (7.1) and (7.2) it follows that

---

*According to Chaplygin, Lyusternik applied jet theory to the planing-plate problem in 1931. Chaplygin's rough notes outlining his solution carry the same year date.

$$z = \int \frac{dz}{dw}\frac{dw}{du}\,du = -\frac{2h^4 q}{\pi v_o}\int \frac{u+i}{u-i}\,\frac{1+u^2}{u(u^2-h^2)^2}\,du$$

$$= -\frac{h^4 q}{\pi v_o}\left[-\frac{h^2-1+2iu}{h^2(u^2-h^2)} + \frac{1}{h^4}\ln\frac{u^2-h^2}{u^2} - \frac{i}{h^3}\ln\frac{u-h}{u+h}\right] . \tag{7.5}$$

By using Eq. (7.1), we find point E corresponds to $u = 1$ in the u-plane. Thus, from Eqs. (7.4) and (7.5),

$$\ell = FB = \text{Re}\,[z(+\infty) - z(1)]$$

$$= \frac{q}{\pi v_o}\left[\cot^2\frac{\alpha_o}{2} + \pi\cot\frac{\alpha_o}{2} + \ln\left(\cot^2\frac{\alpha_o}{2} - 1\right)\right] . \tag{7.6}$$

For small α_o, $\ell \approx 4\delta/(\pi\alpha_o^2)$ where $\delta = q/v_o$.

The normal force P, acting on the gliding plate, can be obtained from the equations of Chapter VI, Section A. However, it is easier to examine Fig. 150, where the model of a planing-plate flow with finite depth is shown. Let the fluid depth at infinity in front of the plate be $y_o + \delta$, where $\delta = q/v_o$ is the thickness of the spray sheet; at infinity behind the plate the depth is y_o. We apply the momentum theorem to the volume of the fluid bounded by the bottom, free surface, the plate, and three infinitely distant plane sections, appropriately perpendicular either to the bottom or to the plate. The equation of the component of momentum in the direction of the approaching flow gives

$$P \sin\alpha_o = \rho\, v_o q(1 + \cos\alpha_o) . \tag{7.7}$$

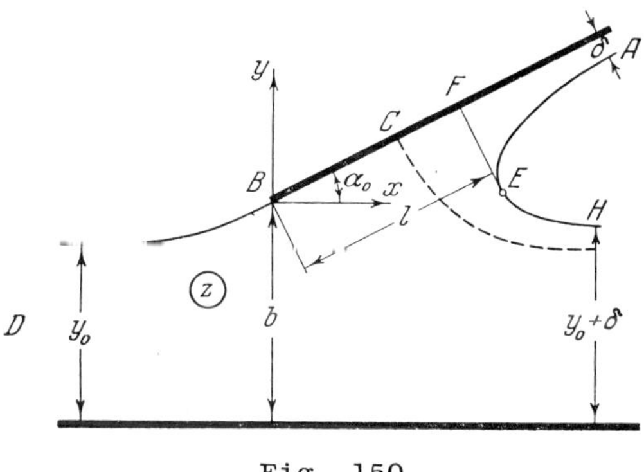

Fig. 150

This last equation is correct for an arbitrary flow depth and, in particular, for infinite depth. From Eqs. (7.6) and (7.7) it is easy to find the normal force coefficient

$$C_n = \frac{2P}{\rho v_o^2 \ell}$$

$$= \frac{2\pi}{\cot(\alpha_o/2) + \pi + \tan(\alpha_o/2)\,\ell n\left[\cot^2(\alpha_o/2) - 1\right]} . \tag{7.8}$$

As α_o tends to 0, C_n becomes, asymptotically, $C_n \approx \pi\alpha_o$, i.e., for small angles of attack the normal force acting on the planing plate is equal to half the normal force acting on a flat wing.

Kalinin [125] computed the moment M of the hydrodynamic force P acting on the entire plate BA relative to the trailing edge. If $M/P\ell = \ell_o$, his result is

$$\frac{\ell_o}{\ell} = \frac{1 + (\cos\alpha_o/2) + 2(1 - \cos\alpha_o)\,\ell n\,2 + (\pi/2)\sin\alpha_o}{(1 - \cos\alpha_o)\,\ell n[2\cos\alpha_o/(1 - \cos\alpha_o)] + 1 + \cos\alpha_o + \pi\sin\alpha_o} . \tag{7.9}$$

As α_0 tends to 0, ℓ_0/ℓ approaches 3/4 (the same result as found for a flat wing at small angles of attack). The results of Kalinin's computations are given in Table 24.

TABLE 24

α_0 deg	ℓ_0/ℓ	α_0 deg	ℓ_0/ℓ	α_0 deg	ℓ_0/ℓ	α_0 deg	ℓ_0/ℓ
0	0.750	10	0.686	20	0.649	45	0.652
3	0.728	12	0.676	25	0.639	50	0.671
5	0.715	15	0.664	30	0.636	60	0.723
7	0.703	18	0.654	35	0.639	70	0.824
				40	0.644	80	1.058

The pressure at any point in the flow is easily computed from Bernoulli's integral. Interestingly, over a wide range of attack angles, the pressure distribution on the section from the trailing edge of the planing plate to the critical point A differs very little from the pressure distribution on the corresponding section of the lower side of a flat wing [24, Chapter VII, 3, Fig. 167]. The pressure distributions in the region of the leading edge of the wing and the planing plate are quite different, primarily because of the leading-edge suction force acting on the wing.

We must examine now which parameters determine the actual motion of a glider or planing surface. Such a surface can, within certain limits, be loaded in an arbitrary manner, but prescription of the loading fixes the magnitude and point of application of the hydrodynamic lift that must oppose the load resultant. Then, in the case of a speedboat, for example, with a given fluid density ρ and a known rpm for the boat's propeller, the planing surface's velocity v_0, its location relative to the undisturbed water level, the length of the wetted surface, and the detailed flow picture can be obtained. Thus, in proceeding from a real physical problem to the planing plate of infinite span, we find that four parameters may be prescribed arbitrarily: ρ, v_o, P, and ℓ_o. Given these four values, it is possible to determine ℓ and α_o from Eqs. (7.8) and (7.9), while h and q are determined from Eqs. (7.4) and (7.6). Then Eqs. (7.1) and (7.3) are used to complete determination of the remainder of the fluid-motion detail. Therefore, it is clear that our problem statement, from the point of view of the number of prescribed parameters, is physically realistic.

Another viewpoint was adopted in many of the first papers on planing [123a, 125, 126, 127]. First, a more general planing problem was considered. Second, in the more general setup, the plate length was prescribed arbitrarily and assumed to be equal to the wetted length. Thus, during the solution, an extra parameter appeared. But, in reality, the fluid does not whip over the leading edge of the planing plate, and the wetted length is less than the planing-surface length because of the influence of gravity and viscosity. Thus, the later trend was away from the more general scheme in favor of the more realistic scheme presented above. However, the more general scheme has both theoretical and practical interest, even if not as a model for a flow past a planing plate. We shall return to this in Section C, where hydrofoils are discussed.

B. PLANING OVER THE SURFACE OF A FLUID OF FINITE DEPTH--TANDEM FLAT PLATES

The flow about a plate, gliding on a surface of a fluid of finite depth, was first solved by S. A. Chaplygin [123a]. Later, more general calculations were carried out by Green [127] and Yu. S. Chaplygin [128]. The general solution is given here.

Let a flow with velocity v_o approach an infinitely long plate BCA that is inclined at an angle α_o to the horizontal (Fig. 150). The fluid depth at infinity ahead of the plate is $y_o + \delta$, while at infinity behind the plate the depth is y_o. At infinity (A) the spray-sheet thickness is δ.

Now we prescribe a parametric variable u that varies over the rectangle ABDH with sides $\omega_1/2$ and $\omega_2/2i$* (Fig. 151). We map the region of change of the dimensionless complex velocity $dw/v_o dz$ and the complex potential derivative dw/du onto the u-plane rectangle ABDH. The boundaries of the rectangle correspond to the streamlines along which $\text{Im}\, dw = 0$. It follows that dw/du is purely imaginary on AH and DB and is purely real on HD and AB. On extending dw/du to the entire u-plane through use of the Schwarz reflection (or symmetry) principle [5], we observe that dw/du is doubly periodic with periods ω_1 and ω_2. Through the parallelogram of periods (Fig. 151; a rectangle or "cell" similar to ABDH but with sides twice as long and equal in length to one period) the values of dw/du on the outer boundaries of the reflected rectangles can be related to the values on the right and upper sides of ABDH.

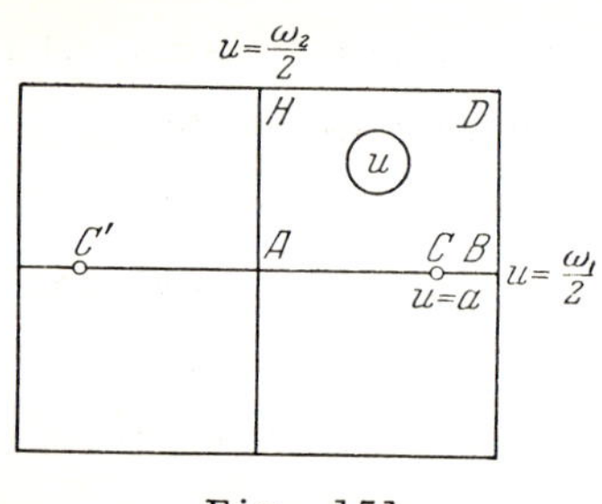

Fig. 151

In the parallelogram of periods, dw/du has simple zeros at $u = \pm a$ (corresponding to the critical point C) and at $B(u = \omega_1/2)$ where the mapping of w onto u is not conformal. The complex potential $w(u)$ has logarithmic singularities at D, H, and A, which correspond to infinitely distant points on the jets. Therefore, dw/du has simple poles at $u = 0$, $u = \omega_2/2$, and $u = (\omega_1 + \omega_2)/2$. As

*The quantity ω_2 is inherently imaginary in this notation.

a result, dw/du is doubly periodic, has only simple zeros and poles, and is accordingly an elliptic function.

When constructing $dw/v_o dz$ from its singularities, the reflected pole corresponding to the pole at $D(u = [\omega_1 + \omega_2]/2)$ is placed at $u = (\omega_1 - \omega_2)/2$, which is separated from D by a period ω_2; etc. Since $\sigma(u)$ is an odd, integral, quasi-periodic function with simple zeros at $u = 0$ and at those points separated from $u = 0$ by an integral number of periods, we can easily obtain*

$$\frac{dw}{v_o du} = N \frac{\sigma(u - a)\ \sigma(u + a)\ \sigma[u - (\omega_1/2)]}{\sigma(u)\ \sigma[u - (\omega_2/2)]\ \sigma[u + (\omega_2 - \omega_1)/2]}, \qquad (7.10)$$

where N is a constant to be determined by the thickness of the spray sheet at infinity.

To construct the dimensionless complex velocity $dw/v_o dz$, we consider first the function

$$\omega(u) = \ell n\ (dw/v_o dz) = \ell n\ (v/v_o) - i\theta,$$

where $v = |dw/dz|$ and θ is the angle between the velocity vector and the positive x-axis. In the flow region, $\omega(u)$ has only one logarithmic signularity (at C). Since the flow boundary consists of segments on which either the real $[\ell n\ (v/v_o)]$, or the imaginary $[-\theta]$ parts of ω are constant, it can be shown that dw/du is an elliptic function with periods ω_1 and ω_2 and that there are only two first-order poles at the points $u = \pm a$ in the parallelogram of

*Refer to Smirnov [30], Birkhoff and Zarantonello [5], or Whittaker and Watson [129] for background material on elliptic functions.

of periods. Since the expansion of $dw/v_o dz$ has a simple zero $u = 0$, then, in the neighborhood of $u = a$,

$$\omega'(u) = \frac{\frac{d}{du}\left(\frac{dw}{v_o dz}\right)}{dw/v_o dz} = \frac{1}{u - a} + \dots \quad ; \tag{7.11}$$

Along AH, $\omega'(u)$ is real; thus, according to the symmetry principle, the expansion of $\omega'(u)$ in the neighborhood of $u = -a$ must have the form

$$\omega'(u) = \frac{-1}{u + a} + \dots \quad . \tag{7.12}$$

Since in the neighborhood of $u = 0$ the expansion of $\zeta(u) = d(\ell n\ \sigma)/du$ has the form $\zeta(u) = 1/u + \dots$, then, by taking into account Eqs. (7.11) and (7.12), we have

$$\omega'(u) = A_1 + \zeta(u - a) - \zeta(u + a) \quad ,$$

where A_1 is a constant. On integrating this result, we obtain

$$\omega(u) = A_1 u + B_1 + \ell n\ \sigma(u - a) - \ell n\ \sigma(u + a) \quad ,$$

and so,

$$\frac{dw}{v_o dz} = \exp\,[A_1 u + B_1]\,\frac{\sigma(u - a)}{\sigma(u + a)} \quad . \tag{7.13}$$

Now we shall determine A_1, B_1, and a. At $H(u = \omega_2/2)$,

$$\left(\frac{dw}{v_o dz}\right)_H = e^{-\pi i} = \exp\left[\frac{A_1\omega_2}{2} + B_1\right]\frac{\sigma[(\omega_2/2) - a]}{\sigma[(\omega_2/2) + a]} = \exp\left[\frac{A_1\omega_2}{2} + B_1 - \eta_2 a\right],$$

and

$$-\pi i = \frac{A_1\omega_2}{2} + B_1 - \eta_2 a \quad . \tag{7.14}$$

On $CB(a < u < \omega_1 2)$, as seen in Fig. 150, θ is constant and equal to $\pi + \alpha_o$; thus, on CB, $\arg (dw/v_o dz) = -(\pi + \alpha_o)$. It is easily shown that the ratio $\sigma(u - a)/\sigma(u + a)$ is real and positive on CB.* Accordingly, we see from Eq. (7.13) that A_1 is real and

$$B_1 = -i(\pi + \alpha_o) \quad . \tag{7.15}$$

From Eqs. (7.14) and (7.15) it follows that

$$A_1 = \frac{2(\alpha_o i + a\eta_2)}{\omega_2} \quad . \tag{7.16}$$

The constant a can be obtained from the condition that

$$\frac{dw}{v_o dz} = \exp\left[-i(\alpha_o + \pi)\right]$$

at point $B(u = \omega_1/2)$. By using this result and Eq. (7.13) we find

$$A_1 \frac{\omega_1}{2} + B_1 - \eta_1 a = -i(\alpha_o + \pi) \quad ,$$

*Along $\mathrm{Im}\, u = 0$, $\sigma(u - a)$ is real. In the neighborhood of $u = a$, $\sigma(u - a) \approx u - a$ and is positive when $u > a$. The sign of $\sigma(u - a)$ changes only when u passes through the point $u = a + \omega_1$. It follows that we have $\sigma(u - a) > 0$ on CB. Similarly, we can prove that $\sigma(u + a) > 0$ on CB.

which, together with Eqs. (7.15) and (7.16), gives

$$a = \frac{\omega_1\alpha_o}{2\pi} ; \qquad A_1 = \frac{\eta_1\alpha_o}{\pi} ; \qquad B_1 = -i(\pi + \alpha_o) \quad . \tag{7.17}$$

On introducing these expressions for a, A_1, and B_1 into Eqs. (7.10) and (7.12), we have finally

$$\frac{dw}{v_o dz} = \frac{\sigma[u - (\omega_1\alpha_o/2\pi)]}{\sigma[u + (\omega_1\alpha_o/2\pi)]} \exp\left[\frac{\eta_1\alpha_o u}{\pi} - i(\pi + \alpha_o)\right], \tag{7.18}$$

and

$$\frac{dw}{v_o du} = N \frac{\sigma[u - (\omega_1\alpha_o/2\pi)]\ \sigma[u + (\omega_1\alpha_o/2\pi)]\ \sigma[u - (\omega_1/2)]}{\sigma(u)\ \sigma[u - (\omega_2/2)]\ \sigma[u + (\omega_2 - \omega_1)/2]} \quad . \tag{7.19}$$

Clearly, in the neighborhood of $A(u = 0)$, $dw/v_o dz$ has an expansion

$$\frac{dw}{v_o du} = -N \frac{\sigma^2(\omega_1\alpha_o/2\pi)\ \sigma(\omega_1/2)}{u\sigma(\omega_2/2)\ \sigma[(\omega_2 - \omega_1)/2]} + \dots \quad . \tag{7.20}$$

By integrating this equation along an infinitesimal quarter of a circle around A in the first quadrant and noting that $\operatorname{Im} w$ jumps by δv_o as A is passed in going from AH to BCA, we obtain

$$\delta = \frac{\pi N}{2} \frac{\sigma^2(\omega_1\alpha_o/2\pi)\ \sigma(\omega_1/2)}{\sigma(\omega_2/2)\ \sigma[(\omega_2 - \omega_1)/2]} \quad . \tag{7.21}$$

Thus, N is determined in terms of δ.

Now we may determine the fluid depth at infinity ahead of the plate. An expansion of $dw/v_o du$ in the neighborhood of $H(u = \omega_2/2)$ has the form, according to Eq. (7.19),

$$\frac{dw}{v_o du} = N \frac{\sigma[(\omega_2/2) - (\omega_1\alpha_o/2\pi)]\,\sigma[(\omega_2/2) + (\omega_1\alpha_o/2\pi)]\,\sigma[(\omega_2 - \omega_1)/2]}{[u - (\omega_2/2)]\,\sigma(\omega_2/2)\,\sigma[\omega_2 - (\omega_1/2)]} + \cdots . \tag{7.22}$$

As before, by an integration of Eq. (7.22), along an infinitesimal quarter of a circle around $H(u = \omega_2/2)$ and accounting for the jump in $\operatorname{Im} w$ of $v_o(y_o + \delta)$ as we pass from the streamline HA to the streamline HD, we find

$$y_o + \delta = \frac{N\pi}{2} \frac{\sigma[(\omega_2/2) - (\omega_1\alpha_o/2\pi)]\,\sigma[\omega_2/2) + (\omega_1\alpha_o/2\pi)]\,\sigma[(\omega_2 - \omega_1)/2]}{\sigma(\omega_2/2)\,\sigma[\omega_2 - (\omega_1/2)]} . \tag{7.23}$$

All the geometric elements of the flow, such as Wagner's wetted length HF of the plate, the height b of the trailing edge of the plate above the bottom, the shape of the streamlines, etc., can be computed by integrating dz/du, which is easily found from Eqs. (7.18) and (7.19) to be

$$\frac{dz}{du} = N \frac{\sigma^2[u + (\omega_1\alpha_o/2\pi)]\,\sigma[u - (\omega_1/2)]\,\exp\left[-\frac{\eta_1\alpha_o}{\pi}u + i(\pi + \alpha_o)\right]}{\sigma(u)\,\sigma[u - (\omega_2/2)]\,\sigma[u + (\omega_2 - \omega_1)/2]} . \tag{7.24}$$

This expression may be integrated after σ [in Eq. (7.24)] is expressed in terms of the known theta elliptic functions and then expanded in a series.

In the above-mentioned Refs. [127] and [128] the results of many numerical computations are given. However, here we give in Table 25 and Fig. 152 some of Green's results. They consist of the normal force P acting on the plate obtained by prescribing the width δ of the spray sheet, the height b of the trailing edge above the bottom, and the flow depth

TABLE 25

α_o = 5 deg		α_o = 10 deg		α_o = 30 deg		a_o = 60 deg	
$\frac{b}{y_o + \delta}$	$\frac{P}{\rho v_o^2(y_o + \delta)}$	$\frac{b}{y_o + \delta}$	$\frac{P}{\rho v_o^2(y_o + \delta)}$	$\frac{b}{y_o + \delta}$	$\frac{P}{\rho v_o^2(y_o + \delta)}$	$\frac{b}{y_o + \delta}$	$\frac{P}{\rho v_o^2(y_o + \delta)}$
1.0012	0.0006	1.0024	0.0013	1.0063	0.0039	1.0085	0.0069
1.0076	0.0069	1.0146	0.0138	1.0345	0.0398	1.0345	0.0679
1.0208	0.0351	1.0383	0.0699	1.0693	0.1963	0.9995	0.3156
1.0255	0.0571	1.0455	0.1133	1.0646	0.3132	0.9291	0.4803
1.0274	0.724	1.0478	0.1435	1.0542	0.3918	0.8747	0.5818
1.0296	0.1140	1.0482	0.2252	1.0108	0.5950	0.7293	0.8113
1.0294	0.1624	1.0434	0.3197	0.9515	0.8127	0.5847	1.0109
1.0248	0.2937	1.0225	0.5714	0.7953	1.3119	0.3314	1.3317
1.0153	0.5049	0.9859	0.9649	0.6003	1.9082	0.1510	1.5507
0.9982	0.8728	0.9245	1.6168			0.0494	1.6729
0	22.9037	0	11.4300	0	3.7320	0	1.7320

$y_o + \delta$ ahead of the plate. Remember that δ and y_o are determined from Eqs. (7.21) and (7.23), b is found by integrating Eq. (7.24), and the normal force is

$$P = \rho v_o^2 \delta \cot (\alpha_o/2) \quad ,$$

which was obtained from Eq. (7.7), where $q = v_o \delta$.

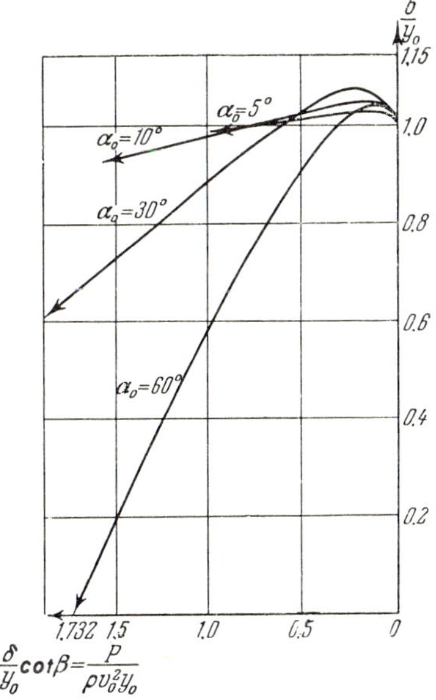

Fig. 152

From examination of Table 25 or Fig. 152 it is seen that, when $b > y_o + \delta$, there are two possible regimes with different jet thicknesses and lift forces. In particular, when $b = y_o + \delta$, the plate can either just touch the undisturbed surface of the flow without experiencing any resistance or substantially disturb the flow and have a finite resistance P. It is not known by the author if the stability of these two regimes has been studied theoretically.

The bottom surfaces of gliding or planing vessels often have a step in the middle. When the jet separates from the forward portion of the stepped bottom, the surface can be represented by two different, but rigidly connected, planing surfaces, placed one behind the other--in tandem. Thus, it is appropriate to give here the general solution to the flow about a pair of tandem planing plates [126] as shown in Fig. 153.

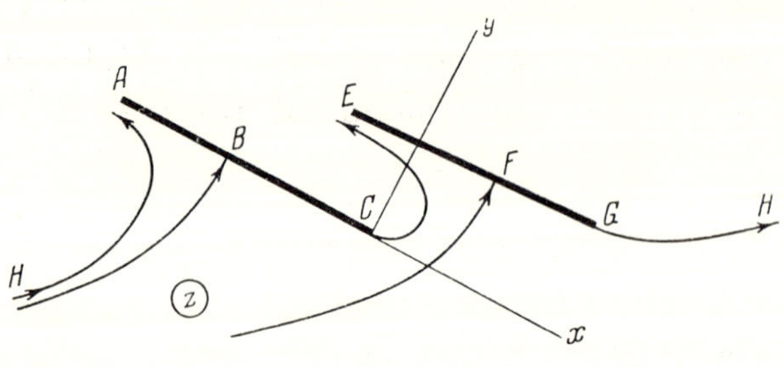

Fig. 153

Let the parametric variable u vary over the inside of a rectangle CAGE with sides $\omega_1/2$ and $\omega_2/2i$ (Fig. 154). The general solution consists of the equations for mapping the regions of change of the dimensionless complex velocity dw/v_0dz and the complex potential derivative dw/du onto the rectangle CAGE. This solution is obtained by the same method used at the beginning of this section for the planing plate on a finite-depth fluid. The differences between these problems are not essential ones. First, instead of one critical point, there are now two--B and F. Further, since the tandem plates are planing over an infinitely deep fluid, dw/du has a second-order pole at H. As a result it may easily be shown that

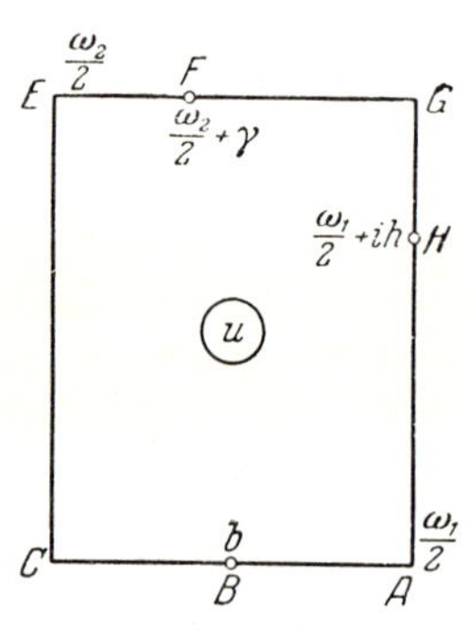

Fig. 154

$$\frac{dw}{v_0dz} = \frac{\sigma(u - b)\,\sigma[u - (\omega_2/2) - \gamma]}{\sigma(u + b)\,\sigma[u + (\omega_2/2) + \gamma]} \exp\left[\left(2\eta_1 \frac{b + \gamma}{\omega_1} + \eta_2\right)u\right] , \tag{7.25}$$

$$\frac{dw}{du} = N \frac{\sigma(u)\,\sigma[u - (\omega_1 + \omega_2)/2]\,\sigma(u - b)\,\sigma(u + b)\,\sigma[u - (\omega_2/2) - \gamma]\,\sigma[u + (\omega_2/2) + \gamma]}{\sigma[u - (\omega_1/2)]\,\sigma[u - (\omega_2/2)]\,\sigma^2[u - (\omega_1/2) - hi]\,\sigma^2[u + (\omega_1/2) + hi]} \cdot \tag{7.26}$$

In these equations the following notation has been adopted. The values of u at B, H, and F are, respectively, b, $(\omega_1/2) + hi$, and $(\omega_2/2) + \gamma$. The constant N can be expressed in terms of the thickness of either spray sheet. In Ref. [126], dw/du is expressed in terms, not of the σ function, but of $\wp$ and $\wp'$, the Weierstrass functions. A simple change in notation plus introduction of the σ functions in the appropriate equation in Ref. [126] leads directly to Eq. (7.25). From Eqs. (7.25) and (7.26) we obtain dz/du, which, after expansion into a series, is integrated to obtain z. The total force acting on the tandem plates was easily deduced in Ref. [126]. There, it is also shown that, when the plates are parallel, dw/du is given in terms of the Weierstrass functions $\wp$ and $\wp'$ and z is given in terms of the sum of a finite number of σ and ζ functions, multiplied by constant coefficients. Unfortunately, no numerical results are available for this planing, tandem-plate problem.

C. HYDROFOILS BENEATH A FREE SURFACE

Our next problem—the submerged wing or hydrofoil running beneath a free surface—has already found practical application. Hydrofoil systems have been successfully used on many passenger vessels and the widespread use of foil systems for ships of all sizes seems to be a promising prospect.

As with the case of unlimited flow past wings or hydrofoils, the flow may be either fully wetted (nonseparated) or cavitational. In the present case we are not precluded from employing the same types of flow models used to study unlimited flows. For example, we show cavity models for flow around a plate with re-entrant jet (Fig. 155) and parallel walls (Fig. 156). In Fig. 157 we show the corresponding fully wetted flow under a free surface. Note that the circulation around the plate is not zero.

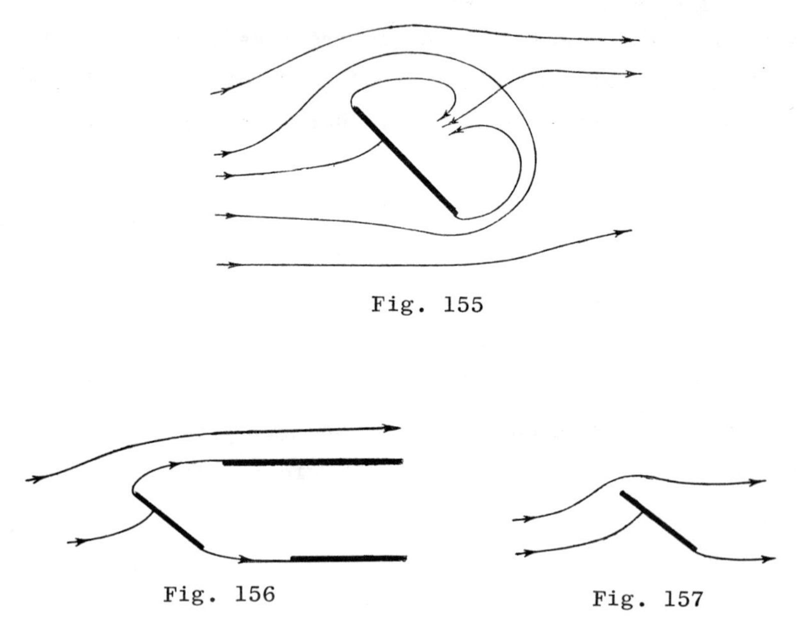

Fig. 155

Fig. 156

Fig. 157

The author does not know of any complete solutions to the flows posed in Figs. 155 - 157. Undoubtedly, solution of these problems, even if possible, is difficult. Considerably simpler is the limiting case of these problems when the cavitation number $Q = 0$. Thus, just as the Rayleigh flow is the limiting case as $Q \to 0$ of a cavity flow around a plate in an unlimited fluid, the flow in Fig. 158 is the limiting case as $Q \to 0$ of the flow models in Fig. 155 and 156. The model in Fig. 158 (as mentioned earlier in Section A of this chapter)

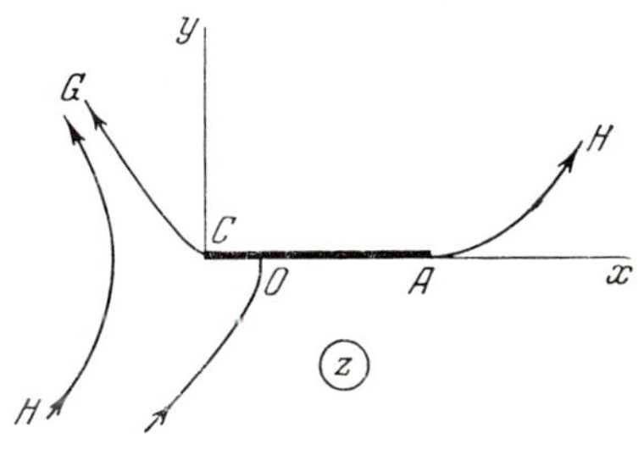

Fig. 158

was used by Chaplygin [124] in his study of the gliding plate, which is obtained when $CO = \infty$. He showed that, for a weightless, infinitely deep fluid, the plate rises infinitely high above the fluid level at infinity. As a result, it seems most logical to take the spray-sheet thickness δ as a submergence "depth" for the hydrofoil. The model in Fig. 158 was recommended as a hydrofoil model by Weinig [130] in 1937; however, his suggestion was not pursued.

An interesting problem along the lines of the above was solved by Fedorov.* He generalized the Chaplygin and Lavrentiev [32] model to the case of a flow with a free surface (Fig. 159). This case includes a very important particular flow. When the jet separation point C, located on the upper side of the plate, coincides with point E at the leading edge of the plate, we obtain a cavity flow around a hydrofoil with the cavitation number equal to 0 (Fig. 158). Another limiting case is shown in Fig. 160. There the separation

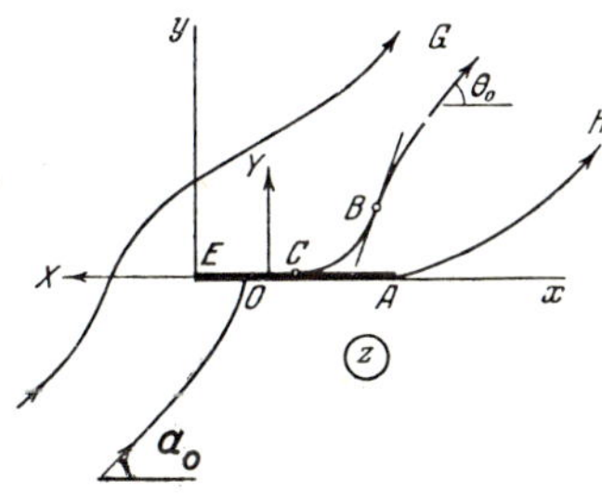

Fig. 159

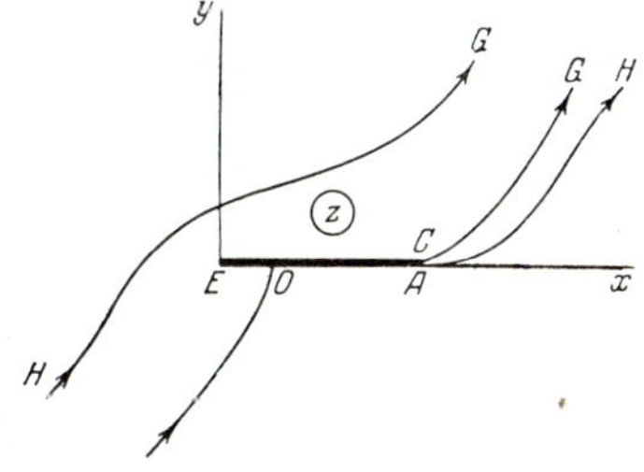

Fig. 160

*Fedorov's work was presented in a seminar at the USSR Academy of Sciences Computing Center.

point C coincides with the trailing edge of the plate. In Chapter III, Section C, we noted that Chaplygin and Lavrentiev showed that, for small angles of attack, the lift on a wing in an infinite, nonseparated, flow with circulation is not appreciably different from the lift calculated for their model flow when the flow-separation point coincides with the plate's trailing edge.

Thus, we are led to attempt solution of the simpler problem of flow around a wing with trailing-edge separation (Fig. 160) in lieu of the nonseparated problem (Fig. 157). The relative simplicity of the former scheme is related to the simply connected flow region. In the case of a circulatory flow around a wing (Fig. 157), the region is doubly connected. In his work Fedorov recommended that the separation point C be chosen so that the inflection point B (Fig. 159) on the surface of the jet is at infinity. He assumed that the presence of the inflection point made the flow unstable. This author feels that the instability of the water flow is related not so much to the presence of the inflection point as to the existence of negative-pressure zones where cavitation may be produced. In the Fedorov flow model, the negative-pressure zones always exist except when $Q = 0$ (Fig. 158). Because of this the case selected by Fedorov--i.e., that for which B goes to infinity--is not unreasonable from the physical point of view. At any rate, we shall proceed to solve the more general problem of Fig. 159.

We let the flow region correspond to the upper right quadrant (Fig. 161) in a parametric u-variable plane. The complex potential derivative dw/du has a first-order pole at $G(u = \gamma)$, which corresponds to the point at infinity on the jet. Furthermore, at $H(u = h)$ corresponding to the point at infinity in the infinite mean flow, dw/du has a second-order pole. Then, we observe that at the critical

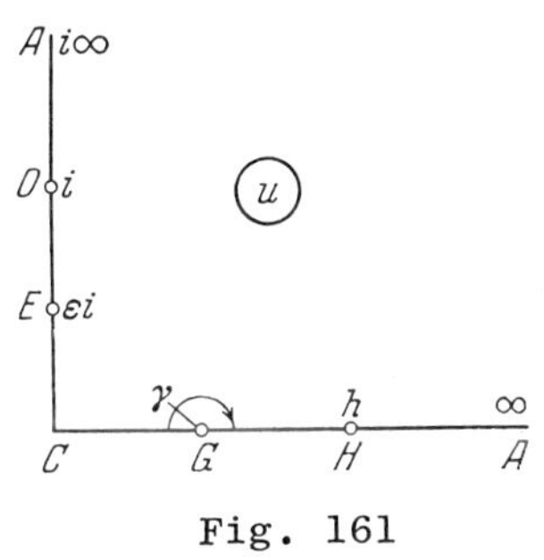

Fig. 161

(stagnation) point $O(u = i)$, dw/du has a first-order zero. Because the conformality of the mapping of w onto u is violated at $C(u = 0)$, dw/du has a zero there also. Since the boundaries of the w region are the lines $\text{Im}\, w = \text{const}$, $\text{Im}\, dw/du = 0$ along the real semi-axis CGHA in the u-plane and $\text{Re}\, dw/du = 0$ along the imaginary semi-axis CEOA. Now, by using the symmetry principle it is possible to extend dw/du to the entire u-plane. As a result, dw/du has a first-order zero at $u = -i$, a first-order pole at $u = -\gamma$, and a second-order pole at $u = -h$.

Now it is easy to construct dw/du from its known zeros and poles as

$$\frac{dw}{du} = N \frac{u(u^2 + 1)}{(u^2 - \gamma^2)(u^2 - h^2)^2} \quad . \tag{7.27}$$

By integrating Eq. (7.27) along an infinitesimal semicircle around G (Fig. 161) it is possible to express the constant N in terms of the discharge $q = v_o\delta$ in the "spray-sheet" or upper jet where δ is the spray-sheet thickness at infinity; then,

$$N = -\frac{2(h^2 - \gamma^2)^2}{\pi(1 + \gamma^2)} q \quad . \tag{7.28}$$

Next we determine the dimensionless complex velocity $dw/v_o dz$. At $E(u = i\epsilon)$ where the velocity is infinite, $dw/v_o dz$ has a pole, while at the critical point $O(u = i)$, $dw/v_o dz$ has a first-order zero. Along OA, OE, and EC the argument of the complex velocity has constant values—i.e., in a plot of $dw/v_o dz$ these parts of the boundaries will be straight lines. Finally, the real semi-axis CGHA will be some part of a unit circle $|dw/v_o dz| = 1$ in the $dw/v_o dz$ plot. By using the symmetry principle again, we extend $dw/v_o dz$ to the entire u-plane. After the extension through the real axis, the pole at $u = i\epsilon$ becomes a zero at $u = -i\epsilon$ and the zero at $u = i$ becomes a pole at $u = -i$. On constructing $dw/v_o dz$ from its zeros and poles, we find that

$$\frac{dw}{v_o dz} = M \frac{(u - i)(u + i\epsilon)}{(u + i)(u - i\epsilon)} .$$

Because $dw/v_o dz = 1$ at $A(u = \infty)$, $M = 1$. Thus, finally

$$\frac{dw}{v_o dz} = \frac{(u - i)(u + i\epsilon)}{(u + i)(u - i\epsilon)} . \tag{7.29}$$

Equations (7.27) and (7.29) give the general solution to the problem. If α_o is the angle between the velocity vector at infinity and the plate, and the angle of inclination of the spray sheet at infinity is θ_o, then by using Eq. (7.29), α_o and θ_o can be expressed in terms of the parameters h, γ, and ϵ. On the segment CGH of the real u-axis we have $dw/v_o dz = e^{-i\theta}$, where θ is the angle between the velocity and the x-axis. Equation (7.29) then gives

$$e^{-i\theta} = \frac{u^2 + \epsilon - iu(1 - \epsilon)}{u^2 + \epsilon + iu(1 - \epsilon)} ,$$

so that

$$\theta = 2 \arctan \frac{u(1 - \epsilon)}{u^2 + \epsilon} . \tag{7.30}$$

From Eq. (7.30), by setting $u = h$ (point H) and $u = \gamma$ (point G), we find

$$\tan \frac{\alpha}{2} = \frac{h(1 - \epsilon)}{h^2 + \epsilon} , \qquad (7.31)$$

$$\tan \frac{\theta_o}{2} = \frac{\gamma(1 - \epsilon)}{\gamma^2 + \epsilon} . \qquad (7.32)$$

To determine the geometric characteristics of the flow it is necessary to find first dz/du and then, by integration, $z(u)$. From the basic Eqs. (7.27), (7.28), and (7.29), which determine dw/du and $dw/v_o dz$, we obtain

$$\frac{dz}{du} = -\frac{2\delta}{\pi} \frac{(h^2 - \gamma^2)^2}{1 + \gamma^2} \frac{(u - i\epsilon)(u + i)^2 u}{(u + i\epsilon)(u^2 - \gamma^2)(u^2 - h^2)^2} . \qquad (7.33).$$

Since $z = 0$ at the point $u = i\epsilon$ (see Fig. 159), we next obtain

$$z = -\frac{2\delta}{\pi} \frac{(h^2 - \gamma^2)^2}{1 + \gamma^2} \int_{i\epsilon}^{u} \frac{(u - i\epsilon)(u + i)^2 u \, du}{(u + i\epsilon)(u^2 - \gamma^2)(u^2 - h^2)^2} . \qquad (7.34)$$

The integral on the right-hand side of this last equation can be evaluated in elementary functions as follows:

$$\frac{\pi(1 + \gamma^2)z}{2\delta(h^2 - \gamma^2)^2} = \frac{A}{2} \ln \frac{(\epsilon^2 + h^2)(u + i\epsilon)^2}{4\epsilon^2(u^2 - h^2)} - \frac{B}{2} \ln \frac{(\epsilon^2 + \gamma^2)(u^2 - h^2)}{(\epsilon^2 + h^2)(u^2 - \gamma^2)}$$

$$- i \frac{C}{2\gamma} \ln \frac{(\gamma - i\epsilon)^2 (u + \gamma)^2}{(\gamma^2 + \epsilon^2)(\gamma^2 - u^2)} - i \frac{2h^2E + G}{4h^3} \ln \frac{(h - i\epsilon)^2 (h + u)^2}{(h^2 + \epsilon^2)(h^2 - u^2)}$$

$$+ \frac{G}{2\beta^2}\left(\frac{iu}{u^2 - h^2} - \frac{\epsilon}{\epsilon^2 + h^2}\right) + \frac{F}{2} \frac{u^2 + \epsilon^2}{(u^2 - h^2)(\epsilon^2 + h^2)} , \qquad (7.35)$$

where

$$A = \frac{2\epsilon^2(1-\epsilon)^2}{(\epsilon^2+\gamma^2)(\epsilon^2+h^2)^2}$$

$$B = -\frac{1+\gamma^2}{(h^2-\gamma^2)^2}\cos\theta_o$$

$$C = -\frac{(1+\gamma^2)\,\gamma}{(h^2-\gamma^2)^2}\sin\theta_o$$

$$E = \frac{2\epsilon^2(1-\epsilon)^2}{(\epsilon^2+\gamma^2)(\epsilon^2+h^2)^2} + \frac{(1+\gamma^2)\,\gamma}{(h^2-\gamma^2)^2}\sin\theta_o \qquad (E = A\epsilon - C)$$

$$F = \frac{1+h^2}{h^2-\gamma^2}\cos\alpha_o$$

$$G = \frac{(1+h^2)h}{h^2-\gamma^2}\sin\alpha_o \quad .$$

Equation (7.35) allows one to find the shape of the free surface and any geometrical element of the flow. In particular, Fedorov found the plate length ℓ as

$$\frac{\pi(1+\gamma^2)}{2\delta(h^2-\gamma^2)^2}\,\ell = \frac{A}{2}\,\ell n\,\frac{\epsilon^2+h^3}{4\epsilon^2} - \frac{B}{2}\,\ell n\,\frac{\epsilon^2+\gamma^2}{\epsilon^2+h^2} + \frac{C}{\gamma}\left(\frac{\pi}{2} - \arctan\frac{\epsilon}{\gamma}\right)$$

$$+ \frac{2h^2E+G}{2h^3}\left(\frac{\pi}{2} - \arctan\frac{\epsilon}{h}\right) + \frac{F}{2(\epsilon^2+h^2)}$$

$$- \frac{G}{2h^2}\,\frac{\epsilon}{\epsilon^2+h^2} \quad . \qquad (7.36)$$

The difference $\ell - d$, where d is the abscissa of the jet separation point C, is given by

$$\frac{\pi(1+\gamma^2)}{2\delta(h^2-\gamma^2)^2}(\ell - d) = A \ln\frac{h}{\epsilon} - B \ln\frac{\gamma}{h}$$

$$+ \frac{\pi}{2}\left(\frac{C}{\gamma} + \frac{2h^2E + G}{2h^3}\right) + \frac{F}{2h^2} \quad . \tag{7.37}$$

This condition (7.37) is an equation for determination of one flow parameter. If the flow is noncavitating, then according to the considerations above, $\ell - d = 0$ in Eq. (7.37). If on the other hand, a fully cavitating flow around a wing with $Q = 0$ is desired, then $d = 0$ in Eq. (7.37).

The resultant force acting on the plate is determined as a combination of normal pressure and suction forces. As in Chaplygin and Lavrentiev's problem (Chapter III, Section C), there is a suction force X acting on the leading edge E of the plate. This force is easily computed from the known result of thin-wing theory [e.g., Eq. (12.20), Chapter II, Section 2, in Sedov, 24],

$$X = -\rho\pi\left[z\left(\frac{dw}{dz}\right)^2\right]_{z=0} \quad . \tag{7.38}$$

Now $z = 0$ corresponds to $E(u = \epsilon i)$ (see Fig. 161). In the neighborhood of E we have from Eq. (7.34), on neglecting higher-order terms in $u - i\epsilon$,

$$z \approx \frac{\delta}{2\pi}\frac{(h^2-\gamma^2)^2}{1+\gamma^2}\frac{(\epsilon+1)^2(u-i\epsilon)^2}{(\epsilon^2+\gamma^2)(\epsilon^2+h^2)^2} \quad . \tag{7.39}$$

Analogously, we obtain from Eq. (7.29) as $u \to i\epsilon$,

$$\frac{dw}{dz} \approx v_o \frac{\epsilon - 1}{\epsilon + 1} \frac{2i\epsilon}{u - i\epsilon} . \tag{7.40}$$

Introduction of Eqs. (7.39) and (7.40) into Eq. (7.38) gives

$$X = -2\rho v_o^2 \delta \frac{(h^2 - \gamma^2)^2 (\epsilon - 1)^2 \epsilon^2}{(1 + \gamma^2)(\epsilon^2 + \gamma^2)(\epsilon^2 + h^2)^2} . \tag{7.41}$$

Now consider for the moment a more general problem of flow around a hydrofoil in the presence of the bottom (Fig. 162). The plate drag R—i.e., the component of the resultant of hydrodynamic forces acting on the foil in the direction of the bottom—is*

$$R = X \cos \alpha_o + Y \sin \alpha_o . \tag{7.42}$$

Now by application of the momentum theorem, R is easily found to be, as in Section A of this chapter,

$$R = \rho v_o^2 \delta \, [1 - \cos (\theta_o - \alpha_o)] . \tag{7.43}$$

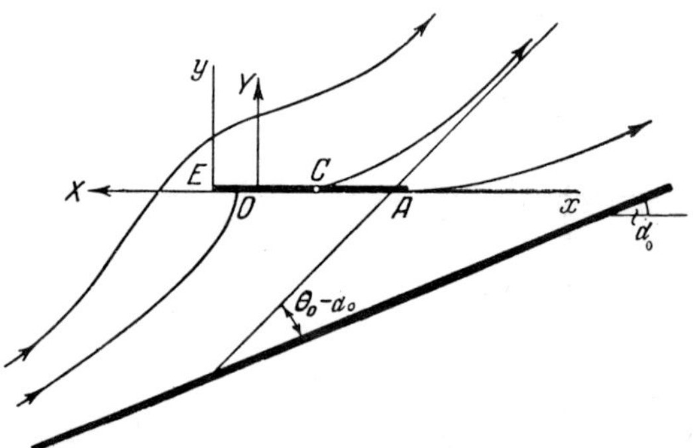

Fig. 162

*The X shown in Fig. 162 is negative.

If $\theta = \pi$, then Eq. (7.7) is regained from Eq. (7.43). From Eqs. (7.41) through (7.43) it is easy to obtain the force acting normal to the plate. We can now, of course, return to the case of a flow with infinite depth.

Fedorov made a series of computations related to the case when the inflection point B (Fig. 159) goes to infinity and to the case when C coincides with E—i.e., when we have a cavitating hydrofoil and zero cavitation number. We now focus our attention on this latter case (Fig. 158). Clearly, when C coincides with E, $\epsilon = 0$. Equation (7.27) for dw/du is unchanged as $\epsilon \to 0$, but Eq. (7.29) becomes

$$\frac{dw}{v_o dz} = \frac{u - 1}{u + i} \quad . \tag{7.44}$$

From Eq. (7.33) or from Eqs. (7.27) and (7.44) it follows that

$$\frac{dz}{du} = -\frac{2\delta}{\pi} \frac{(h^2 - \gamma^2)^2 (u + i)^2 u}{(1 + \gamma^2)(u^2 - \gamma^2)(u^2 - h^2)^2} \quad . \tag{7.45}$$

After an elementary transformation Eq. (7.36) gives, with $\epsilon = 0$, for the plate length

$$\ell = \frac{\delta}{\pi} \left[\frac{(h^2 - 1)(h^2 - \gamma^2)}{h^2 (1 + \gamma^2)} + \frac{1 - \gamma^2}{1 + \gamma^2} \ln \frac{h^2}{\gamma^2} + \frac{\pi (h - \gamma)^2}{h(1 + \gamma^2)} \right] . \tag{7.46}$$

From physical reasoning and from Eq. (7.41) it is seen that $X = 0$. Because of this Eqs. (7.42) and (7.43) give

$$C_y = \frac{2Y}{\rho \ell v_o^2} = \frac{2\delta}{\ell \sin \alpha_o} [1 - \cos (\theta_o - \alpha_o)] \quad . \tag{7.47}$$

The moment M of Y relative to the trailing edge of the plate was found by Kalinin [125] to be

$$M = \frac{\rho v_o^2 \delta^2}{\pi} \frac{\sin \alpha_o}{b - a} \Big([b - (b^2 - 1)^{1/2}] (1 + a) - \frac{a}{2}$$

$$+ \frac{\pi}{2} (1 - a^2)^{1/2} [b - (b^2 - 1)^{1/2}]^2$$

$$+ (1 - ab) \big\{ [b + (b^2 - 1)^{1/2}] \; \ell n \, 2 \, [b - (b^2 - 1)]$$

$$+ (b^2 - 1)^{1/2} \, \ell n \, (b - 1) + b \, \ell n \, (b + 1) \big\} \Big) \, , \qquad (7.48)$$

where

$$a = \frac{h^2 - 1}{h^2 + 1} \, , \qquad b = \frac{h^2 + \gamma^2}{h^2 - \gamma^2} \, .$$

In many practical applications of hydrofoils one seeks to avoid cavitation because it materially reduces the foil's effectiveness. Thus, it is important to examine various typical flow configurations. For example, Fedorov's results for $\ell - d = 0$ are of particular value, but even more interesting will be the solution to the flow shown in Fig. 157.

Jet-theory methods make it possible to solve the flows past curvilinear planing surfaces and curvilinear hydrofoils. We shall present Weinig's [130] and Franke's [131] solutions to these problems. The flow picture is shown in Fig. 163. At infinity (point B) the velocity is horizontal, directed along the negative x-axis, and equal in absolute value to v_o. The regions of change of the complex variable w and the dimensionless complex velocity $dw/v_o dz$ are mapped onto the lower t-plane outside the semicircle $|t| < 1$ (Fig. 164). The

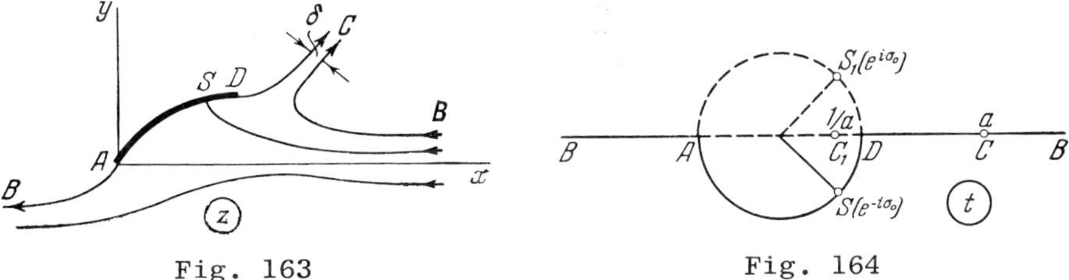

Fig. 163

Fig. 164

semicircle ASD ($|t| = 1$) corresponds to the hydrofoil or wing; the free surfaces correspond to segments of the real axis ($t^2 > 1$). The complex velocity is bounded everywhere in the flow region and zero at the critical point $S(t = \exp[-i\sigma_0])$. We shall denote by w_0 the complex potential for a plane wing. On extending dw_0/v_0dz by using the symmetry principle, we see that in the entire t-plane dw_0/v_0dz has only one zero (at S) and only one singularity [which is the pole at $S_1(t = \exp[-i\sigma_0])$] symmetric to S relative to the real axis. It follows that dw_0/v_0dz has the form

$$\frac{dw_0}{v_0dz} = N \frac{t - \exp[-i\sigma_0]}{t - \exp[i\sigma_0]},$$

It is easily seen that because $t - \infty$ at B_1 the constant $N = 1$. In Levi-Civita's method, where the interior of a unit semicircle serves as a region of change of the parametric variable, dw_0/v_0dz is multiplied by $\exp[F]$, where F is a series in positive powers of the parametric variable with purely imaginary coefficients, in order to obtain dw/v_0dz. Franke's alteration of the Levi-Civita method was to use the outside of the unit circle as the region of the parametric variable. Then F takes the form of a series in negative powers of t. The result is

$$\frac{dw}{v_o dz} = -\frac{t - \exp[-i\sigma_o]}{t - \exp[i\sigma_o]} \exp\left[i \sum_{n=i}^{\infty} \frac{A_n}{t^n}\right], \qquad (7.49)$$

where the constant coefficients A_n are real.

We shall now construct $w(t) = \varphi + i\psi$. Let the stream function $\psi = 0$ along SAB and SDC. Then along BC, $\psi = v_o\delta$, where δ is the jet thickness. In constructing $w(t)$ we can use the symmetry principle. At $C(u = a)$, corresponding to infinity on the jet, there must be a sink, which absorbs the discharge of the spray sheet. An equivalent sink must occur at $C_1(t = 1/a)$, symmetric to C relative to the unit circle. Along BCDSAB, ψ is constant and $w(t)$ represents the complex potential of some flow about the interior and exterior of the unit circle in the t-plane. Accordingly, in addition to the sinks in the t-plane, there must be sources of the same intensity. Outside the unit circle the source must be at infinity; inside the unit circle the source will be at a point symmetric to infinity—i.e., at the origin. The complex potential corresponding to the above combination of sources and sinks is

$$\frac{q}{\pi} \ln\left(t - \frac{1}{a}\right) + \frac{q}{\pi} \ln(t - a) - \frac{q}{\pi} \ln t \quad .$$

The flow presented in Fig. 163 is composed of not only sources and sinks with finite discharge but also a mean flow with infinite discharge and velocity v_o at infinity. The velocity potential of such a flow must have a pole at $B(t = \infty)$ and a corresponding pole at $t = 0$. Now, knowing all the singularities of $w(t)$, we can write

$$w(t) = M\left(t + \frac{1}{t}\right) + \frac{q}{\pi}\left[\ln\left(t - \frac{1}{a}\right) + \ln(t - a) - \ln t\right] \quad . \qquad (7.50)$$

Then,

$$\frac{dw}{dt} = M\left(1 - \frac{1}{t^2}\right) + \frac{q}{\pi}\left[\frac{1}{t - (1/a)} + \frac{1}{t - a} - \frac{1}{t}\right] \tag{7.51}$$

or

$$\frac{dw}{dt} = \frac{M(t - a)[t - (1/a)] + (q/\pi)t}{t^2[t - (1/a)](t - a)}\,(t^2 - 1)\ . \tag{7.52}$$

At the critical (stagnation) point $S(t = \exp[-i\sigma_o])$, $dw/dt = 0$. Thus, it follows directly that

$$\frac{q}{\pi} = M\left(a + \frac{1}{a} - 2\cos\sigma_o\right)\ . \tag{7.53}$$

From Eqs. (7.52) and (7.53) we obtain, finally,

$$\frac{dw}{dt} = M\,\frac{\{t - \exp[i\sigma_o]\}\{t - \exp[-i\sigma_o]\}}{t^2[t - (1/a)](t - a)}\,(t^2 - 1)\ . \tag{7.54}$$

The planing-surface problem can be considered a particular case of the hydrofoil problem that occurs when D and C coincide (Fig. 165). Expression (7.49) for the hydrofoil's complex velocity is not changed by moving C and D together. The complex potential w or dw/dt is obtained from the general Eqs. (7.50) and (7.54) with $a = 1$. Therefore, in the case of a planing surface, we have

$$\left.\begin{aligned} w &= M\left(t + \frac{1}{t}\right) + 2M(1 - \cos\sigma_o)\,[2\,\ell n\,(t - 1) - \ell n\,t] \\ \frac{dw}{dt} &= M\,\frac{\{t - \exp[i\sigma_o]\}\{t - \exp[-i\sigma_o]\}}{t^2} \end{aligned}\right\}. \tag{7.55}$$

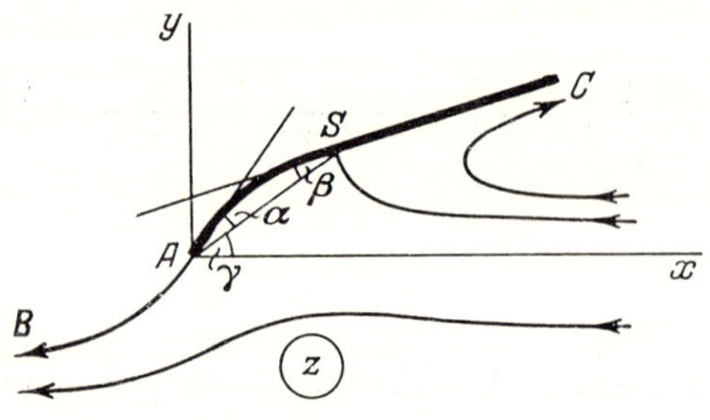

Fig. 165

Thus, Eqs. (7.49) or (7.55) give the general solution for flow about either a curvilinear hydrofoil with $Q = 0$ or a curvilinear planing surface.

Franke [131] gave much attention to the case $a = 1$. By using the general solution and Bernoulli's integral, he obtained all the necessary formulas for determination of surface shape and the resultant force and moment and, furthermore, he carried out some numerical computations. In Eq. (7.49) and in all the other computation equations Franke retained only A_1 and A_2 and set the rest of the A_n $(n > 2)$ coefficients equal to zero. He characterized the shape of the planing surface by the two angles α and β, which the contour forms with the chord AS at A and S (Fig. 165). The attack angle γ of the gliding surface is the angle between the same chord AS and the x-axis. The angles α and β are easily found from Eq. (7.49). To determine γ it is necessary to compute the coordinates of S. This can be done by integrating dz/dt along t. For this, dz/dt is easily found from Eqs. (7.49) and (7.54). The integration must be done numerically in the general case. When A_1 and A_2 are small, Franke replaces $\exp\left[i\{(A_1/t) + (A_2/t)\}\right]$ by the approximation

$$1 + i\left[(A_1/t) + \left(A_2/t^2\right)\right] ,$$

after which the evaluated integral is given in terms of elementary functions. Franke used this same approximation in determining α and β. Unfortunately, this does not lighten the already simple computations, but leads to some formulas more complicated than the exact ones.

The flow about a flat-plate hydrofoil in a finite depth fluid with $Q = 0$ was solved in Refs. [124] and [127]. However, those flows were interpreted as flows past a gliding plate (Fig. 166). In Figs. 167 through 169 we present some of Green's numerical results [127]. In Fig. 167 the normal force coefficient results are given; in Fig. 168, M_B is the moment of the normal force relative to the hydrofoil trailing edge B; and finally, in Fig. 169, d is the distance between the center of pressure and the center of the plate.

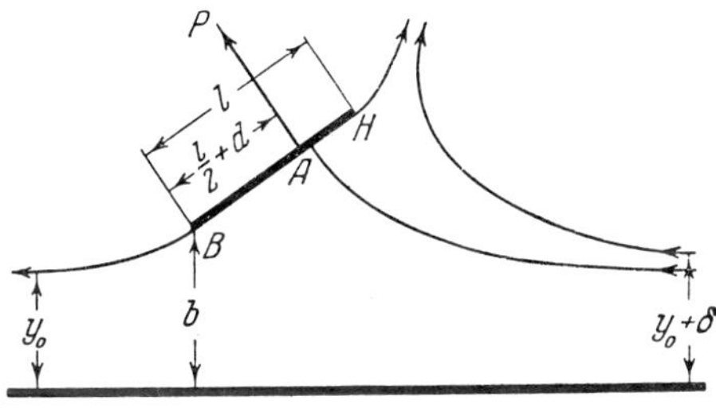

Fig. 166

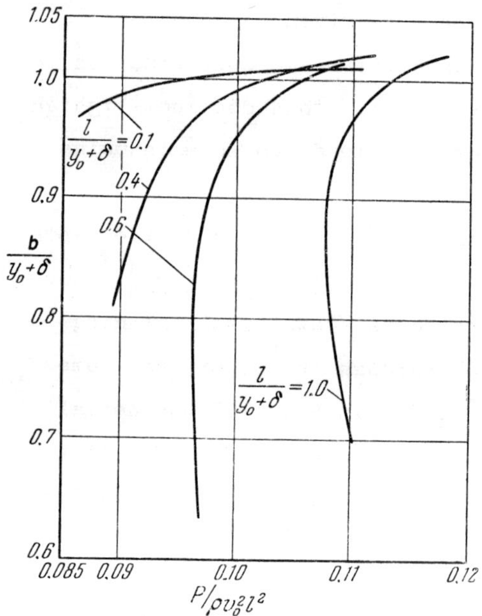

Fig. 167

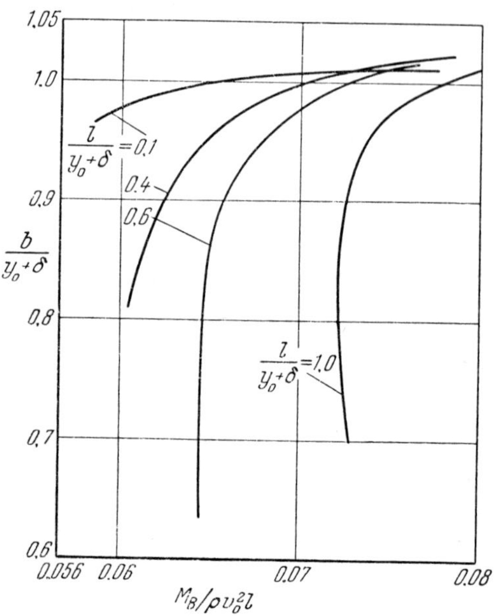

Fig. 168

1.04
1.02
0.98
0.94
0.90
0.1725
0.1825
0.1925
0.2025
d/l
$\frac{l}{y_0+\delta}$ = 1.0
0.1
0.2
0.4
$\frac{l}{y_0+\delta}$ = 0.4
0.1
0.2

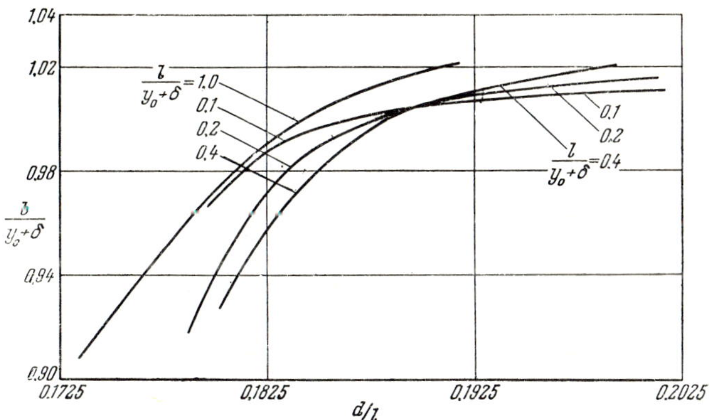

Fig. 169

CHAPTER VIII. VARIOUS FREE-JET PROBLEMS

A. COLLISION OF JETS—HOLLOW CHARGES AND ARMOR-PIERCING JETS

Until now we have studied separated flow around bodies and the jet flow from orifices. However, there is a series of jet problems that are difficult to place within one of these categories. These special problems have both practical and and theoretical value, and their possible varieties are manifold. In this chapter we shall limit the description to that of characteristic free-jet problems.

The collision of jets is a classical problem. In several more-or-less general versions it has been solved in a whole series of old works, [e.g., 10, 132, 133, 134, 135, and 136]. A detailed presentation can be found in Volume I of Cisotti's monograph [51], in which analytical solutions to problems about collision of any number of jets (Fig. 170) or of two jets with formation of a stagnation zone (Fig. 171) are presented. Also, we must mention the group of problems about collision of jets flowing from two channels with rectilinear

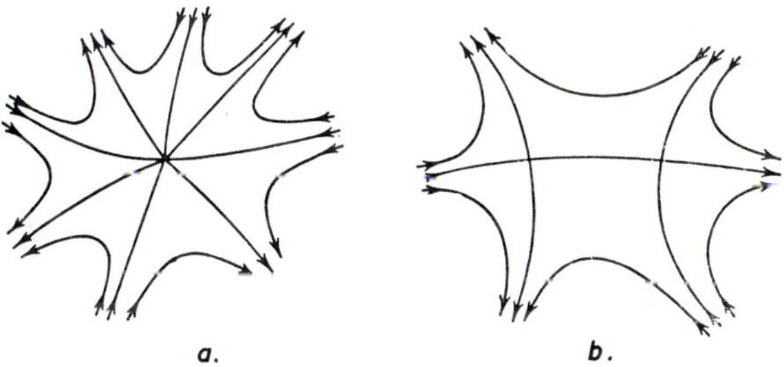

Fig. 170

walls [51]. Mathematical analysis of one such flow (Fig. 172) is given by Birkhoff and Zarantonello [5]. Here we limit the discussion to the collision of two free jets.

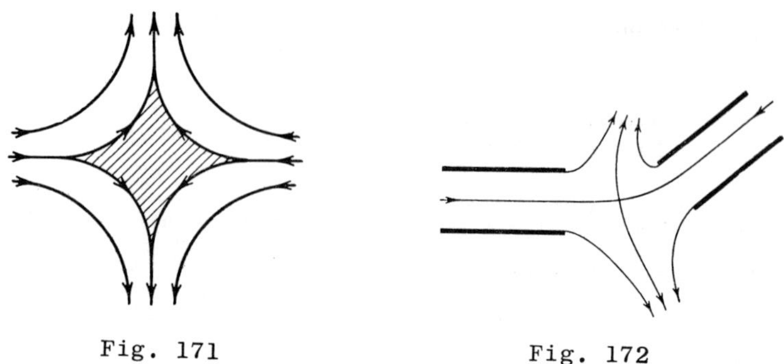

Fig. 171 Fig. 172

Let the two jets A_1 and A_3 (Fig. 173) collide and scatter to the sides in the form of jets A_2 and A_4 under the condition that the pressure and the modulus v of the velocity are respectively the same on all the free surfaces. We choose our time unit so that $v = 1$ on the free surfaces. Thus, the flowrate in each jet is equal to the width of the jet at infinity. We consider a flow with one* critical point

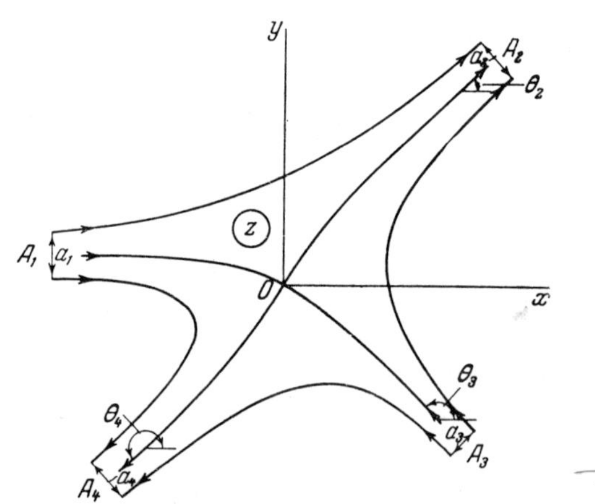

Fig. 173

*Figure 171 shows another possible jet-collision pattern.

0. The origin of the Cartesian coordinate system is placed at 0 and the system is oriented so that the x-axis is parallel to the velocity of the approaching flow in jet A_1 (Fig. 173).

We denote the complex velocity of the flow $dw/dz = ve^{-i\theta}$ by ζ. From Fig. 173 it is easy to see that, as we circle the region boundaries in a clockwise direction (A_1, A_2, A_3, and A_4), the angle θ changes from 0 to 2π, while the argument of $\zeta = dw/dz$ varies from 0 to -2π. Since the maximum value $v = 1$ is achieved on the flow boundaries, the flow region is the unit circle $|\zeta| = 1$ in the ζ-plane (Fig. 174).

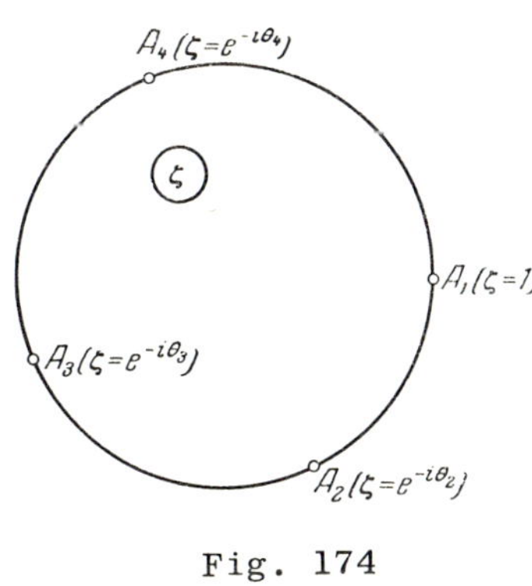

Fig. 174

Now, let the width of the jets A_1, A_2, A_3, and A_4 at infinity be represented by a_1, a_2, a_3, and a_4 respectively. On computing the flowrate in the jets, it is easy to see that, if the stream function $\psi = \psi_o$ on A_1A_2, then on A_2A_3, $\psi = \psi_o - a_2$; on A_3A_4, $\psi = \psi_o - a_2 + a_3$; and on A_4A_1, $\psi = \psi_o - a_2 + a_3 - a_4$. In passage through $A_1(\zeta = 1)$, $A_2(\zeta = \exp[-i\theta_2])$, $A_3(\zeta = \exp[-i\theta_3])$, and $A_4(\zeta = \exp[-i\theta_4])$ the imaginary part of the complex potential experiences jumps of a_1, a_2, a_3, and a_4 respectively. Thus in the ζ-plane, $w(\zeta)$ must have logarithmic singularities at these points. Extension of $w(\zeta)$ to the entire ζ-plane by a "mirror" or reflection mapping does not produce any new singularities, so we can write

$$w(\zeta) = \frac{1}{\pi}\{a_1 \ln(\zeta - 1) + a_3 \ln(\zeta - \exp[-i\theta_3]) - a_2 \ln(\zeta - \exp[-i\theta_2]) - a_4 \ln(\zeta - \exp[-i\theta_4])\} + \text{const.} \tag{8.1}$$

Here it is convenient to remember that the amount of fluid carried in by jets A_1 and A_3 is equal to the amount of fluid carried away by jets A_2 and A_4. Thus,

$$a_1 + a_3 = a_2 + a_4 \quad . \tag{8.2}$$

From condition (8.2) we conclude that there is no logarithmic singularity at infinity in the ζ-plane.

From Eq. (8.1) we obtain

$$\frac{dw}{d\zeta} = \frac{1}{\pi}\left[\frac{a_1}{\zeta - 1} + \frac{a_3}{\zeta - \exp[-i\theta_3]} - \frac{a_2}{\zeta - \exp[-i\theta_2]} - \frac{a_4}{\zeta - \exp[-i\theta_4]}\right] . \tag{8.3}$$

But $\zeta = dw/dz$; so

$$\frac{dz}{d\zeta} = \frac{dz}{dw}\frac{dw}{d\zeta} = \frac{1}{\zeta}\frac{dw}{d\zeta}$$

$$= \frac{1}{\pi}\left[\frac{a_1}{\zeta - 1} - \frac{a_1}{\zeta} + \frac{a_3 \exp[i\theta_3]}{\zeta - \exp[-i\theta_3]} - \frac{a_3 \exp[i\theta_3]}{\zeta} - \frac{a_2 \exp[i\theta_2]}{\zeta - \exp[-i\theta_2]} + \frac{a_2 \exp[i\theta_2]}{\zeta} - \frac{a_4 \exp[i\theta_4]}{\zeta - \exp[-i\theta_4]} + \frac{a_4 \exp[i\theta_4]}{\zeta}\right] . \tag{8.4}$$

In the flow region, $z(\zeta)$ is single-valued, and the integral $\int (dz/d\zeta)\, d\zeta$ taken along a circle of infinitesimal radius with center at $\zeta = 0$ must be zero. It follows that the coefficient of the $1/\zeta$ term in the expansion (8.4) must be 0 and therefore that

$$-a_1 - a_3 \exp [i\theta_3] + a_2 \exp [i\theta_2] + a_4 \exp [i\theta_4] = 0. \quad (8.5)$$

Equation (8.5) can be obtained directly also by applying the momentum theorem; separating the real and imaginary parts leads to

$$\left.\begin{aligned} -a_1 - a_3 \cos \theta_3 + a_2 \cos \theta_2 + a_4 \cos \theta_4 &= 0 \\ - a_3 \sin \theta_3 + a_2 \sin \theta_2 + a_4 \sin \theta_4 &= 0 \end{aligned}\right\} . \quad (8.6)$$

By integrating Eq. (8.4) and introducing Eq. (8.5) into the result, we obtain

$$\begin{aligned} z(\zeta) = \frac{1}{\pi} \{a_1\, \ell n\, (1 - \zeta) &+ a_3 \exp [i\theta_3]\, \ell n\, (1 - \zeta \exp [-i\theta_3]) \\ &- a_2 \exp [i\theta_2]\, \ell n\, (1 - \zeta \exp [-i\theta_2]) \\ &- a_4 \exp [i\theta_4]\, \ell n\, (1 - \zeta \exp [-i\theta_4])\} . \end{aligned} \quad (8.7)$$

The free surfaces are mapped to arcs on the unit circle in the ζ-plane. The shapes of the jets are obtained by setting $\zeta = e^{i\sigma}$ in Eq. (8.7)—see, e.g., [51]. Note that, if at each point in the flow the direction of the velocity is reversed without changing its magnitude, then the streamlines are not altered.

From the physical point of view the solution of the problem must be completely determined by the widths a_1 and a_3 of the colliding jets and the angle θ_3 between them. Four parameters need to be determined: θ_2, θ_4, a_2, and a_4. For the determination of these four parameters we have only three conditions, incorporated in Eqs. (8.2) and (8.6), thereby making the problem indeterminate.* However, when jets A_1 and A_3 are parallel—i.e., $\theta_3 = \pi$—the problem is determinate. In this case, in addition to the angle $\theta_3 = \pi$ and the width of jets A_1 and A_3, it is possible to prescribe also the displacement of the jets relative to each other (Fig. 175).

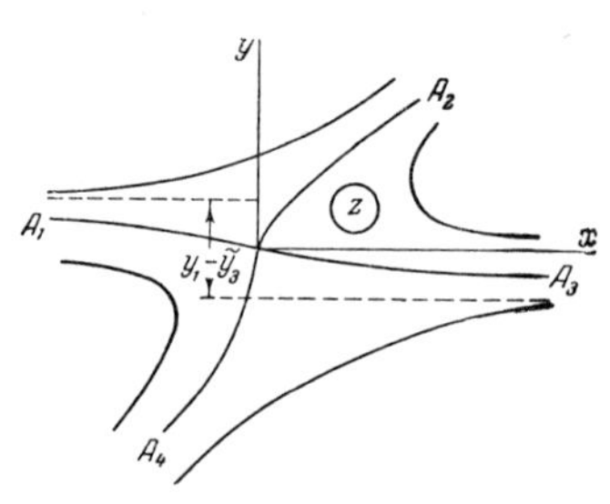

Fig. 175

This displacement can be characterized by the distance between the centerlines of jets A_1 and A_3 at infinity or, as shown in Fig. 175, by the distance $y_1 - \tilde{y}_3$ between the upper free surface of jet A_1 at infinity and the lower free surface of jet A_3 at infinity. Note, incidentally, that if this difference exceeds in absolute value the sum of the jets' widths, the jets will not collide. The distance $y_1 - \tilde{y}_3$ can be computed from Eq. (8.6). Thus,

$$y_1 - \tilde{y}_3 = a_1 - a_4 \cos\theta_4$$

$$- \frac{1}{\pi}\left[a_2 \sin\theta_2 \,\ell n\left|\tan\frac{\theta_2}{2}\right| + a_4 \sin\theta_4 \,\ell n\left|\tan\frac{\theta_4}{2}\right|\right].$$

If $\theta_3 = \pi$ and the centerlines of jets A_1 and A_2 coincide, then the flow picture is symmetric with respect to

*An attempt to make the problem determinate by introducing a complementary arbitrary hypothesis was made by Palatini [137].

the x-axis (Fig. 176). Also, the x-axis is then a streamline and can be replaced by a solid wall. In the particular case under consideration, $\theta_2 = 2\pi - \theta_4$. Thus, from Eqs. (8.2) and (8.6), we have

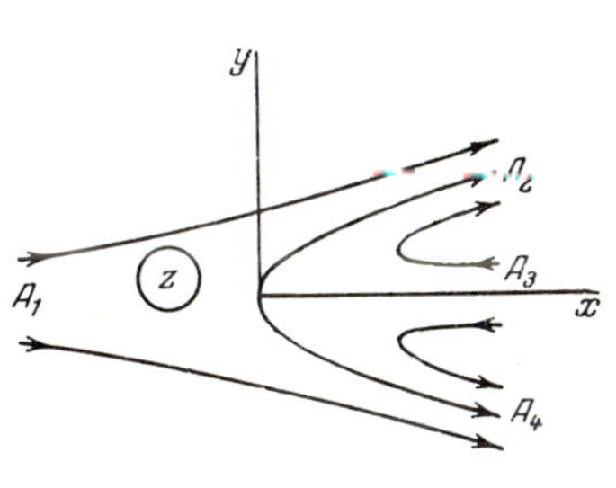

Fig. 176

$$\left.\begin{aligned} a_2 &= a_4 \\ a_1 + a_3 &= 2a_2 \\ a_1 - a_3 &= 2a_2 \cos \theta_2 \end{aligned}\right\} , \qquad (8.8)$$

and then

$$\cos \theta_2 = \frac{a_1 - a_3}{a_1 + a_3} . \qquad (8.9)$$

As a result, Eq. (8.3) can be transformed into

$$\frac{dw}{d\zeta} = \frac{8a_1a_3\zeta}{\pi(a_1 + a_3)(\zeta^2 - 1)(\zeta - \exp[i\theta_2])(\zeta - \exp[-i\theta_2])} . \qquad (8.10)$$

Another interesting case occurs when a jet of finite width $a_3 = a$ collides with a flow of infinite width $a_1 = \infty$. Clearly, Eq. (8.9) shows that $\theta_2 = 0$ now, and Eq. (8.10) gives then

$$\frac{dw}{d\zeta} = \frac{8a\zeta}{\pi(\zeta + 1)(\zeta - 1)^3} . \qquad (8.11)$$

If at each point in the flow the direction of the velocity is reversed, the streamlines of the flow are not altered (Fig. 177); but the signs of the complex potential and complex velocity change. Equations (8.8) and (8.9) remain unchanged because the sign of $\cos \theta_2$ does not depend on the sign of θ_2. The resulting flow in the upper or lower halves of Fig.

177 is then, in essence, the flow of a jet along a semi-infinite plate.

During World War II an important and unexpected application of jet theory to armor-piercing hollow charges was made. In Fig. 178 we show a simplified model of such a charge. The

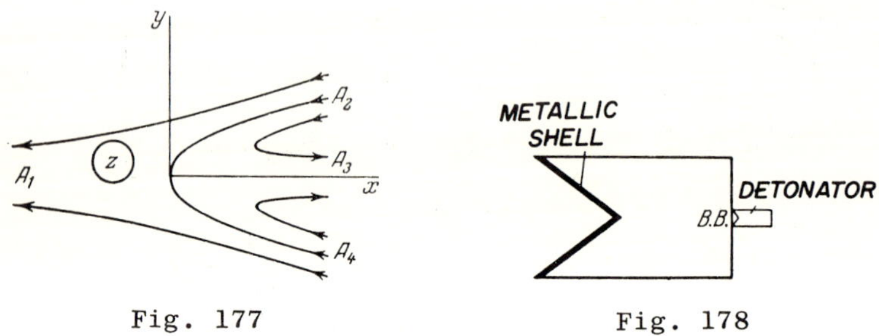

Fig. 177

Fig. 178

detonation wave travels through the exploding substance with a velocity of 7 to 10 km/sec. Behind the wave front the pressure is of the order of 100,000 atmospheres. Under these pressures, the strength of the material and plastic resistance are very small compared to the inertial forces, and the metallic shell acts as an ideal fluid. The collapse of the walls of the conical or wedge-shaped shell produces a flow similar to that obtained in the collision of jets. The resulting thin metal jet moves forward with a tremendous velocity and striking force.

The first applications of charges with cavities, but without the metallic shell, were made in rock-blasting as early as the end of the 19th Century. The first patent for the use of the shell charge with a cavity—covered by a metallic shell—for armor-piercing was issued in 1914, but wide practical application of armor-piercing hollow charges was made only during the Second World War. The first unclassified publication in which the theoretical bases for analysis of hollow charges with metallic shells were presented was by

Birkhoff, MacDougall, Pugh and Taylor [138]. Afterwards, a whole series of articles on the same subject was published in the same Journal of Applied Physics. A detailed survey of these articles was made by Ivanova and Rozantseva [139], who included a large bibliography in their survey. In relation to the theory of hollow charges, Lavrentiev [140] described a series of interesting mathematical problems.* We, of course, can dwell on only the simplest basic theory of the hollow charge with a wedge-shaped metallic shell and of armor piercing. A series of important effects, which serve only to complicate portrayal of the phenomenon, will be ignored for our presentation. These neglected effects and experimental results are discussed in Ref. [139].

To reduce the hollow-charge problem to a classical jet-collision problem (Fig. 177), the following approximating assumptions are made:

1. After the detonation wave passes, the walls of the metallic shell move in with a constant velocity until they meet on the axis of the projectile.
2. Under the action of the huge pressure produced by the collision, the metal of the shell behaves as an ideal fluid.
3. Relative to an axis, connected to the "junction"—i.e., to the point of the meeting of the metallic walls—the flow is steady.
4. The surfaces of the fluid-metal jet are free surfaces.

A schematic drawing of the hollow-charge jet formation is given in Fig. 179. The initial position of the shell is represented by the angle DBC. In passing through the shell

*Lavrentiev's work was done before publication of [138] but came to light after considerable delay.

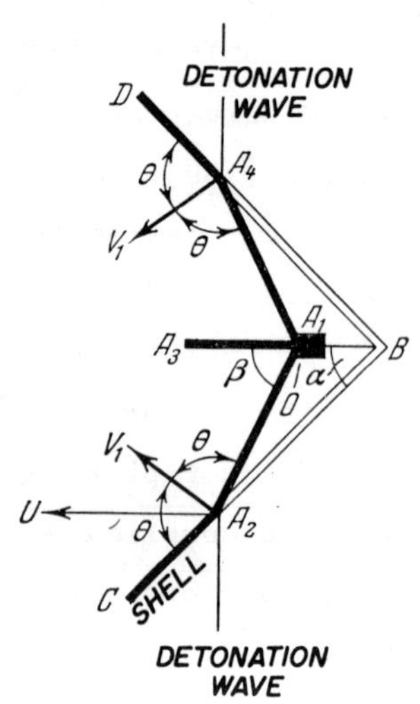

Fig. 179

with a horizontal velocity U, the detonation wave transfers impulses to successive parts of the shell. From elementary geometric considerations it is possible to show [e.g., 139], that those parts of the shell affected by the detonation wave's passage up through point A_2 move along the bisector of the angle OA_2C with a velocity

$$V_o = \frac{2U \sin [(\beta - \alpha)/2]}{\cos \alpha} .$$

Colliding on the axis of symmetry in the junction 0, the parts of the shell form a thin jet OA_3 and a so-called core OA_1.

The absolute velocity of the junction 0 in a fixed coordinate system is

$$V_1 = V_o \frac{\cos [(\beta - \alpha)/2]}{\sin \beta} = \frac{U \sin (\beta - \alpha)}{\sin \beta \cos \alpha} . \tag{8.12}$$

According to assumption 3, the flow relative to the junction 0 is steady, and 0 is a stagnation or critical point. The velocity in the jets relative to 0 is

$$V_2 = V_o \frac{\cos [(\beta + \alpha)/2]}{\sin \beta} = \frac{U}{\cos \alpha} - \frac{U \tan \alpha}{\sin \beta} . \tag{8.13}$$

In a fixed coordinate system, the jet moves to the left and has a velocity

$$V_j = V_1 + V_2 . \tag{8.14}$$

Thus, the jet provides the basic armor-piercing action. The core also moves to the left but has the considerably lower absolute velocity

$$V_s = V_1 - V_2 \quad . \tag{8.15}$$

On substituting V_1 and V_2 from Eqs. (8.12) and (8.13) in Eqs. (8.14) and (8.15), we find after an elementary transformation that

$$\left.\begin{aligned} V_j &= 4U \frac{\cos(\beta/2)\cos(\alpha/2)\sin[(\beta-\alpha)/2]}{\cos\alpha \sin\beta} \\ V_s &= 4U \frac{\sin(\alpha/2\beta)\sin(\beta/2)\sin[(\beta-\alpha)/2]}{\cos\alpha \sin\beta} \end{aligned}\right\} \quad . \tag{8.16}$$

It follows immediately that

$$\lim_{\alpha\to 0} V_j \leqq 2U; \qquad \lim_{\alpha\to 0} V_s = 0 \quad .$$

However, as $\alpha \to 0$, our elementary theory no longer agrees even approximately with experiments. We note, in passing, that the theory and experiments agree more in the early part of jet formation, while they are most divergent in the final part, when the material in the metallic shell becomes exhausted.

Since the velocities in the jets relative to 0 are equal, the ratio of the mass of the jet m_j to the mass of the core m_s is equal to the ratio of the widths of the jet and the core at "infinity." Obviously, we can use Eq. (8.9) to find m_j/m_s simply by replacing a_1/a_3 by m_j/m_s and θ_2 by $\pi - \beta$. As a result, we are led to

$$\cos\beta = \frac{1 - (m_j/m_s)}{1 + (m_j/m_s)}$$

and

$$\frac{m_j}{m_s} = \frac{1 - \cos\beta}{1 + \cos\beta} \quad . \tag{8.17}$$

If the metallic-shell mass is

$$m = m_j + m_s \quad , \tag{8.18}$$

then, from Eqs. (8.17) and (8.18),

$$m_j = \frac{m}{2}(1 - \cos\beta) \;, \qquad m_s = \frac{m}{2}(1 + \cos\beta) \quad . \tag{8.19}$$

Now, we consider the jet as it strikes the armor. As in the jet formation in the hollow charge, the tremendous jet velocity (in the armor-charges the usual velocity is 9 km/sec [139]) causes the armor to behave as an ideal fluid. Also, in comparison to the thin projectile jet, the armor flow can be considered a jet flow of infinite width. Thus, the general solution can be obtained, as we shall see below, from Eq. (8.10). The flow picture is given in Fig. 180. It is important to remember that the armor density ρ_I is not necessarily

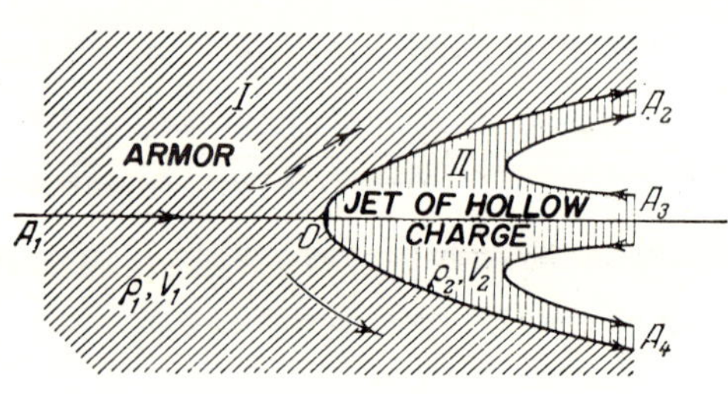

Fig. 180

equal to the jet density ρ_{II}, while Eq. (8.10) was obtained for the case $\rho_I = \rho_{II}$. In Fig. 180, A_2OA_4 is a separation line between the armor (Region I) and the jet (Region II). At infinity the armor is fixed (has zero velocity) and the absolute velocity U_o of 0 is taken to be the striking velocity of the armor-piercing jet. As before, the flow is steady relative to the coordinate axis with fixed origin at 0.

Along the line A_2OA_4 the velocity is discontinuous, but the pressure must vary continuously across this line. Thus, if the moduli of the armor and jet velocities are V_I and V_{II} respectively, then, according to Bernoulli's theorem, the following relation must hold along A_2OA_4:

$$\frac{1}{2}\rho_I V_I^2 = \frac{1}{2}\rho_{II} V_{II}^2 \quad . \tag{8.20}$$

Hence,

$$\frac{V_{II}}{V_I} = \left[\frac{\rho_{II}}{\rho_I}\right]^{1/2} = \lambda \quad . \tag{8.21}$$

In the fixed coordinate system the modulus of the jet velocity is V_j and the velocity of the jet at infinity (point A_3) is $-V_j + U_o$, relative to that axis connected to 0. The armor flow velocity at infinity (point A_1) is U_o. Since the pressures at A_1 and A_3 are equal, Bernoulli's integral gives

$$\frac{1}{2}\rho_I U_o^2 = \frac{1}{2}\rho_{II}(U_o - V_j)^2 \quad ;$$

now, if V_j is known, it is easy to find

$$U_o = \frac{\lambda V_j}{1 + \lambda} \quad . \tag{8.22}$$

The equivalent problem of jet collision in a channel was studied by Alekseevskii [27].

Now we can solve the hydrodynamic problem of the motion of the armor and jet "fluids." First, we note that multiplying the velocities at each point by a constant factor does not alter the flow streamlines; such a multiplication is equivalent to a simple change in the units for velocity measurement. In obtaining Eq. (8.11) we set the jet-surface velocity equal to unity everywhere and held the density equal and constant everywhere. Here, the flow represented by Eq. (8.11) becomes equivalent to the real fluid flow if

1. The density in Region I is ρ_I and in Region II is ρ_{II}.
2. All velocities in Region I are multipled by U_o and in Region II by $V_j - U_o = U_o/\lambda$.

Now Eq. (8.11) can be adapted to describe the present flow, but it is convenient to consider the variable ζ as equal to $dw/U_o dz$ in Region I and $\lambda\, dw/U_o dz$ in Region II.

B. JET FLOWS WITH SINGULARITIES IN THE REGION OCCUPIED BY THE FLUID

A theory for jet flows containing sources, sinks, and other singularities in the flow region was given by Hopkinson [141]. The problems were solved by mapping the region of change of the complex potential and the logarithm of the complex velocity onto the upper half-plane of the variable u. In the absence of singularities, Hopkinson's equations reduce to Zhukovskii's (see Chapter I, Section E, or [10]). Hopkinson studied some particular examples in detail, namely: 1) a vortex in a finite region that is bounded partly by a flat plate and partly by a free surface, 2) a vortex and a doublet in a finite region bounded by a free surface, and 3) a doublet in a jet flowing from a channel. Examples related to Hopkinson's are discussed in [5]. In Figs. 181 and 182 we show a vortex between two plates and two free surfaces and a source between two plates.

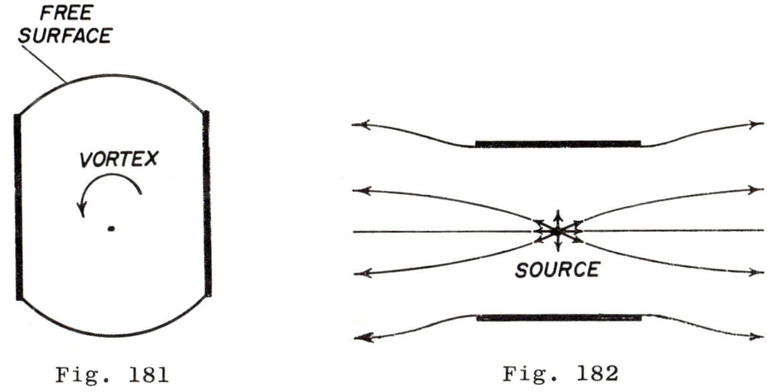

Fig. 181 Fig. 182

The above jet theory with singularities can be applied to jet flow around a body. The solution to this problem is useful in correction of experimental results for wall effects in wind and cavitation tunnels where free surfaces are present.

We assume that a vortex with circulation $-\Gamma$ is placed in a free jet with a finite discharge q (Fig. 183). It is obvious that to a first approximation this flow can be considered a free jet flow around a wing; it was first studied in 1919 by Banzi [5, pg. 62]. This and a more general flow with a vortex located in an open section of a wind tunnel (Fig. 184)* were solved by Simmons [142, 143]. The vortex

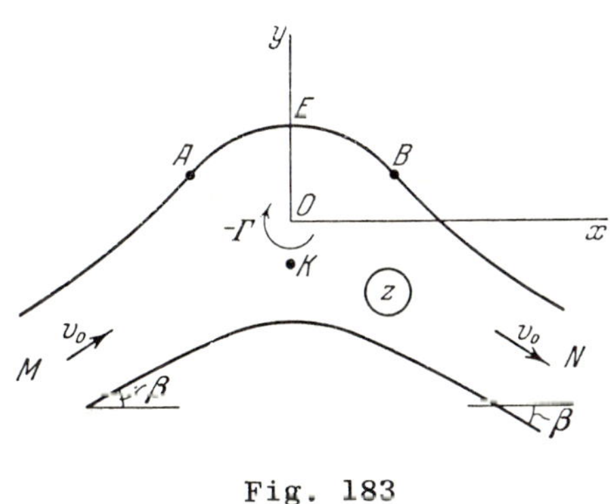

Fig. 183

*In Fig. 184 the walls DC and DE are parallel to the x-axis. The walls BA and FA of the collector sections are actually

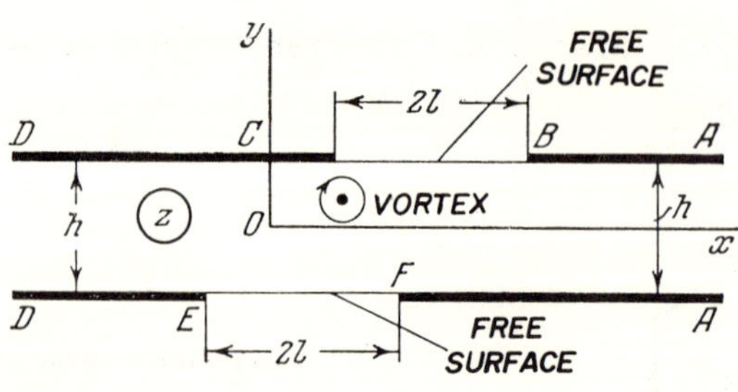

Fig. 184

in a free jet was studied also by Nikolskii [144], who carried out a detailed analysis and did some numerical computations (with $\Gamma/q = 0.5$).

We shall be concerned here only with a vortex in a free jet. We put the coordinate origin at point O, where the vortex is located, and set the x-axis so that the approaching and the departing jets form equal angles $\pm\beta$ (Fig. 183) with the x-axis. The solution is constructed from the complex potential w and the dimensionless complex velocity $\zeta = dw/v_o dz$, where v_o is the constant velocity on the free surface. Let the parametric variable t vary over a circle of radius R so that the center of the circle $t = 0$ corresponds to point O (Fig. 185). The points M and N at infinity correspond to the points $t_M = Re^{i\alpha}$ and $t_N = Re^{-i\alpha}$ on the circle $|t| = R$. At these points $w(t)$ has logarithmic singularities. During passage around these points on an infinitesimal semicircle $\text{Im } w = \psi$ jumps by $\pm q$. In other words, there is a source at M and a sink at N. At point O $(t = 0)$, where the vortex is located, $w(t)$ also has a logarithmic singularity. Under a passage around $t = 0$ along

inclined downward from the x-axis by a very small angle δ (the inclination is not shown in Fig. 184).

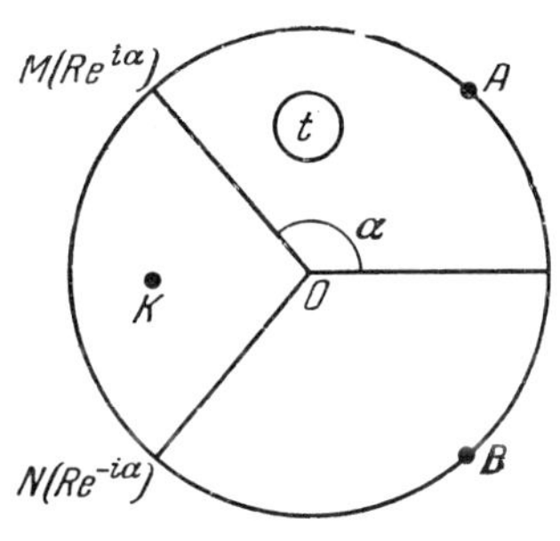

Fig. 185

a small contour, $\mathrm{Re}\, w = \varphi$ jumps by $-\Gamma$. Since the circle $|t| = R$ corresponds to the streamlines—i.e., constant values of $\mathrm{Im}\, w$—$w(t)$ can be extended over the entire t-plane by the reflection-mapping principle. As a result, in addition to the previously existing vortex, source, and sink, we must have a vortex at infinity. It follows that

$$w = \frac{q}{\pi} \ln \frac{t - Re^{i\alpha}}{t - Re^{-i\alpha}} + \frac{i\Gamma}{2\pi} \ln t \quad , \tag{8.23}$$

and

$$\frac{dw}{dt} = \frac{q}{\pi} \left[\frac{1}{t - Re^{i\alpha}} - \frac{1}{t - Re^{-i\alpha}} \right] + \frac{i\Gamma}{2\pi t} \quad . \tag{8.24}$$

Equation (8.24) could have been obtained directly by considering that dw/dt has simple poles at $t = Re^{i\alpha}$, $t = Re^{-i\alpha}$, and $t = 0$, and that as $t \to \infty$, $dw/dt \approx \Gamma i/(2\pi t)$. On setting $\Gamma/q = \gamma$ we find from Eq. (8.24)

$$\frac{dw}{dt} = \frac{\Gamma i \, \{t^2 + 2Rt \, [(2 \sin \alpha/\gamma) - \cos \alpha] + R^2\}}{2\pi t(t - Re^{i\alpha})(t - Re^{-i\alpha})} \quad . \tag{8.25}$$

Since the mapping of the flow region z onto the interior of the unit circle in the t-plane is conformal, dz/dt is bounded and nonzero inside of this circle. Because of this, the point $t = t_o$, where $dw/dt = 0$, is a critical point of the flow and, at this point, $dw/dz = (dw/dt)(dt/dz) = 0$. Equation (8.25) now yields a quadratic equation

$$t_o^2 + 2Rt_o\left(\frac{2 \sin \alpha}{\gamma} - \cos \alpha\right) + R^2 = 0 \quad . \tag{8.26}$$

for t_o. Thus,

$$t_o = -R\left(\frac{2 \sin \alpha}{\gamma} - \cos \alpha\right) \pm \left[R^2\left(\frac{2 \sin \alpha}{\gamma} - \cos \alpha\right)^2 - R^2\right]^{1/2} \quad . \tag{8.27}$$

If $[(2 \sin \alpha/\gamma) - \cos \alpha]^2 \leqq 1$, $|t_o| = R$—i.e., the critical points lie on the free surface, a configuration which is impossible. Thus,

$$\left(\frac{2 \sin \alpha}{\gamma} - \cos \alpha\right)^2 > 1 \quad , \tag{8.28}$$

and the roots t_o are real. The physical meaning of the inequality (8.28) is obvious. The ratio $\Gamma/q = \gamma$ must be sufficiently small for the flow picture of Fig. 183 to be possible.

Since the product of the roots of Eq. (8.26) is R^2, one of the values of t_o lies inside the circle $|t| = R$ and the other lies outside. Obviously, only $|t_o| < R$ has physical meaning. We can choose a circle of any radius R as a region of change of the parametric variable. It is convenient, however, to choose R so that $t_o = -1$. Then from Eq. (8.26) we have

$$R^2 - 2R\left(\frac{2 \sin \alpha}{\gamma} - \cos \alpha\right) + 1 = 0 \tag{8.29}$$

for determination of R. On solving this equation, we find

$$R = \frac{2 \sin \alpha}{\gamma} - \cos \alpha + \left[\left(\frac{2 \sin \alpha}{\gamma} - \cos \alpha\right)^2 - 1\right]^{1/2} \quad . \tag{8.30}$$

Since the product of the roots of Eq. (8.29) is equal to 1, then the smallest root gives $R < 1$, which is not usable because then $|t_o| = |-1|$ is larger than R.

Since on the basis of Eq. (8.30) one of the roots of Eq. (8.26) is $t_o = -1$, the second root is, obviously, $-R^2$. Therefore, Eq. (8.25) can be written in the form

$$\frac{dw}{dt} = \frac{\Gamma i(t+1)(t+R^2)}{2\pi t(t - Re^{i\alpha})(t - Re^{-i\alpha})} . \tag{8.31}$$

Next $dw/v_o dz = \zeta$ is found. In the neighborhood of 0, where the vortex is located, $w \approx -(\Gamma/2\pi i)\,\ell n\, z$ and, consequently, $\zeta \approx -\Gamma/(2\pi i v_o z)$; therefore, ζ has a simple pole at $t = 0$. At $K(t = t_o = -1)$, as shown above, ζ has a zero. When $|t| = R$, $|dw/v_o dz| = 1$. Thus, on extending $\zeta(t)$ to the entire t-plane we find that $\zeta(t)$ has another pole at $t = -R$ and a zero at infinity. By constructing $\zeta(t)$ from its poles and zeros, we find

$$\zeta = \frac{dw}{v_o dz} = \frac{R^2(t+1)}{t(R^2+t)} . \tag{8.32}$$

The constant factor in Eq. (8.32) is chosen so that $|\zeta| = 1$ when $|t| = R$ and thus the arguments of ζ at M and N differ only in sign. Now we let $t = Re^{i\sigma}$ on the bounded circle. Then, since on the free surface $\zeta = e^{-i\theta}$, where θ is the angle between the velocity and the x-axis, we have from Eq. (8.32)

$$e^{-i\theta} = \frac{R + e^{-i\sigma}}{R + e^{i\sigma}}$$

and

$$\theta = 2 \arctan \frac{\sin \sigma}{R + \cos \sigma} . \qquad (8.33)$$

Now it is easy to see that β, the angle between the velocity and the x-axis in the approaching flow (point M), is

$$\beta = 2 \arctan \frac{\sin \alpha}{R + \cos \alpha} . \qquad (8.34)$$

The angle θ has maximum and minimum values at $\sigma = \pm\arccos(1/R)$. These values of σ correspond to the inflection points A and B on the bounding streamlines (Fig. 183). It is easy to see that the solution obtained is completely determined when the following are given: Γ, q, v_o, and α. Clearly, when the other parameters are given, knowledge of α is equivalent to knowledge of the vortex location in the jet. Knowing $dz/dt = (v_o dz/dw)(dw/dt)(1/v_o)$, we easily find $z(t)$ by integration. The streamlines are symmetric with respect to the y-axis.

We proceed now to determine the force acting on the vortex. By applying the momentum theorem we find that the force projections X and Y on the coordinate axes are

$$X = 0 ; \qquad Y = 2\rho q\, v_o \sin \beta . \qquad (8.35)$$

From Eqs. (8.29) and (8.34) it follows that

$$\sin \beta = 2 \sin \left(\arctan \frac{\sin \alpha}{R + \cos \alpha}\right) \cos \left(\arctan \frac{\sin \alpha}{R + \cos \alpha}\right)$$

$$= 2 \frac{\sin \alpha(R + \cos \alpha)}{R^2 + 2R \cos \alpha + 1} = \frac{(R + \cos \alpha)\gamma}{2R} ;$$

thus Eq. (8.35) is transformed to

$$Y = \rho\Gamma v_o\left(1 + \frac{\cos\alpha}{R}\right). \qquad (8.36)$$

In an infinite ideal-fluid flow a wing profile has a lift equal to $\rho v_o\Gamma$ according to the Zhukovskii theorem. If the lift L is considered a projection of Y on the perpendicular to the direction of approaching flow at M, then $L = Y\cos\beta$. In addition the wing (vortex) experiences a drag $D = Y\sin\beta$ in a free jet of finite width. Using the circle of variable radius R as the region of change of the parametric variable makes conversion of the finite jet to an unlimited fluid flow ($\gamma = \Gamma/q \to 0$) easy. From Eqs. (8.30) and (8.34) it is seen that as $\gamma \to 0$, $R \to \infty$ and $\beta \to 0$. Therefore, in the limit $\gamma \to 0$, Eq. (8.36) becomes equivalent to Zhukovskii's theorem and $Y = L = \rho v_o\Gamma$.

Another interesting flow worthy of brief examination is a doublet in a free jet. A doublet in an infinite fluid flow produces a flow around a circle, but in a free jet it produces a free-jet flow around an almost circular contour.*

Figure 186 shows the upper half of a flow of a symmetric free jet, with thickness h and velocity v_o, past a doublet placed on the axis of symmetry at A. Points H and B are critical points; F and D mark the inflection points on the free surface. The line HNB is a streamline that approximates a circular arc. However, we consider the flow outside and the auxiliary flow inside the contour HNB as a single flow.

*We note, incidentally, that Woods [145] in solving the free-jet flow about an oscillating wing solved as a particular case a symmetric free-jet flow around a thin symmetric profile at zero angle of attack.

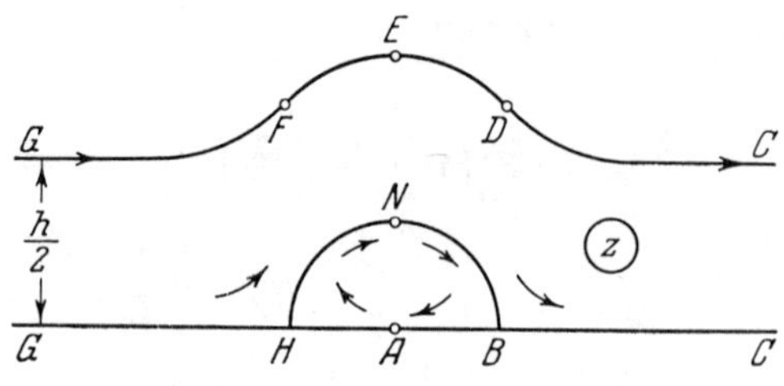

Fig. 186

Whitehead [146] examined the complex potential w and the function $\omega = \ell n\,(dw/v_o dz) = \ell n\,(v/v_o) - i\theta$ for this flow. The region of change of ω, corresponding to that part of the flow shown in Fig. 186, is given in Fig. 187. There, the vertical cut corresponds to the free surface where $\ell n\,(v/v_o) = 0$. The horizontal cut, where $\theta = 0$, corresponds to GH and BC on the axis of symmetry of the flow. The lines $-\theta = \pm\pi$ correspond to the segments HA and BC inside the circle. Since the boundary of the region of change of ω consists of straight lines, Whitehead was able to map the region onto the upper half-plane of the parametric variable t (Fig. 188) by using the Schwarz-Christoffel formula

$$\frac{d\omega}{dt} = -\frac{2b^2 i}{d^2}\,\frac{t^2 - d^2}{t(t^2 - b^2)(t^2 - 1)^{1/2}}\,, \tag{8.37}$$

from which

$$\omega = -\frac{2b^2 i}{d^2}\int_{\infty}^{t}\frac{t^2 - d^2}{t(t^2 - b^2)(t^2 - 1)^{1/2}}\,dt\;. \tag{8.38}$$

The lead constant-factor in Eqs. (8.37) and (8.38) was chosen so that the angle θ jumps by 2π when we pass through A (from BA onto HA). The lower limit in the integral in Eq. (8.38) was chosen so that $\omega = 0$ at E. Equation (8.38) may

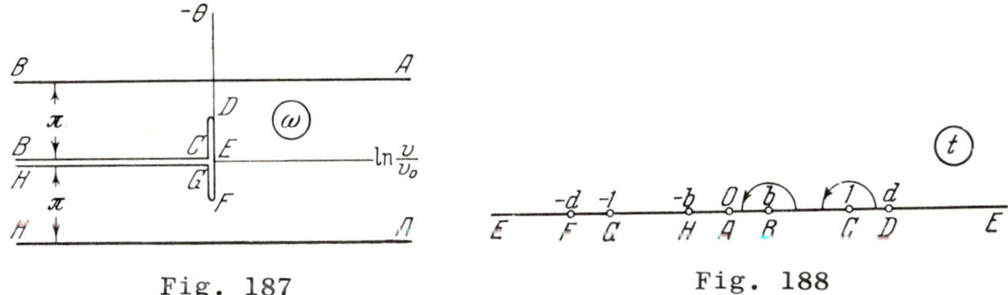

Fig. 187

Fig. 188

be verified directly. It is sufficient to trace the change of the function under the integral as we move along the real t-axis from $+\infty$ to $-\infty$. Under a passage around B $(t = b)$ in a counterclockwise direction along an infinitesimal semicircle, $\operatorname{Im} \omega = -\theta$ jumps by π. This gives a condition relating the constants b and d:

$$\frac{2b^2}{d^2} \cdot \frac{d^2 - b^2}{2b^2(1 - b^2)^{1/2}} = 1 \quad ,$$

from which we obtain:

$$d^2 = \frac{b^2}{1 - (1 - b^2)^{1/2}} = 1 + (1 - b^2)^{1/2} \quad . \qquad (8.39)$$

Performing the integration in Eq. (8.38), using Eq. (8.39), and exponentiating both sides of the result leads to

$$\frac{dw}{v_o dz} = \frac{(t^2 - 1)^{1/2} + i(t^2 - 1)^{1/2} - i(1 - b^2)^{1/2}}{(t^2 - 1)^{1/2} - i(t^2 - 1)^{1/2} + i(1 - b^2)^{1/2}} \quad . \qquad (8.40)$$

Obviously, $w(t)$ has logarithmic singularities at G $(t = -1)$ and C $(t = 1)$ and a pole at A $(t = 0)$, where the doublet is located. Thus, $dw/v_o dt$ has simple poles at G and C and a second-order pole at A. Furthermore, $dw/v_o dt$ has simple zeros at the critical points H and B $(t = \pm b)$. Since the boundaries of the flow region are streamlines, we have $\operatorname{Im}(dw/v_o dt) = 0$ along the real t-axis. On extending $dw/v_o dt$ in accordance with the symmetry principle to the entire t-plane, we do not add any new singularities or zeros. Therefore, by making use of the singular point method, we write

$$\frac{dw}{v_o dt} = -\frac{h(t^2 - b^2)}{\pi(1 - b^2)t^2(t^2 - 1)} . \qquad (8.41)$$

The constant factor (h/π) in Eq. (8.41) was chosen so that the jet flowrate is $v_o h$. It is possible to find dz/dt from Eqs. (8.39) and (8.40). Then, integration gives $z(t)$.

Denoting the contour's horizontal diameter HB by 2f and its vertical diameter 2AN by 2g, Whitehead finds the following approximate expression for small b:

$$\left.\begin{aligned} \frac{\pi f}{h} &= b + \frac{5}{6}b^3 + \frac{61}{80}b^5 + \frac{481}{672}b^7 + \ldots \\ \frac{\pi g}{h} &= b + \frac{5}{6}b^3 + \frac{577}{720}b^5 + \frac{7967}{10080}b^7 + \ldots \end{aligned}\right\} . \qquad (8.42)$$

By an analogous method Whitehead [146] solved the problem of a doublet in a jet where symmetric plates covered the front and back of the doublet (Fig. 189).

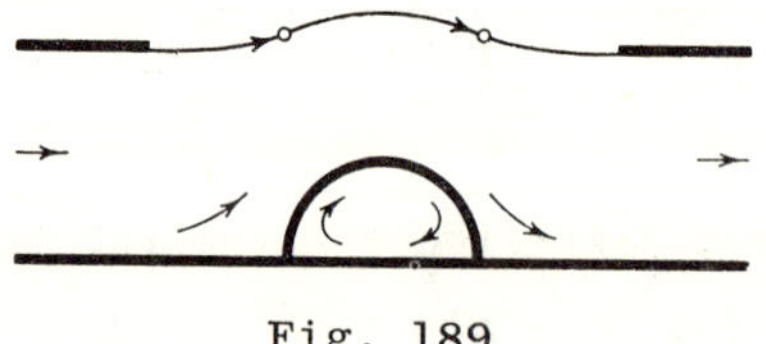

Fig. 189

C. OTHER PROBLEMS

It is not our object here to survey all the jet theory problems not discussed previously. Such a survey would require a special report in itself because of the abundance of jet-theory literature in a vast array of published sources. On the other hand, we shall discuss a heterogeneous collection of problems that are united by their dependence on the jet theory of weightless, ideal, incompressible fluid for solution. Our objective in presenting these problems is to stimulate the reader to find new applications for jet theory. In the interest of brevity we have omitted from this section many of the problems found in the oft-mentioned Cisotti [51] and Birkhoff and Zarantonello [5] monographs.

A problem closely associated to those in the preceding section concerns circulatory flow around a region of constant pressure (hollow vortex) located between two walls (Fig. 190).

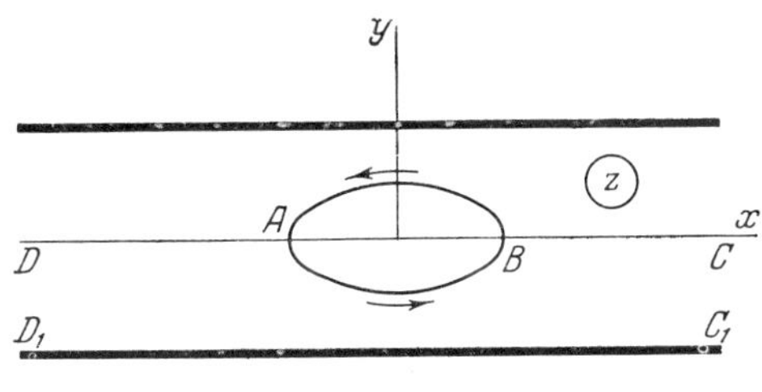

Fig. 190

We need to study only the lower half of the flow. The velocity is vertical all along the straight lines DA and BC, and they are equipotentials because the flow is symmetric and is assumed to be stagnant at infinity. Along the streamline D_1C_1 the stream function $\psi = 0$, and along the streamline AB, $\psi = \text{const.}$ The circulation around the hollow vortex is Γ. We shall map the regions of change of w and ζ onto a rectangle in some u-plane with vertices at points C $(u = K)$,

B $(u = K + iK/2)$, A $(u = -K + iK/2)$, and D $(u = -K)$ (Fig. 191). Assuming that the complex potential $w = 0$ at the coordinate origin 0 in Figs. 190 and 191, we have

$$w = \frac{\Gamma u}{4K} . \tag{8.43}$$

Thus, $w_C - w_D = w_B - w_A = \Gamma/2$; along AB and DC the imaginary part of w is constant, and along AD and BC $\text{Re } w = \phi$ is constant.

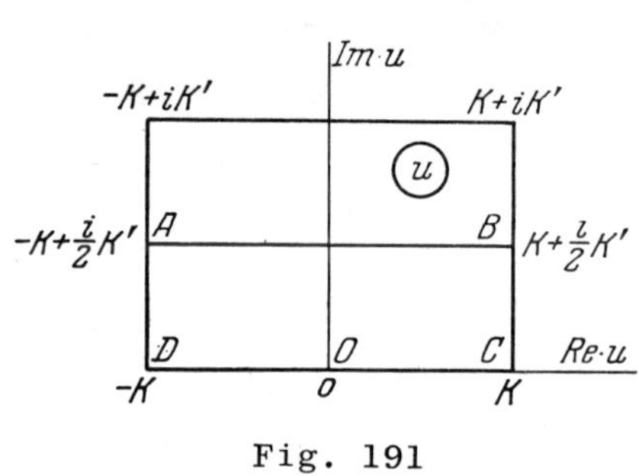

Fig. 191

At points D and C (at infinity) the velocity is zero. Along the wall D_1C_1 the velocity is horizontal. On the free streamline AB, $|\zeta| = 1$, where $\zeta = dw/v_o dz$ and v_o is the magnitude of the velocity on the boundary of the constant-pressure region.

The function $\zeta(u)$ can be extended by applying the symmetry principle to a rectangle with vertices at $u = -K$, $u = K$, $u = K + iK'$, and $u = -K + iK'$ (Fig. 191). Then, since $|\zeta| = 1$ on AB, a zero at $u = 0$ will correspond to a simple pole at $u = iK'$. Again on extending $\zeta(u)$ to the entire plane of the parametric variable u by applying the symmetry principle, we observe that: 1) $\zeta(u)$ is doubly periodic with periods $4K$ and $2iK'$, 2) has zeros at points congruent to $u = 0$ and $u = 2K$, and 3) has poles at points congruent to $u = iK'$ and $u = 2K + iK'$. The unique function of the complex variable u which satisfies these conditions is

$$\zeta = \sqrt{k} \text{ sn } (u - K) = -\sqrt{k} \frac{\text{cn } u}{\text{dn } u} , \tag{8.44}$$

where the factor $\sqrt{k}$ is chosen so that $|\zeta| = 1$ on AB.

From Eqs. (8.43) and (8.44) we find

$$dz = \frac{dw}{v_o \zeta} = - \frac{\Gamma \, dn \, u}{4\sqrt{k} \, K \, cn \, u} \, du \quad , \tag{8.45}$$

from which

$$z = \frac{\Gamma}{8\sqrt{k} \, K} \, \ell n \, \frac{1 - sn \, u}{1 + sn \, u} \quad . \tag{8.46}$$

The above problem was first solved by Michell [11]. Other more general problems with a hollow vortex in a regular polygon have been studied [5, 11, 147]. The "square" flow is shown in Fig. 192.

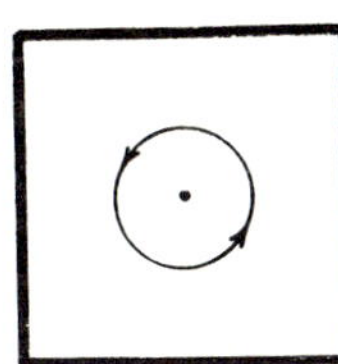

Fig. 192

Next we examine Ehrich's attempts [148] to apply jet theory to the flow of a fluid jet into a main stream from an orifice or slot. He studied four schemes; two are related to jet theory and they are shown in Figs. 193 and 194. Figure 193 shows a slot, while Fig. 194 shows an orifice. The lines EA in these figures represent free

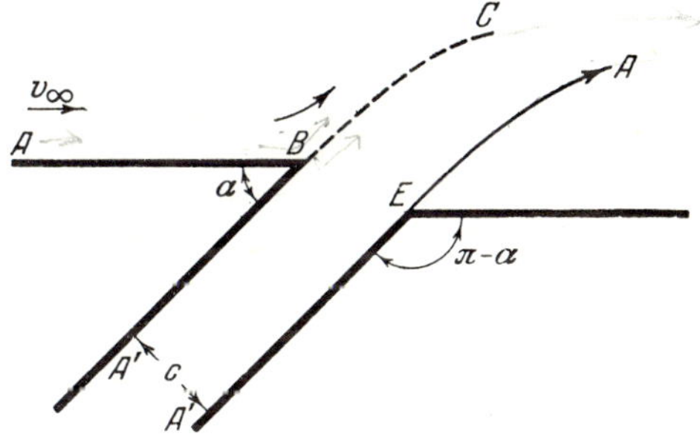

Fig. 193

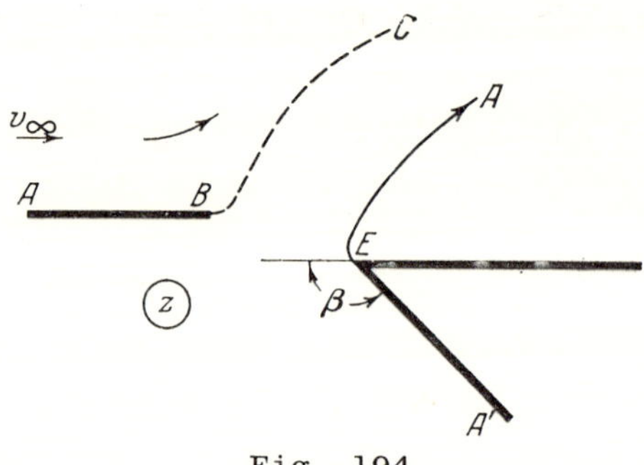

Fig. 194

streamlines along which the pressure and magnitude of the velocity are assumed constant. Along the separation lines BC between the jet and mean flows, the pressures and velocities are continuous. Furthermore, the lines are horizontal at infinity where the velocity is v_∞. The densities of the fluid in the main flow and in the jet are the same. In both cases the problems are solved by a conformal transformation of the regions of change of the complex potential w and of $\omega = \ell n\ (v_\infty\ dz/dw)$ onto the upper half-plane of the parametric variable t (Fig. 195).

In both problems the complex potential has both a pole and a logarithmic singularity at point A, C $(t = 1)$ and a logarithmic singularity at A' $(t = -h)$. The derivative dw/dt has a second-order pole at A, C and a simple pole at A'. Now, as we have done repeatedly, it is easy to write an expression for dw/dt in terms of its singularities. We must note, however, that the constant factor in the following expression is chosen so that the discharge through the opening is $v_\infty c$, where in the first problem c is the distance between the parallel walls. Thus,

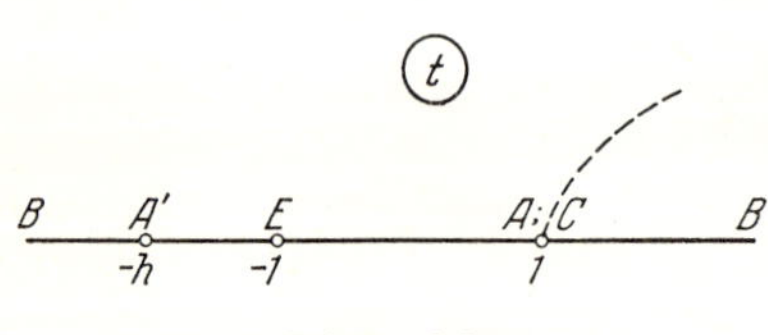

Fig. 195

$$\frac{dw}{dt} = \frac{(1 + h^2)\, v_\infty c}{\pi(t + h)(t - 1)^2} . \tag{8.47}$$

For both problems the region of change of $\omega = \ell n\,(v_\infty\, dz/dw)$ is a semi-infinite strip; however, the point correspondence, as well as the strip widths, is different. Figure 196 shows ω for a slot (see Fig. 193), while Fig. 197 gives ω for the orifice of Fig. 194. The mapping

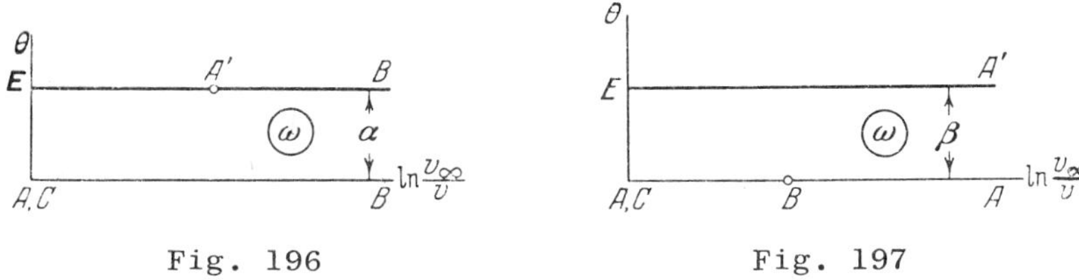

Fig. 196

Fig. 197

of ω onto the upper half t-plane is found by Ehrich by using the Schwarz-Christoffel theorem. The final results are

$$\omega = \frac{\alpha}{\pi}\, \ell n\, [t + (t^2 - 1)^{1/2}] \qquad \text{(slot)} , \tag{8.48}$$

$$\omega = \frac{\beta}{\pi}\, \ell n\, \frac{ht + 1 - [(h^2 - 1)(t^2 - 1)]^{1/2}}{t + h} \qquad \text{(orifice)} . \tag{8.49}$$

From knowledge of dw/dt and ω it is possible, of course, to compute any or all flow characteristics. Ehrich computed the shapes of the separation streamline BC and the free surface EA for slots with $\alpha = \pi$ and $\alpha = \pi/2$ and for an orifice with $\beta = \pi$.

The total history of the development of jet theory indicates that good agreement between theory and experiment can be expected only when the density of a jet is quite different from that of the main stream. However, the density-adjustment technique described earlier, under the theory of armor-piercing jets [see Eq. (8.19)] permits us to generalize the theory of this section to cases of different densities in the jet and mean flows without additional computations.

In the design selection of a wing profile or a duct (closed-channel) shape, it is frequently useful to require that the pressure be constant (constant velocity) along part of the profile or duct boundary. It will be seen that a natural extension of jet-theory methods can be, and has been, useful for such problems. For example, we have Schmieden's study [149] of a profile consisting of two rectilinear segments and a region along which the velocity is constant* (Fig. 198), and Refs. [150, 151] by Nazarov, and Gibbins and Dixon on duct shape. In particular, in [151] one of the elements studied as part of the solution to the general problem is a typical jet theory flow (Fig. 199). Even Zhukovskii [10] studied a particular form of the Fig. 199 flow—i.e., the plane walls AB and EF are infinitely far apart and only the plate CD covers the free surface. Another interesting problem is that studied by Lighthill [152]. He examined the deflection of jets

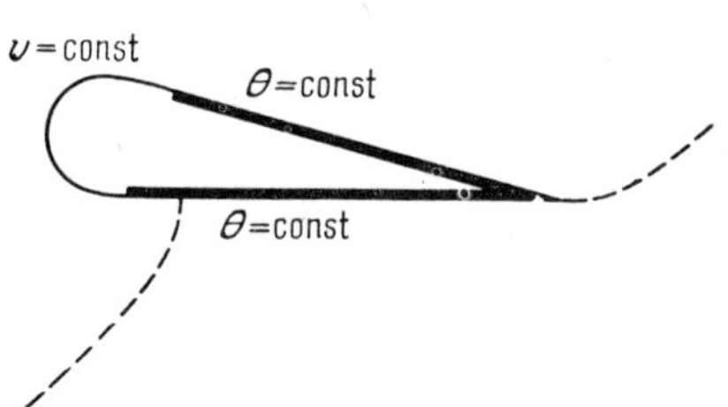

Fig. 198

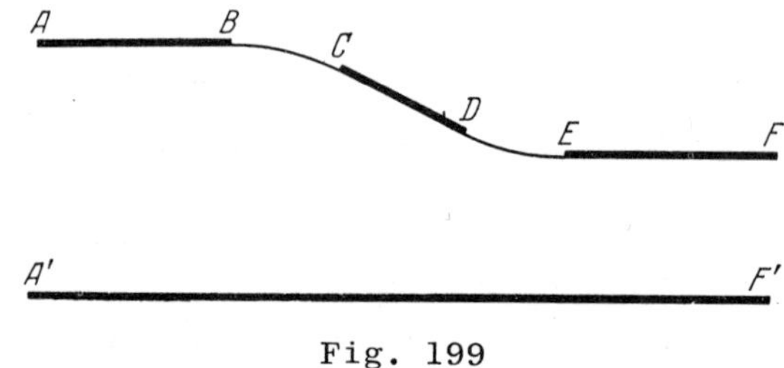

Fig. 199

*Schmieden also examined a more common type of wing profile along parts of which the velocity is constant.

as they rounded curved wing surfaces (Fig. 200). The region of change of the complex potential w is an infinite strip bounded by two straight lines ψ = const. The region of change of his $\omega = \ell n\ (dw/v_o dz)$ is given in Fig. 201. The free surfaces then correspond to the straight line $\operatorname{Im} \omega = \ell n\ (v_o/v_o) = 0$. In Fig. 201 the wetted part DEC of the contour corresponds to some curve. A change in the latter's form changes

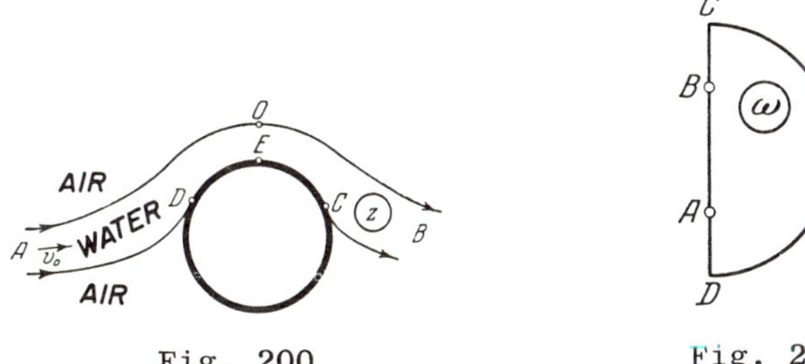

Fig. 200

Fig. 201

the form of DEC in the physical plane. Lighthill examined the particular cases when DEC is either a semicircle or an isosceles right triangle with hypotenuse DC in Fig. 201. In both of these cases the regions of change of w and ω are easily mapped onto the upper half-plane of a parametric variable; thus, the problems are solved.*

Now let us consider the curious "teapot effect" described by Keller [154]. He noted that, on occasion, the water flowing from the spout of a teapot reverses direction and flows around the lower side of the spout and onto the teapot itself. Keller assures us that this phenomenon is related neither to viscosity nor to capillarity, but is produced only by the difference between atmospheric pressure and the pressure in the flowing fluid. Figure 202 shows the corresponding plane flow,

---

*Woods [153] generalized the Lighthill problem to the case of a subsonic gas jet.

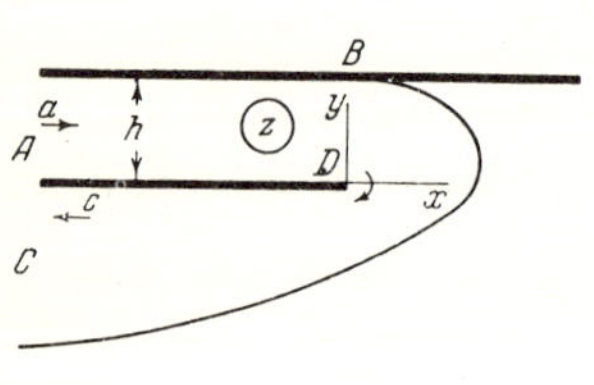

Fig. 202

where the teapot's spout is considered to be infinitely long and represented by two plane walls separated by a distance h. Gravity effects are neglected.

Along the free surface BC the magnitude of the velocity is constant and equal to c. At infinity (point A), the velocity is a. We map the region of change of the complex potential w and the dimensionless complex velocity $(dw/c\ dz) = \zeta$ onto the upper right quarter of a τ-plane (Fig. 203) so that the free surface corresponds to the imaginary semi-axis of τ and the wall corresponds to the real semi-axis.

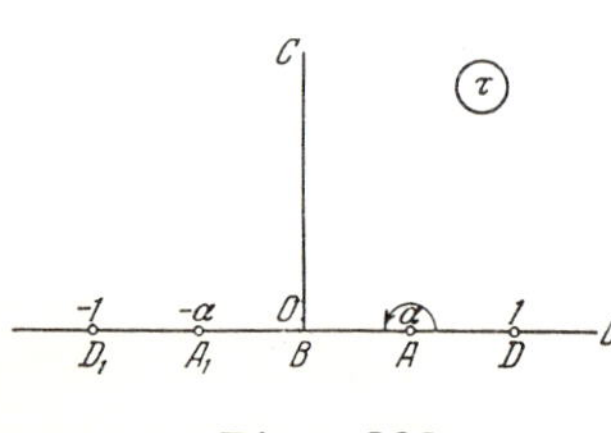

Fig. 203

The complex potential has logarithmic singularities at A (source) and C (sink). Correspondingly, $dw/d\tau$ has a pole at A $(\tau = \alpha)$ and $w = O(1/\tau)$ at C $(\tau = \infty)$. In addition, $dw/d\tau$ has a simple zero at B $(\tau = 0)$, where the mapping is not conformal. By applying the symmetry principle and extending $dw/d\tau$ to the entire τ-plane, we find that, besides the abovementioned zeros and poles, $dw/d\tau$ also has a pole at A_1 $(\tau = -\alpha)$. Under a passage around A along an infinitesimal semicircle, Im w changes by $q = ha$, which is the discharge of fluid in the jet. Thus, we obtain finally

$$\frac{dw}{d\tau} = \frac{2q\tau}{\pi(\tau^2 - \alpha^2)} \quad . \tag{8.50}$$

Integration now gives

$$w = \frac{q}{\pi} \ln (\tau^2 - \alpha^2) + \text{const} \quad . \tag{8.51}$$

This equation is easily verified directly.

We pass now to the determination of ζ. In the flow region the velocity is always greater than zero and is infinite at D $(\tau = 1)$. Therefore, $\zeta(\tau)$ has a simple pole at D. Since we have $|\zeta| = 1$ on the free surface, extension of $\zeta(\tau)$ through the imaginary axis of the τ-plane produces a simple zero in $\zeta(\tau)$ at $\tau = -1$. The function $\zeta(\tau)$ has no other zeros or singularities in the τ-plane. It now follows that

$$\zeta = \frac{dw}{c\ dz} = \frac{1 + \tau}{1 - \tau} \quad . \tag{8.52}$$

If we let the coordinate origin coincide with point D, then, by using Eqs. (8.50) and (8.52), we find

$$z = \frac{1}{c}\int_1^{\tau} \frac{c\ dz}{dw}\frac{dw}{d\tau}\,d\tau = \frac{2q}{\pi c}\int_1^{\tau} \frac{1 - \tau}{1 + \tau}\,\frac{\tau}{\tau^2 - \alpha^2}\,d\tau \quad .$$

Evaluation of the last integral gives

$$z = \frac{q}{\pi c}\left[-\frac{4}{1 - \alpha^2}\,\ell n\,\frac{1 + \tau}{2} + \frac{1 - \alpha}{1 + \alpha}\,\ell n\,\frac{\tau - \alpha}{1 - \alpha} + \frac{1 + \alpha}{1 - \alpha}\,\ell n\,\frac{\tau + \alpha}{1 + \alpha}\right] . \tag{8.53}$$

We may now compute any geometrical element of the flow; for example, from Eq. (8.53) the abscissa of point B is found to be

$$x_B = \frac{4}{1 - \alpha^2}\,\ell n\ 2 + \frac{1 - \alpha}{1 + \alpha}\,\ell n\,\frac{1}{1 - \alpha} + \frac{1 + \alpha}{1 - \alpha}\,\ell n\,\frac{1}{1 + \alpha} + \frac{2(1 + \alpha^2)}{1 - \alpha^2}\,\ell n\,\alpha \quad . \tag{8.54}$$

Then from Eq. (8.52) it follows that

$$\frac{a}{c} = \frac{1 + \alpha}{1 - \alpha} \geqq 1 \quad ,$$

from which, according to Bernoulli's integral, the pressure at A is less than or equal to the pressure on the free surface. An interesting limiting case occurs when $a = c$ and the pressures at points A and C are equal. Then points A and B coincide (Fig. 204)—i.e., $\alpha = 0$. Now it follows from Eq. (8.54) that $x_B = -\infty$—i.e., the upper wall is absent and Eqs. (8.51)(with const = 0) and (8.53) take the form

$$\left.\begin{aligned} w &= \frac{2q}{\pi}\,\ell n\,\tau \;, \qquad \tau = \exp\,[\pi w/2q] \\ z &= \frac{2q}{\pi c} - 2\ell n\,\frac{1 + \tau}{2} + \ell n\,\tau \end{aligned}\right\} . \tag{8.55}$$

From Eqs. (8.55) we obtain

$$\frac{\pi c z}{4q} + \frac{\pi z}{4h} = -\,\ell n\,\cosh\,\frac{\pi w}{4q} \quad . \tag{8.56}$$

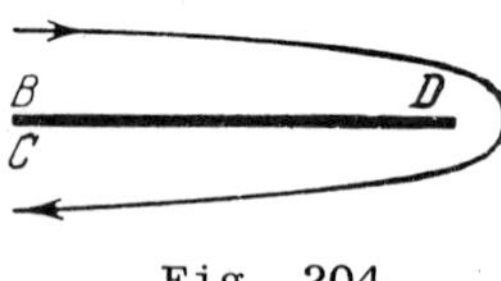

Fig. 204

Now by solving Eq. (8.56) for w, it is possible to express the complex potential w in terms of elementary functions of z—a very rare occurrence in jet theory.

In concluding this section we discuss Khmelnik's problem [155]. Khmelnik's work is concerned with the flow of a thin layer of ideal, incompressible fluid over arbitrary surfaces. In the process of investigating the flow on a cone* Khmelnik solved several plane

*Khmelnik's work is developed on the basis of the general theory of fluid flow in thin layers over surfaces [156].

flows of a jet around plates by using sources. These flows are shown in Fig. 205. The most interesting flow is the last one, Fig. 205d, which is a jet flow in a circular cascade formed by $k = \pi/\alpha$ elements. The flow is produced by a source

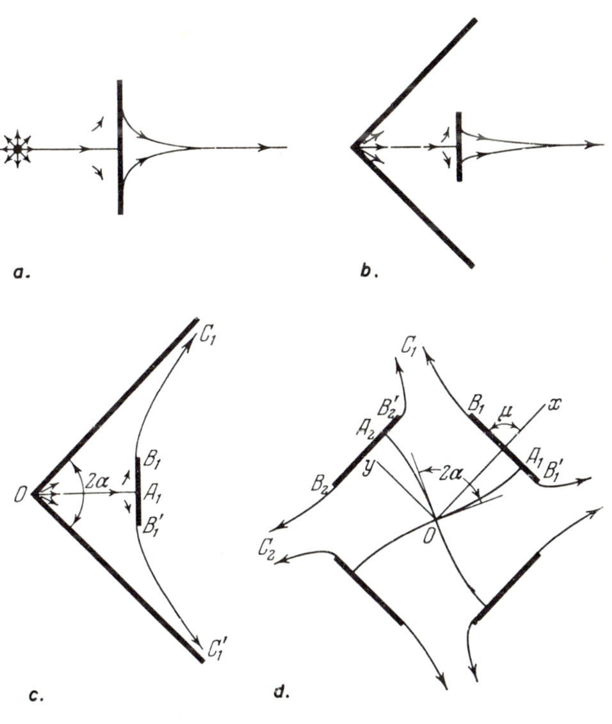

Fig. 205

located at point 0. On Fig. 205d the x-axis passes through the middle of the plate $B_1'B_1$. To facilitate solution of this problem it is possible to define the period of the cascade, bounded by the streamlines $OA_1B_1C_1$ and $OA_2B_2'C_1$. We shall map the region of change of the dimensionless complex velocity $dw/v_o dz$, where v_o is the velocity on the jet surfaces, and of the derivative dw/dt of the complex potential onto the upper unit semicircle in a t-plane (Fig. 206). The streamlines OA_1 and OA_2 (Fig. 205d) correspond to the different sides of the cut A_1OA_2 in Fig. 206. The general solution to the problem, obtained by Khmelnik's method of singular points, has the form

$$\frac{dw}{dt} = M \frac{(t - e^{i\lambda})(t - e^{-i\lambda})(t^2 - 1)\,\{t - (\exp[i\mu_o]/m)\}^{-1}\,\{t - (\exp[-i\mu_o]/m)\}^{-1}}{(t - \delta)\,[t - (1/\delta)]\,(t - m\exp[i\mu_o])\,(t - m\exp[-i\mu_o])} \tag{8.57}$$

and

$$\frac{dw}{v_o dz} = N \frac{t - e^{i\lambda}}{t - e^{-i\lambda}} \left[\frac{(t - m\exp[-i\mu_o])\,\{t - (\exp[-i\mu_o]/m)\}}{(t - m\exp[i\mu_o])\,\{t - (\exp[i\mu_o]/m)\}}\right]^{\alpha/\pi}, \tag{8.58}$$

where M and N are constants. The geometric meaning of the t-plane constants m, δ, and μ_o is seen from an examination of Fig. 206. The validity of Eqs. (8.57) and (8.58) is easily verified directly. It is convenient to remember that on the part A_1B_1 of the plate the argument of dw/v_odz must be some constant $-\mu$ (Fig. 205d) and on the part A_2B_2' of the other plate $\arg(dw/v_odz) = \pi - \mu - 2\alpha$. On the jet surfaces $B_2'C_1$ and B_1C_1, $|dw/v_odz| = 1$.

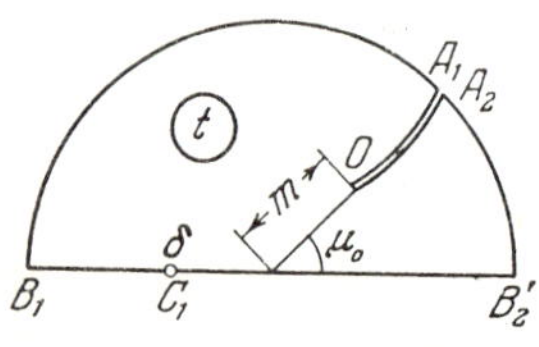

Fig. 206

Then, since along the streamlines $OA_1B_1C_1$ and $OA_2B_2'C_1$, $\text{Im}\, dw = 0$, $t\, dw/dt$ is real on the diameter $B_1C_1B_2'$ of the semicircle (Fig. 206) and purely imaginary on the circle $t = e^{i\sigma}$ $(0 \leq \sigma \leq \pi)$. The flow of Fig. 205c with $\pi/\alpha = k$ (k being a whole number) is a particular case of a circular cascade where the angle $\mu = \pi/2$, and the critical point A_1 coincides with the middle of the plate $B_1'B_1$. Also in this case, $\delta = 0$, $\mu_o = \pi/2$, $\lambda = \pi/2$, and

$$\lim_{\delta \to 0} (-\delta M) = M_1 \quad .$$

The regions of change of dw/dt and dw/v_odz are mapped on the same unit semicircle, but the cut is different (Fig. 207) and circumference of the upper semicircle corresponds to the whole plate. $B_1'A_1B_1$. The sides of the corner (with included angle 2α) become the sides of the cut and*

$$\frac{dw}{dt} = M_1 \frac{t^4 - 1}{t(t^2 + m^2)[t^2 + (1/m^2)]} , \tag{8.59}$$

and

$$\frac{dw}{v_o dz} = N \frac{t - i}{t + i} \left[\frac{t^2 - 1 + it\,[m + (1/m)]}{t^2 - 1 - it\,[m + (1/m)]}\right]^{\alpha/\pi} . \tag{8.60}$$

The constant M_1 is defined in terms of the fluid discharge. The constant N is determined from the condition that at B_1 $(t = -1)$, $dw/v_o dz = i$. Thus, $N = -e^{-i\alpha}$. The detailed solutions of the problems in Fig. 205 are found in Refs. [155, 157].

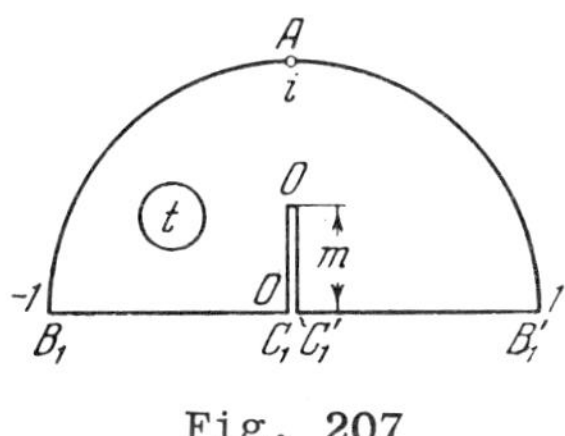

Fig. 207

The problem about a free jet flowing from the interior of a wedge with a source located at its vertex was solved by Weinig [158].

Until now our discussion has been limited to the steady, plane, incompressible flows of classical jet theory. As seen in the Table of Contents, the further chapters consider problems in which the limitations of classical theory are eliminated in turn. Since jet theory is so closely associated with other branches of hydrodynamics, the exact scope of jet theory can be defined only conditionally. Consequently, we limit out later discussions to such problems as can be solved, in our view, by a natural development or extension of the classical methods of jet theory.

*This solution for the corner is useful even when π/α is not a whole number.

CHAPTER IX. UNSTEADY FLOWS

A. FLAT PLATE IN AN ACCELERATED FLOW

In spite of its obvious practical importance, unsteady flow is the youngest and least developed area of jet theory. In fact, the first solution to the accelerated flow around a plate with a trailing, attached, constant-pressure zone was published by von Karman [159] only in 1949. We shall examine his solution now.

The flat plate of width 2h is placed normal to the approaching flow, which has a velocity U(t) directed along the x-axis at infinity, where t is time. A cavity is located behind the plate, and the cavity pressure is constant (Fig. 208). Von Karman searched only for for flows in which the flow geometry was time invariant. The complex potential W of the flow is sought in the form

$$\Phi + i\Psi = W(z,t) = U(t)\ w(z) = U(\varphi + i\psi) \quad . \qquad (9.1)$$

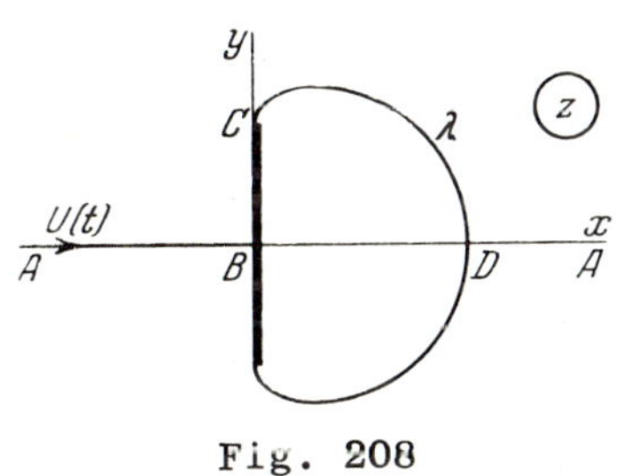

Fig. 208

We shall examine the flow's upper half that is bounded by parts AB and DA of the axis of symmetry (they can be replaced by solid walls), the plate BC, and the constant-pressure surface that is located between points C and D. The corresponding region of change of of w(z) is the upper half-plane $\operatorname{Im} w(z) = \psi \geqq 0$. We map this region onto the upper unit semicircle $|\tau| \leqq 1$, $\operatorname{Im} \tau \geqq 0$

in a parametric variable τ-plane (Fig. 209). The mapping is made in a manner that makes λ map onto the circumference of the semicircle and the solid walls map onto its diameter.

The above mapping is given by

$$w = -hN\left[1 + \frac{1}{2}\left(\tau + \frac{1}{\tau}\right)\right] = -\frac{hN}{2\tau}(1 + \tau^2)^2 \quad , \tag{9.2}$$

where the constant factor N is not dependent on the coordinates. Equation (9.2) was obtained in an obvious manner and is easily verified. Note that an additive constant was used in Eq. (9.2) to make $w = 0$ at D. On the solid walls the normal velocity must be zero. Thus, $\mathrm{Im}\,(dw/dz) = 0$ on AB and DA, and $\mathrm{Re}\,(dw/dz) = 0$ on BC. The boundary condition on the unknown free streamline λ is determined from the Lagrange integral. For the present unsteady plane flow of an ideal, incompressible, and weightless fluid, this integral is

$$\frac{\partial\Phi}{\partial t} + \frac{U^2}{2}\left|\frac{dw}{dz}\right|^2 + \frac{p}{\rho} = c(t) \quad , \tag{9.3}$$

where p is the pressure and ρ is the density. Also note that $p = p_o$ everywhere on λ (the cavity pressure is uniform). If it is assumed that D is a singular point, then $dw/dz = 0$ there. But, then $p_o/\rho = c(t)$ everywhere on the free surface and the λ boundary condition (9.3) reduces to

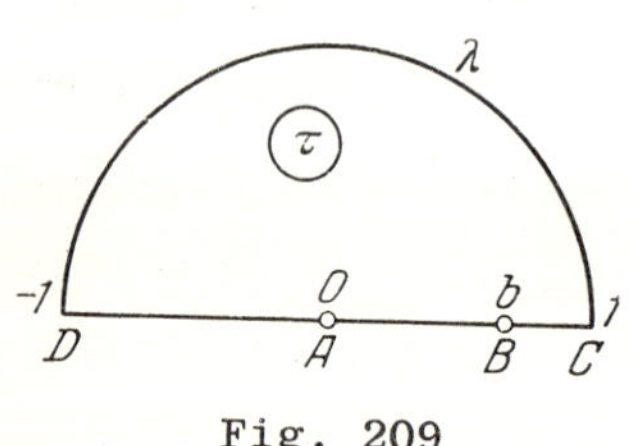

Fig. 209

$$\frac{\partial\Phi}{\partial t} + \frac{U^2}{2}\left|\frac{dw}{dz}\right|^2 = 0 \quad .$$

Since $W = \Phi$ on λ, then according to Eq. (9.1) the above equation becomes

$$-\frac{U^2}{2aw}\left|\frac{dw}{dz}\right|^2 = 1 \quad , \tag{9.4}$$

where the acceleration $a = dU/dt$.

Now consider the function

$$\omega(\tau) = \frac{U^2}{2aw}\left(\frac{dw}{dz}\right)^2 = -\frac{U^2\tau\,(dw/dz)^2}{ahN\,(1+\tau)^2} \quad . \tag{9.5}$$

On the walls AB, BC, and DA

$$\operatorname{Im}\omega(\tau) = 0 \quad . \tag{9.6}$$

On the free surface λ, we have, according to condition (9.4)

$$|\omega(\tau)| = 1 \quad . \tag{9.7}$$

Inside the unit semicircle, $\omega(\tau)$ has no zeros or singularities. Thus, we need to investigate ω only in the neighborhood of points A, B, and D. Since the flow velocity is U at A, Eq. (9.5) shows that $\omega(\tau)$ has a simple zero at A. Under a passage from λ to DA along an infinitesimal quarter-circle around D, the argument of dw/dz varies from $\pi/2$ to 0. Therefore, $dw/dz = O(\tau + 1)$ and $(dw/dz)^2 = O(\tau + 1)^2$ in the neighborhood of D. According to Eq. (9.5) then, $\omega(\tau)$ has neither zeros nor poles at D. In passing from AB to BC along an infinitesimal semicircle around B, the argument of dw/dz varies from 0 to $-\pi/2$. Therefore, $dw/dz = O(\tau - b)^{1/2}$ and consequently $\omega(\tau) = O(\tau - b)$ in the neighborhood of $B(\tau = b)$.

By using Eqs. (9.6) and (9.7), we apply the symmetry principle to extend $\omega(\tau)$ analytically to the entire τ-plane. Then, we see that $\omega(\tau)$ has first-order poles at $\tau = \infty$ and $\tau = 1/b$. Constructing $\omega(\tau)$ from its zeros and poles gives

$$\omega(\tau) = M \frac{\tau(\tau - b)}{[\tau - (1/b)]} . \tag{9.8}$$

Since $dw/dz = 1$ at point A, $\omega(\tau)$ is equal to $-U^2\tau/ahN$ plus higher-order small terms in the neighborhood of A, and we can express M in terms of the other parameters as $M = -U^2/ahNb^2$. Thus, Eq. (9.8) can be written in the form

$$\omega(\tau) = - \frac{U^2}{ahNb^2} \frac{\tau(\tau - b)}{[\tau - (1/b)]} . \tag{9.9}$$

From Eqs. (9.9) and (9.5) we find

$$\frac{dw}{dz} = (1 + \tau) \left[\frac{1 - (\tau/b)}{1 - \tau b}\right]^{1/2} . \tag{9.10}$$

The parameters appearing in the general solution of the problem given by Eqs. (9.2) and (9.9) must satisfy three relationships that permit determination of the constants b and N and of the law for U(t).

Our Eqs. (9.9) and (9.10) for $\omega(\tau)$ and dw/dz satisfy all the boundary conditions except Eq. (9.4), which is satisfied only partially. Actually, on introducing the results for $\omega(\tau)$ and dw/dz in Eq. (9.4), we obtain, on the left side of Eq. (9.4), a quantity that is independent of the coordinates, but not necessarily unity. By equating this quantity from condition (9.4) to unity, we obtain the first of the above-mentioned relationships.

From Eq. (9.10) and (9.2) it follows that, on the free surface λ—i.e., when $\tau = e^{i\sigma}$ and $0 \leqq \sigma \leqq \pi$—we have

$$2aw = - haN \cdot 4 \cos^2 \frac{\sigma}{2}$$

and

$$- U^2 \left|\frac{dw}{dz}\right|^2 = - \frac{U^2}{b} \cdot 4 \cos^2 \frac{\sigma}{2} \quad .$$

From these results and Eq. (9.4) we obtain, in accordance with the above procedure,

$$\frac{U^2}{habN} = 1 \quad . \tag{9.11}$$

The same result can be obtained directly from Eqs. (9.7) and (9.9)

Since $a = dU/dt$, Eq. (9.11) can be considered a differential equation from which it is possible to find $U(t)$. On integrating (9.11), we are led to

$$\frac{U}{U_o} = \frac{1}{1 - (U_o/hNb)t} \quad , \tag{9.12}$$

where U_o is the velocity when $t = 0$.

We now determine b. Clearly, both AB and AD must lie on the x-axis and, in passing from AB to AD, $\operatorname{Im} z = \operatorname{Im} \int (dz/d\tau)\, d\tau$ must not experience any jump. Thus the residue of $(dz/d\tau) = (dz/dw)(dw/d\tau)$ must be 0 at A. Thus, we obtain the condition* $b^2 + 2b - 1 = 0$. Solving this quadratic equation and taking the root $0 < b < 1$ gives

$$b = \sqrt{2} - 1 \approx 0.414 \quad . \tag{9.13}$$

Finally, the constant N is determined from the condition that the distance between B and C in the z-plane must be h (half of the plate width). Thus,

---

*This condition is analogous to condition (6.100) for a cavitational flow around a wedge in a channel.

$$ih = -\frac{ihN}{2}\int_b^1 \left[\frac{1-\tau b}{(\tau/b)-1}\right]^{1/2} \frac{1-(1/\tau^2)}{1+\tau}\, d\tau \quad .$$

The integral is easily evaluated, and since $b = \sqrt{2} - 1$, we obtain

$$\frac{1}{N} = \frac{1}{2}\left[\sqrt{2}(\sqrt{2}-1)^{1/2} + (\sqrt{2}-1)\arccos(\sqrt{2}-1)\right] \approx 0.692 \quad . \tag{9.14}$$

From the known values of N and b given in Eqs. (9.13) and (9.14) and from Eq. (9.12) the U-variation law

$$\frac{U}{U_o} = \frac{1}{1 - 1.675\,(U_o t/h)} \tag{9.15}$$

is obtained.

Von Karman's work has been extended by a number of investigators. Thus, while von Karman solved the first example of an accelerated flow of a constant-shape cavity with a stagnation-point closure, Gilbarg [160] derived the entire set of flows. He studied symmetric cavities with cusped ends B (Fig. 210), which are not critical points, and with inflection points A_1 and A_2 on the free surfaces. Thus, von Karman's solution is the limiting case of Gilbarg's, as the concave parts A_1B and A_2B of the cavity vanish. Gilbarg investigated also a symmetric polygonal obstacle and indicated a method for solving nonsymmetric problems. Furthermore, he suggested a generalization of the solutions to the case when the cavity shape changes slowly in time. Woods [161], on the other hand, generalized

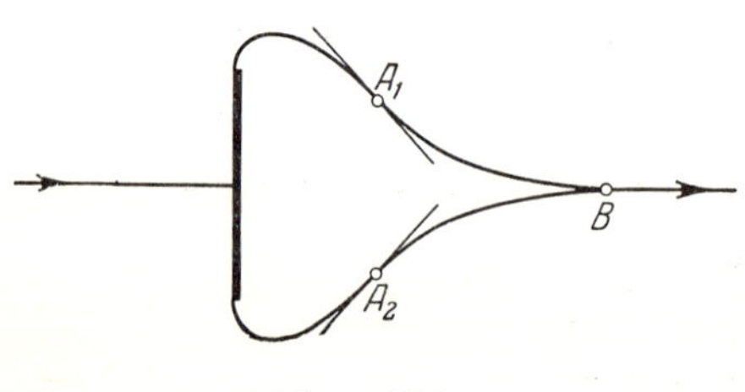

Fig. 210

von Karman's theory to the case of Riabouchinsky's flow model, and he investigated the general case of a curved obstacle.

Returning now to von Karman's problem, we observe that it is not difficult to compute the pressure on the plate. From Eq. (9.3) it follows that the pressure difference $p - p_o$ acting on the plate is

$$p - p_o = - \rho \left[\frac{\partial \Phi}{\partial t} + \frac{U^2}{2} \left| \frac{dw}{dz} \right|^2 \right] .$$

Since $\Phi = W = Uw$ on the plate and $U^2 = hbN(dU/dt)$ according to Eq. (9.11),

$$p - p_o = - \rho \frac{dU}{dt} \left[w + \frac{hbN}{2} \left| \frac{dw}{dz} \right|^2 \right] . \qquad (9.16)$$

As a result, the total pressure force X on the entire plate of width $2h$ is

$$X = - 2\rho \frac{dU}{dt} \int_{\tau=b}^{\tau=1} \left[w + \frac{hbN}{2} \left| \frac{dw}{dz} \right|^2 \right] \frac{dy}{d\tau} \, d\tau . \qquad (9.17)$$

Introduction of the expressions for w, dw/dz, and $dy = \mathrm{Im}\,(dz/dw)(dw/dt)\,dt$, obtained from Eqs. (9.2) and (9.10) produces

$$X = \rho \frac{h^2 N^2}{2} \frac{dU}{dt} \int_b^1 \frac{(1 + \tau)\,(1 - \tau^2)^2 \, d\tau}{\tau^3 (1 - \tau b)^{1/2} \, [(\tau/b) - 1]^{1/2}} . \qquad (9.18)$$

The change of variables $(\tau - b)/(1 - \tau b) = \eta^2$, when introduced into Eq. (9.18), gives

$$X = \rho \frac{dU}{dt} h^2 N^2 \sqrt{b}\,(1 + b)(1 - b^2)^2$$

$$\cdot \int_0^1 \frac{(1 + \eta^2)(1 - \eta^4)^2}{(b + \eta^2)^3 (1 + b\eta^2)^3}\, d\eta \tag{9.19}$$

or, after numerical computations,

$$X = 6.3\rho h^2 \frac{dU}{dt} \quad . \tag{9.20}$$

The maximum pressure difference occurs at $B(\tau = b)$. Thus, according to Eqs. (9.2), (9.10), and (9.16) we have, at the critical point B,

$$p - p_o = \rho \frac{dU}{dt} hN \frac{(1 + b)^2}{2b} = 3.5\rho h \frac{dU}{dt} \quad . \tag{9.21}$$

The coefficient $6.3\rho h^2$ in Eq. (9.20) should not, in general, be considered an additional mass m for a jet flow around a plate (although $m' = 6.3\rho h^2$ can be called a "cavity-induced" mass). To determine the additional or virtual mass associated with acceleration, it is more appropriate to shift the problem's viewpoint and study a plate that is moving along the x-axis with a velocity $-U(t)$ and through a fluid that is at rest at infinity. Then on the left side of Lagrange's Eq. (9.3) a new term $-x(dU/dt)$ appears. This term has a double influence. First, as we can see from an integration, it decreases the drag force by $\rho S(dU/dt)$, where S is the area of the cavity behind the plate. Second, it changes the boundary condition on the free surface, thus making it considerably more difficult to find the general solution to the hydrodynamic problem; the solution to the new problem cannot be obtained directly from the solution to the von Karman problem.

On the other hand, consider a fully wetted flow. We make use of the known solution [1] to an unseparated flow about a flat plate of width 2h. If the flow velocity is normal to the plate and equal to $U(t)$ at infinity, then the maximum pressure difference across the plate is $2\rho h(dU/dt)$ and the total pressure force on the plate is $\pi\rho h^2(dU/dt)$. Because the plate area (in the x-y plane) is 0 and the free surfaces are absent, the total force acting on a plate moving with velocity $U(t)$ through a stagnant fluid is the same as found for the other viewpoint—i.e., $\pi\rho h^2(dU/dt)$. Here the coefficient $m = \pi\rho h^2$ is called the "additional or virtual mass" of the plate [24]. In particular, m can be computed by determining the kinetic energy of the fluid surrounding the moving plate and dividing the result by $U^2/2$.

Now consider a classical, separated, "Kirchhoff-type" flow about a plate (Fig. 1). Assume that we adopt a viewpoint wherein the flow velocity is 0 at infinity. We cannot find the virtual mass of the plate with this separated flow around it by using the kinetic-energy computation because, as is easily seen, the kinetic energy is infinite (cf. Chapter III, Section D). Our next section is devoted to just such a problem of determining the virtual mass of a contour in a separated flow.

B. MOTION OF A STREAMLINED CONTOUR IN A SEPARATED FLOW

We consider [162] a separated Kirchhoff model flow about an arbitrary stationary contour AB (Fig. 211). The velocity at infinity v_∞ is directed along the x-axis. The coordinate origin is placed at the only critical (stagnation) point 0, which is located on the contour.

Suppose points on the contour suddenly acquire a normal velocity U_n, where U_n is an arbitrary known function of arc length. In general, the contour is deformed during the stroke or period of motion. However, the most interesting problems belong to that class in which the contour shape remains unchanged. Our objective is to describe the flow arising as a result of the stroke of unsteady motion.

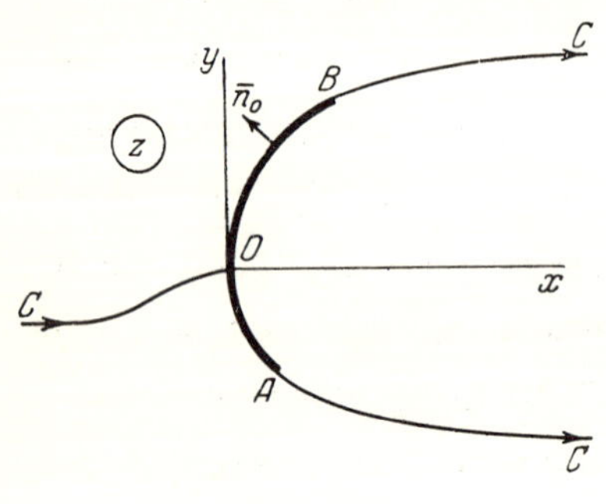

Fig. 211

In accordance with the general theory of impulsive (or impact) motion in an incompressible flow [24] the additional flow produced by the stroke possesses a velocity potential φ, which is related to the impulse pressure p_i and the fluid density ρ by

$$p_i = \rho\varphi \quad . \tag{9.22}$$

The velocity potential φ is a harmonic function of the fixed Cartesian coordinates in the flow plane $z = x + iy$ and satisfies the following boundary conditions:

1. On free surfaces $p_i = 0$ and then, according to Eq. (9.22),

$$\varphi = 0 \quad . \tag{9.23}$$

2. On the contour the normal velocity U_n is given—i.e.,

$$\frac{\partial\varphi}{\partial n} = U_n \quad , \tag{9.24}$$

where the positive normal to the contour is directed into the fluid.

We find the general solution to the above-formulated problem by proceeding on the assumption that the steady flow around the contour AOB (Fig. 211) is known.

The steady-flow problem is solved by mapping the regions of change of the complex potential w_o and the complex velocity dw_o/dz onto the upper half-plane of the parametric variable u (Fig. 212). Then it is obvious that $dz/du = (dz/dw_o)(dw_o/du)$ and $z(u) = \int (dz/du)\, du$ are also known. Now, we neglect the particle displacement that occurs during the unsteady stroke. Thus, z(u) is the same for both the steady and the additional, impulsive flows. Because of this, the complex potential w of the additional, unsteady motion can be found in the u-plane. On the parts of the real u-axis corresponding to the jet surfaces BC and CA, it is possible to apply the alternate condition

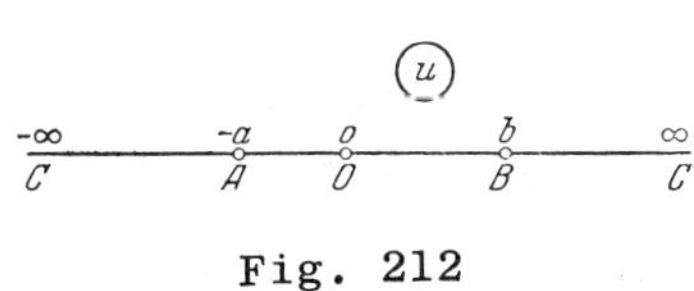

Fig. 212

$$\mathrm{Re}\,\frac{dw}{du} = 0 \quad , \tag{9.25}$$

in lieu of the condition $\varphi = 0$, Eq. (9.23). We see later that dw/du has a zero at $|u| \to \infty$.

We now transform Eq. (9.24). Under the conformal mapping the normal direction on a boundary remains normal. Therefore, by using the normal derivative $\partial\varphi/\partial n$ on a boundary in the z-plane to obtain the normal derivative of the velocity potential

$$-\,\mathrm{Im}\,(dw/du) = -\,\mathrm{Im}\,[(\partial\varphi/\partial u_1) + i(\partial\psi/du_1)] = \partial\varphi/\partial u_2 \quad ,$$

where $u = u_1 + iu_2$, it is necessary only to multiply $\partial\varphi/\partial n$ by the scale factor $|dz/du|$. Thus, Eq. (9.24) can be written in the form

$$\operatorname{Im} \frac{dw}{du} = - U_n \left|\frac{dz}{du}\right| \quad . \tag{9.26}$$

Since $z(u)$ is known, we can consider that on the contour U_n is a known function, not only of arc length, but also of u. Now the problem of determing w or, equivalently, dw/du, reduces to finding a function of the complex variable in the upper half u-plane with the conditions that on the real axis either the real or the imaginary part of dw/du is known.

As in the case of an impact on an unperturbed fluid surface [24], dw/du must have a zero of order u^{-2} at infinity; at the edges $A(u = -a)$ and $B(u = b)$ of the plate dw/du has the singular order $(u + a)^{-1/2}$ and $(u - b)^{-1/2}$ respectively. Our present problem is easily solved by methods adopted from thin-wing theory and the solution to an impact on an incompressible fluid. We introduce the function

$$f(u) = \frac{dw}{du} [(u + a)(u - b)]^{1/2} \quad .$$

According to Eqs. (9.25) and (9.26) the function must satisfy the following boundary conditions

$$\operatorname{Re} f(u) = 0$$

on BC and CA, and

$$\operatorname{Re} f(u) = U_n \left|\frac{dz}{du}\right| [(u + a)(b - u)]^{1/2}$$

on AOB.

By employing Schwarz's formula [4, 163] to find $f(u)$ in the upper half-plane from its known real part on the real axis, we are led to

$$f(u) = \frac{dw}{du}\left[(u + a)(u - b)\right]^{1/2}$$

$$= \frac{1}{\pi i}\int_{-a}^{b} U_n(\xi)\left|\frac{dz}{d\xi}\right|\left[(\xi + a)(b - \xi)\right]^{1/2}\frac{d\xi}{\xi - u} . \qquad (9.27)$$

Equation (9.27) is the general solution to the problem under consideration if only the steady flow around the contour is known. It is obvious that, by making use of the boundary conditions in the forms of Eqs. (9.25) and (9.26), it is possible to solve the impulsive-motion problem with more complicated flow schemes—e.g., impact of several plates.

We consider as an example the straight stroke of a flat plate of width $2h$. The steady, separated flow around the plate (Fig. 213) is symmetric and so, on Fig. 212, we can set $a = b = 1$.

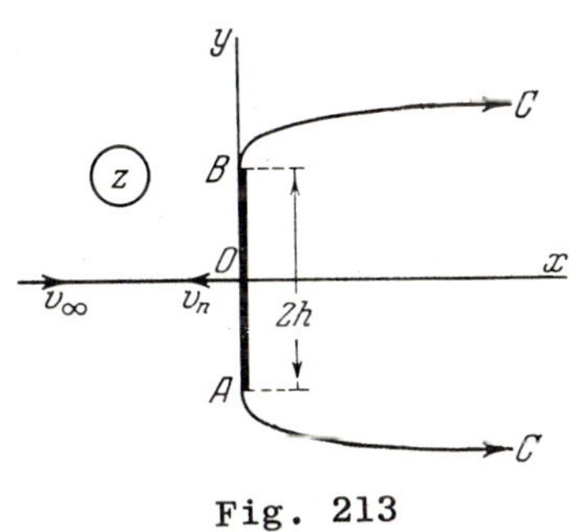

Fig. 213

The steady-flow solution was given in Chapter I, Section E, by Eqs. (1.38) and (1.44). In accordance with the nomenclature of the present section and because the plate AOB in Fig. 213 is located located along the y-axis, and not along the x-axis as in Section E, we rewrite Eqs. (1.38) and (1.44) as the easily verified equations

$$w_0 = \varphi_0 u^2 ; \qquad \frac{v_\infty dz}{dw} = i\,\frac{(1 - u^2)^{1/2} + 1}{u} , \qquad (9.28)$$

where φ_o is a constant. From Eq. (9.28) it is easy to find

$$z(u) = \int_0^u \frac{dz}{dw_o}\frac{dw_o}{du}\,du = \frac{2i\varphi_o}{v_\infty}\int_0^u [1 + (1 - u^2)^{1/2}]\,du$$

$$= \frac{i\varphi_o}{v_\infty}[2u + u(1 - u^2)^{1/2} + \arcsin u] \quad . \qquad (9.29)$$

Since $z(1) = ih$, we obtain from Eq. (9.29)

$$ih = \frac{i\varphi_o}{v_\infty}\left[2 + \frac{\pi}{2}\right] ,$$

or, cf. Eq. (3.7),

$$\frac{\varphi_o}{v_\infty} = \frac{2h}{4 + \pi} \quad .$$

By introducing this expression for φ_o/v_∞ in Eq. (9.29), we obtain $z(u)$ in its final form

$$z(u) = \frac{2ih}{4 + \pi}[2u + u(1 - u^2)^{1/2} + \arcsin u] \quad . \qquad (9.30)$$

Then,

$$\left|\frac{dz}{d\xi}\right| = \frac{4h}{4 + \pi}[1 + (1 - \xi^2)^{1/2}] \quad . \qquad (9.31)$$

Let $U_n = \text{const} > 0$, which represents a straight stroke of a solid flat plat in the direction of the positive x-axis. Now from Eqs. (9.27) and (9.31) we obtain

$$f(u) = \frac{dw}{du}(u^2 - 1)^{1/2} = \frac{2hU_n}{\pi i(\pi + 4)} \int_{-1}^{1} \frac{1 - \xi^2 + (1 - \xi^2)^{1/2}}{\xi - u} d\xi .$$

After evaluating the integral we achieve

$$\frac{dw}{du} = \frac{4hU_n}{i\pi(\pi + 4)} \left[(u^2 - 1)^{1/2} \ln \frac{u + 1}{u - 1} - \frac{(2 + \pi)u}{(u^2 - 1)^{1/2}} + \pi \right] . \tag{9.32}$$

Knowing dw/du we can compute the impulsive forces I_x acting on the plate during the impact. According to Eq. (9.22)

$$I_x = \int_{-h}^{h} p_i \, dy = -\rho \int_{-1}^{1} \varphi \frac{dy}{du} du = \rho \int_{-1}^{1} y \frac{d\varphi}{du} du . \tag{9.33}$$

because $\varphi = 0$ at $u = \pm 1$. Use of $d\varphi/du = \mathrm{Re}\,(dw/du)$ from Eq. (9.32) and $y = \mathrm{Im}\,[z(u)]$ from Eq. (9.30) in Eq. (9.33) gives

$$I_x = \frac{\rho U_n}{\pi} \left(\frac{4h}{\pi + 4} \right)^2 \int_{-1}^{1} \left[(1 - u^2)^{1/2} \ln \frac{1 + u}{1 - u} + \frac{(2 + \pi) u}{(1 - u^2)^{1/2}} \right]$$

$$\cdot \left[\frac{u}{2} (1 - u^2)^{1/2} + \frac{1}{2} \arcsin u + u \right] du . \tag{9.34}$$

In [162] it was found that

$$I_x = 0.4224 \, \rho (2h)^2 U_n . \tag{9.35}$$

According to the general nomenclature of fluid impact theory, the coefficient ahead of U_n—i.e., $m = 0.4224 \, \rho(2h)^2$—can be considered as a fluid virtual mass under an impact of the plate in a separated jet flow.* The virtual mass m_o for the impact of a plate on an undisturbed fluid is $m_o = \pi\rho h^2/2$ [24]. Thus, the ratio m/m_o is

$$\frac{m}{m_o} = 1.077 \quad . \tag{9.36}$$

The flow caused by the contour's impact is independent of the velocity distribution in the fluid before the impact, but depends on the contour shape, the free surface shape, and U_n. The highest additional velocities are achieved by the fluid particles in the neighborhood of the body. Since the fluid particles separate smoothly from the flat plate—i.e., tangent to the plate, the shape of the free surface in the neighborhood of the plate in the separated flow differs very little from an undisturbed fluid surface being impacted by a flat plate. Thus, it is apparent why m/m_o is so close to unity.

On the other hand, the free surface in a separated jet flow around a wedge differs substantially from the undisturbed surface in the neighborhood of the floating wedge [5, Chapter 9, Section 6]. Therefore, the ratio of the virtual masses m/m_o for wedges should increase as the included angle $2\pi\kappa$ of the wedge decreases (Fig. 214). For arbitrary κ the symmetric, linear impact of a wedge in a separated jet was solved by Berman [164], who carried out numerical computations for $\kappa = 1/3$ (included angle 120 deg) and for infinitesimal κ. When $\kappa = 1/3$ he found $m/m_o = 1.146$, and when κ was very small, $m/m_o = 1.444$.

*In order to avoid any misunderstanding, we note that the virtual mass m can also be computed from the kinetic energy of the additional or perturbed fluid flow as determined by the complex potential.

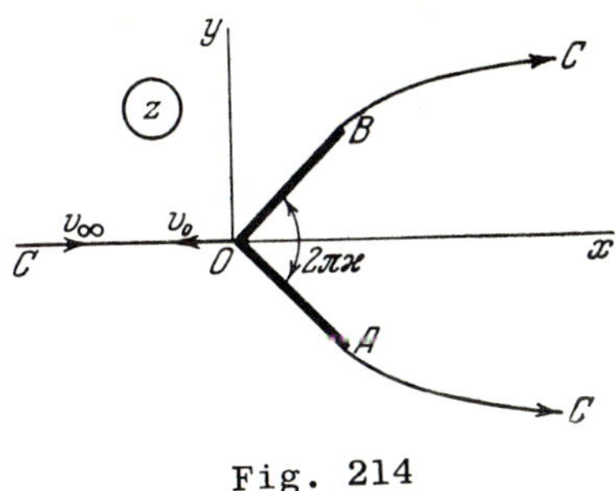

Fig. 214

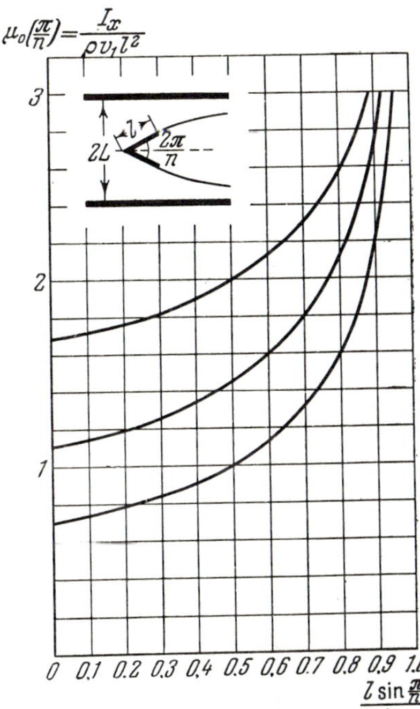

Fig. 215

Finally, Parkhomovskii [165 - 168] published a series of papers in which he computed virtual masses for a wedge, an inclined plate, a cascade of wedges, and some curvilinear contours. Figure 215 shows the virtual mass $\mu_o(\pi/n) = I_x(\rho v_1 \ell^2)$ of a symmetric wedge located between parallel walls and in a separated jet flow of the Kirchhoff type. The included angle of the wedge is $2\pi/n$, the length of the wedge's side is ℓ, and the distance between the parallel walls is 2L. The velocity, which the wedge suddenly obtains under the impact, is directed along the axis of symmetry x, but opposed to the approaching flow, and is equal to v_1. Finally, the projection on the x-axis of the resultant of the impulsive pressure on the wedge is I_x. In the figure, the upper curve is for a flat plate with n = 2, the middle curve is for n = 3, and the lower curve is for n = 4.

Birkhoff [5, 169] used a different approach to determine the virtual mass of a body in a separated jet flow. He introduced the concept of the acceleration potential A, whose gradient is a vector $\mathbf{a}$ that is the acceleration of the fluid under an impact. Thus,

$$\mathbf{a} = \mathbf{i}\frac{\partial u_x}{\partial t} + \mathbf{j}\frac{\partial u_y}{\partial t} + \mathbf{k}\frac{\partial u_z}{\partial t} = \nabla A \quad .$$

where t is time, (u_x, u_y, u_z) are the projections of the velocity vector on a Cartesian coordinate system fixed in space, and $\mathbf{i}$, $\mathbf{j}$, and $\mathbf{k}$ are unit vectors. He then proved several interesting general theorems related to the virtual or induced mass and presented a limiting problem for determining A for small t. The problem of determining the acceleration potential A is equivalent to the problem of determining the velocity potential $\varphi = \int A\, dt$, where the integration is carried over the infinitesimal time of the impact.

An impact problem for a contour in a separated jet flow can, in a sense, be treated as a particular case of a weakly perturbed steady fluid flow. We shall discuss this in the next section.

C. WEAKLY PERTURBED JET FLOW

Assume that we select one of the many steady-jet-flow problems with a known solution, such as those studied in the preceding chapters. Clearly, we shall then know the conformal mappings that map the regions of change of the complex potential w_o, the complex velocity dw_o/dz, and, from these, the flow plane z onto the upper half-plane of the parametric variable u. Now, consider an unsteady jet flow that differs very little from our selected, known, steady flow. This unsteady flow could take place, for example, as a result of small vibrations of solid walls or with fixed walls as a result of flow instability.

The complex potential of the unsteady flow F may be given as the sum of a complex potential for the steady flow w_o and a complex potential of the perturbed flow w—i.e.,

$$F = w_o + w \quad . \tag{9.37}$$

To find w we must first formulate the unsteady boundary conditions on the walls and free surfaces. As in the theory of thin wings and small-amplitude waves, the unsteady boundary conditions on the fluctuating walls and free surfaces can, by neglecting small high-order quantities, be transferred to the boundaries of the unperturbed steady flow. Finally, we shall find it convenient not to vary our known function $z(u)$.*

Now, during the unsteady motion the contour points oscillate in a direction normal to the steady-flow contour according to a known relationship. These velocities U_n are expressed by the known relationship $U_n = f(u,t)$, where t is time. Since U_n is known, the normal component U_n of the velocity of the perturbed flow is known. Now we examine this problem in detail.

Figure 216 shows part of a contour around which fluid is flowing. The velocity of the contour points and the contour's shape and location are known at any instant of time. An infinitesimal element of the contour ΔS is isolated in Fig.

*As Fox and Morgan [170] point out, two properly selected mathematical perturbations on z and w—i.e., z_1, z_2 and w_1, w_2, can represent the same physical perturbation since two of the four perturbations on z, w, p, and ω are independent. The difference of such perturbations—i.e., $z_I = z_1 - z_2$—leaves the physical flow unchanged. The perturbation in which the space variable $z(u)$ is not perturbed is called a stationary perturbation by Fox and Morgan.

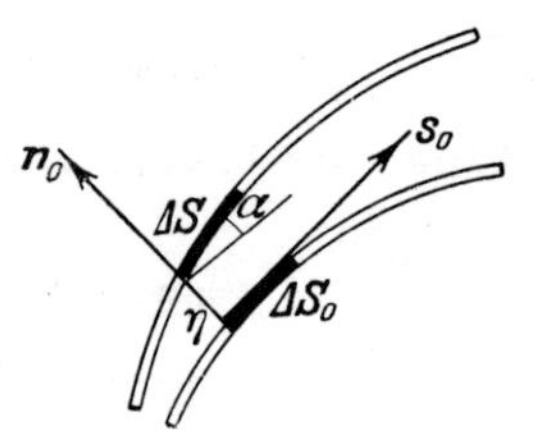

Fig. 216

216. At the present moment ΔS is inclined at a known small angle α with respect to the corresponding element ΔS_o of the fixed contour. The positive normal n_o is directed into the fluid. Along the normal to ΔS_o, the distance from ΔS to ΔS_o is equal to a known quantity $\eta = \int U_n \, dt$. The projections of the fluid velocity on the tangent s_o and the normal n_o to the element ΔS_o are

$$\left. \begin{aligned} V_s &= v_o + \Delta v_{os} + v_s \\ V_n &= \Delta v_{on} + v_n \end{aligned} \right\} . \tag{9.38}$$

The velocity on the steady-flow contour is v_o. The projections on s_o and n_o of the steady-flow velocity increment produced by the translation of the element ΔS are Δv_{os} and Δv_{on}. Finally, v_s and v_n are the projections of the perturbed-flow velocities on s_o and n_o. If we neglect small quantities of higher order, the perturbed flow can be related to the fixed element ΔS_o. The projections on the s_o- and n_o-axes of the unit normal to ΔS are $\sin \alpha = \alpha$ and $\cos \alpha \approx 1$ respectively. Now we can find the projections on the normal to ΔS of the contour velocity U_n and of the fluid velocity; these projections must be equal. If small values of higher order are neglected, we find

$$U_n = - \alpha v_o + \Delta v_{on} + v_n \quad . \tag{9.39}$$

When the line of reasoning applied to derive Eq. (9.26) is applied here, it leads to

$$v_n = \frac{\partial \varphi}{\partial n_o} = - \operatorname{Im} \frac{dw}{du} \left| \frac{du}{dz} \right| . \tag{9.40}$$

The increment Δv_{on} is a known function of u and t. In particular,

$$\Delta v_{on} = \frac{\partial v_{on}}{\partial n_o} \eta = \frac{\partial n_o}{\partial s_o} \eta = \pm v_o \frac{\partial v_o}{\partial \varphi_o} \eta . \tag{9.41}$$

Here $v_o(\partial v_o/\partial \varphi_o)$ can be evaluated on the fixed contour.* In Eq. (9.41) the plus sign is used when both s_o and φ_o increase in the same direction; otherwise, the minus sign is used. The velocity potential of the steady flow φ_o and the velocity v_o are known functions of u on the contour. From Eqs. (9.39) through (9.41) we deduce the boundary condition on the movable or fixed walls in the form

$$\operatorname{Im} \frac{dw}{du} = \left| \frac{dz}{du} \right| \left[- U_n - \alpha v_o \pm v_o \frac{\partial v_o}{\partial \varphi_o} \eta \right] = \nu(u,t) , \tag{9.42}$$

where $\nu(u,t)$ is a known function of u and t.

The derivation of free-surface boundary conditions follows. For this derivation we assume that, at the point at infinity in the flow the velocity is constant and equal to v_∞. An example of such a flow is an unbounded flow around an oscillating contour with separation (see Fig. 211). Other examples are easily constructed. On the free surface the pressure p is constant and, according to the Lagrange integral,

*In the calculation of Δv_{on} we implicitly assume that, when the element ΔS leaves the steady-flow region, $w_o(z)$ can be analytically extended through the elements ΔS_o.

$$\frac{\partial\varphi}{\partial t} + \frac{1}{2}\left(\frac{\partial\varphi_o}{\partial x} + \frac{\partial\varphi}{\partial x}\right)^2 + \frac{1}{2}\left(\frac{\partial\varphi_o}{\partial y} + \frac{\partial\varphi}{\partial y}\right)^2 = \frac{1}{2} v_\infty^2 \quad ,$$

from which, neglecting second-order small terms, we find

$$\frac{\partial\varphi}{\partial t} + \frac{\partial\varphi_o}{\partial x}\frac{\partial\varphi}{\partial x} + \frac{\partial\varphi_o}{\partial y}\frac{\partial\varphi}{\partial y} + \frac{1}{2}\left[\left(\frac{\partial\varphi_o}{\partial x}\right)^2 + \left(\frac{\partial\varphi_o}{\partial y}\right)^2 - v_\infty^2\right] = 0 \quad . \qquad (9.43)$$

The derivatives in Eq. (9.43) are evaluated on the perturbed free surface, which can leave the unperturbed-(steady-) flow region. Thus, it is again necessary to consider that $w_o(z)$ can be analytically extended outside the steady region to an infinitesimal strip extending along the free surface of the unperturbed flow. However, within the assumed limits of accuracy, the first three terms on the left side of Eq. (9.43) can be evaluated on the unperturbed free surface. The quantity in the square brackets must be evaluated more carefully.

We begin by assuming that ds_o and $d\varphi_o$ have the same sign. On the unperturbed free surface we have

$$\frac{\partial\varphi_o}{\partial x} = v_\infty \cos\theta_o \ ; \qquad \frac{\partial\varphi_o}{\partial y} = v_\infty \sin\theta_o \ ; \quad d\varphi_o = v_\infty ds_o \quad , \qquad (9.44)$$

where θ_o is the angle between the unperturbed-flow velocity and the x-axis. Equation (9.44) is used to transform Eq. (9.43) to the form

$$\frac{\partial\varphi}{\partial t} + v_\infty^2\frac{\partial\varphi}{\partial\varphi_o} + \frac{1}{2}\Delta v_o^2 = 0 \quad , \qquad (9.45)$$

where

$$\Delta v_o^2 = v_o^2 - v_\infty^2 = \left(\frac{\partial\varphi_o}{\partial x}\right)^2 + \left(\frac{\partial\varphi_o}{\partial y}\right)^2 - v_\infty^2 \quad .$$

Gurevich and Khaskind [171] attempted to simplify the problem by dropping $\Delta v_o^2/2$ from Eq. (9.45) and thereby arrived at the boundary condition

$$\frac{\partial\varphi}{\partial t} + v_\infty^2 \frac{\partial\varphi}{\partial\varphi_o} = 0 \quad . \tag{9.46}$$

On the other hand, Woods [172] assumed that the regions of change of the complex potentials in the steady and unsteady flows were the same, but that the functions

$$-\omega = \ell n\ (v_\infty dz/dF) = \ell n\ (v_\infty/V) + i\theta = -\tau + i\theta$$

and

$$-\omega_o = \ell n\ \frac{v_\infty dz}{dw_o} = \ell n\ \frac{v_\infty}{v_o} + i\theta_o = -\tau_o + i\theta_o$$

differed to the first order.* On this basis he obtained the free-surface boundary condition

$$-\left[\frac{\partial}{\partial\varphi_o}(v_\infty^2\tau) + \frac{\partial\tau}{\partial t}\right] = \frac{\partial}{\partial\varphi_o}\left\{v_\infty^2\ \ell n\ \frac{v_\infty}{V}\right\} + \frac{\partial}{\partial t}\ \ell n\ \frac{v_\infty}{V} = 0 \quad , \tag{9.47}$$

*It is obvious that such an approach makes the dependence of z different on the parametric variable in the steady and unsteady flows; hence, the perturbations used by Woods are not stationary according to the Fox and Morgan definition.

where $V = v_o + v$. But,

$$\ell n \frac{v_\infty}{V} = \ell n \frac{v_\infty}{v_\infty + v} \approx - \frac{v}{v_\infty} = - \frac{\partial\varphi}{v_\infty \partial s_o} = - \frac{\partial\varphi}{\partial\varphi_o} ,$$

and the Woods's condition trasforms to

$$v_\infty^2 \frac{\partial^2\varphi}{\partial\varphi_o^2} + \frac{\partial^2\varphi}{\partial t \partial\varphi_o} = 0 .$$

This condition is obtained directly from Eq. (9.46) by differentiation with respect to φ_o. Therefore, conditions (9.46) and (9.47) are practically equivalent.

Now we return to boundary condition Eq. (9.45). Let the positive normal to the surface point into the fluid. Denote by η the distance from points of the actual free surface to the free surface of the unperturbed flow; η is positive when a point of the actual free surface is inside the unperturbed flow. Thus, if we exclude the jet-separation points (at which the curvature of the free surface can be infinite), then to first-order accuracy

$$\frac{1}{2} \Delta v_o^2 = v_\infty \Delta v_o = v_\infty \frac{\partial v_o}{\partial n_o} \eta = v_\infty^2 \frac{\partial\theta_o}{\partial s_o} \eta = v_\infty^3 \frac{\partial\theta_o}{\partial\varphi_o} \eta , \quad (9.48)$$

and Eq. (9.45) takes the form

$$\frac{\partial\varphi}{\partial t} + v_\infty^2 \frac{\partial\varphi}{\partial\varphi_o} + v_\infty^3 \frac{\partial\theta_o}{\partial\varphi_o} \eta = 0 . \quad (9.49)$$

Here, contrary to the condition on the contour of the body, the value of the unsteady displacement η is unknown. However, η can be eliminated by using the condition that the normal component of the fluid velocity $\partial\varphi/\partial n_o$ must be equal to η's total time derivative--i.e.,

$$\frac{\partial\varphi}{\partial n_o} = D\eta = \frac{\partial\eta}{\partial t} + v_\infty \frac{\partial\eta}{\partial s_o} = \frac{\partial\eta}{\partial t} + v_\infty^2 \frac{\partial\eta}{\partial\varphi_o} \quad . \tag{9.50}$$

Elimination of η between Eqs. (9.49) and (9.50) gives

$$v_\infty^3 \frac{\partial\varphi}{\partial n_o} = - D\left[\frac{\partial\varphi_o}{\partial\theta_o} D\varphi\right] \quad ,$$

or, since $\partial\varphi/\partial n_o = -\partial\psi/\partial s_o$,

$$v_\infty^3 \frac{\partial\psi}{\partial s_o} = v_\infty^4 \frac{\partial\psi}{\partial\phi_o} = D\left[\frac{\partial\varphi_o}{\partial\theta_o} D\right] \quad . \tag{9.51}$$

We considered the case when the arc distance increases downstream in the direction of the velocity. However, in the opposite case, when $d\varphi_o = -v_\infty ds$, Eqs. (9.47) and (9.51) are unchanged even though some terms in the intermediate equations have different signs.

If $\omega_o = \ell n(dw/v_\infty dz) = \tau_o - i\theta_o$, then Eq. (9.51) becomes

$$\text{Im}\left[v_\infty^4 \frac{dw}{d\omega_o} - D\left(\frac{dw_o}{d\omega_o} Dw\right)\right] = 0 \quad . \tag{9.52}$$

An equation in a form equivalent to Eq. (9.52) was used by Fox and Morgan [170]. However, their equation was given without a detailed derivation and with only a reference to Ablow and Hayes's work [173].

Curle [174] took the velocity potential of the perturbed flow in the form $\varphi_1 e^{-\lambda t}$, where λ is a constant, and obtained a free-surface boundary condition

$$\frac{\partial \varphi_1}{\partial \tau_o} = - \left[- \frac{\partial \varphi_o}{\partial \theta_o} \frac{\lambda}{v_\infty^2} + \frac{\partial}{\partial \theta_o} \right]^2 \varphi_1 \quad . \tag{9.53}$$

This condition is easily obtained from Eq. (9.51).

Now we survey the results obtained in the references cited in this section. In [171] steady, harmonic oscillations of a contour in an unlimited jet flow with separation at the contour (Fig. 211) were examined. There, $\nu(u,t)$—see Eq. (9.42)—was given as

$$\nu(u,t) = \nu_1 \cos kt + \nu_2 \sin kt$$

and w as

$$w = w_1 \cos kt + w_2 \sin kt \quad ,$$

where k is the frequency of the oscillation and ν_1, ν_2, w_1, and w_2 are independent of time. These equations can be simplified by introducing a new imaginary unit $j = \sqrt{-1}$ that is independent of $i = \sqrt{-1}$. In equations containing j and i we retain as final results only the real parts relative to j but both the real and imaginary parts relative to i. Now the preceding expressions become

$$\nu = ce^{jkt} , \qquad w = We^{jkt} \qquad (c = \nu_1 - j\nu_2 ; \qquad W = w_1 - jw_2) \quad .$$

Introducing these results into the boundary condition Eqs. (9.42) and (9.46) produces the time independent equations

$$\text{Im} \frac{dW}{du} = c(u) \tag{9.54}$$

and

$$jk\Phi + v_\infty^2 \frac{d\Phi}{d\varphi_o} = 0 \qquad (W = \Phi + i\Psi) \quad . \tag{9.55}$$

In Eq. (9.54) Im indicates the imaginary part relative to i.

The condition on the free surface, Eq. (9.55), can be considered a differential equation for determining Φ. Integrating this equation gives, on the free surface,

$$\Phi = a \exp\left[-\frac{jk\varphi_o}{v_\infty^2}\right] \quad . \tag{9.56}$$

The arbitrary constant a has different values on the different jet surfaces AC and BC. For computational brevity we assume that the flow is symmetric about the x-axis. Then, a has the same value on the free surfaces to either side of the plate. Next, it is possible to make points A and B correspond to the points $u = \mp 1$ and to map points C and O onto $u = \infty$ and $u = 0$, respectively. The mapping function is

$$w_o = Nu^2 \quad , \tag{9.57}$$

where N is a real, positive constant (see, e.g., Chapter I, Section E). By using Eq. (9.57), Eq. (9.56) is reduced to

$$\mathrm{Re}\, W = a \exp\left[-j\kappa u^2\right] \qquad \left(u^2 > 1 \; ; \qquad \kappa = \frac{kN}{v_\infty^2}\right) \quad . \tag{9.58}$$

The function $W(u)$ is to be found in the upper halfplane of the parametric variable u. Since $W(u)$ is to satisfy the boundary condition Eqs. (9.42) and (9.58), we divide $W(u)$

into two parts, W_1 and W_2; the sum of these two parts is W(u), and they satisfy the following conditions:

1. On the contour $(u^2 \le 1)$,

$$\operatorname{Im} W_1 = 0 , \qquad \operatorname{Im} \frac{dW_2}{du} = c(u) . \tag{9.59}$$

2. On the free surface $(u^2 > 1)$,

$$\operatorname{Re} W_1 = a \exp\left[-j\kappa u^2\right] , \qquad \operatorname{Re} \frac{dW_2}{du} = 0 . \tag{9.60}$$

From the methods of thin-wing theory [24] and Schwarz's formula for the upper half-plane, we obtain

$$\frac{W}{(u^2 - 1)^{1/2}} = -\frac{a}{\pi i}\int_{-\infty}^{-1} \frac{\exp\left[-j\kappa\xi^2\right] d\xi}{(\xi^2 - 1)^{1/2}(\xi - u)}$$

$$+ \frac{a}{\pi i}\int_{1}^{\infty} \frac{\exp\left[-j\kappa\xi^2\right] d\xi}{(\xi^2 - 1)^{1/2}(\xi - u)}$$

$$= \frac{a}{\pi i}\int_{1}^{\infty} \frac{\exp\left[-j\kappa\xi^2\right]}{(\xi^2 - 1)^{1/2}}\left(\frac{1}{\xi + u} + \frac{1}{\xi - u}\right) d\xi$$

$$= \frac{2a}{\pi i}\int_{1}^{\infty} \frac{\exp\left[-j\kappa\xi^2\right]\xi \, d\xi}{(\xi^2 - 1)^{1/2}(\xi^2 - u^2)} . \tag{9.61}$$

Analogously, we may also obtain

$$\frac{dW_2}{du} = \frac{1}{\pi(1 - u^2)^{1/2}}\int_{-1}^{1} \frac{c(\xi)\,(1 - \xi^2)^{1/2}}{\xi - u} d\xi . \tag{9.62}$$

In [171] a is selected so that the perturbed-flow velocity at the separation points is finite. Note that the potential $W_2 e^{jkt}$ is analogous to the potential arising from an impact and gives an oscillation that does not promote wave formation. The potential $W_1 e^{jkt}$ cancels the infinite velocities at the edges of the arc, which are produced by the "impact" flow (with a potential $W_2 e^{jkt}$), and gives waves that propagate from the contour on the free surface of our weightless fluid.

Woods [172] investigated the problem of a perturbed-jet flow around a contour from several other viewpoints. For example, as a region of change of the parametric variable ζ he chose a semi-infinite strip of width 2π (Fig. 217). The region of change of the steady-flow complex potential w_o for the Fig. 211 flow is a plane with a cut along the real axis $\psi = 0$. The mapping of this cut plane onto the semi-infinite strip of Fig. 217 is given by

$$w_o = 4a\left(i \sinh \frac{\zeta}{2} + \sin \frac{\lambda}{2}\right)^2 , \qquad (9.63)$$

where

$$\sin \frac{\lambda}{2} = \frac{(\varphi_A)^{1/2} - (\varphi_B)^{1/2}}{(\varphi_A)^{1/2} + (\varphi_B)^{1/2}} ; \qquad 4a = \frac{1}{4}\left[(\varphi_A)^{1/2} + (\varphi_B)^{1/2}\right]^2 ,$$

and φ_A and φ_B are the values of w_o at A and B. As noted above, Woods does not vary the complex potential, and his unsteady, perturbed-flow complex potential is the same as w_o, determined by Eq. (9.63). However, he allows $-\omega_o = \ln (v_\infty dz/dw_o) = -\tau_o + i\theta_o$ to vary because the difference $-\omega + \omega_o$ is a first-order small quantity. If on the contour the imaginary part of $-\omega + \omega_o$ is known—$\text{Im}(-\omega + \omega_o) = \theta - \theta_o$—and on the free surfaces the real part is known—$\text{Re}(-\omega + \omega_o) = \tau_o - \tau$—then $-\omega + \omega_o$ can be obtained by solving a mixed boundary-value problem for a semi-infinite strip. The result is

$$-\omega + \omega_o = \frac{\cosh(\zeta/2)}{2\pi}\left\{\int_{-\pi}^{\pi} \frac{(\theta - \theta_o)\, d\gamma^*}{\sin(\gamma^*/2) + i \sinh(\zeta/2)} - \int_{-\infty}^{0}\left(\frac{\tau_1 - \tau_{1o}}{\cosh(\eta^*/2) + i \sinh(\zeta/2)} + \frac{\tau_2 - \tau_{2o}}{\cosh(\eta^*/2) - i \sinh(\zeta/2)}\right) d\eta^*\right\} . \tag{9.64}$$

In the last integral the subscripts 1 and 2 refer to the upper jet BC and the lower jet AC, respectively. Equation (9.64) was obtained directly by Woods. It is also possible to obtain it from the solution of the mixed problem for the half-plane [24] by employing the conformal mapping of the half-plane onto a semi-infinite strip. From Eqs. (9.63) and (9.64) it follows that the expansions of w_o and $-\omega + \omega_o$ in the neighborhood of $C(\eta \to \infty)$, the point at infinity, have the form

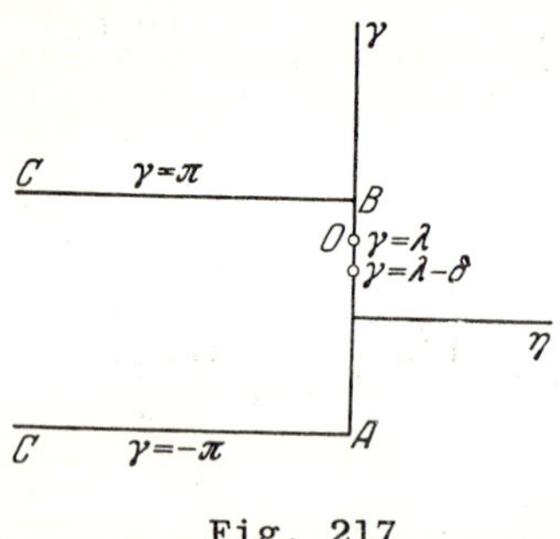

Fig. 217

$$\frac{w_o}{a} = e^{-\zeta}\left\{1 + 4i \sin\frac{\lambda}{2} \exp[\zeta/2] + O(e^{\zeta})\right\} , \tag{9.65}$$

$$\omega_o - \omega = iA + B \exp[\zeta/2) + iCe^{\zeta} + O(\exp[3\zeta/2] . \tag{9.66}$$

Woods assumes that the unsteady motion has existed for a finite time. It then follows that

$$\left.\begin{aligned}
A &= \frac{1}{2\pi}\int_{-\pi}^{\pi}(\theta-\theta_o)\,d\gamma^* - \frac{1}{2\pi}\int_{-\infty}^{0}[(\tau_1-\tau_{1o})-(\tau_2-\tau_{2o})]\,d\eta^* = 0\\
B &= \frac{1}{\pi}\int_{-\pi}^{\pi}(\theta-\theta_o)\sin\frac{\gamma^*}{2}\,d\gamma^*\\
&\quad -\frac{1}{\pi}\int_{-\infty}^{0}[(\tau_1-\tau_{1o})+(\tau_2-\tau_{2o})]\cosh\frac{\eta^*}{2}\,d\eta^* = 0\\
C &= \frac{1}{\pi}\int_{-\pi}^{\pi}(\theta-\theta_o)\cos\gamma^*\,d\gamma^*\\
&\quad +\frac{1}{\pi}\int_{-\infty}^{0}[(\tau_1-\tau_{1o})-(\tau_2-\tau_{2o})]\cosh\eta^*\,d\eta^* = 0
\end{aligned}\right\} . \qquad (9.67)$$

The value $\theta - \theta_o$ is expressed in terms of known quantities and δ, which is the ζ-plane displacement of the critical point (Fig. 217). As a result, after the exclusion of δ from Eqs. (9.67), they become a system of two integral equations with two unknowns τ_1 and τ_2. Considering Eq. (9.47) and carrying out a proper change of variables, Woods solves the above system of equations by employing the Laplace transformation—i.e., by the methods of operational calculus. Using this method to find the general problem solution, Woods obtained, in addition, equations for the pressure distribution, drag, lift, and total moment on the contour.

For example, Woods studied two cases of the motion of a flat plate that is normal to the approaching flow. First, he investigated the case when the constant velocity v_∞ of the plate with respect to the fluid changes suddenly to $v_\infty + \Delta v_\infty$ at $t = 0$ and then suddenly returns to v_∞ at $t = t_1$. For a plate of width 2ℓ he found for the drag coefficient C_x

$$C_x = \frac{2\pi}{4+\pi} + 2\,\frac{\Delta v_\infty}{v_\infty}\begin{cases} 1 + \dfrac{8}{\pi}\left(\dfrac{\pi+2}{\pi+4}\right)\eta_1 F(\eta_1) & \text{when } 0 < t < t_1 \\[2ex] \dfrac{9}{\pi}\left(\dfrac{\pi+2}{\pi+4}\right)\eta_1 F(\eta_1) - \eta_2 F(\eta_2) & \text{when } t > t_1 \end{cases}$$

where:

$$\eta_1 = (\tau + 1)^{-1/2}, \qquad \eta_2 = (\tau - \tau_1 + 1)^{-1/2},$$

$$\tau = v_\infty^2 t/4a, \qquad \tau_1 = v_\infty^2 t_1/4a = (4+\pi)\, v_\infty t_1/2\ell,$$

$$F(k) = k^{-2}E(k) - (1 - k^2)\, k^{-2}K(k).$$

Here $K(k)$ and $K(k)$ are the complete elliptic integrals of the first and second kind. Then, increasing the range of applicability of his results, Woods obtained the drag on a flat plate performing harmonic oscillations as a second case.

Consider now Curle's work [174], which encompassed the following problem: a motionless fluid fills the left half-plane and is separated from a region of constant pressure by a solid wall, coinciding with the y-axis. If an opening of width 2ℓ appears suddenly in the solid wall, then, because of the pressure difference, fluid begins to flow from the opening. After an infinite time the flow becomes steady.

The jet-formation process is the subject of study. However, no suitable theory has been derived to provide a complete solution to the problems. Curle studied only two limiting cases:

1. The initial instant of jet formation.
2. The motion long after the initial instant and at a finite distance from the wall when the shape of the unsteady jet differs very little from that of the steady jet.

While the first case is solved relatively easily and has little in common with the material in this section, the second case can serve as an instructive example of a solution to a slightly perturbed jet flow.

The solution to the steady jet flow from an opening in a plane was given in Chapter I, Section E. On eliminating t from Eqs. (1.47) and (1.48), replacing v_o by v_∞, and denoting $\ln(dw/v_\infty dz)$ by $\omega_o = \tau_o - i\theta_o$, we find $w_o = -(Q/\pi) \ln \cosh \omega_o$; from this and Eq. (1.51) after denoting BA by 2ℓ (see Figs. 8 and 218) we finally obtain

$$w_o = -\frac{2\ell v_\infty}{2+\pi} \ln \cosh \omega_o \quad . \tag{9.68}$$

From Fig. 218, $\theta_o = 0$ on AC and $\theta_o = \pi$ on BC. Furthermore, $\tau_o = 0$ on AD and BD, and $\omega_o = -\pi i/2$ at D, the point at infinity. Now it follows that the region of change of ω_o is a semi-infinite strip, as shown in Fig. 219. To verify the accuracy of Eq. (9.68) it is sufficient to show that along the streamline CAD, $\text{Im } w_o = \psi_o = 0$, and along the streamline CBD, $\text{Im } w_o = \psi_o = -2\pi\ell v_\infty/(2+\pi)$.

Long after the orifice is opened, the unsteady-flow velocity potential is given approximately, according to Curle, by $\varphi_o + \varphi_1 \exp[-\lambda t]$, where λ is a positive constant. The approximation arises because hereafter quantities of the order of $\exp[-2\lambda t]$ are neglected—i.e., t is sufficiently large to make such terms negligible. Along the solid walls the derivative of the velocity potential with respect to the

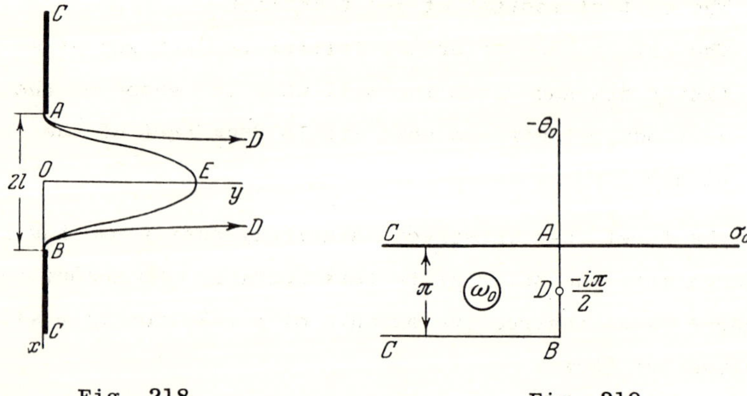

Fig. 218

Fig. 219

interior normal $\partial\varphi/\partial n$ is zero; therefore, it is easy to see that when $-\theta_o = 0$ or $-\theta_o = \pi$,

$$\frac{\partial\varphi_1}{\partial\theta_o} = 0 \quad . \tag{9.69}$$

On the free surfaces—i.e., when $\tau_o = 0$—condition (9.53) must be satisfied. It is convenient to introduce $\partial\varphi_o/\partial\theta_o$, obtained from Eq. (9.68)—i.e.,

$$\frac{\partial\varphi_o}{\partial\theta_o} = \text{Im}\,\frac{\partial w_o}{\partial\omega_o} = -\,\text{Im}\,\frac{2\ell v_\infty}{2+\pi}\tanh\,\omega_o$$

into Eq. (9.53). But first note that, on the free surface, $\omega_o = -i\theta_o$, so

$$\frac{\partial\varphi_o}{\partial\theta_o} = \frac{2\ell v_\infty}{2+\pi}\tan\,\theta_o \quad . \tag{9.70}$$

With the help of Eq. (9.70) the boundary condition, Eq. (9.53), can be written in the form

$$\frac{\partial\varphi_1}{\partial\tau_o} = -\left[\frac{\partial}{\partial\theta_o} - \frac{2\ell\lambda\tan\theta_o}{(2+\pi)\,v_\infty}\right]^2 \varphi_1$$

$$= -\left[\frac{\partial}{\partial\theta_o} - \frac{2\ell\lambda\tan\theta_o}{(2+\pi)\,v_\infty}\right]\left[\frac{\partial\varphi_1}{\partial\theta_o} - \frac{2\ell\lambda\tan\theta_o}{(2+\pi)\,v_\infty}\varphi_1\right] .$$

Then, if $\lambda_1 = 2\ell\lambda/(2+\pi)v_\infty$, we have (with $\tau_o = 0$)

$$\frac{\partial\varphi_1}{\partial\tau_o} = -\frac{\partial^2\varphi_1}{\partial\theta_o^2} + 2\lambda_1 \tan\theta_o \frac{\partial\varphi_1}{\partial\theta_o} - \lambda_1^2 \tan^2\theta_o\varphi_1 + \lambda_1\varphi_1 \sec^2\theta_o . \tag{9.71}$$

Now, the solution is sought in the form of a series

$$\varphi_1 = \frac{2\ell v_\infty}{\pi+2}\sum_0^\infty a_n \exp\left[n\tau_o\right]\cos n\theta_o . \tag{9.72}$$

Clearly, each term of the series satisfies Laplace's equation. Also the φ_1, determined by Eq. (9.72), satisfies the boundary condition (9.69) for any a_n when $\theta_o = 0$ and $\theta_o = \pi$. It remains only to choose the coefficients a_n so that condition (9.71) is satisfied. By introducing Eq. (9.72) into Eq. (9.71) we find

$$\sum_0^\infty\left(n^2 - n + \lambda_1^2\right) a_n \cos n\theta_o = 2\lambda_1 \tan\theta_o \sum_0^\infty n a_n \sin n\theta_o$$

$$+ \left(\lambda_1^2 - \lambda_1\right)\sec^2\theta_o \sum_0^\infty a_n \cos n\theta_o ;$$

after multiplying this by $4 \cos^2 \theta_o = 2(1 + \cos 2\theta_o)$ and making some simple transformations, we obtain

$$-2 \sum_{0}^{\infty} \left(n^2 - n + 2\lambda_1 - \lambda_1^2\right) a_n \cos n\theta_o = \sum_{0}^{\infty} \left(n^2 - n + 2\lambda_1 n + \lambda_1^2\right) a_n \cos (n + 2) \theta_o$$

$$+ \sum_{0}^{\infty} \left(n^2 - n - 2\lambda_1 n + \lambda_1^2\right) a_n \cos (n - 2) \theta_o \ . \tag{9.73}$$

If Eq. (9.73) is to be satisfied, then the coefficients of terms $\cos (r\theta_o)$ on each side of the equal sign must be equal. Consequently, we obtain the system of equations

$$\left.\begin{aligned}
-2\left(2\lambda_1 - \lambda_1^2\right)a_o &= \left(\lambda_1^2 - 4\lambda_1 + 2\right)a_2 \\
-3\left(2\lambda_1 - \lambda_1^2\right)a_1 &= \left(6 - 6\lambda_1 + \lambda_1^2\right)a_3 \\
-2\left(2 + 2\lambda_1 - \lambda_1^2\right)a_2 - 2\lambda_1^2 a_o &= \left(12 - 8\lambda_1 + \lambda_1^2\right)a_4 \\
-2\left(r^2 - r + 2\lambda_1 - \lambda_1^2\right)a_r &= \left[(r - 2)^2 - (r - 2) + 2\lambda_1(r - 2) + \lambda_1^2\right]a_{r-2} \\
&\quad + \left[(r + 2)^2 - (r + 2) - 2\lambda_1(r + 2) + \lambda_1^2\right]a_{r-2} \\
&(\text{with } r \geqq 3) \ .
\end{aligned}\right\} \tag{9.74}$$

Equations (9.74) are two independent systems: one is for even r and one is for odd r. The even-r set corresponds to a symmetric flow, while the odd-r set corresponds to an asymmetric flow. For symmetric flow, we set all a_r equal to zero for odd r. Further, if the pressure at point C at infinity is constant, then $\partial\varphi/\partial t$ at $C(\tau_o = -\infty)$ must be zero. Therefore, according to Eq. (9.72)

$$a_o = 0 \ . \tag{9.75}$$

Now from Eqs. (9.74) and (9.75) it follows that either $a_2 = 0$ or $\lambda_1^2 - 4\lambda_1 + 2 = 0$. Continuing this process, we see from Eq. (9.74) that either $\varphi_1 = 0$ or, for some r,

$$\lambda_1^2 - 2\lambda_1(r + 2) + (r + 2)^2 - (r + 2) = 0 \quad ,$$

from which

$$\lambda_1 = r + 2 \pm (r + 2)^{1/2} \qquad (r = 0,\ 2,\ 4,\ \ldots)\ .^{*} \tag{9.76}$$

To the smallest value $\lambda_1 = 2 - \sqrt{2}$ corresponds

$$\lambda = \frac{(2 + \pi)\, v_\infty (2 - \sqrt{2})}{2\ell} \approx 1.506\ v_\infty/\ell \quad .$$

From knowledge of a_1 and λ_1 and with Eq. (9.74), all the other coefficients a_r for even r can be found—i.e., φ_1 can be found. To fix a_2, Curle assumed $a_2 = 1$.

Knowing φ_1, it is possible to find the shape of the jet for any sufficiently large t. The shape of the steady-flow jet is known and is easily obtained from Eq. (9.68) after integration of

$$z = \frac{1}{v_\infty} \int \exp\,[-\omega_0]\, dw_0 = -\frac{2\ell}{2 + \pi} \int \exp\,[-\omega_0]\, \frac{\tanh \omega_0}{\cosh \omega_0}\, d\omega_0$$

with $\omega_0 = -i\theta_0$. On AD $(0 \leq \theta_0 \leq \pi/2)$ the parametric equations of the steady free surface are

*Fox and Morgan [170] obtained the same family of values for odd r—i.e., for the asymmetric perturbations.

$$x = -\frac{\pi\ell}{2+\pi} - \frac{2\ell}{2+\pi}\cos\theta_o ,$$

$$y = \frac{2\ell}{2+\pi}\left[\ell n\,(\sec\theta_o + \tan\theta_o) - \sin\theta_o\right] .$$

To obtain the shape of the perturbed free surface it is sufficient to find the value η, the distance between points of the perturbed and the unperturbed, steady free surfaces. To find η, we take advantage of Eq. (9.49), into which we now substitute $\varphi_1 e^{-\lambda t}$ in lieu of φ; $\partial\theta_o/\partial\varphi_o$ is given by Eq. (9.70). The remaining and quite obvious calculations that lead to determination of the parametric equations for the free surface of the perturbed flow, together with the numerical results, are found in [174].

In concluding the present section we briefly examine the question of the stability of jet flows. As mentioned at the beginning of the book, for a long period of time it was assumed that, in the region of constant pressure, bounded by the free surfaces, there existed a fluid with the same density as that in the main flow. However, experiments have shown that such flows are unstable. The bases of our elementary, theoretical analysis of the stability of a free surface—that is, a surface of discontinuity of the tangential velocities—are well known [2, 175].

Let the fluid be motionless in the upper half-plane $y > 0$ and have a horizontal velocity v in $y < 0$. We now assume that an unsteady motion arises, in which the velocity potentials φ_1 and φ (in the upper and lower half-planes respectively) and the elevation of the perturbed free surface η have the forms

$$\varphi_1 = \mathrm{Re}\left[c_1 e^{-ky} e^{ikx}\right] , \qquad (9.77)$$

$$\varphi = v + \mathrm{Re}\left[c e^{ky} e^{ikx}\right] , \qquad (9.78)$$

$$\eta = \mathrm{Re}\left[M e^{ikx}\right] . \qquad (9.79)$$

The constant $k > 0$ so that the perturbations die out at $y = \pm\infty$. The complex coefficients C_1, C, and M depend on time t. During our examination of the stability problem, we omit for brevity the designation "Re". On assuming that the pressures at $y = \pm\infty$ are both equal to p_∞, we can write the Lagrange integrals for the upper and lower halves of the flow as

$$\frac{p_1}{\rho} + \frac{1}{2}\left[\left(\frac{\partial\varphi_1}{\partial x}\right)^2 + \left(\frac{\partial\varphi_1}{\partial y}\right)^2\right] + \frac{\partial\varphi_1}{\partial t} = \frac{p_\infty}{\rho} , \qquad (9.80)$$

$$\frac{p}{\rho} + \frac{1}{2}\left[\left(\frac{\partial\varphi}{\partial x}\right)^2 + \left(\frac{\partial\varphi}{\partial y}\right)^2\right] + \frac{\partial\varphi}{\partial t} = \frac{p_\infty}{\rho} + \frac{v^2}{2} . \qquad (9.81)$$

Since the pressure varies continuously across the boundary between the two fluids, we obtain from Eqs. (9.77), (9.78), (9.80), and (9.81)

$$\frac{dc_1}{dt} = \frac{dc}{dt} + vikc \qquad (9.82)$$

after neglecting terms containing the squares and higher order products of the small numbers c and c_1. On the other hand, the conditions that fluid particles located in the upper and lower half-planes cannot mix have the form {cf. Eq. (9.50)}

$$\frac{\partial\eta}{\partial t} = \left(\frac{\partial\varphi_1}{\partial y}\right)_{y=\eta} , \qquad \frac{\partial\eta}{\partial t} + v\,\frac{\partial\eta}{\partial x} = \left(\frac{\partial\varphi}{\partial y}\right)_{y=\eta} .$$

On neglecting small values of higher order, the same conditions can be written in more convenient form as

$$\frac{\partial\eta}{\partial t} = \left(\frac{\partial\varphi_1}{\partial y}\right)_{y=0}, \qquad \frac{\partial\eta}{\partial t} + v\,\frac{\partial\eta}{\partial x} = \left(\frac{\partial\varphi}{\partial y}\right)_{y=0} . \tag{9.83}$$

By using Eqs. (9.77) through (9.79), condition (9.83) can be given in the form of equations that do not contain the x-coordinate, as

$$\frac{dM}{dt} = -kc_1 , \qquad \frac{dM}{dt} + ikvM = kc . \tag{9.84}$$

Equations (9.82) and (9.84) represent a system of three ordinary, linear, differential equations with constant coefficients for the unknowns c, c_1, and M. By eliminating c and c_1, we reduce the system to

$$\frac{d^2M}{dt^2} + vik\,\frac{dM}{dt} - \frac{v^2k^2}{2}\,M = 0 . \tag{9.85}$$

The general solution to Eq. (9.85) is

$$M = \exp\left[-\frac{vik}{2}\,t\right]\left(A\exp\left[\frac{vk}{2}\,t\right] + B\exp\left[-\frac{vk}{2}\,t\right]\right), \tag{9.86}$$

where A and B are arbitrary constants. Since either $vk/2$ or $-vk/2$ must be positive, $|M| \to \infty$ when $t \to \infty$. Therefore, the surface of discontinuity (of the horizontal velocities) is unstable.

As repeatedly mentioned above, modern jet theory is applied to cavitational flow around bodies, planing flow, and flow of water into air (in short, to problems in which the "dead zone" is filled by a medium whose density is considerably less than that of the flowing fluid). Stability analyses of the separation surface between two fluids with different densities (including capillary and gravity effects) have also been made [2, 176, and 177 § 61, problem 3]. It is of greatest interest to us to examine the limiting case when the fluid density in the upper half-plane is zero. In addition, we shall consider capillary effects.*

The velocity potential φ of the flow in the lower half-plane and the disturbed free surface shape $\eta(x,t)$ are given as usual by Eqs. (9.78) and (9.79). Also, Eq. (9.81) must be satisfied. However, the flow in the upper half-plane no longer exists, and the pressure p_1 there is constant. According to the capillary wave theory [177, § 60 and 61], the pressure difference $p_1 - p$ (where p is the pressure on the free surface as we approach from below) is, on neglecting small terms of higher order,

$$p_1 - p = \alpha \frac{\partial^2 \eta}{\partial x^2} , \tag{9.87}$$

where α is a coefficient of surface tension. From Eqs. (9.87), (9.78), (9.79) and (9.81) we find the free surface boundary condition to be

$$\frac{dc}{dt} + vikc + \frac{\alpha k^2 M}{\rho} = 0 . \tag{9.88}$$

---

*We shall not account for gravity effects. The basic physical applications of jet theory are concerned with high velocities (where gravity effects are in general small); the fundamental question of the stability of jet free surfaces must be answered, regardless of the angle of inclination of these surfaces to the horizontal.

The additional Eqs. (9.83) and (9.84) remain unchanged. By using Eq. (9.84) to exclude c from Eq. (9.88) we find

$$\frac{d^2M}{dt^2} + 2ikv\frac{dM}{dt} - k^2v^2M + \frac{\alpha k^3}{\rho}M = 0 \quad . \tag{9.89}$$

The characteristic equation for Eq. (9.89) is

$$\lambda^2 + 2ikv\lambda - k^2v^2 + \frac{\alpha k^3}{\rho} = 0 \quad ,$$

which has the solutions

$$\lambda_{1,2} = -ikv \pm i\left(\frac{\alpha k^3}{\rho}\right)^{1/2} \quad .$$

Thus, the two roots of the characteristic equation are different and purely imaginary. As a result, the amplitude of oscillations of φ and η is constant.

If $\alpha = 0$, then the system of equations, consisting of Eq. (9.84) and (9.88) becomes

$$\left.\begin{aligned} &\frac{dc}{dt} + vikc = 0 \\ &\frac{dM}{dt} + ikvM = kc \end{aligned}\right\} \quad . \tag{9.90}$$

By integrating the first equation of this system, we find

$$c = c_o \exp\left[-ikvt\right] \quad , \tag{9.91}$$

where c_o is an arbitrary constant. Then, by placing this expression for c in the second equation of Eqs. (9.90) and integrating it, we obtain

$$M = M_o \exp\left[-ikvt\right] + tc_ok \exp\left[-ikvt\right] \quad . \tag{9.92}$$

Therefore, we observe that, if capillary forces are not considered, harmonic oscillations of the velocity potential lead to an unbounded increase in the amplitude of the free surface as a function of time. Note, however, that the speed of this increase in amplitude is considerably less than the corresponding speed of increase for the amplitude of the oscillations (of the horizontal velocities' discontinuity surface) when the density in the "dead zone" is the same as the density in the mean flow—cf. Eq. (9.86).

The most substantial work dedicated to the stability of jet flows appears to be the above-mentioned work by Fox and Morgan [170]. They investigated the stability of classical jet flows when the free surfaces of the fluid are bounded by a void. Considering as known the mean, steady flow, Fox and Morgan gave the complex potential of the additional, perturbed flow w in the form

$$w = G_1 e^{\lambda t} + G_2 e^{\bar{\lambda} t} ,$$

where G_1 and G_2 are functions of the complex velocity of the steady flow. The perturbations were considered small, and terms of higher order in these perturbations were neglected everywhere. On the solid wall the perturbed flow's normal velocity was taken as zero. On the free surfaces, condition (9.52) was used. Fox and Morgan called the perturbations steady (stable), if $\mathrm{Re}\,\lambda < 0$, and unsteady (unstable), if $\mathrm{Re}\,\lambda > 0$. The perturbation for which $\mathrm{Re}\,\lambda = 0$ was called neutral. The basic mathematical part of Fox and Morgan's work consists in finding eigenvalues λ, for which the boundary conditions can be satisfied.

Thus, Fox and Morgan investigated the stability of the flows shown in Fig. 220 and arrived at the following results:

1. For a jet that strikes a symmetrically placed plate that is perpendicular to the jet, the flow is stable or neutrally stable (Fig. 220a).
2. For the collision of symmetric jets, it was found that, in addition to the stable perturbations, there are also unstable ones with $0 \leqq \operatorname{Re} \lambda < 1$ (Fig. 220b).
3. For a jet flowing from a slot between two plane plates with an included angle β (Fig. 220c) all the perturbations are stable, except when $\beta = 2\pi$ (the Borda nozzle). When $\beta = 2\pi$ an isolated, unsteady perturbation exists.
4. For a hollow vortex, confined in a pipe whose axis coincides with that of the vortex, the flow has neutral stability (Fig. 220d).

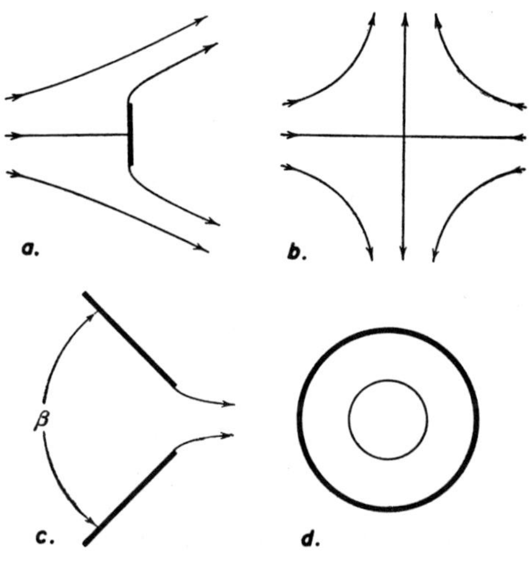

Fig. 220

Unfortunately, the theory is as yet unable to explain the observed stability of real jet flows. One problem is that neutral stability in the velocity potential does not prevent the free surface from being unstable. However, as demonstrated above, in general capillary forces probably act to convert free-surface instability to neutral stability. Clearly then, by analogy with Liapunov's stability theory, it is necessary to investigate the higher-order perturbations for the neutrally stable cases in order to reach a firm conclusion. It is quite possible that a completely new mathematical formulation of the stability problem for jet flows will be required. For example, possibly it is advisable to limit the stability analysis to the neighborhood of the body around which the fluid flows and to ignore the question of the stability of the jet flow as a whole.

D. SURFACE IMPACT OF A WEDGE

The solution to the problem of the surface impact of a wedge on water is a requisite for theoretical computations on landing a seaplane. In spite of the clarity of the problem formulation for a wedge entering a fluid and the abundance of literature dedicated to this topic, an exact, analytical solution to the problem has yet to be obtained. In this section we give only the problem formulation and a brief, historical review of analyses containing concepts related to jet theory.

We begin initially with a fluid that is at rest and occupies the lower half-plane (Fig. 221a). The wedge entering the fluid has a vertical axis of symmetry. The angle α formed by the sides of the wedge and the undisturbed fluid level is called the careening angle (Fig. 221). Thus for small angles the wedge is blunt; for large careening angles (close to $\pi/2$), the wedge is sharply pointed. The angle between the sides of the wedge $2\pi\kappa$ is related to the careening angle α

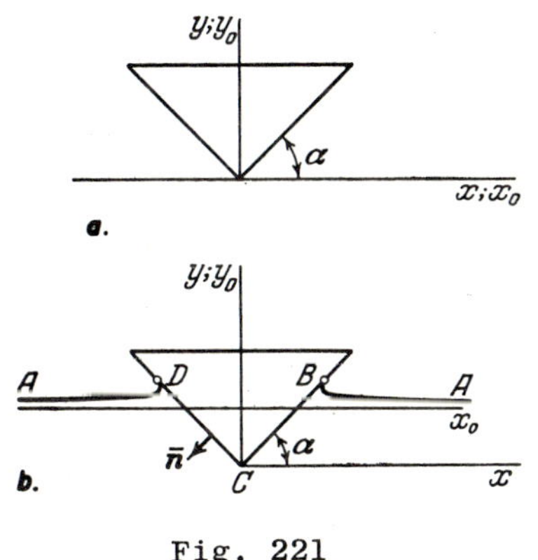

Fig. 221

by $2\pi\kappa = \pi - 2\alpha$. The vertical velocity v of the wedge—i.e., its rate of submergence in the fluid—is assumed to be given by

$$v = ct^{\gamma} \quad , \tag{9.93}$$

where t is time, and c and γ are constants.

When the wedge first enters the fluid, the motion will be governed by a velocity potential $\varphi(x_o, y_o, t)$ that satisfies the Laplace equation

$$\frac{\partial^2 \varphi}{\partial x_o^2} + \frac{\partial^2 \varphi}{\partial y_o^2} = 0 \quad , \tag{9.94}$$

where x_o and y_o are fixed Cartesian coordinates.

On the wedge surfaces the normal velocity of the fluid $\partial\varphi/\partial n$ is equal to the normal velocity of the wedge surface, so

$$\frac{\partial \varphi}{\partial n} = v \cos \alpha \qquad \text{on} \quad ACB \quad , \tag{9.95}$$

where the positive normal is directed into the fluid (Fig. 221b). The fluid velocity at infinity is zero. On the free surface S the pressure is constant; by using the Lagrange integral, it is possible to ascertain the boundary condition on the free surface in the form

$$\frac{\partial \varphi}{\partial t} + \frac{1}{2}\left[\left(\frac{\partial \varphi}{\partial x_o}\right)^2 + \left(\frac{\partial \varphi}{\partial y_o}\right)^2\right] = 0 \qquad \text{on} \quad S \quad . \tag{9.96}$$

However, the shape of the free surface is not known in advance. We assume that the free-surface equation has the form

$$y_o = f(x_o, t) \qquad f(x_o, 0) = 0 \quad . \tag{9.97}$$

The function $f(x,t)$ must satisfy the kinematic condition

$$\frac{\partial f}{\partial t} = \left(\frac{\partial \varphi}{\partial y_o}\right)_{y_o=f} . \tag{9.98}$$

Finally, in addition to the indicated conditions, the initial condition

$$\varphi(x_o, y_o, 0) = 0 \tag{9.99}$$

must be satisfied.

The problem determined by Eqs. (9.93) through (9.99) is, according to Sedov's terminology, "self-similar" [178], and the solution depends only on two dimensionless combinations of the variables x_o, y_o, and t; in particular, we introduce the dimensionless variables

$$x_1 = \frac{x_o}{ct^{\gamma+1}} , \qquad y_1 = \frac{y_o}{ct^{\gamma+1}} . \tag{9.100}$$

The region of flow in the variables x_o and y_o changes with time but remains, in a sense, geometrically similar. The region of change of the variables x_1 and y_1 is time invariant. In the region (x_1, y_1) the equation for the fixed, but unknown, boundary $\bar{S}$ (corresponding to the free surface S) can be written in the form

$$y_1 = f_1(x_1) . \tag{9.101}$$

Next, it is possible to express the velocity potential in terms of x_1 and y_1 as

$$\varphi = c^2 t^{2\gamma+1} \Phi(x_1, y_1) . \tag{9.102}$$

Finally, we transform Eqs. (9.94) through (9.96) and (9.98) into the dimensionless variables. Obviously, Eq. (9.94) transforms without difficulty into

$$\frac{\partial^2 \Phi}{\partial x_1^2} + \frac{\partial^2 \Phi}{\partial y_1^2} = 0 \quad . \tag{9.103}$$

The derivatives $\partial\varphi/\partial x_o$, $\partial\ /\partial y_o$, $\partial\varphi/\partial t$, and $\partial\varphi/\partial n$ are:

$$\left.\begin{aligned}
&\frac{\partial\varphi}{\partial x_o} = ct^{\gamma}\,\frac{\partial\Phi}{\partial x_1} \qquad \frac{\partial\varphi}{\partial y_o} = ct^{\gamma}\,\frac{\partial\Phi}{\partial y_1} \\
&\frac{\partial\varphi}{\partial t} = c^2 t^{2\gamma}\left[(2\gamma + 1)\Phi - (\gamma + 1)x_1\,\frac{\partial\Phi}{\partial x_1} - (\gamma + 1)y_1\,\frac{\partial\Phi}{\partial y_1}\right] \\
&\frac{\partial\varphi}{\partial n} = ct^{\gamma}\left(\frac{\partial\Phi}{\partial x_1}\sin\alpha - \frac{\partial\Phi}{\partial y_1}\cos\alpha\right)
\end{aligned}\right\} . \tag{9.104}$$

Thus, Eq. (9.95) (the condition on the wedge's surface) becomes

$$\frac{\partial\Phi}{\partial x_1}\sin\alpha - \frac{\partial\Phi}{\partial y_1}\cos\alpha = \cos\alpha \quad , \tag{9.105}$$

and Eq. (9.96) is transformed into

$$(2\gamma + 1)\Phi - (\gamma + 1)x_1\,\frac{\partial\Phi}{\partial x_1} - (\gamma + 1)y_1\,\frac{\partial\Phi}{\partial y_1} + \frac{1}{2}\left[\left(\frac{\partial\Phi}{\partial x_1}\right)^2 + \left(\frac{\partial\Phi}{\partial y_1}\right)^2\right] = 0 \,. \tag{9.106}$$

This last condition must be satisfied on $\overline{S}$, which is determined by the kinematic condition, Eq. (9.98). Finally, Eq.

(9.98) is transformed to dimensionless variables. First, by using Eqs. (9.97), (9.100), and (9.101), we get

$$f(x_o, t) = ct^{\gamma+1} \, f_1(x_1) \quad .$$

Then,

$$\left.\begin{aligned} \frac{\partial f}{\partial t} &= (\gamma + 1) \, ct^{\gamma} \, f_1(x) \\ \frac{\partial f}{\partial x_1} &= ct^{\gamma+1} \, \frac{df_1}{dx_1} \end{aligned}\right\} \quad . \tag{9.107}$$

Furthermore, according to Eqs. (9.100) and (9.102), we have

$$\frac{dx_1}{dt} = \frac{\partial x_1}{\partial t} + \frac{\partial x_1}{\partial x_o} \frac{\partial \varphi}{\partial x_o} = - \frac{\gamma + 1}{t} x_1 + \frac{\partial \Phi}{t \partial x_1} \quad . \tag{9.108}$$

From Eqs. (9.107) and (9.108) we easily find

$$\frac{df}{dt} = (\gamma + 1) \, ct^{\gamma} \, f_1(x_1) + ct^{\gamma+1} \frac{df_1}{dx_1} \left[- \frac{\gamma + 1}{t} x_1 + \frac{\partial \Phi}{\partial x_1} \right] .$$

Thus, it follows that Eq. (9.98) takes the form

$$(\gamma + 1) \, f_1(x_1) + \frac{df_1}{dx_1} \left[- \frac{\gamma + 1}{t} x_1 + \left(\frac{\partial \Phi}{\partial x_1} \right)_{y_1 = f_1} \right] = \left(\frac{\partial \Phi}{\partial y_1} \right)_{y_1 = f_1} \quad . \tag{9.109}$$

Therefore, the problem is now to determine the harmonic function $\Phi(x_1, y_1)$, satisfying the boundary condition Eqs. (9.105), (9.106), and (9.109), all of which contain the unknown function $f_1(x_1)$. As already noted, no exact analytical solution to this problem is yet available. Thus, a short, historical resume of the problem and possible solutions is appropriate.

Wagner [123] formulated the problem for the impact and submergence of a wedge with constant velocity. Because an exact solution did not appear feasible, Wagner proposed an approximate method which gives good, practical results for small or large careening angles. His basic concept was to replace the continuous submergence process with a series of discontinuous impacts on the water by a wedge or a plate. Wagner's idea produced an intense interest in impact theory, which was later developed extensively by Keldysh, Lavrentiev, and Sedov. But this approach is aside from the jet theory presented in this book, so we will not discuss it further, except to indicate some works in which Wagner's ideas are presented and approximate computations made for submergence of a wedge [179, 180, 181, 182] and of a cone [183]. We are, however, interested in another aspect of Wagner's work. First, we note that, for the case of a constant velocity of submergence, Wagner observed that a similarity existed between the flows at several instants of time. Furthermore, he introduced

$$h = \int_{\infty}^{z} \left(\frac{d^2 w}{dz^2}\right)^{1/2} dz \quad ,$$

where w is a complex potential and $z = x + iy$ is a complex variable in the flow plane. Suppose we now consider some particular fluid particle on the free surface at the initial instant of time, when the vertex of the wedge just touches the unperturbed free surface. Let the distance from this particle to the vertex of the wedge be s, a variable that might possibly be considered a Lagrangian coordinate. Then, taking into account the similarity of the flow picture at different instants of time t, $z(t,s)$ has the form

$$z(t,s) = ct\zeta\left(\frac{s}{t}\right) \quad . \tag{9.110}$$

Since the pressure on the free surface is constant, the pressure gradient and the acceleration of the particle $\partial^2 z/\partial t^2$ are perpendicular to the free surface. Mathematically this condition on the free surface can be written

$$\mathrm{Re}\left\{\frac{\partial^2 z}{\partial t^2}\,\overline{\frac{\partial z}{\partial t}}\right\} = 0 \quad . \tag{9.111}$$

Since $\partial z/\partial t = \overline{dw/dz}$, Eqs. (9.110) and (9.111) lead to the conclusion that on the free surface $(d^2w/dz^2)dz^2$ is a purely imaginary quantity; thus, the argument of $(d^2w/dz^2)^{1/2}dz$ is $\pm\pi/4$. On the wedge's surface the normal velocity is constant; it follows that on the surface of the wedge $d^2\psi = 0$ and $(d^2w/dz)^{1/2}dz$ is real.

Consider now some particular instant of time—e.g., $t = 1$—and locate the coordinate origin at the vertex C of the wedge. Wagner erroneously considered that the region of change of h is an open triangle with vertex A at infinity. In Khan Hi Man's dissertation, entitled "Studies of some problems about unsteady fluid motion," written under the direction of Sedov and defended in 1957 at the Moscow State University, it was proven that the region of change of h is an isosceles right triangle of finite dimensions (Fig. 222). If, in addition to h, it were possible to find another complex variable function whose region of change is known and which can be expressed in terms of w and z or their derivatives by some parametric variable with a known region of change, then the hydrodynamic problem would be reduced to a problem of conformal mappings. However, such a function has yet to be found.

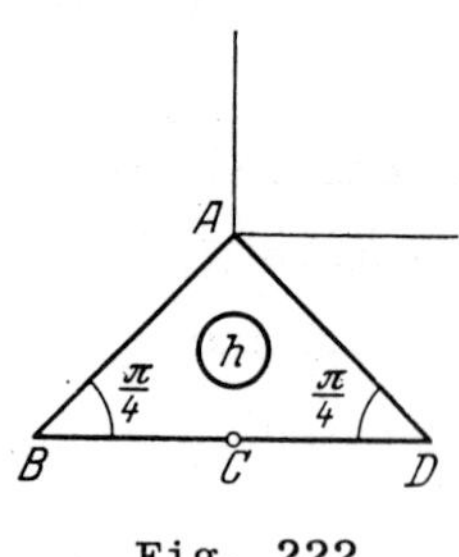

Fig. 222

Wagner's investigations were extended by several authors. Of these we touch upon only Garabedian's work [184], where additional references can be found. As did Wagner, Garabedian studied a wedge submerging with a constant velocity. Assuming that s is an analytic function of z, he extended s over the entire flow plane. The free surface corresponds to $\operatorname{Im} s = 0$—i.e., a part of the real axis. Unfortunately, the shape of the region's boundary corresponding to the wedge is not known in advance. Garabedian did find a particular form of $s(z)$ for which the boundary conditions on the surface of the wedge are satisfied. Thus, he found an "inverse" solution to the problem of submergence of a nonsymmetric wedge. Additionally, in his solution the pressure on the free surface to the right of the wedge differs from that to the left.

A series of interesting results were given in the above-mentioned Khan Hi Man dissertation, even though the posed problem was not completely solved. In the first part of his work, Man studied the submergence of a wedge with a velocity that varied exponentially with time—see Eq. (9.93). However, our interest in this work lies in the systematic investigation of the singularities that $s(z)$ must possess. Also interesting is a new problem formulation for an explosion on the free surface. From the characteristics of the boundary conditions, this problem is very similar to that of wedge submergence.

Moiseev, Borisova, and Koriavov [28] examined the following problem: a symmetric wedge with included angle $\pi - 2\alpha$ is submerged in a fluid; at the initial instant of time $(t = 0)$ the fluid is motionless and occupies the interior of the angle 2β (Fig. 223). Their velocity of submergence depends exponentially on time according to Eq. (9.93). They investigated two special cases:

1. $\beta = \pi/2$—i.e., the above-described case of submergence of a wedge into an unperturbed fluid.
2. $\alpha = 0$—i.e., the impact of a plane wall on a fluid wedge or the spreading of a fluid wedge over a solid surface.

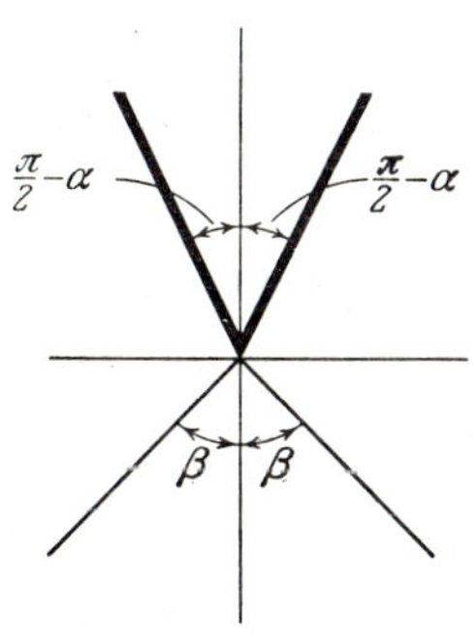

Fig. 223

If we investigate a symmetric collision of two fluid wedges with equal included angles then, in addition to the vertical axis of symmetry that coincides with the symmetric axis of the wedges, there is also a horizontal axis of symmetry, which can be considered a solid wall. Thus, the spreading of a fluid wedge over a plane wall is equivalent to to collision of fluid wedges. Hence, Moiseev, Borisova, and Koriavov [28] studied this scheme as a model of a flow for unsteady collisions of hollow jets.

While Man expressed the problem's boundary condtions in terms of a complex potential, the boundary conditions' derivation given in this section was adopted from Moiseev, Borisova and Koriavov [28], who, in their work, also evinced the possibility of computing the resultant force Y, acting on the wedge, and of ascertaining the velocity distribution on the free surface when the shape of the surface is known. The free-surface velocity is found as the solution of a first-order differential equation with two boundary conditions, that accordingly place some restrictions on the unknown shape of the free surface. They solved the wedge submergence problem as follows: the shape of the free surface is given approximately by an appropriate equation with three constant coefficients, which are determined by three conditions:

1. The free surface asymptotically approaches the unperturbed-fluid level at infinity.
2. The volume of fluid above the free surface is equal to the volume of the submerged part of the wedge.
3. A combination of boundary conditions and the above-mentioned differential equation is used to find the velocity distribution on the free surface.

Also given in [28] is a formula that can be used to find the drag of the submerged wedge when the shape of the free surface is known.

The spreading of a fluid wedge (Fig. 224) is also solved in the same manner in [28]. Furthermore, the indicated method can be extended to the asymmetric problem. Finally, together with the problems about wedge submergence and spreading of a fluid wedge, Moiseev, Borisova, and Koriavov investigated one more problem that serves as an approximate model of a hollow jet. This problem (Fig. 225) is outlined as follows: let the fluid initially occupy a volume bounded from below by a solid conical surface with an included vertex angle 2δ and from above by a free boundary that is also a cone with an included angle $2(\delta - \beta)$. It is assumed that initially all fluid particles have the same velocity, directed along the bounding cones, and that the flow is "self-similar."

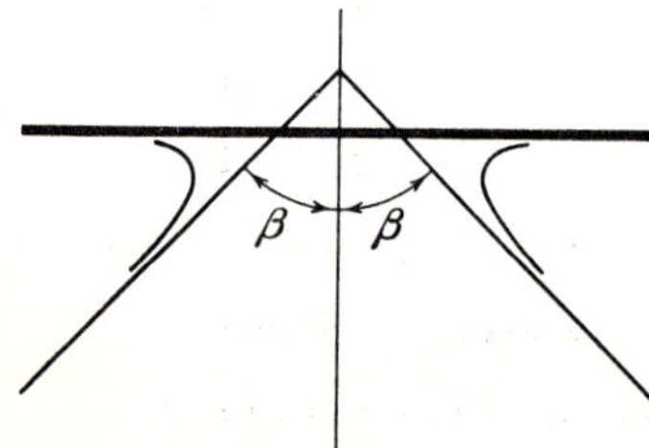

Fig. 224

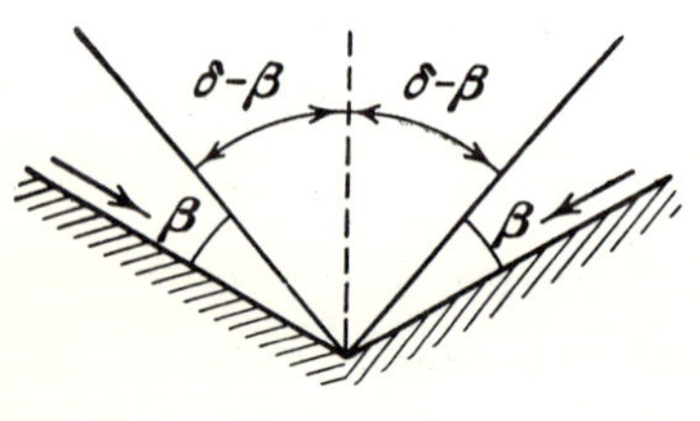

Fig. 225

The above analyses led to a series of useful computations that were executed on a high-speed computer. Figure 226 shows

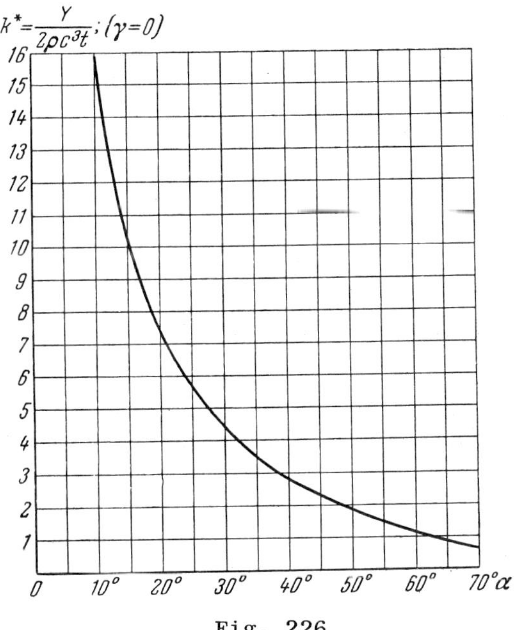

Fig. 226

one of the many graphs of the results; in particular, the computed results for the drag coefficient k^* of the submerging wedge are shown, where

$$k^* = \frac{Y}{2\rho c^3 t} \qquad \text{with } \gamma = 0, \quad v = c \quad .$$

Furthermore, the reader will also find in [28] comparisons of the computations with the results of other authors [182]. Moiseev, Borisova, and Koriavov's results seem valid for medium careening angles (note that Wagner's are valid for large and small angles). For small careening angles, a plate analogy is suggested [86, 179]. For large careening angles—i.e., for sharp wedges—it is possible to neglect the rising of the water. Then, if t is time, m is the virtual mass, H is the submergence (Fig. 227), Y is the resultant pressure

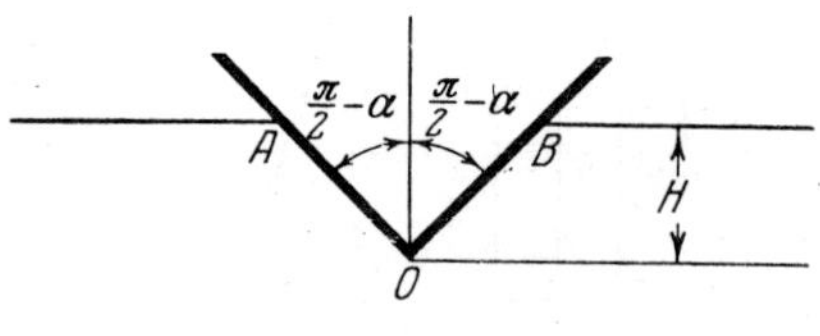

Fig. 227

force on the wedge, and v is the submergence velocity of the wedge (which for simplicity we consider constant)* it follows from the momentum theorem that

$$Y = \frac{d(mv)}{dt} = \frac{dm}{dH}\frac{dH}{dt} v = \frac{dm}{dH} v^2 \quad . \tag{9.112}$$

Finally, we employ Sedov's formula [181]

$$m = \rho H^2 \cot \alpha \left[\frac{\Gamma\left(\frac{3}{2} - \frac{\alpha}{\pi}\right)\Gamma\left(\frac{\alpha}{\pi}\right)}{\Gamma\left(\frac{\alpha}{\pi} + \frac{1}{2}\right)\Gamma\left(1 - \frac{\alpha}{\pi}\right)} - 1 \right] \tag{9.113}$$

to determine the virtual mass m.

*Sedov [180] computed the submergence of a sharp wedge with a given mass. The velocity of submergence of such a wedge will obviously be variable.

CHAPTER X. JET FLOW OF COMPRESSIBLE FLUID

A. CHAPLYGIN'S EQUATION FOR TWO-DIMENSIONAL STEADY FLOW OF A GAS

The theory of compressible (gas) jet flow is a significant part of gas dynamics, and a complete exposition of this theory would require a separate monograph. Here we present an outline of Chaplygin's exact and approximate methods, which are closely related to incompressible-jet theory, and a brief survey of subsequent developments in gas jet theory. We shall be particularly brief in our survey of transonic and supersonic gas jets to avoid the extensive discourse on gas dynamics and its mathematical methods that would have to precede an in-depth survey. The bases for our discussion here and, in fact, for gas-jet theory, were laid in S. A. Chaplygin's doctoral dissertation [6], which has been reprinted many times.

The required equations for the steady, plane flow of an inviscid gas are given without proof (for the derivations see [1]). The Euler equations are in Lamb's form

$$\left.\begin{aligned} \frac{1}{\rho}\frac{\partial p}{\partial x} &= -\frac{\partial v^2}{2\partial x} + v_y\left(\frac{\partial v_y}{\partial x} - \frac{\partial v_x}{\partial y}\right) \\ \frac{1}{\rho}\frac{\partial p}{\partial y} &= -\frac{\partial v^2}{2\partial y} - v_x\left(\frac{\partial v_y}{\partial x} - \frac{\partial v_x}{\partial y}\right) \end{aligned}\right\} . \tag{10.1}$$

We assume that the pressure p is a function of the density only. Under the irrotationality condition

$$\frac{\partial v_y}{\partial x} - \frac{\partial v_x}{\partial y} = 0 \quad , \tag{10.2}$$

it is possible to obtain from Eq. (10.1) Bernoulli's integral

$$\int_{p_o}^{p} \frac{dp}{\rho} = - \frac{v^2}{2} \quad , \tag{10.3}$$

where p_o is the pressure when the velocity v is zero. The continuity equation

$$\frac{\partial(\rho v_x)}{\partial x} + \frac{\partial(\rho v_y)}{\partial y} = 0 \tag{10.4}$$

is added to Eqs. (10.1) and (10.2) to complete the set required to describe our flows.

For an adiabatic process the relation between pressure and density is

$$\frac{p}{p_o} = \left(\frac{\rho}{\rho_o}\right)^{\gamma} \quad , \tag{10.5}$$

where ρ_o is the density when $v = 0$, and γ is the ratio of specific heat at constant pressure to the specific heat at constant volume (for air $\gamma \approx 1.4$). For an adiabatic process, Bernoulli's integral is rewritten in the form

$$\rho = \rho_o \left(1 - \frac{v^2}{[(\gamma + 1)/(\gamma - 1)]\, a_*^2}\right)^{1/(\gamma - 1)} \quad . \tag{10.6}$$

Note that the speed of sound $a = (dp/d\rho)^{1/2}$ depends on the flow velocity v.

A flow in which $v < a$ or $\mathbf{M} = v/a < 1$ is called subsonic, and a flow in which $v > a$ or $\mathbf{M} > 1$ is called supersonic. In Eq. (10.6) for a given flow, the constant a_*, the critical speed of sound, corresponds to the critical velocity $v = v_*$, which is equal to the speed of sound or to $\mathbf{M} = v_*/a_* = 1$. Chaplygin denotes by τ tho ratio

$$\tau = \frac{v^2}{[(\gamma + 1)/(\gamma - 1)]\, a_*^2} = \frac{v^2}{[2/(\gamma - 1)]\, a_o^2} = \frac{v^2}{v_{max}^2} ,$$

where a_o is the speed of sound when $v = 0$ and v_{max} is the maximum possible speed of sound in a gas. It is obvious that $\tau < (\gamma - 1)/(\gamma + 1)$ for subsonic speeds. At the speed of sound or sonic speed, $\tau = (\gamma - 1)/(\gamma + 1)$.

Next we derive Chaplygin's equation. From Eq. (10.2) it follows that there exists a velocity potential φ such that

$$v_x = \frac{\partial\varphi}{\partial x} \qquad v_y = \frac{\partial\varphi}{\partial y} . \tag{10.7}$$

From Eq. (10.4) it follows that there is a stream function ψ, which, according to Chaplygin's notation, satisfies

$$\frac{\rho}{\rho_o} v_x = \frac{\partial\psi}{\partial y} \qquad \frac{\rho}{\rho_o} v_y = -\frac{\partial\psi}{\partial x} . \tag{10.8}$$

Thus, from Eqs. (10.7) and (10.8)

$$v_x dx + v_y dy = d\varphi ,$$

and

$$-v_y dx + v_x dy = \frac{\rho_o}{\rho} d\psi .$$

If we multiply the second equation by i and add it to the first one, then

$$(v_x - iv_y)\, d(x + iy) = d\varphi + i \frac{\rho_o}{\rho} d\psi \quad .$$

Finally, if θ is the angle between the velocity and the x-axis (so that $v_x - iv_y = ve^{-i\theta}$) and the notation $z = x + iy$ is introduced, we obtain

$$dz = \left(d\varphi + i \frac{\rho_o}{\rho} d\psi\right) \frac{e^{i\theta}}{v} \quad . \tag{10.9}$$

The quantities θ and v are introduced as independent variables, and Eq. (10.9) now becomes

$$\frac{\partial z}{\partial v} dv + \frac{\partial z}{\partial \theta} d\theta = \left[\frac{\partial \varphi}{\partial v} dv + \frac{\partial \varphi}{\partial \theta} d\theta + i \frac{\rho_o}{\rho} \left(\frac{\partial \psi}{\partial v} dv + \frac{\partial \psi}{\partial \theta} d\theta\right)\right] \frac{e^{i\theta}}{v} \quad .$$

Since dv and $d\theta$ are independent, this equation is equivalent to the two following:

$$\left.\begin{aligned} \frac{\partial z}{\partial v} &= \left(\frac{\partial \varphi}{\partial v} + i \frac{\rho_o}{\rho} \frac{\partial \psi}{\partial v}\right) \frac{e^{i\theta}}{v} \\ &\text{and} \\ \frac{\partial z}{\partial \theta} &= \left(\frac{\partial \varphi}{\partial \theta} + \frac{i\rho_o}{\rho} \frac{\partial \psi}{\partial \theta}\right) \frac{e^{i\theta}}{v} \end{aligned}\right\} \quad . \tag{10.10}$$

Now z is eliminated from Eqs. (10.10) by differentiating the first with respect to θ and the second with respect to v and equating the results. Note that ρ/ρ_o depends on v but not on θ. Thus,

$$\left(\frac{\partial^2\varphi}{\partial v\,\partial\theta} + i\,\frac{\rho_o}{\rho}\,\frac{\partial^2\psi}{\partial v\,\partial\theta}\right)\frac{e^{i\theta}}{v} + \left(\frac{\partial\varphi}{\partial v} + \frac{i\rho_o}{\rho}\,\frac{\partial\psi}{\partial v}\right)\frac{e^{i\theta}}{v}\,i$$

$$= \left(\frac{\partial^2\varphi}{\partial\theta\,\partial v} + \frac{i\rho_o}{\rho}\,\frac{\partial^2\psi}{\partial\theta\,\partial v}\right)\frac{e^{i\theta}}{v} + \left[\frac{\partial\varphi}{\partial\theta}\left(-\frac{1}{v^2}\right) + i\,\frac{d}{dv}\left(\frac{\rho_o}{\rho v}\right)\frac{\partial\psi}{\partial\theta}\right]e^{i\theta} \; .$$

By executing obvious simplifications and separating the real and imaginary parts, we obtain

$$\left.\begin{aligned} \frac{\partial\varphi}{v\,\partial v} &= \frac{d}{dv}\left(\frac{\rho_o}{\rho v}\right)\frac{\partial\psi}{\partial\theta} \\ \frac{\partial\varphi}{v\,\partial\theta} &= \frac{\rho_o}{\rho}\,\frac{\partial\psi}{\partial v} \end{aligned}\right\} . \qquad (10.11)$$

By introducing τ in place of v we obtain from Eqs. (10.11) and (10.6) Chaplygin's equations

$$\left.\begin{aligned} \frac{\partial\varphi}{\partial\theta} &= \frac{2\tau}{(1-\tau)^{1/(\gamma-1)}}\,\frac{\partial\psi}{\partial\tau} \\ \frac{\partial\varphi}{\partial\tau} &= -\,\frac{1-\tau[(\gamma+1)/(\gamma-1)]}{2\tau(1-\tau)^{\gamma/(\gamma-1)}}\,\frac{\partial\psi}{\partial\theta} \end{aligned}\right\} . \qquad (10.12)$$

Eliminating φ from Eqs. (10.12) leads to a second-order, linear partial differential equation for the stream function

$$\frac{\partial}{\partial\tau}\left[\frac{2\tau}{(1-\tau)^{\beta}}\,\frac{\partial\psi}{\partial\tau}\right] + \frac{1-\tau(2\beta+1)}{(1-\tau)^{\beta+1}\,2\tau}\,\frac{\partial^2\psi}{\partial\theta^2} = 0 \; , \qquad (10.13)$$

where $\beta = 1/(\gamma - 1)$. This equation is elliptic when

$$\tau < \frac{\gamma-1}{\gamma+1} = \frac{1}{2\beta+1} \; ,$$

i.e., at subsonic speeds, because then the coefficients of $\partial^2\psi/\partial\tau^2$ and $\partial^2\psi/\partial\theta^2$ are positive. At supersonic speeds Eq. (10.13) is hyperbolic. Also, Eqs. (10.11) are brought to canonical form by introducing a new independent variable s given by

$$\frac{ds}{dv} = \frac{[1 - (v^2/a^2)]^{1/2}}{v} , \qquad (10.14)$$

in place of v. As a result,

$$\frac{\partial\varphi}{\partial\theta} = \sqrt{K}\,\frac{\partial\psi}{\partial s} \qquad \frac{\partial\varphi}{\partial s} = -\sqrt{K}\,\frac{\partial\psi}{\partial\theta} . \qquad (10.15)$$

The function K, given for an arbitrary $p(\rho)$ by [24], is

$$K = \left(\frac{\rho_o}{\rho}\right)^2 \left(1 - \frac{v^2}{a^2}\right) = \frac{\rho_o^2}{\rho^2}\left[1 + \frac{2\int_{p_o}^{p}(dp/\rho)}{dp/d\rho}\right] . \qquad (10.16)$$

For adiabatic processes, Chaplygin's equations were first brought into the canonical form of Eqs. (10.15) by Leibenzon [185]. They were used for solving gas-dynamics problems by Khristianovich, Tsien, and others.

B. EXACT SOLUTIONS TO CHAPLYGIN'S EQUATION FOR SUBSONIC FLOW

Consider the particular solutions of Eq. (10.13)

$$\psi_n = z_n(\tau)\,\sin\,(2n\theta + \alpha_n) , \qquad (10.17)$$

where $n > 0$ and α_n are constants. The unknown $z_n(\tau)$ are determined from the following equation derived from Eq. (10.13) by substitution of Eq. (10.17):

$$\frac{d}{d\tau}\left[\frac{\tau}{(1-\tau)^{\beta}}\frac{dz_n}{d\tau}\right] - n^2\,\frac{1-\tau(2\beta+1)}{\tau(1-\tau)^{\beta+1}}\,z_n = 0$$

or, in expanded form,

$$\tau^2(1-\tau)\frac{d^2z_n}{d\tau^2} + \tau[1+(\beta-1)\tau]\frac{dz_n}{d\tau} - n^2[1-(2\beta+1)\tau]z_n = 0\,. \tag{10.18}$$

Setting

$$z_n = \tau^n y_n \tag{10.19}$$

in Eq. (10.18) leads to

$$\tau(1-\tau)\frac{d^2y_n}{d\tau^2} + [2n+1+(\beta-2n-1)\tau]\frac{dy_n}{d\tau}$$

$$+\ \beta n(2n+1)y_n = 0\quad . \tag{10.20}$$

Thus, the $y_n(\tau)$ are found as the solutions of the hypergeometric Eq. (10.20). It is known [30, 129] that the solution to Eq. (10.20) in the neighborhood of $\tau = 0$ can be sought in the form

$$y_n(\tau) = \tau^r\left(c_o + c_1\tau + c_2\tau^2 + \dots\right)\quad . \tag{10.21}$$

Here, r is determined by a characteristic equation*

$$r(r-1) + (2n+1)r = 0\quad ;$$

*This equation is easily obtained since it is sufficient to substitute Eq. (10.21) in Eq. (10.20) and set the coefficient of τ^{r-1} equal to 0.

the solutions are

$$r_1 = 0 \qquad r_2 = -2n \quad . \tag{10.22}$$

Chaplygin used only the first solution,* so that $y_n(r)$ are finite when $\tau = 0$. The first solution then is represented, except for the arbitrary c_o, by a hypergeometric series

$$y_n^{(1)} = F(a_n, b_n, 2n+1, \tau) \quad , \tag{10.23}$$

where a_n and b_n are found from

$$a_n + b_n = 2n - \beta \quad ,$$

$$a_n b_n = -\beta n(2n+1) \quad .$$

Chaplygin studied those jet problems in which ψ could be expressed by

$$\lambda\psi = A + B\theta + \sum_{n=1}^{\infty} B_n \psi_n \quad , \tag{10.24}$$

where λ, A, B, and B_n are constants and the ψ_n are determined from Eqs. (10.17), (10.19) and (10.23), so that each separate term of the series, Eq. (10.24), satisfies the basic Eq. (10.13).

Now we determine the boundary conditions for our problems. Since the gas must be bounded by streamlines in a steady flow, ψ must be constant along the boundary contour of the (τ, θ) region. Thus, if the part under consideration is a

*If n is an integer, the second solution of Eq. (10.20) cannot be given in the form of Eq. (10.21).

plane wall, θ (the angle between the velocity and the x-axis) must be constant on the wall. On the surfaces of the jets the pressure p = const., and consequently, according to Bernoulli's integral, the velocity v must equal a constant v_1. It follows that $\tau = \tau_1$ = constant along the surfaces of the jets also. If τ is considered a radius-vector and θ an angle in a polar coordinate system, then the boundary of the (τ, θ) region will be composed of straight lines θ = const (rectilinear solid walls) and an arc of a circle $\tau = \tau_1$ (free surfaces). The variable τ loses its meaning in the case of an incompressible flow $(\mathbf{M} = 0)$. However, it is actually more useful to use the variable $\tau/\tau_1 = v^2/v_1^2$, which remains constant and retains its meaning when we pass from compressible to incompressible flow.

We now compare a compressible-fluid flow with the corresponding incompressible flow with the same boundary conditions (i.e., identical wall placement, equal velocities at infinity, and equal velocities on the boundary of the jets separating from the obstacle). Assume that a general solution to some incompressible-fluid jet flow is obtained by relating the complex potential $w_H = \varphi_H + i\psi_H$ and the variable

$$\ell n \frac{v_H \, dz}{dw_H} = \omega_H = \vartheta + i\theta = \ell n \left(\frac{v_1}{v}\right) + i\theta$$

$$= \ell n \left(\frac{\tau_1}{\tau}\right)^{1/2} + i\theta = -\frac{1}{2} \ell n \left[\frac{\tau}{\tau_1} \exp\left[-2i\theta\right]\right] . \tag{10.25}$$

Then, $w_H = f(\omega_H)$ is known. Assume further that $f(\omega_H)$ can be expanded in a series of the form

$$w_H = H + B\left(\ell n\left(\frac{\tau_1}{\tau}\right)^{1/2} + i\theta\right) - \sum_{n=1}^{\infty} B_n\left(\frac{\tau}{\tau_1}\right)^n \exp\left[-2ni\theta\right] ,$$

where B, H, and B_n are constants, so that

$$\psi_H = A + B\theta + \sum_{n=1}^{\infty} B_n\left(\frac{\tau}{\tau_1}\right)^n \sin\left(2n\theta + \alpha_n\right) . \quad (10.26)$$

The same problem for a gas flow is solved by

$$\lambda\psi = A + B\theta + \sum_{n=1}^{\infty} B_n\left(\frac{\tau}{\tau_1}\right)^n \sin\left(2n\theta + \alpha_n\right) \frac{y_n(\tau)}{y_n(\tau_1)} \quad (10.27)$$

{cf. Eq. (10.24)}.

Clearly, when $\tau = \tau_1$, the right-hand sides of Eqs. (10.26) and (10.27) agree to the extent that, for $\tau = \tau_1$, both ψ_H = const and ψ = const. Furthermore, if, for some value $\theta = \theta_o$, ψ_H is to be independent of τ, then we must have $\sin(2n\theta_o + \alpha_n) = 0$ for all n. However, then the right-hand side of Eq. (10.27) also has a constant value when $\theta = \theta_o$. Thus, the boundary conditions imposed on ψ are satisfied.

The series, Eq. (10.27) or, equivalently, Eq. (10.24), formally satisfies Eq. (10.13). However, before considering this series as a solution to the problem or using it, together with Eqs. (10.9) and (10.12), to determine ϕ, x, and y, it is necessary to show that this series converges for all $\tau < \tau_1$ and tends to the same limit as Eq. (10.26) when $\tau \to \tau_1$. In addition, it must be proven that the series Eq. (10.26), together with the series obtained from it by term-by-term differentiation with respect to τ or θ, converges absolutely and uniformly. These difficult and elegant proofs were given by Chaplygin [6]. We shall not repeat them, but, before passing to specific examples, we present without derivation the formula for φ, which is obtained from Eqs. (10.13), (10.12) and (10.27),

$$\varphi = C + \frac{B}{(1-\tau)^\beta} - \frac{B}{2}\int \frac{d\tau}{\tau(1-\tau)^\beta}$$

$$- \frac{1}{(1-\tau)^\beta}\sum_{n=1}^{\infty} B_n \left(\frac{\tau}{\tau_o}\right)^n \frac{y_n(\tau)}{y_n(\tau_1)}\left(1 + \frac{\tau}{n}\frac{y_n'(\tau)}{y_n(\tau)}\right)\cos(2n\theta + \alpha_n) . \tag{10.28}$$

The function $1 + (\tau/n)(y_n'/y_n)$ occurs frequently, so we denote it by

$$x_n = 1 + \frac{\tau}{n}\frac{y_n'}{y_n} . \tag{10.29}$$

We shall study Chaplygin's first example: a gas jet flowing from an orifice in a plane (Fig. 228). This problem's solution for an incompressible fluid is given in Chapters I and II. On placing $\kappa = 1/2$ in Eq. (2.1), and replacing w by w_H in Eqs. (2.2) and (2.26) and q by $q/2$, we obtain a solution for an incompressible flow in the form

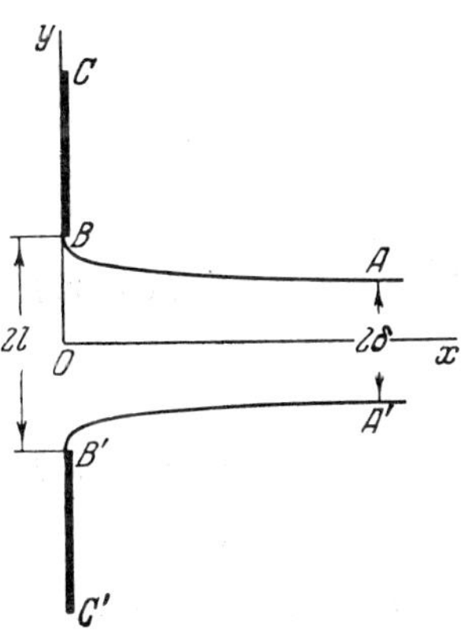

Fig. 228

$$\frac{dw_H}{v_o\,dz} = t^{1/2} \qquad w_H = \frac{q}{2\pi}\ln\frac{t}{(1-\iota)^2} , \tag{10.30}$$

where t is the parametric variable. The upper half of the unit circle in the t-plane (Fig. 18) corresponds to the upper half-plane in Fig. 228 (the flow above the x-axis). Replacing t by $(dw_H/v_H dz)^2 = \exp[-2\omega_H]$, according to Eq. (10.25) and the first of Eqs. (10.30), gives, from the second of Eqs. (10.30),

$$w_H = \varphi_H + i\psi_H = -\frac{q}{\pi}\omega_H - \frac{q}{\pi}\ln(1 - \exp[-2\omega_H]).$$

On expanding the logarithm in a series we obtain

$$\frac{\pi}{q}(\varphi_H + i\psi_H) = -\vartheta - i\theta + \sum_{n=1}^{\infty}\frac{\exp[-2n\vartheta]}{n}(\cos 2n\theta - i\sin 2n\theta),$$

from which

$$\frac{\pi}{q}\psi_H = -\theta - \sum_{n=1}^{\infty}\frac{\exp[-2n\vartheta]}{n}\sin 2n\theta \quad .$$

Introducing the variable τ/τ_1, given by

$$\frac{\tau}{\tau_1} = \frac{v^2}{v_1^2} = e^{-2\vartheta} \quad , \tag{10.31}$$

in this formula, we achieve the final expansion for ψ_H:

$$\frac{\pi}{q}\psi_H = -\theta - \sum_{n=1}^{\infty}\left(\frac{\tau}{\tau_1}\right)^n \frac{\sin 2n\theta}{n} \quad . \tag{10.32}$$

This series converges absolutely. Thus, from Eqs. (10.27) and (10.26), we now obtain for the stream function ψ, which determines the flow of a compressible fluid from an orifice in a plane,

$$\frac{\pi}{q}\psi = -\theta - \sum_{n=1}^{\infty} \frac{1}{n}\left(\frac{\tau}{\tau_1}\right)^n \frac{y_n(\tau)}{y_n(\tau_o)} \sin 2n\theta \quad . \tag{10.33}$$

Note that the velocities on the jets are the same in both compressible and incompressible flows—i.e., $v_o = v_H = v_1$. The contraction coefficient of the jet δ/ℓ, where 2δ and 2ℓ are the width of the jet and the orifice, respectively (Fig. 228), can now be found.

Along the free surface $dv = 0$. Thus, to determine the difference $y_B - y_A = b - a$ by integration along the streamline BA, it is sufficient to compute $\int_{AB} (\partial y/\partial\theta)\, d\theta$. From Eq. (10.10),

$$\frac{\partial y}{\partial\theta} = \frac{\rho_o}{v\rho}\frac{\partial\psi}{\partial\theta}\cos\theta + \frac{1}{v}\frac{\partial\varphi}{\partial\theta}\sin\theta \quad .$$

Along the free surface $\psi = \text{const}$; therefore,

$$\frac{\partial y}{\partial\theta} = \frac{1}{v}\frac{\partial\varphi}{\partial\theta}\sin\theta$$

and

$$\ell - \delta = -\int_{-\pi/2}^{0} \frac{1}{v}\frac{\partial\varphi}{\partial\theta}\sin\theta\, d\theta \quad . \tag{10.34}$$

It is most convenient to evaluate this integral along some line $\tau = \text{const}$ that passes inside the fluid and then later to pass to the limit $\tau \to \tau_1$. This order of operations is needed to insure that the series we use converges at all times. Using Eq. (10.12), we rewrite Eq. (10.34) in the form

$$\ell - \delta = \lim_{\tau\to\tau_1} \frac{-2\tau}{(1-\tau)^\beta v}\int_{-\pi/2}^{0} \sin\theta\,\frac{\partial\psi}{\partial\tau}\, d\theta \quad .$$

Determining $\partial\psi/\partial\tau$ from Eq. (10.33) and making use of the values x_n from Eq. (10.29), we find from the above equation,

$$\ell - \delta = \frac{q}{\pi} \lim_{\tau\to\tau_1} \left\{ \frac{-2\tau}{(1-\tau)^{\beta} v} \int_{-\pi/2}^{0} - \sum_{n=1}^{\infty} \left[\left(\frac{\tau}{\tau_1}\right)^n \frac{y_n(\tau)}{y_n(\tau_1)} \frac{1}{\tau} + \left(\frac{\tau}{\tau_1}\right)^n \frac{y_n'(\tau)}{y_n(\tau_1)} \frac{1}{n} \right] \sin 2n\theta \sin\theta \, d\theta \right\}$$

$$= \frac{q}{\pi} \lim_{\tau\to\tau_1} \left\{ \frac{2}{(1-\tau)^{\beta} v} \int_{-\pi/2}^{0} \sum_{n=1}^{\infty} \left(\frac{\tau}{\tau_1}\right)^n \frac{y_n(\tau)}{y_n(\tau_1)} x_n(\tau) \sin 2n\theta \sin\theta \, d\theta \right\} .$$

Now

$$\sin 2n\theta \sin\theta = \frac{1}{2} [\cos (2n-1)\theta - \cos (2n+1)\theta] .$$

Therefore, by executing the above-indicated integration, we obtain

$$\ell - \delta = \lim_{\tau\to\tau_1} \frac{q}{\pi} \left\{ \frac{1}{(1-\tau)^{\beta} v} \sum_{n=1}^{\infty} \left[\left(\frac{\tau}{\tau_1}\right)^n \frac{y_n(\tau)}{y_n(\tau_1)} x_n(\tau)(-1)^{n-1} \frac{4n}{4n^2 - 1} \right] \right\} .$$

Passing to the limit produces

$$\ell - \delta = \frac{q}{\pi(1-\tau_1)^{\beta} v_1} \sum_{n=1}^{\infty} x_n(\tau_1) \frac{4n(-1)^{n-1}}{4n^2 - 1} , \quad (10.35)$$

where v_1 is the gas velocity on the free surface.

Since the gas density in the jet is $\rho_o(1 - \tau_1)^\beta$ at infinity according to the Bernoulli integral, Eq. (10.6), the gas flowrate in the jet is {cf. Eq. (10.8)}

$$\rho_o q = v_1 \rho_o (1 - \tau_1)^\beta \, 2\delta \quad . \tag{10.36}$$

From Eqs. (10.35) and (10.36)

$$\ell - \delta = \frac{8\delta}{\pi} \sum_{n=1}^{\infty} x_n(\tau_1) \, \frac{n(-1)^{n-1}}{4n^2 - 1} \quad .$$

Accordingly, the jet contraction coefficient is

$$\frac{\delta}{\ell} = \pi \left[\pi + 8 \sum_{n=1}^{\infty} x_n(\tau_1) \, \frac{n(-1)^{n-1}}{4n^2 - 1} \right]^{-1} \quad . \tag{10.37}$$

On the basis of numerical computations with Eq. (10.37) Chaplygin proposed an approximate formula

$$\frac{\delta}{\ell} = \frac{\pi}{\pi + 2 - 5s_1 + 2s_1^2} \quad , \tag{10.38}$$

where $s_1 = \tau_1/(1 - \tau_1)$ or $p_o/p_1 = (1 + s_1)^{\beta+1}$ (p_1 is the free-surface pressure). The results of computations [186] using the exact formula, Eq. (10.37), are presented in Table 26.

Chaplygin analyzed series convergence [6] and also showed that, in the limit $\tau_1 \to 0$, Eq. (10.37) gives the contraction coefficient for an incompressible-fluid flow as $\delta/\ell = \pi/(\pi + 2)$.

Figure 299a shows the flow of a gas jet through an opening between two walls. This flow was examined in [1] for an included angle of $\pi\alpha$ between the walls. The contraction coefficient in this case is expressed by

$$\frac{\delta}{\ell} = \pi \left[\pi + \frac{8}{\alpha^2} \sin \frac{\pi\alpha}{2} \sum_{n=1}^{\infty} (-1)^{n-1} x_{n/\alpha} (\tau_1) \frac{n}{(4n^2/\alpha^2) - 1} \right]^{-1} . \tag{10.39}$$

Approximate computations based on Eq. (10.39) for small angles between the walls were carried out by Arynov [187], who also generalized the solution to the case of $\mathbf{M} = 1$ or sonic flow on the jet surface. These results are given in Table 27 for $\gamma = 1.4$.

TABLE 26. $\gamma = 1.4$

τ_1	δ/ℓ	τ_1	δ/ℓ
0	0.611	0.10	0.681
0.02	0.623	0.12	0.699
0.04	0.636	0.14	0.717
0.06	0.650	0.16	0.738
0.08	0.665	0.1667	0.745

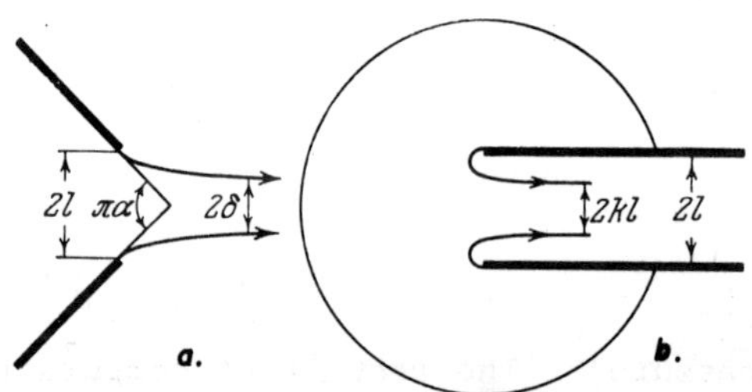

Fig. 229

For $\alpha = 2$—i.e., the Borda nozzle (Fig. 229b)—several undetermined expressions appear in the solution, thereby requiring special treatment. Sekerzh-Zenkovich [188] solved the Borda-nozzle problem by Chaplygin's method and computed the contraction coefficient $k = \delta/\ell$. However, if determination of the contraction coefficient is our only goal, the

TABLE 27. THE CONTRACTION COEFFICIENT δ/ℓ

M	90 α (deg)		
	5	10	15
0.1	0.9640	0.9293	0.8964
0.2	0.9642	0.9303	0.898
0.3	0.9653	0.9316	0.9016
0.4	0.9664	0.9343	0.9043
0.5	0.9682	0.9377	0.909
0.6	0.9706	0.9424	0.9155
0.7	0.9738	0.9487	0.9222
0.8	0.9785	0.9575	0.9366
1	0.9880	0.9737	0.9547

momentum theorem may be used, and it is thus unnecessary to solve the hydrodynamic problem.

We will show that there is no need to restrict the problem to the plane case in calculating the contraction coefficient of the Borda-nozzle jet. In fact, the pipe can have an arbitrary cross section if only the incoming flow is parallel to the walls at infinity.

From Bernoulli's integral for an adiabatic gas flow, {see also Eq. (10.6)},

$$p = p_o(1 - \tau)^{\gamma/(\gamma-1)} \qquad \rho = \rho_o(1 - \tau)^{1/(\gamma-1)} . \quad (10.40)$$

Let 2ℓ represent the cross-section area of the nozzle and $2k\ell$ the cross-section area of the outgoing jet at infinity. The flowrate in the jet is $k2\ell v_1$, where v_1 is the gas velocity on the free surface. The control surface in the gas consists of the walls of the Borda nozzle, the free surface of the jet, a normal cross section through the jet at infinity, and the surface of a "sphere" with infinitely large radius (Fig. 229b). The projection of the net resultant pressure force (acting on the control surface) in a direction parallel to the nozzle walls is $-(p_1 - p_o)2\ell$. Here, p_1 is the pressure on the free surface and p_o is the pressure at infinity. The corresponding horizontal component of the momentum increment (imparted in a unit of time to the fluid within the control surface at the initial instant of time) is $\rho_1 k 2\ell v_1^2$. According to the momentum theorem for the horizontal projections,

$$\rho_1 k 2\ell v_1^2 = -(p_1 - p_o)2\ell \ .$$

From this,

$$k = \frac{p_o - p_1}{\rho_1 v_1^2} \ ,$$

where ρ_1 is the gas density on the free surface. Introduction of Eqs. (10.40) (with τ_1 corresponding to p_1 and ρ_1) into this result gives, after some simplification,

$$k = \frac{(1 - \tau_1)^{-\beta} - (1 - \tau_1)}{2(1 + \beta)\,\tau_1} \ , \qquad (10.41)$$

where, as above, $\beta = 1/(\gamma - 1)$. The contraction coefficient can also be expressed in terms of the Mach number $\mathbf{M}$ [1]

$$k = \frac{\{1 + [(\gamma - 1)/2]\mathbf{M}^2\}^{\gamma/(\gamma-1)} - 1}{\gamma \mathbf{M}^2} \ .$$

The solution to the plane, Borda-nozzle problem by Chaplygin's method leads to an equation for k, containing a hypergeometric function $F(1, -\beta, 2, \tau_1)$. However, this function actually degenerates into an algebraic function

$[1 - (1 - \tau_1)^{\beta+1}]/[\tau_1(\beta + 1)]$ for this case, and Eq. (10.41) is again obtained for k. Some of the Sekerzh-Zenkovich results [188] for the plane problem are given in Table 28 but, as we have already noted, they are also suitable for the equivalent three-dimensional problem.

TABLE 28. $\gamma = 1.4$

τ_1	k	τ_1	k
0.02	0.5129	0.12	0.5911
0.04	0.5266	0.14	0.6102
0.06	0.5412	0.16	0.6307
0.08	0.5567	0.1667	0.6378
1.10	0.5734		

The study of Chaplygin's problem of perfect gas flow from a vessel with rectilinear walls led to the discovery of a remarkable condition, the existence of which was proven by Ovsiannikvov [189]. He showed that, when the pressure on the jet surface is such that the velocity there is exactly equal to the speed of sound, then the flow in the jet is equalized a finite distance from the opening. Thus, all the gas on the various streamlines in the jet reaches the speed of sound at a particular cross section defined by a single plane-normal to the jet and a finite distance from the opening. A more general result, applicable when the density-pressure relation is arbitrary and the jet is flowing from an arbitrarily shaped vessel, was obtained by Rudnev [24, 190]. These first flows with a straight sonic line were used for nozzle design by Khristianovich and his collaborators in 1943.

Chaplygin also solved the flow around a plate of finite width located perpendicular to an approaching jet. The problem is solved in a manner analogous to the preceding ones. The drag R of the plate is expressed by

$$R = \frac{2\ell\rho_1 v_o^2 \pi}{\pi + \frac{8}{1 - \cos m} \sum_{n=1}^{\infty} (-1)^{n-1} \frac{n x_n(\tau_1)}{4n^2 - 1} (1 - \cos 2nm)} ,$$

where 2ℓ is the plate width, $\rho_1 = \rho_o(1 - \tau_1)^\beta$ is the density of the gas in the jet at infinity, and m is the angle between the inclined downstream jets and the axis of symmetry. For small $\mathbf{M} = v_1/a_1$ (where a_1 is the speed of sound corresponding to the velocity v_1) Chaplygin deduced, on the basis of exact calculations, an approximate equation for the case of an infinitely wide jet:

$$R = \frac{\pi}{\pi + 4 - 2\mathbf{M}_1^2} 2\ell\rho_1 v_1^2 .$$

In light of what was presented in Chapter V, Section A, subsonic jet flow around bodies, in its pure theoretical form, appears to be very difficult to accomplish in practice. On the other hand, it is perfectly reasonable to expect that Chaplygin's theory will give good results for a flow of an inviscid gas into a medium with considerably less density.

Attempts to expand the class of problems solvable by Chaplygin's method met many obstacles because it was difficult to find new problems for which the Chaplygin series converged everywhere in the flow region. Nevertheless, several works dedicated to new, exact solutions of gas-jet theory problems have appeared. First, Rudnev [190] investigated by a new method the flow of a subsonic jet around a cascade; his method differs from Chaplygin's and is cumbersome. We shall consider

Falkovich's work [191] because, while solving a new problem example, he showed how to widen the region of applicability of Chaplygin's method. Falkovich's method is also interesting because he did not proceed from an incompressible-fluid-flow solution, but solved the gas-dynamics problem independently.

To begin, let a gas jet flow at subsonic speed from a rectangular vessel of finite width 2L through an opening of dimension 2ℓ (Fig. 230). Assume that the stream function ψ along the upper flow boundary A'B'C'D' takes the value $\psi = q/2$ and that, along the lower boundary ABCD, $\psi = -q/2$. We denote the gas velocity at a great distance from the opening inside the vessel as v_∞.

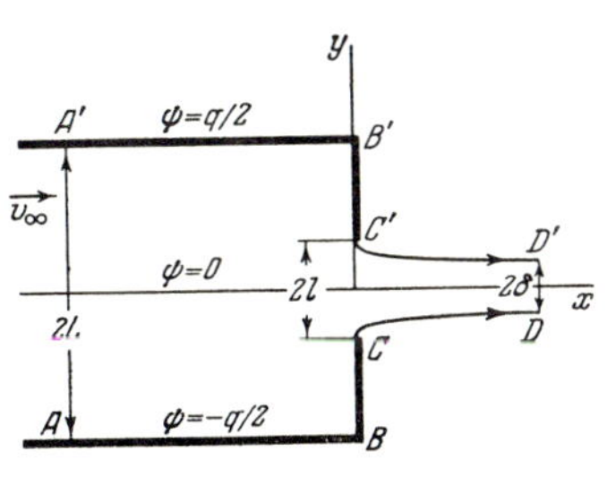

Fig. 230

In the velocity or hodograph plane the physical flow region is represented by a semicircle of radius

$$\tau_1 = \frac{v_1^2}{[(\gamma + 1)/(\gamma - 1)]a_*^2}$$

with a cut of length

$$\tau_\infty = \frac{v_\infty^2}{[(\gamma + 1)/(\gamma - 1)]a_*^2}$$

along the ray $\theta = 0$ (Fig. 231). The polar coordinates are the radius τ and angle θ. The values taken by the stream function ψ along the boundaries of the hodograph region are the following:

$$\psi = -q/2 \quad \text{when} \quad \tau = \tau_1 \qquad 0 < \theta < \pi/2 \tag{10.42}$$

$$\psi = -q/2 \quad \text{when} \quad \tau_1 \geqq \tau \geqq 0 \qquad \theta = \pi/2 \tag{10.43}$$

$$\psi = -q/2 \quad \text{when} \quad 0 \leqq \tau < \tau_\infty \qquad \theta = +0 \tag{10.44}$$

$$\psi = q/2 \quad \text{when} \quad \tau = \tau_1 \qquad -\pi/2 \leqq \theta < 0 \tag{10.45}$$

$$\psi = q/2 \quad \text{when} \quad \tau_1 \geqq \tau > 0 \qquad \theta = -\pi/2 \tag{10.46}$$

$$\psi = q/2 \quad \text{when} \quad 0 \leqq \tau < \tau_\infty \qquad \theta = -0 \ . \tag{10.47}$$

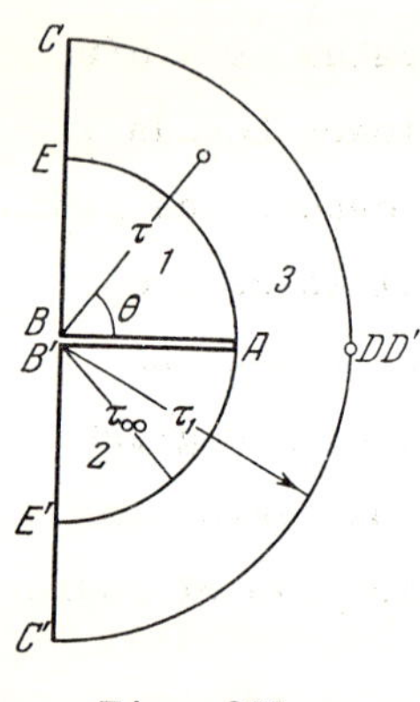

Fig. 231

Thus, determination of the flow is reduced to finding the solution to Eq. (10.13) in the region shown in Fig. 231 with given values {Eqs. (10.42) through (10.47)} on the region's boundaries—i.e., to a Dirichlet problem for Chaplygin's Eq. (10.13).

If we draw an arc EAE' of radius $\tau = \tau_\infty$, then the region in which the solution is sought is divided into three regions (1, 2, and 3 indicated in Fig. 231).

We assume that in Regions 1 and 2 the solution to Eq. (10.13) has the forms

$$\psi^{(1)}(\theta,\tau) = -\frac{q}{2} + \sum_{n=1}^{\infty} a_n z_n(\tau) \sin 2n\theta \ , \tag{10.48}$$

$$\psi^{(2)}(\theta,\tau) = \frac{q}{2} + \sum_{n=1}^{\infty} a_n z_n(\tau) \sin 2n\theta \ , \tag{10.49}$$

where $z_n(\tau)$ is the solution to Eq. (10.18), bounded at $\tau = 0$. From Eqs. (10.19) and (10.23) it follows that we can write

$$\left.\begin{aligned} z_n(\tau) &= \tau^n F(a_n,\ b_n,\ 2n+1;\ \tau) \\ a_n + b_n = 2n - \beta \qquad a_n b_n &= -\beta n(2n+1) \end{aligned}\right\} . \tag{10.50}$$

The second solution to Eq. (10.18), which is linearly independent of $z_n(\tau)$, is called $\zeta_n(\tau)$.* There are several expressions for this solution [186 or 192]. Furthermore, $\zeta_n(\tau)$ has a logarithmic singularity at $\tau = 0$, but the function is used only in Region 3.

Because Region 3 is a half ring CDC'E'AEC, the function ψ, which satisfies Eq. (10.13), is sought in the form

$$\psi^{(3)}(\theta,\tau) = -\frac{q}{\pi}\theta + \sum_{n=1}^{\infty} (A_n z_n(\tau) + B_n \zeta_n(\tau)] \sin 2n\theta \quad . \tag{10.51}$$

Equation (10.48) for Region 1 satisfies the boundary conditions on DE and BA, and Eq. (10.49) for Region 2 satisfies condition Eqs. (10.47) and (10.46) on B'E' and B'A. Equation (10.51) for the ring-shaped Region 3 satisfies the boundary condition Eqs. (10.43) and (10.46) on CE and C'E'.

---

*For integer n Falkovich takes the Cherry solution [192] ζ_n as more convenient for calculations—i.e.,

$$\zeta_n(\tau) = \lim_{\nu\to -n}\left[z_n(\tau) + \frac{(2n-1)h_n\tau^{-\nu}F(a_\nu - 2\nu,\ b_\nu - 2\nu,\ 1-2\nu;\ \tau)}{(2n+1)(2\nu+2n)}\right],$$

where

$$h_n = \frac{a_n(a_n - 1)\ldots(a_n - 2n+1)(2n-1-b_n)(2n-2-b_n)\ldots(-b_n)}{(2n-1)!(2n)!} \quad .$$

Finally, we must satisfy the boundary condition Eqs. (10.42) and (10.45) on the free surface CDC' and match the solution along E'AE so that $\psi^{(3)}$ is an analytic extension of $\psi^{(1)}$ and $\psi^{(2)}$. Then the unknown coefficients a_n, A_n, and B_n can be found.

To satisfy the boundary condition Eqs. (10.42) and (10.45) on the arc C'DC $(\tau = \tau_1)$, we must have

$$\frac{q}{\pi}\,\theta \mp \frac{q}{2} = \sum_{n=1}^{\infty} [A_n z_n(\tau_1) + B_n \zeta_n(\tau_1)] \sin 2n\theta \quad . \tag{10.52}$$

The minus sign is used when $\theta > 0$; the plus sign is used when $\theta < 0$. Now it can be shown that, when $-\pi/2 \leqq \theta \leqq \pi/2$,

$$\frac{q}{\pi}\,\theta \mp \frac{q}{2} = -\frac{q}{\pi} \sum_{n=1}^{\infty} \frac{\sin 2n\theta}{n} \quad . \tag{10.53}$$

Thus, on comparing Eqs. (10.52) and (10.53), we obtain an equation for A_n and B_n:

$$A_n z_n(\tau_1) + B_n \zeta_n(\tau_1) = -\frac{q}{\pi n} \quad . \tag{10.54}$$

Now we require that $\psi^{(3)}$ be an analytic extension of $\psi^{(1)}$ and $\psi^{(2)}$ in passing from Regions 1 and 2 into Region 3 $(\tau_\infty \leqq \tau \leqq \tau_1;\ -\pi/2 \leqq \theta \leqq \pi/2)$. Thus, the following conditions must be satisfied on the arc EAE':

$$\psi^{(3)}(\theta,\tau_\infty) = \psi^{(1)}(\theta,\tau_\infty) \qquad \frac{\partial\psi^{(3)}}{\partial\tau} = \frac{\partial\psi^{(1)}}{\partial\tau} \qquad (0 \leqq \theta \leqq \pi/2)$$

$$\psi^{(3)}(\theta,\tau_\infty) = \psi^{(2)}(\theta,\tau_\infty) \qquad \frac{\partial\psi^{(3)}}{\partial\tau} = \frac{\partial\psi^{(2)}}{\partial\tau} \qquad (0 \geqq \theta \geqq -\pi/2).$$

On substituting Eqs. (10.48), (10.49), and (10.51) for $\psi^{(1)}$, $\psi^{(2)}$, and $\psi^{(3)}$ in the first and third conditions, we have

$$\mp \frac{q}{2} + \frac{q}{\pi}\theta = \sum_{n=1}^{\infty} [(A_n - a_n) z_n(\tau_\infty) + B_n\zeta_n(\tau_\infty)] \sin 2n\theta$$

$$(-\ \text{when}\ \theta > 0)$$

$$(+\ \text{when}\ \theta < 0)\ .$$

By using Eq. (10.53) we now can write

$$(A_n - a_n)z_n(\tau_\infty) + B_n\zeta_n(\tau_\infty) = -\frac{q}{\pi n}\ ; \qquad (10.55)$$

from the second and fourth conditions, it follows that

$$(A_n - a_n)z_n'(\tau_\infty) + B_n\zeta_n'(\tau_\infty) = 0\ . \qquad (10.56)$$

The system of Eqs. (10.54) through (10.56) determines the unknown coefficients A_n, B_n and a_n. Solving these equations simultaneously leads to

$$A_n = -\frac{q}{\pi n}\left[1 - \frac{\zeta_n(\tau_1)z_n'(\tau_\infty)}{W(\tau_\infty)}\right]\frac{1}{z_n(\tau_1)}\ ,$$

$$B_n = -\frac{q}{\pi n}\,\frac{z_n'(\tau_\infty)}{W(\tau_\infty)}\ ,$$

$$a_n = -\frac{q}{\pi n}\left[1 - \frac{\zeta_n(\tau_1)z_n'(\tau_\infty) - z_n(\tau_1)\zeta_n'(\tau_\infty)}{W(\tau_\infty)}\right]\frac{1}{z_n(\tau_1)}\ ,$$

where $W(\tau_\infty)$ is the Wronskian determinant

$$W(\tau) = \Delta(\zeta_n, z_n) = \zeta_n(\tau)z_n'(\tau) - \zeta_n'(\tau)z_n(\tau)$$

for the linearly independent $z_n(\tau)$ and $\zeta_n(\tau)$ when $\tau = \tau_\infty$. It is easy to note [30, Vol. II, Chap. 2] that for Eq. (10.18) the Wronskian W has the form

$$W(\tau) = H_n \exp\left[-\int \frac{1 + (\beta - 1)\tau}{\tau(1 - \tau)} d\tau\right] = H_n \frac{(1 - \tau)^\beta}{\tau}, \tag{10.57}$$

where H_n are constants that depend on the selection of $\zeta_n(\tau)$.* On introducing the values of A_n and B_n in Eq. (10.51), we find the Region 3 solution:

$$\frac{\pi}{q}\psi^{(3)}(\theta,\tau) = -\theta - \sum_{n=1}^{\infty} \frac{z_n(\tau)}{z_n(\tau_1)} \frac{\sin 2n\theta}{n}$$

$$+ \frac{\tau_\infty}{(1 - \tau_\infty)^\beta} \sum_{n=1}^{\infty} \left[\frac{\zeta_n(\tau_1)z_n(\tau) - \zeta_n(\tau)z_n(\tau_1)}{z_n(\tau_1)} \cdot z_n'(\tau_\infty) \frac{\sin 2n\theta}{nH_n}\right]. \tag{10.58}$$

When the vessel is infinitely wide, $\tau_\infty = 0$, the second series in Eq. (10.58) vanishes, and $\psi^{(3)}$ represents ψ in the entire region and coincides with Chaplygin's solution, Eq. (10.33).

*For Cherry's solution, $H_n = 2n$ [191].

For brevity we define

$$\chi_n(\tau) = \frac{z_n(\tau)}{z_n(\tau_1)} - \frac{\tau_\infty}{(1-\tau_\infty)^\beta} \frac{\zeta_n(\tau_1)z_n(\tau) - \zeta_n(\tau)z_n(\tau_1)}{H_n z_n(\tau_1)} z_n'(\tau_\infty) \quad . \tag{10.59}$$

Thus, Eq. (10.58) takes the form

$$\frac{\pi}{q}\,\psi^{(3)}(\theta,\tau) = -\theta - \sum_{n=1}^{\infty} \frac{\chi_n(\tau)}{n} \sin 2n\theta \quad . \tag{10.60}$$

Equation (10.60) can now be used to find the jet contraction coefficient. If the jet width at infinity is 2δ (Fig. 230), we can again use to advantage Eq. (10.34) and the equation following it, namely,

$$\ell - \delta = \lim_{\tau\to\tau_1} \frac{2\tau}{(1-\tau)^\beta v} \int_0^{-\pi/2} \sin\theta \frac{\partial\psi}{\partial\tau}\, d\theta \quad . \tag{10.61}$$

Introduction of Eq. (10.60) for $\psi^{(3)}$ into Eq. (10.61) gives

$$\ell - \delta = -\frac{2\tau_1}{(1-\tau_1)^\beta v_1} \lim_{\tau\to\tau_1} \frac{q}{\pi} \sum_{n=1}^{\infty} \int_0^{-\pi/2} \frac{\sin\theta \sin 2n\theta}{n} \chi_n'(\tau)\, d\theta \quad ;$$

but

$$-\int_0^{-\pi/2} \frac{\sin\theta\ \sin 2n\theta}{n}\, d\theta = \frac{(-1)^{n-1}}{2n} \frac{4n}{4n^2 - 1} \quad .$$

Therefore,

$$\ell - \delta = \frac{4q\tau_1}{\pi(1 - \tau_1)^\beta v_1} \sum_{n=1}^{\infty} \frac{(-1)^{n-1} \chi_n'(\tau_1)}{4n^2 - 1} . \quad (10.62)$$

According to Eq. (10.36), $q/v_1(1 - \tau_1)^\beta$ can be replaced by the jet width 2δ in Eq. (10.62). If, furthermore, we let $\ell/\delta = 1/k$, where k is the contraction coefficient of the jet, then we have

$$\frac{1}{k} = \frac{\ell}{\delta} = 1 + \frac{2\tau_1}{\pi} \sum_{n=1}^{\infty} \frac{(-1)^{n-1} \chi_n'(\tau_1)}{4n^2 - 1} . \quad (10.63)$$

From Eqs. (10.57) and (10.59)

$$\chi_n'(\tau_1) = \frac{z_n'(\tau_1)}{z_n(\tau_1)} - \frac{\tau_\infty}{(1 - \tau_\infty)^\beta} \frac{W(\tau_1)}{H_n z_n(\tau_1)} z_n'(\tau_\infty)$$

$$= \frac{z_n'(\tau_1)}{z_n(\tau_1)} - \frac{\tau_\infty(1 - \tau_1)^\beta}{\tau_1(1 - \tau_\infty)^\beta} \cdot \frac{z_n'(\tau_\infty)}{z_n(\tau_1)} .$$

Substituting these results into Eq. (10.63) leads to

$$\frac{1}{k} = 1 + \frac{8\tau_1}{\pi} \left[\sum_{n=1}^{\infty} \frac{(-1)^{n-1}}{4n^2 - 1} \frac{z_n'(\tau_1)}{z_n(\tau_1)} - \frac{\tau_\infty}{\tau_1} \frac{(1 - \tau_1)^\beta}{(1 - \tau_\infty)^\beta} \cdot \sum_{n=1}^{\infty} \frac{(-1)^{n-1}}{4n^2 - 1} \frac{z_n'(\tau_\infty)}{z_n(\tau_1)} \right] . \quad (10.64)$$

For an infinitely wide vessel $\tau_\infty = 0$, as noted above, and Eq. (10.64) degenerates to Chaplygin's Eq. (10.37). If the ratio ℓ/δ obtained from Eq. (10.37) is called $1/k_\infty$, then the quantity $1/k$ given by Eq. (10.64) can be written as

$$\frac{1}{k} = \frac{1}{k_\infty} + \frac{8\tau_\infty}{\pi} \frac{(1 - \tau_1)^\beta}{(1 - \tau_\infty)^\beta} \sum_{n=1}^{\infty} \frac{(-1)^n}{4n^2 - 1} \frac{z_n'(\tau_\infty)}{z_n(\tau_1)} \quad . \qquad (10.65)$$

Fortunately, from a computational viewpoint, the functions ζ_n do not appear in this final expression. To this final result we must add the condition that the gas flowrates at infinitely distant cross sections to the left and to the right are equal— i.e.,

$$v_\infty(1 - \tau_\infty)^\beta \, 2L = v_1(1 - \tau_1)^\beta \, 2\delta = v_1(1 - \tau_1)^\beta \, k2\ell \quad . \qquad (10.66)$$

The system of Eqs. (10.65) and (10.66) is now conveniently written in the following final form:

$$k = \frac{L}{\ell} \frac{\sqrt{\tau_\infty}\,(1 - \tau_\infty)^\beta}{\sqrt{\tau_1}\,(1 - \tau_1)^\beta} ,$$

$$\frac{\ell}{L} = \frac{\sqrt{\tau_\infty}\,(1 - \tau_\infty)^\beta}{k_\infty\sqrt{\tau_1}\,(1 - \tau_1)^\beta} + \frac{8}{\pi}\left(\frac{\tau_\infty^3}{\tau_1}\right)^{1/2} \sum_{n=1}^{\infty} \frac{(-1)^n}{4n^2 - 1} \frac{z_n'(\tau_\infty)}{z_n(\tau_1)} \quad . \qquad (10.67)$$

Falkovich also solved the problem of gas flow from a vessel of finite width, where the vessel's walls form an arbitrary angle with the axis of symmetry. The computations of the jet's contraction coefficient according to Falkovich's technique were carried out by Aslanov and Legkova [193]. These results are given below in Table 29.

TABLE 29

τ_1	τ_∞	ℓ/L	k	τ_1	τ_∞	ℓ/L	k
0.02	0	0	0.6233	0.10	0	0	0.6815
	0.0025	0.5543	0.6668		0.0025	0.2957	0.6914
	0.01	0.9091	0.7973		0.01	0.5574	0.7200
	0.02	1.0000	1.0000		0.02	0.7308	0.7572
					0.04	0.8978	0.8277
					0.06	0.9672	0.8928
					0.10	1.0000	1.0000
0.04	0	0	0.6364	0.12	0	0	0.6988
	0.0025	0.4184	0.6580		0.0025	0.2792	0.7073
	0.01	0.7312	0.7246		0.01	0.5291	0.7324
	0.02	0.9174	0.8115		0.02	0.6988	0.7646
	0.04	1.0000	1.0000		0.04	0.8698	0.8251
					0.06	0.9478	0.8798
					0.08	0.9831	0.9281
					0.12	1.0000	1.0000
0.06	0	0	0.6504	0.14	0	0	0.7175
	0.0025	0.3559	0.6653		0.0025	0.2670	0.7252
	0.01	0.6548	0.7097		0.1	0.5108	0.7438
	0.02	0.8340	0.7683		0.02	0.6747	0.7766
	0.04	0.9725	0.8849		0.04	0.8476	0.8303
	0.06	1.0000	1.0000		0.08	0.9721	0.9204
					0.10	0.9908	0.9557
					0.14	1.0000	1.0000
0.08	0	0	0.6654	0.1667	0	0	0.7447
	0.0025	0.3196	0.6914		0.0025	0.2554	0.7516
	0.01	0.5968	0.7116		0.01	0.4882	0.7719
	0.02	0.7740	0.7565		0.02	0.6513	0.7977
	0.04	0.8432	0.7818		0.04	0.8254	0.8454
	0.06	0.9878	0.9251		0.06	0.9135	0.8877
	0.08	1.0000	1.0000		0.08	0.9601	0.9241
					0.1667	1.0000	1.0000

In 1958 and 1959 Sretenskii [194, 195] published reports of exact solutions to gas-jet problems. His method is based on a transformation of Chaplygin's series into definite integrals. Without doubt, this method deserves attention; however, it is difficult to evaluate its advantages now because the final expressions for the stream functions are complicated and numerical computations have not yet been published.

Also, in 1958 Mackie [196] produced an exact solution to a gas flow around a wedge using the Zhukovskii-Roshko model (Fig. 84). Mackie allowed for an arbitrary relation between p and ρ. He solved the equation (for the stream function ψ)

$$\frac{\partial^2\psi}{\partial\sigma^2} + K(\sigma)\,\frac{\partial^2\psi}{\partial\theta^2} = 0 \quad ,$$

where σ is a known function only of velocity, by separation of variables. The region of change of the variables (σ, θ) is a horizontal semi-infinite strip. A solution for ψ is given as a definite integral containing an arbitrary function. This solution satisfies the boundary conditions on the upper horizontal and on the vertical boundaries of the semi-infinite strip. An attempt to satisfy the boundary condition on the lower horizontal boundary produces an integral equation for the above-mentioned arbitrary function. This integral equation is solved by using the Sherman inversion formulas [66].

C. CHAPLYGIN'S APPROXIMATE METHOD

For small Mach numbers $\mathbf{M}$, Chaplygin proposed an approximate method that now forms the basis of many approximate methods used in modern gas dynamics. To illustrate his method we introduce a new variable σ, where

$$\sigma = \int_{\tau}^{\tau_o} \frac{(1 - \tau)^{\beta}}{2\tau} \, d\tau \quad . \tag{10.68}$$

Equations (10.12) can now be written

$$\left.\begin{aligned} \frac{\partial\varphi}{\partial\theta} &= -\frac{\partial\psi}{\partial\sigma} \\ \frac{\partial\varphi}{\partial\sigma} &= K \frac{\partial\psi}{\partial\theta} \end{aligned}\right\} , \tag{10.69}$$

where

$$K = \frac{1 - (2\beta + 1)\tau}{(1 - \tau)^{2\beta+1}} \quad . \tag{10.70}$$

In adiabatic processes the K from Eq. (10.16) is the same as that from Eq. (10.70). Clearly, $dK/d\tau < 0$ when $\tau > 0$. It follows that K is a decreasing function and when $\tau = 0$, $K = 1$. Simple arithmetic calculations show that for $0 < \tau < 1/31$ (corresponding to $\mathbf{M} < 0.4$), $1 > K > 0.982$. Thus, Chaplygin proposed that $K \approx 1$ for small τ. Under this assumption Eqs. (10.69) are transformed into the Cauchy-Riemann equations; it them follows that the flow can be represented in complex form by

$$w = \varphi + i\psi = F(\sigma + i\theta) \quad . \tag{10.71}$$

Consider a subsonic jet flow of a compressible fluid in which all the bounding walls are plane. We investigate simultaneously an incompressible-jet flow with the same plane-wall and free-surface configuration. Suppose that the incompressible flow has a solution given by

$$w_H = \varphi_H + i\psi_H = F(\omega_H)$$

$$\omega_H = \ln \frac{v_1 dz_H}{dw_H} = \ln \frac{v_1}{v_H} + i\theta_H = \vartheta_H + i\theta_H \quad ,$$

where w_H is the complex potential of the incompressible flow, v_1 is the velocity on the free surface, and θ_H is the angle between the velocity and the x-axis. On all the boundaries, ψ_H has particular constant values. On the walls, θ_H = const. and on the jets, $v_H = v_1$; consequently, $\vartheta_H = 0$.

It is clear that on finding $F(\omega_H)$—the solution to a given incompressible flow problem—we can obtain the solution to the same problem for a gas by placing

$$\varphi + i\psi = F(\sigma + i\theta) \quad ,$$

i.e., simply by replacing ω_H by $\sigma + i\theta$. Now on the boundaries of the region of θ and σ coinciding* with the boundaries of the region of ϑ_H and θ_H, ψ takes the same constant values as ψ_H. Once $\varphi + i\psi$ is found as a function of $\sigma + i\theta$, it is easy to find the physical plane coordinates as functions of these variables σ and θ, to study the contours of the resulting jet, and to determine characteristic constants.

By using Eqs. (10.9) and (10.6) and replacing

$$\frac{v^2}{[(\gamma + 1)/(\gamma - 1)]a_*^2} = v^2/v_{max}^2$$

*From Eq. (10.68) it is obvious that if $\sigma = 0$ (corresponding to $\vartheta_H = 0$), $\tau = \tau_1$.

by τ, we obtain

$$v_{max} z + \int \left(d\varphi + i \frac{\rho_o}{\rho} d\psi\right) \frac{e^{i\theta}}{v} v_{max} = \int \left(d\varphi + \frac{i d\psi}{(1-\tau)^{\beta}}\right) \frac{e^{i\theta}}{\sqrt{\tau}} ,$$

from which, on introducing $\overline{w} = \varphi - i\psi$, we find

$$2v_{max} z = \int \left[dw + d\overline{w} + \frac{dw - d\overline{w}}{(1-\tau)^{\beta}}\right] \frac{e^{i\theta}}{\sqrt{\tau}} . \qquad (10.72)$$

Now from Eq. (10.68) it follows that

$$\frac{d}{d\sigma}\left(\frac{1}{\sqrt{\tau}}\right) = -\frac{1}{2\tau\sqrt{\tau}} \frac{d\tau}{d\sigma} = \frac{1}{\sqrt{\tau}\,(1-\tau)^{\beta}} . \qquad (10.73)$$

Furthermore, in accordance with the notation of Eq. (10.70),

$$\frac{d}{d\sigma} \frac{1}{\sqrt{\tau}\,(1-\tau)^{\beta}} = \frac{1 - (2\beta + 1)\,\tau}{(1-\tau)^{2\beta+1}\sqrt{\tau}} = \frac{K}{\sqrt{\tau}} . \qquad (10.74)$$

In the approximate method, K is constant and $K \approx 1$; then from Eqs. (10.73) and (10.74) we find

$$\frac{d^2}{d\sigma^2}\left(\frac{1}{\sqrt{\tau}}\right) = \frac{1}{\sqrt{\tau}} ,$$

from which

$$\frac{1}{\sqrt{\tau}} = \frac{C_1 e^{\sigma} + C_2 e^{-\sigma}}{2} , \qquad (10.75)$$

where C_1 and C_2 are constants. Substituting Eq. (10.75) into the left side of Eq. (10.73) gives

$$\frac{1}{\sqrt{\tau}\,(1-\tau)^{\beta}} = \frac{C_1 e^{\sigma} - C_2 e^{-\sigma}}{2} \; . \tag{10.76}$$

Since $\tau = \tau_1$ when $\sigma = 0$, Eqs. (10.75) and (10.76) lead to

$$\frac{1}{\sqrt{\tau_1}} = \frac{C_1 + C_2}{2} \qquad \frac{1}{\sqrt{\tau_1}\,(1-\tau_1)^{\beta}} = \frac{C_1 - C_2}{2} \; . \tag{10.77}$$

Now, using Eqs. (10.75) and (10.76), we obtain from Eq. (10.72) the final expression for z

$$2zv_{max} = \int \{C_1 \exp\,[\sigma + i\theta]\; dw + C_2 \exp\,[-\sigma + i\theta]\; d\overline{w}\} \; . \tag{10.78}$$

The integration in this equation can be performed since $w = \sigma + i\theta$, and $\overline{w} = -\sigma + i\theta$.

As an example of application of his approximate method, Chaplygin examined a gas-jet flow around a flat plate; Fig. 232 shows the flow. The plate forms some arbitrary angle α_o with the x-axis, and the velocity at infinity is directed along the x-axis. For brevity, we consider only a particular case—a flow symmetric with respect to the x-axis—i.e., $\alpha_o = \pi/2$ (Fig. 233).

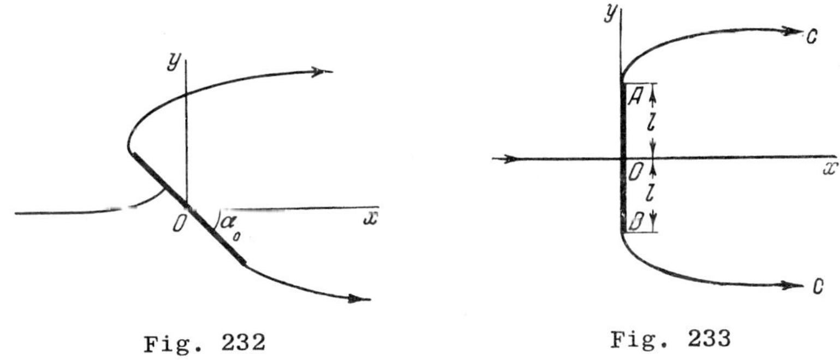

Fig. 232 Fig. 233

The corresponding incompressible-flow problem was investigated several times in Chapter I (see Fig. 1). The solutions presented there can be used here if only we remember that the flows in Figs. 233 and 1 are rotated 90 deg relative to each other. For convenience, the results from Chapter I are summarized and discussed here.

The regions of change of the complex potential w_H and the dimensionless complex velocity dw_H/v_1dz are mapped onto the upper half-plane of the parametric variable u (Figs. 233 and 234); thus,

$$w_H = \varphi_H + i\psi_H = ku^2$$

$$\frac{dw_H}{v_1dz_H} = \exp\left[-\vartheta_H - i\theta_H\right] = \frac{-iu}{1 + (1 - u^2)^{1/2}} , \qquad (10.79)$$

where the radical $(1 - u^2)^{1/2}$ is positive on the segment $-1 < u < 1$. From Eqs. (10.79) it is seen that $\psi_H = 0$ along the real axis in u. At point 0 where $u = 0$ and the streamline bifurcates, $dw_H/du = 0$. Everywhere in the upper half-plane both $w_H(u)$ and dw_H/v_1dz_H are analytic. Obviously, $\arg\left[dw_H/v_1dz_H\right]$ is $-\theta_H = -\pi/2$ along OA and $-\theta_H = \pi/2$ along OB. $|dw_H/v_1dz_H|$ varies from 0 at point 0 to 1 at A and B. On AC and CB, dw_H/v_1dz_H takes the values

$$-iu/[1 - i(u^2 - 1)^{1/2}] \qquad \text{and} \qquad -iu/[1 + i(u^2 - 1)^{1/2}]$$

respectively. Clearly, in both cases

$$\left|\frac{dw_H}{v_1dz_1}\right| = \left\{\frac{u^2}{1 + [\pm(u^2 - 1)^{1/2}]^2}\right\}^{1/2} = 1 \quad .$$

The angle θ varies monotonically along AC and BC from $\pm\pi/2$ at A and B respectively to 0 at C.

It is possible to eliminate u from Eqs. (10.79) and to obtain

$$w_H = \frac{k}{\sin^2(\theta_H - i\vartheta_H)} . \qquad (10.80)$$

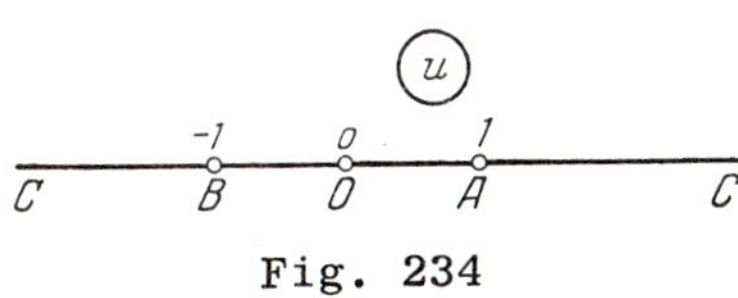

Fig. 234

Now in accordance with Chaplygin's outline of his approximate method, we study the gas flow by replacing ϑ_H with σ and w_H with w in Eq. (10.80). The result is the general solution for the gas-flow problem in the form

$$w = \frac{k}{\sin^2(\theta - i\sigma)} . \qquad (10.81)$$

Next, we find the relationship between the known coefficient k and the plate length 2ℓ. To do this, we use Eq. (10.78) which, after an integration by parts, is

$$2zv_{max} = C_1 \exp[\sigma + i\theta]w + C_2\overline{w} \exp[-\sigma + i\theta]$$

$$- C_1 \int w \exp[\sigma + i\theta] d(\sigma + i\theta)$$

$$+ C_2 \int \overline{w} \exp[-\sigma + i\theta] d(\sigma - i\theta) . \qquad (10.82)$$

Because of the flow symmetry, only computations on OA are required; there we have $w = \overline{w} = \phi$ and $\theta = \pi/2$. From Eq. (10.82) we obtain

$$2zv_{max} = iC_1 e^{\sigma} w + iC_2 e^{-\sigma} w - iC_1 \int we^{\sigma}\, d\sigma$$

$$+ iC_2 \int we^{-\sigma}\, d\sigma \quad . \quad (10.83)$$

From Eq. (10.81), with $\pi/2 = 0$, we find

$$w = \frac{k}{\sin^2 [(\pi/2) - i\sigma]} = \frac{k}{\cos^2 i\sigma} = \frac{k}{\cosh^2 \sigma} \quad . \quad (10.84)$$

Introduction of Eq. (10.84) for w into Eq. (10.83) and replacement of e^{σ} by t leads to

$$2zv_{max} = 4ki \left[\frac{C_1 t^3}{(1 + t^2)^2} + \frac{C_2 t}{(1 + t^2)^2} - C_1 \int \frac{t^2\, dt}{(1 + t^2)^2} \right.$$

$$\left. - C_2 \int \frac{dt}{(1 + t^2)^2} \right] \quad .$$

These integrals are easily evaluated to yield

$$2zv_{max} = 4ki \left[\frac{C_1 t^3}{(1 + t^2)^2} + \frac{C_2 t}{(1 + t^2)^2} - \frac{1}{2} C_1 \left(\arctan t - \frac{t}{t^2 + 1} \right) \right.$$

$$\left. + \frac{1}{2} C_2 \left(\arctan t + \frac{t}{1 + t^2} \right) \right]$$

$$+ \text{const} \quad . \quad (10.85)$$

From the definition of σ [see Eq. (10.68)], it is seen that at point 0 (where $\tau = 0$), $\sigma = \infty$ and $t = \infty$, whereas at point A (where $\tau = \tau_1$), $\sigma = 0$ and $t = 1$. Thus, by introducing these limits into Eq. (10.85) and after performing certain simplifications, we find

$$2\ell i v_{max} = 2(z_A - z_o)v_{max} = 4ki\left[\frac{C_1 + C_2}{2} + \frac{C_1 - C_2}{2}\frac{\pi}{4}\right] .$$

Now on substituting in this result the values of $(C_1 + C_2)/2$ and $(C_1 - C_2)/2$ from Eq. (10.77) and making additional simplifications, we finally have

$$\frac{2\ell v_{max}}{k}\sqrt{\tau_1} = 4 + \pi(1 - \tau_1)^{-\beta} . \tag{10.86}$$

The drag X is found next. From Eqs. (10.5) and (10.6) we find the pressure

$$p = p_o(1 - \tau)^{\gamma/(\gamma-1)} = p_o(1 - \tau)^{\beta+1} . \tag{10.87}$$

If the pressure on the free surface and at infinity is p_1, then from Eq. (10.87)

$$p_1 = p_o(1 - \tau_1)^{\beta+1} . \tag{10.88}$$

The drag X is the difference between the total pressures acting on either side of the plate. Therefore, on allowing for the flow symmetry, we write

$$X = 2\int_0^{\ell} p_o(1 - \tau)^{\beta+1}\, dy - 2p_1\ell ,$$

from which, after integrating by parts, we find

$$X = 2p_o\,(\beta + 1)\int_0^{\tau}(1 - \tau)^{\beta}\, y\, d\tau . \tag{10.89}$$

However, according to Eqs. (10.68) and (10.75),

$$(1 - \tau)^{\beta}\, d\tau = -2\tau\, d\sigma = -\frac{8}{(C_1 e^{\sigma} + C_2 e^{-\sigma})^2}\, d\sigma \quad .$$

Thus, by considering that $\sigma = \infty$ when $\tau = 0$, and $\sigma = 0$ when $\tau = \tau_o$, we can obtain from Eq. (10.89)

$$X = 16 p_o\, (\beta + 1) \int_0^{\infty} \frac{y}{(C_1 e^{\sigma} + C_2 e^{-\sigma})^2}\, d\sigma \quad .$$

By integrating by parts once again, we achieve

$$\frac{C_1}{8 p_o (\beta + 1)}\, X = \frac{-y}{C_1 e^{2\sigma} + C_2}\Bigg|_0^{\infty} + \int_0^{\infty} \frac{\partial y}{\partial \sigma}\, \frac{d\sigma}{C_1 e^{2\sigma} + C_2} \quad .$$

Next, since $y = \ell$ when $\sigma = 0$ and $z = iy$, $w = \varphi$ and $\theta = \pi/2$ on the upper half OA of the plate, the above expression can be written

$$\frac{C}{8 p_o (\beta + 1)}\, X = \frac{\ell}{C_1 + C_2} + \frac{1}{2 v_{max}} \int_0^{\infty} \frac{\partial \varphi}{\partial \sigma}\, \frac{C_1 e^{\sigma} + C_2 e^{-\sigma}}{C_1 e^{2\sigma} + C_2}\, d\sigma \quad .$$

Further reduction is achieved by cancelling the fraction under the integral sign and by integrating by parts again; thus,

$$\frac{C_1}{8 p_o (\beta + 1)}\, X = \frac{\ell}{C_1 + C_2} + \frac{1}{2 v_{max}} \left[\varphi e^{-\sigma}\Big|_0^{\infty} + \int_0^{\infty} \varphi e^{-\sigma}\, d\sigma \right] \quad .$$

Then, using Eq. (10.84) leads to

$$\frac{C_1}{8 p_o (\beta + 1)}\, X = \frac{\ell}{C_1 + C_2} + \frac{1}{2 v_{max}} \left[-k + k \int_0^{\infty} \frac{e^{-\sigma}}{\cosh^2 \sigma}\, d\sigma \right] \quad . \qquad (10.90)$$

The integral in Eq. (10.90) is easily evaluated. The change of variable $e^{\sigma} = t$ reduces the integral to that of a rational fraction. After elementary computations and substitution of $k/(2v_{max})$ from Eq. (10.86), we will have

$$\frac{C_1}{8p_o(\beta + 1)} X = \frac{\ell}{C_1 + C_2} + \frac{\ell\sqrt{\tau_1}}{4 + \pi(1 - \tau_1)^{-\beta}} \left(\frac{\pi}{2} - 2\right) .$$

Equations (10.77) can be used to replace C_1 and C_2 by τ_1, and subsequent simple algebraic transformations yield

$$X = \frac{4p_o(\beta + 1)\ \pi\tau_1 \ell(1 - \tau_1)^{\beta}}{4(1 - \tau_1)^{\beta} + \pi} . \qquad (10.91)$$

Finally, we re-introduce physical variables in Eq. (10.91). First, $\tau_1 = v_1^2 / \left[2a_o^2/(\gamma - 1)\right]$ (see Section A of this chapter). Second, $a^2 = dp/d\rho = \gamma p/\rho$ for adiabatic processes [see Eq. (10.5)]; clearly, when $v = 0$, $a_o^2 = \gamma p_o/\rho_o$. Third, $\beta + 1 = \gamma/(\gamma - 1)$. Fourth, the density ρ_1 corresponding to v_1 is $\rho_1 = \rho_o(1 - \tau_1)^{\beta}$. Then, after rearrangement and simplification we have finally

$$X = \frac{2\pi\ell\rho_1 v}{4(1 - \tau_1)^{\beta} + \pi} . \qquad (10.92)$$

For an arbitrary angle of attack of the plate (see Fig. 232) Chaplygin obtained the simple formula

$$P = \frac{\pi \sin \alpha_o}{4(1 - \tau_1)^{\beta} + \pi \sin \alpha_o} 2\ell v_1^2 \rho_1 , \qquad (10.93)$$

where P is the normal force on the plate. For an incompressible flow $\tau_1 = 0$ and Chaplygin's formula reduces to the well-known Rayleigh equation [see Eq. (3.11)].

Chaplygin's approximate method can be applied to the solution of any gas jet problem, if its incompressible counterpart can be solved. Slezkin [197], for example, examined the problem of gas-stream flow past a curvilinear contour, joining the methods of Chaplygin and Levi-Civita.

Slezkin mapped the regions of change of $w = \varphi + i\psi$ and $\omega = \sigma + i\theta$ onto the upper unit semicircle in the parametric-variable u-plane. The mapping equations are

$$w(u) = A^2 \left[\cos \epsilon_o - \frac{1}{2}\left(u + \frac{1}{u}\right)\right]^2 , \qquad (10.94)$$

$$\omega(u) = \nu + 2\kappa \,\ell n \frac{\exp [i\epsilon_o] - u}{1 - \exp [i\epsilon_o] u} + \Omega(u) \quad , (10.95)$$

where A, ϵ_o, ν, and κ are constants and $\Omega = \theta + iT$ is a function, regular inside the unit circle and on its boundary. As a result, an integral equation analogous to the Villat and Nekrasov equations is obtained for determining T. As an example, Slezkin solved by successive approximations a jet flow around a circular arc and found the drag on the arc. An analogous method, which uses an expansion in a trigonometric series to determine T (in lieu of an integral equation), is given in [5].

Bunimovich [198] extended Slezkin's work using a slight variation of Chaplygin's method. This change consisted of making the function K equal to a constant value, less than unity. Then, as in Chaplygin's method, the problem of determining $\varphi + i\psi\sqrt{K}$ can be reduced to a problem in the theory of complex variables. Bunimovich investigated the flow of a gas from vessels of finite width (including curvilinear vessels), such as are shown in Fig. 235. Flows from c, d, e, f, and g were described in Chapter II for incompressible fluid. The

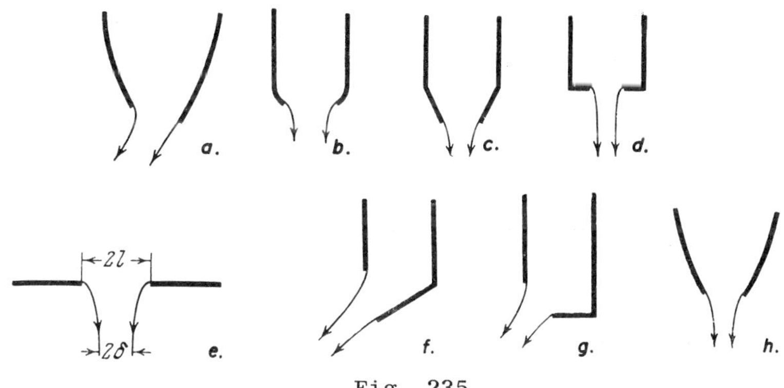

Fig. 235

symmetric vessel shown in Fig. 235b consists of two parallel walls that pass smoothly onto two symmetric circular arcs of equal radius. In [198] an integro-differential equation for the general problem of flow from a vessel with arbitrary curvilinear walls is derived. Furthermore, the solutions to the flows in Figs. 235b through 235g are given there in more-or-less detailed form, and an example is presented of an inverse solution to the flow from a symmetric curvilinear vessel (Fig. 235h). As part of the solutions [198], a formula is given for calculating the total pressure of the gas on the walls (a generalization of Levi-Civita's formulas).* A particularly simple result obtained by Bunimovich is a formula for the contraction coefficient of a jet, flowing from a vessel of infinite width (Fig. 235e):**

---

*It should be possible to compute the pressure force on the plate in the example investigated above by the same method.

**Analogous formulas were obtained by Busemann [199] and Jacob [200].

$$\frac{\delta}{\ell} = \frac{\pi}{\pi + 2\sqrt{K}\,(\rho_1/\rho)} \quad . \tag{10.96}$$

Bunimovich's computations showed that the values of the contraction coefficient obtained by this approximate formula differ very little from the values obtained by the exact result, Eq. (10.37).

D. A SURVEY OF EXTENSIONS OF CHAPLYGIN'S APPROXIMATE METHOD

As pointed out above, Chaplygin's approximate method has been extended in many different ways. To gain an understanding of these extensions, we shall study his method from a new point of view.

From Eq. (10.16) it follows that, from knowledge of p as a function of ρ, we can find K as a function of ρ. In particular, for the adiabatic relationship, Eq. (10.5), Chaplygin's K is given by Eq. (10.70). On the other hand, if $K(\rho)$ is given, then Eq. (10.16) gives the relationship between p and ρ. This equation can be solved for p. After isolating the integral in Eq. (10.16) and differentiating with respect to ρ, we obtain the differential equation

$$\frac{d^2p}{d\rho^2} = \frac{dp}{d\rho}\left[-\frac{d}{d\rho}\,\ell n\left(\frac{\rho^2}{\rho_o^2}K - 1\right) + \frac{2}{\rho\left[\left(\rho^2/\rho_o^2\right)K - 1\right]}\right]$$

for $p(\rho)$. The solution to this equation gives a family of functions $p(\rho, C_1, C_2)$ where C_1 and C_2 are the arbitrary constants obtained during the integration of the following [24, 201]:

$$p = \int \frac{\exp\left\{2 \int d\rho/\rho\left[\left(\rho^2/\rho_o^2\right) K - 1\right]\right\}}{\left(\rho^2/\rho_o^2\right) K - 1} d\rho \quad . \tag{10.97}$$

Now we pose the following question: can $K(\rho)$ be chosen so that the basic gas-dynamics equation is reduced to some well-studied equation of mathematical physics and so that the relationship $p(\rho)$, given by Eq. (10.97), is sufficiently close to the adiabatic one?

Chaplygin set $K = 1$. As we have seen, the equations relating ϕ and ψ to the independent variables σ and θ are then reduced to the Cauchy-Riemann equations. Thus, the second-order equation for ψ is reduced to the Laplace equation in the variables σ and θ.

If $K = 1$, then Eq. (10.16) is satisfied by

$$p = p_o + a_o^2\rho_o - \frac{a_o^2\rho_o^2}{\rho} , \tag{10.98}$$

where a_o is the speed of sound with $\mathbf{M} = 0$. The adiabatic equation, Eq. (10.5), can be represented as a curve in the coordinates $(1/\rho, p)$ for which the general form is shown in Fig. 236. Equation (10.98) is the equation of the tangent to this curve at $(1/\rho_o, p_o)$. Thus, the straight line, Eq. (10.98), passes through $(1/\rho_o, p_o)$, and

$$\left(\frac{dp}{d(1/\rho)}\right)_{\rho=\rho_o} = - \left(\frac{dp}{d\rho} \rho^2\right)_{\rho=\rho_o} = a_o^2\rho_o^2 .$$

In a more general case, where $K = \text{const.}$ still, the basic gas-dynamics equation is also reduced to Laplace's equation, and the general expression for p takes the form

$$p = \frac{C_1}{\rho} + C_2 , \tag{10.99}$$

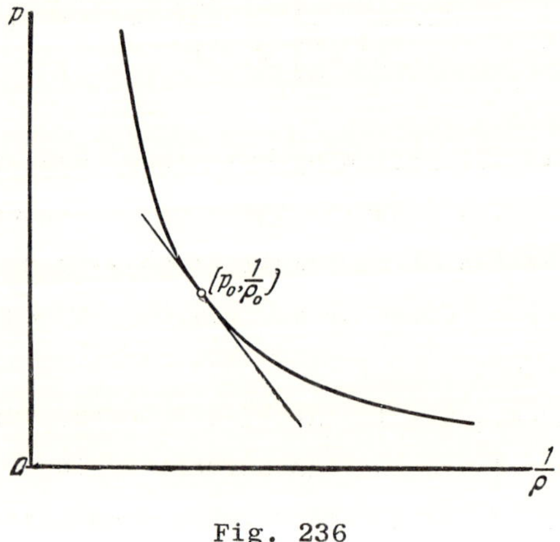

Fig. 236

where C_1 and C_2 are arbitrary constants. The constants are determined by imposing the requirement that Eq. (10.99) either be tangent to the adiabatic curve at some characteristic point [6, 202, 203, and 204] or pass through two special points on the adiabatic curve [205]. The modified forms of Chaplygin's approximate method have been employed by many authors for gas-jet as well as for other gas-dynamics problems, such as smooth flow around profiles and cascades. With regard to jet theory, it is well to note not only the studies of Slezkin [197] and Bunimovich [198] mentioned above, but also those of Busemann [199], Demtchenko [206] and Jacob [200, 207, 208].

Now, however, let us observe that it is not absolutely necessary to replace the adiabatic curve by a straight line as was done above. It is then natural to seek a better approximation of the adiabatic curve by using some appropriate curve. For example, Sauer [209] tried

$$K(s) = Cs^4 , \tag{10.100}$$

where C is a constant and s is determined by Eq. (10.14). Then, $\psi = s^{-1}\ \mathrm{Im}\ F(\mathfrak{z})$, where $F(\mathfrak{z})$ is an arbitrary analytic function of $\mathfrak{z} = s - i\theta$.

Gas flows can also be analyzed by means of a change of variables from φ and ψ to some new, unknown functions Φ and χ. In particular, the Legendre transformation is useful [24]. For the present case, it is given by

$$\varphi + \frac{i}{\rho}\psi = zv \exp[-i\theta] - \left(\Phi + \frac{i}{\rho}\chi\right) . \tag{10.101}$$

Thus, for the new Φ and χ we obtain

$$\frac{\partial\Phi}{\partial\theta} = \frac{1}{\rho^2\sqrt{K}}\frac{\partial\chi}{\partial s} \qquad \frac{\partial\Phi}{\partial s} = -\frac{1}{\rho^2\sqrt{K}}\frac{\partial\chi}{\partial\theta} . \tag{10.102}$$

By analogy with Chaplygin's approximate method, Pérès [210] set $\rho^2\sqrt{K} = \mathrm{const}$. However, his approximation for subsonic regimes is less accurate than Chaplygin's approximate method.

Returning now to the original equations for φ and ψ, we note that Dombrovskii [211] achieved a relationship leading to a third order of tangency between the adiabatic curve and his approximate curve. He set

$$K(s) = [n \tanh(ms)]^4 , \tag{10.103}$$

where n and m are arbitrary constants. This assumed form again reduces the problem of subsonic gas flow to a problem in complex-function theory, and we have for φ and ψ

$$\left.\begin{aligned} \varphi &= n\ \mathrm{Re}\left[-mF + \tanh(ms)\frac{dF}{d\mathfrak{z}}\right] \\ \psi &= n^{-1}\ \mathrm{Im}\left[-mF + \coth(ms)\frac{dF}{d\mathfrak{z}}\right] , \end{aligned}\right\} \tag{10.104}$$

where $F(\zeta)$ is an arbitrary analytic function. The applications of these solutions to jet theory are given in Ref. [212].

The transformations used by Péres and Dombrovskii were known even to Euler (see his Integral Calculations, Vol III). Furthermore, the above ideas were applied not only to subsonic flow $(\mathbf{M} < 1)$, but also to supersonic flow $(\mathbf{M} > 1)$ and to mixed subsonic-supersonic flows. Mathematically, supersonic and subsonic flows differ primarily because supersonic flows are described by hyperbolic-type equations and subsonic flows by elliptic-type equations. Presently, the wave- and Darboux-type equations [49] are used for the study of supersonic flows, and Tricomi's equation [213] is used for the investigation of mixed flows.

For the supersonic flow $(v/a = \mathbf{M} > 1)$ the parameter s, determined by Eq. (10.14), becomes imaginary, and the function K becomes negative. Therefore, in lieu of s and K, the parameters t and the function K_1 are used for supersonic flows, and very simply

$$ds = i\ dt \qquad K = -K_1 \quad . \tag{10.105}$$

Then, Eqs. (10.15) become

$$\frac{\partial\varphi}{\partial\theta} = \sqrt{K_1}\frac{\partial\psi}{\partial t} \qquad \frac{\partial\varphi}{\partial t} = \sqrt{K_1}\frac{\partial\psi}{\partial\theta} \quad . \tag{10.106}$$

The method of replacing the adiabatic curve by a linear relation can be extended also to supersonic flows [214, 215]. Clearly then, it is necessary to put $K_1 = \text{const.}$ in Eqs. (10.106). It follows that the general solution to Eqs. (10.106) is given in a simple form as

$$\varphi = -\sqrt{K_1}\,(f_1 + f_2) \qquad \psi = (f_1 - f_2) \quad , \tag{10.107}$$

where $f_1(\xi)$ and $f_2(\eta)$ are arbitrary functions of the characteristic variables

$$\xi = \frac{1}{2}(t - \theta) \qquad \eta = \frac{1}{2}(t + \theta) \quad . \tag{10.108}$$

The solution to the basic, limiting case problems can be found, e.g., [215]. Good approximations were obtained for supersonic flows by Khristianovich [216], who used

$$K_1(t) = Ct^4 \quad , \tag{10.109}$$

where C is an arbitrary constant. By using this assumed relation one can achieve a second-order tangency between the adiabatic and the approximate curve. The solutions to the basic, limiting-case problems are simplified because in the characteristic variables (ξ,η) the equations for Φ and ψ are transformed into a well-known Darboux-type equation. Among the specific problems solved by this method, we note particularly a problem concerning supersonic gas flow from a plane nozzle at an off-design condition—i.e., when the pressure in the region into which the jet flows is not equal to the pressure in the jet at the exit plane of the nozzle [217].

The Khristianovich approximation noted above corresponds in the subsonic case to the above-mentioned Sauer approximation. The Legendre transformation can be used for supersonic flows as well as for subsonic ones. Then, instead of Eq. (10.102), we will have

$$\frac{\partial\Phi}{\partial\theta} = -\frac{1}{\rho^2\sqrt{K_1}}\frac{\partial\chi}{\partial t} \qquad \frac{\partial\Phi}{\partial t} = -\frac{1}{\rho^2\sqrt{K_1}}\frac{\partial\chi}{\partial\theta} \quad . \tag{10.110}$$

As noted above, Pérès [210] set $\rho^2\sqrt{K_1}$ = const. in Eq. (10.110). His method yields a better approximation for supersonic than subsonic flows; however, the second order of tangency can be obtained only at the one point $M = 1.58$ [217a, 218]. Dombrovskii [211] also outlined an approximation for supersonic flows analogous to the one that he gave for subsonic flows [see Eqs. (10.103) and (10.104)]. If the Chaplygin function for supersonic flow is taken in the form

$$K_1(t) = (n \tan mt)^4 , \qquad (10.111)$$

then the general solution to Eqs. (10.106) is given by

$$\begin{aligned} \varphi &= n \left[-m(f_1 + f_2) + \frac{1}{2} \tan mt (f_1' + f_2') \right] , \\ \psi &= n^{-1} \left[m(-f_1 + f_2) + \frac{1}{2} \cot mt \, (-f_1' + f_2') \right] , \end{aligned} \qquad (10.112)$$

where $f_1(\xi)$ and $f_2(\eta)$ are arbitrary functions.

By employing the Laplace method, Yurev [219] showed that Khristianovich's and Dombrovskii's approximations for supersonic flows can be obtained as particular cases of a more general class of approximation. Finally, in [220], Vorobiev obtained an approximation in which a fourth order of tangency to the adiabatic curve is achieved.

A basic problem of supersonic-jet theory is the remarkably important and practical problem of supersonic-jet flow from a nozzle. The gas in the outer exhaust region either is at rest or is moving with some velocity (frequently supersonic). When the pressure p_b in the exhaust region is equal to the pressure p_c in the jet at the exit plane of the nozzle, the nozzle is operating at design conditions. The other conditions, when $p_c < p_b$ or $p_c > p_b$, are called off-design conditions. Then, depending on the ratio p_c/p_b, shock waves or expansion waves can appear in the jet. The different configurations and shapes of supersonic jets are investigated in references on gas dynamics.* In the first approximation, the "exhausting" jet has a periodic structure that Prandtl [222] first analyzed in terms of linearized gas-dynamic equations. The periodicity of the jet is also found in the solution obtained by the approximate formulations of Chaplygin [Eq. (10.12)] and Khristianovich [Eq. (10.109)]. But, in an approximate formulation that meets the requirements of Eq. (10.103), Dombrovskii [223] showed that, for design-condition flow, the jet periodicity does not occur. Furthermore, at a sufficient distance from the jet orifice, shock waves can appear in the previously continuous flow in the jet.

The most difficult and interesting problems are those concerned with jets passing through the speed of sound; the jet is supersonic in one flow region and subsonic in others. A simple approximation for such flows was suggested by Sedov [24], who proposed an approximate relationship for the $(p, 1/\rho)$ plane in the form of a broken line with the break at the sonic point (Fig. 237).

In [24] Sedov gives an equation that is useful for both subsonic and supersonic speeds—i.e.,

$$\frac{\partial^2 \psi}{\partial \sigma^2} + \frac{d}{d\sigma} \ell n \left[\frac{d\sigma}{d\rho} (\rho^2 K - 1)\right] \frac{\partial \psi}{\partial \sigma} + \frac{K}{(d\sigma/d\rho)^2 (\rho^2 K - 1)^2} \frac{\partial^2 \psi}{\partial \theta^2} = 0 , \tag{10.113}$$

where $\sigma(\rho)$ is an arbitrary, known function. The freedom of choice of $K(\sigma)$ and $\sigma(\rho)$ can be used to simplify Eq. (10.113).

One of the simplest equations of mixed type, whose important applications for solving gas-dynamics problems was first indicated by Frankl [224], is the Tricomi equation

*Trans. Note: see Shapiro [221] for a general discussion.

$$\frac{\partial^2\psi}{\partial\sigma^2} + \sigma\frac{\partial^2\psi}{\partial\theta^2} = 0 \quad . \tag{10.114}$$

The general theory of the Tricomi equation is given by him in [213]. In [224] Frankl showed that the problem of a supersonic-jet flow can be reduced to the so-called Tricomi boundary problem for the Chaplygin equation. In the neighborhood of the sonic line, Chaplygin's equation reduces directly to the Tricomi equation.

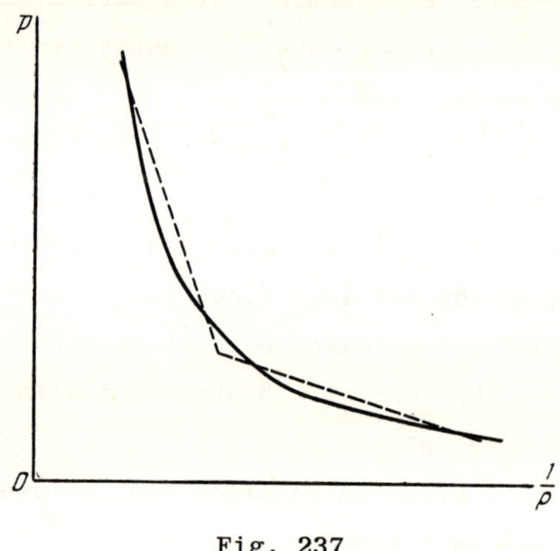

Fig. 237

Equation (10.113) is transformed into Eq. (10.114) if

$$\frac{d\sigma}{d\rho}\left(\rho^2 K - 1\right) = A \qquad \frac{K}{A^2} = \sigma \quad , \tag{10.115}$$

where A is an arbitrary constant, determined from the conditions of the approximation. By using Eqs. (10.115) and (10.97), it is possible to find $p'(\rho)$ or $p(\rho)$ up to the constant of integration.

An approximation using the Tricomi equation provides good accuracy only in the region of the sonic point (where

$M = 1$) (second order of tangency to the adiabatic curve in the sonic point). At large supersonic or small subsonic speeds, such an approximation becomes unsatisfactory. The case of a jet flowing at sonic speed from an orifice between parallel walls is, on the other hand, an excellent example for successfully applying the Tricomi equation. This problem was solved by Skripkin [225].

To obtain good approximations over a wider range of velocities, Sedov [201] used the Fourier method and adopted the conditions

$$\frac{d\sigma}{d\rho} = \frac{A\sigma}{\rho^2 K - 1} \qquad \frac{K}{\sigma'^2(\rho^2 K - 1)^2} = \frac{a}{A^2}\left(\frac{1}{\sigma^2} - 1\right) ,$$

where a and A are arbitrary constants. He thus reduced the problem of determining ψ to finding the solution to Bessel's equation. The same approximation was used by Tomotika and Tamada [226] to construct the flow with a local supersonic zone close to a symmetric profile.

M = 1) (sonic [illegible] of tangency to the [illegible] curve in the sonic [illegible]. For large supersonic or small subsonic speeds, such an approximation becomes unsatisfactory. The case of a jet flowing at sonic speed from an orifice between parallel walls [illegible] successfully [illegible] the Tricomi equation [illegible] was solved by Frankl [illegible].

To obtain good approximations [illegible] velocities, [illegible] [illegible] used the [illegible] method and adopt the conditions

$$[illegible]$$

where [illegible] and [illegible] are [illegible] the problem of determining [illegible] [illegible] equation. The same approximation was used by [illegible] and Yamada [225] to construct [illegible] flow [illegible] supersonic zone close to a [illegible] profile.

CHAPTER XI. AXISYMMETRIC FLOW

A. PROBLEM STATEMENT AND APPROXIMATE METHODS OF SOLUTION

Attempts to solve three-dimensional jet problems have led to great mathematical difficulties. At the present time (1961) the only known three-dimensional results are for axisymmetric jet flows. However, even for these relatively simple three-dimensional flows, no mathematical techniques, such as the powerful complex variable analyses in two dimensions, are available. Thus authors of papers on axisymmetric jet flows have been able only to give either approximate, numerical problem solutions or theorems of a general or qualitative nature.

We shall investigate a steady, axisymmetric, irrotational flow of an ideal, weightless, incompressible fluid. The x-axis lies along the axis of symmetry of the flow. The velocity potential φ and the stream function ψ are functions only of the cylindrical coordinates x and y, where y is the distance from the x-axis. Because the flow is axisymmetric, we need only to study the flow in the meridian half-plane $y \geqq 0$, where we now use the Cartesian coordinates x and y.

For axisymmetric flow it is known [1, 2] that

$$\left.\begin{aligned} \frac{\partial \varphi}{\partial x} &= \frac{\partial \psi}{y\,\partial y} = v_x \\ \frac{\partial \varphi}{\partial y} &= -\frac{\partial \psi}{y\,\partial x} = v_y \end{aligned}\right\}, \qquad (11.1)$$

where v_x and v_y are the velocity's projections on the x and y axes. By first eliminating φ and then ψ from Eqs. (11.1), we obtain

$$\frac{\partial^2\varphi}{\partial x^2} + \frac{\partial^2\varphi}{\partial y^2} + \frac{\partial\varphi}{y\,\partial y} = 0 \tag{11.2}$$

$$\frac{\partial^2\psi}{\partial x^2} + \frac{\partial^2\psi}{\partial y^2} - \frac{\partial\psi}{y\,\partial y} = 0 \quad . \tag{11.3}$$

The hydrodynamic problem can be considered solved if either $\varphi(x,y)$ or $\psi(x,y)$ is found. In addition to Eqs. (11.2) and (11.3) for φ and ψ, there are flow-boundary conditions. On a free surface and on the surface of a body the normal velocity is zero—i.e.,

$$\frac{\partial\varphi}{\partial n} = 0 \quad , \tag{11.4}$$

where n is the inward normal (into the fluid). Also, the stream function ψ is constant on these surface—i.e.,

$$\psi = \text{const.} \tag{11.5}$$

Equations (11.4) and (11.5) are equivalent. Clearly, the constant in Eq. (11.5) takes different values on different boundaries. For example, Fig. 238 shows the meridian half-plane xOy for flow around a circular cone in a tube. Since the stream function is determined only up to a constant factor, it is possible to set $\psi = 0$ on the x-axis, the cone, and the free surface. Then, since 2π times the difference in ψ values on the flow surfaces is the flowrate between surfaces, $\psi = \pi v_\infty h^2/(2\pi)$ on the walls of the tube.* Here, h is the

*This same result can be obtained by integrating (with respect to y) the first of Eqs. (11.1) when $x = -\infty$.

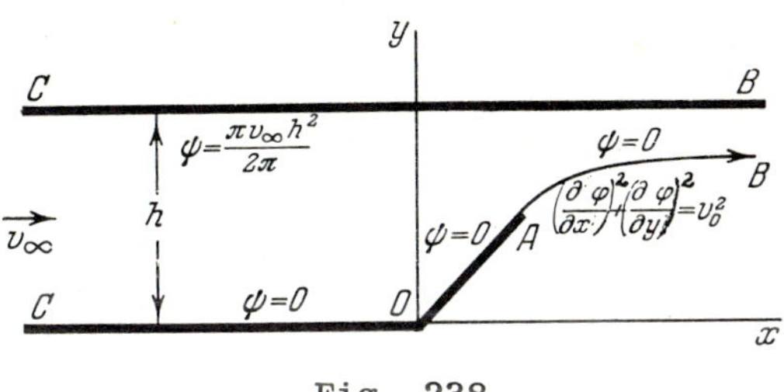

Fig. 238

radius of the tube and v_∞ is the velocity of the approaching flow at infinity to the left.

The shape of the free surface is not known in advance, but on the free surface an additional condition is known. In particular, the modulus of the velocity v is constant or, equivalently, the pressure is constant. This condition can be written as

$$\frac{1}{y^2}\left[\left(\frac{\partial\psi}{\partial x}\right)^2 + \left(\frac{\partial\psi}{\partial y}\right)^2\right] = \left(\frac{\partial\varphi}{\partial x}\right)^2 + \left(\frac{\partial\varphi}{\partial y}\right)^2 = v_o^2 , \qquad (11.6)$$

where v_o is the value of v on the free surface.*

Trefftz [227] made the first major effort to calculate an axisymmetric jet flow theoretically. For simplicity, his basic technique is described here in terms of an example he solved for flow of a jet from a circular orifice in a plane. However, Trefftz's method is clearly general in character and can probably be extended for the solution of nonsymmetric three-dimensional problems.

We choose a simply connected region in the flow bounded by a closed surface Σ. Let S and T be arbitrary points

*It is possible that in some problems v has different values on different free surfaces within the flow (flows with multiple cavities, for example).

inside Σ and on the boundary Σ respectively. If R is the distance between these points, then we know [2] that the velocity potential at S can be expressed in terms of sources and doublets located along the boundary surfaces as

$$4\pi\,(S) = \iint_{\Sigma} \varphi(T)\,\frac{\partial(1/R)}{\partial n}\,d\sigma - \iint_{\Sigma} \frac{1}{R}\,\frac{\partial\varphi(T)}{\partial n}\,d\sigma\ , \tag{11.7}$$

where $d\sigma$ is an element of Σ and the differentiations of φ and $1/R$ are with respect to a normal directed into the fluid. Furthermore, we will need to pass to the limit in Eq. (11.7) as S approaches a point on the boundary surface. To accomplish this limiting process, we must transform Eq. (11.7).

In Fig. 239a, a schematic representation of an element of the surface Σ'' is given; the point T is located on Σ''. From the triangle TT_1S it follows that

$$(R + \Delta R)^2 = R^2 + \Delta n^2 - 2R\,\Delta n\,\cos\left[(\pi/2) - \alpha\right]\ ,$$

from which we have

$$\Delta R \approx -\Delta n\,\sin\alpha$$

and

$$\frac{\partial}{\partial n}\left(\frac{1}{R}\right) = -\frac{1}{R^2}\,\frac{\partial R}{\partial n} = \frac{\sin\alpha}{R^2}\ . \tag{11.8}$$

From Fig. 239b it is seen that, to first-order accuracy,

$$\Delta\sigma\,\sin\alpha \approx R^2\,\Delta\theta\ , \tag{11.9}$$

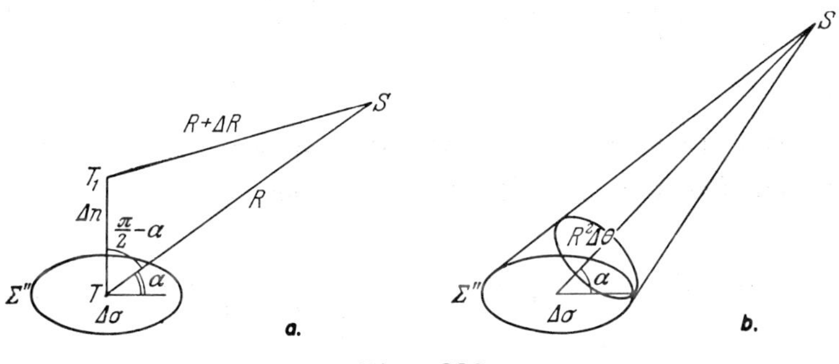

Fig. 239

where $\Delta\theta$ is the solid angle through which the element of the surface Σ'' is viewed. From Eqs. (11.8) and (11.9) we have

$$\frac{\partial}{\partial n}\left(\frac{1}{R}\right) d\sigma = d\theta \quad . \tag{11.10}$$

By using Eq. (11.10), Eq. (11.7) is transformed to

$$4\pi\varphi(S) = \iint_{\Sigma} \varphi(T)\, d\theta - \iint_{\Sigma} \frac{1}{R} \frac{\partial\varphi(T)}{\partial n}\, d\sigma \quad . \tag{11.11}$$

If S now moves to some point on the boundary surface, then in the limit the infinitely small element Σ'' of the surface with its center at the boundary point will be viewed through a solid angle 2π. After passing to the limit, we obtain

$$\iint_{\Sigma} \varphi(T)\, d\theta = 2\pi\ (S) + \iint_{\Sigma'} \varphi(T)\, d\theta \quad , \tag{11.12}$$

where the region of integration Σ' is the region Σ from which an infinitesimal element Σ'' with center at S has been cut. By using Eq. (11.9) we see that the second integral on the right side of Eq. (11.11) is

$$\iint_{\Sigma} \frac{1}{R} \frac{\partial\varphi(T)}{\partial n}\, d\sigma = \iint_{\Sigma'} \frac{1}{R} \frac{\partial\varphi(T)}{\partial n}\, d\sigma \quad . \tag{11.13}$$

After a passage to the limit as outlined above, and with Eqs. (11.12) and (11.13), Eq. (11.11) is transformed to

$$2\pi\varphi(S) = \iint_{\Sigma'} \varphi(T)\, d\theta - \iint_{\Sigma'} \frac{1}{R} \frac{\partial\varphi(T)}{\partial n}\, d\sigma \quad . \tag{11.14}$$

Now let us consider Trefftz's problem about jet flow from a circular orifice in an E-plane, as shown in Fig. 240. For his numerical solution of the problem, Trefftz bounded the flow to the left with the surface of a sphere CC_1 of large radius R_o and, to the right at a considerable distance from the orifice, with a normal section on the jet BB_1. The velocity potential can be set equal to zero at infinity to the left. Since on the sphere CC_1 the normal velocity $\partial\varphi/\partial n$ is of the order of $1/R_o^2$, φ is of the order of $1/R_o$ on CC_1. Thus, the parts of the integrals in Eq. (11.14), which are evaluated along the sphere CC_1, have small values, which can be neglected if R_o is large enough.

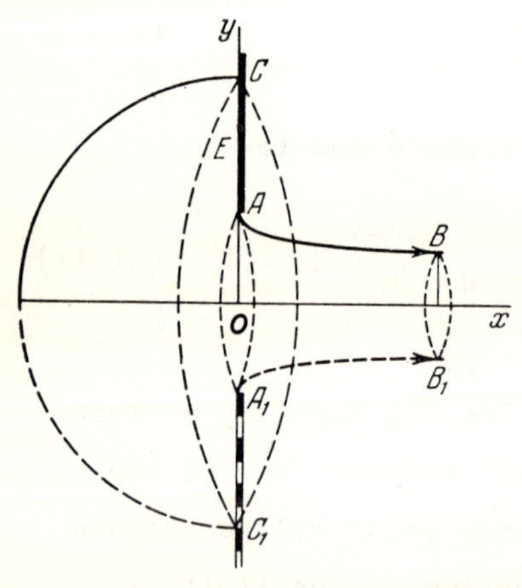

Fig. 240

On the E-plane and on the free surface, the normal derivative of the velocity potential is zero, so $\partial\varphi(T)/\partial n = 0$. At section BB_1, $\partial\varphi(T)/\partial n \approx -v_o$ and is approximately constant in value. Because of the above, the second integral in Eq. (11.14) needs to be evaluated only along the surface BB_1 and becomes a known function of S. We denote the result by

$2\pi f(S)$. The velocity potential φ at the cross section BB_1, as well as its normal derivative $\partial\varphi/\partial n$, can be assumed constant. Consequently,

$$2\pi\varphi(S) = \iint_{\Sigma'} \varphi(T)\, d\theta + 2\pi f(S) \quad . \qquad (11.15)$$

If the shape of the free surface were known, then the last equation could be considered an integral equation for determining $\varphi(T)$. However, since the shape of the free surface it not known in advance, Trefftz suggests the following solution technique.

The free surface in the meridian section xOy (Fig. 240) is represented by the lines AB and A_1B_1. If the arc length along the streamline AB is denoted by ℓ, then Eq. (11.6) along this line is reduced to

$$\frac{\partial\varphi}{\partial\ell} = v_o \quad . \qquad (11.16)$$

Ordinarily, one formulates the present problem in order to seek the velocity potential φ that satisfies Laplace's equation everywhere inside the region occupied by the fluid, the boundary condition $(\partial\varphi/\partial n) = 0$ on the E-plane and the free surface, and condition Eq. (11.16) on the free surface. Trefftz formulates the problem in a new way. He arranges to determine the shape of the jet such that the solution to the integral equation (11.15) satisfies the boundary condition $\partial\varphi/\partial\ell = v_o$ on the jet.

The first step of the solution is to prescribe arbitrarily the shape of the jet without observing condition Eq. (11.16). Then, the velocity potential on the surface of the jet is calculated as a first approximation under the assumption that Eq. (11.16) is satisfied. As a result,

$$\varphi_1 = \ell + \varphi_o \quad , \tag{11.17}$$

where φ_o is the value of φ at the separation point A and v_o is set equal to unity. Clearly, Eq. (11.17) is valid on the exact free surface. Furthermore, the value of φ is determined at an arbitrary point S on the E-plane under the assumption that the shape of the jet is given correctly. To accomplish this it is necessary to transform Eq. (11.15).

First, we shall show that $\iint_{\Sigma'} d\theta = 0$, if the cut-out infinitesimal element Σ'' lies on the E-plane. Actually, if the surface Σ of the half-sphere CC_1 is closed, then $\iint_{CC_1+\Sigma} d\theta = 4\pi$. But $\iint_{CC'} d\theta = 2\pi$ and $\iint_{\Sigma''} d\theta = 2\pi$; thus,

$$\iint_{\Sigma'} d\theta = \iint_{CC_1+\Sigma} d\theta - \iint_{CC'} d\theta - \iint_{\Sigma''} d\theta = 4\pi - 2\pi - 2\pi = 0 \quad .$$

Since any element of the E-plane is viewed from any other point of the plane with an angle $d\theta = 0$,

$$\iint_{\Sigma'-E} d\theta = \iint_{\Sigma'} d\theta - \iint_{E} d\theta = 0 \quad , \tag{11.18}$$

where $\Sigma'-E$ is the jet surface plus the surface of the normal cross section of the jet BB_1.

Clearly, $\iint_E \varphi d\theta = 0$ (because $d\theta = 0$); therefore, by using Eqs. (11.15), (11.17), and (11.18), we can compute the value of the velocity potential at any point on the E-plane—i.e.,

$$\varphi_1(S) = \iint_{\Sigma'-E} \ell_t d\theta + 2\pi f(S) \quad , \tag{11.19}$$

where the integral [see Eq. (11.18)] is taken along the region Σ'-E (along the surface of the jet and the surface of the cross section BB_1). The value $\varphi_1(S)$ is considered a first approximation to the true value of the velocity potential $\varphi(S)$.

To calculate the second approximation φ_2 to φ on the surface of the jet, the value of the first approximation φ_1 is introduced into Eq. (11.15), so that

$$\varphi_2(S) = \frac{1}{2\pi} \iint_{\Sigma'} \varphi_1(T)\, d\theta + f(S) \quad . \tag{11.20}$$

If $\varphi_2 - \varphi_1 = 0$, then the problem is solved. Wherever $\varphi_2 - \varphi_1 < 0$ (i.e., $\partial\varphi_2/\partial\ell < 1$), the velocity on the surface of the jet is too small, and Trefftz suggests increasing it by thinning the jet locally. This procedure presumably increases the velocity. If $\varphi_2 - \varphi_1 > 0$, then the jet is increased in size to reduce the velocity.

The process of selecting successive approximations can be continued indefinitely. Trefftz relies entirely on the skill and experience of the person doing the computations and does not indicate any rational method of obtaining the successive approximations.

As a result of the problem's axial symmetry, the computations can be greatly reduced. If the cylindrical coordinates (x, y, ϑ) are introduced, where y is the distance from the axis of symmetry x, then the distance between S and T (Fig. 241) is expressed by

$$R = \left[(x_s - x_t)^2 + y_t^2 + y_s^2 - 2y_s y_t \cos(\vartheta_s - \vartheta_t)\right]^{1/2} \quad . \tag{11.21}$$

Accordingly, the surface element of Σ is

$$d\sigma = y_t d\ell_t d\vartheta_t \quad , \tag{11.22}$$

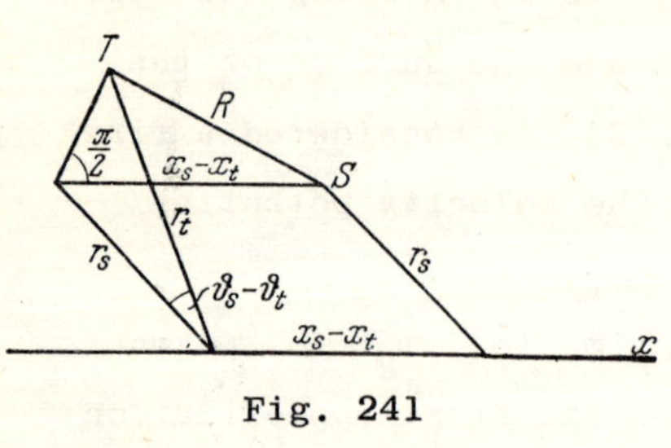

Fig. 241

where $d\ell_t$ is the arc differential of the boundary curve. In particular, on the straight line CA (Fig. 240) $d\ell = -dy$.

Since φ is independent of the angle ϑ_t, the integration over ϑ_t in Eq. (11.7) and in the resultant equations following Eq. (11.7) can be evaluated for the general case by using elliptic integrals. The integrals in Eq. (11.7) can be rewritten as follows:

$$\iint \varphi(T) \frac{\partial(1/R)}{\partial n} d\sigma = 2 \int \varphi y_t d\ell \frac{\partial V(s,t)}{\partial n}$$

$$\iint \frac{\partial\varphi(T)}{\partial n} \frac{\partial\sigma}{R} = 2 \int \frac{\partial\varphi}{\partial n} y_t d\ell V(s,t) \quad ,$$

where

$$2V(S,T) = \int_0^{2\pi} \frac{d\vartheta_t}{\left[(x_s - x_t)^2 + y_t^2 + y_s^2 - 2y_s y_t \cos(\vartheta_s - \vartheta_t)\right]^{1/2}} .$$

Thus,

$$2V(S,T) = \int_0^{2\pi} \frac{d\omega}{\left[(x_s - x_t)^2 + y_t^2 + y_s^2 - 2y_s y_t \cos\omega\right]^{1/2}} , \tag{11.23}$$

where $\omega = \vartheta_s - \vartheta_t$. This is an elliptic integral of the first kind and is easily reduced to a definite form. The detailed computation equations (related to the transformations of the elliptic integrals and their expansion in series in the neighborhood of some points) are given by Trefftz [227]. Even though the velocity potential is computed only at a finite number of points along the boundary, the computations were cumbersome.

Trefftz showed that the contraction coefficient of the jet lies between 0.6 and 0.62. If we remember that the contraction coefficient of the equivalent plane jet is $\pi/(\pi + 2) \approx 0.61$, then we may have a feeling of dissatisfaction with the accuracy of Trefftz's result. However, it would now appear natural to accept the suggestion of Kretzschmer [228] that the contraction coefficient of the jet at a distance from the orifice is independent of the shape of the orifice. We note, incidentally, that Kretzschmer's hypothesis is in fair agreement with experiments.

The function $V(S,T)$ [see Eq. (11.23)] can be interpreted as the total potential of sources uniformly distributed along a boundary circle. Schach [229], in solving the problem of the impact of a round jet on a flat plate, was able to simplify Trefftz's analysis somewhat. Schach directly analyzed the flow produced by sources and doublet rings. We gave a more general presentation of Trefftz's analysis in the hope that some readers would attempt to apply it to a three-dimensional problem of the jet theory in which the axial symmetry is absent. Is it not natural, for example, to attempt to solve the problem about a jet flow from a noncircular orifice in a plane?

A further development of Trefftz's method was provided by Salamatov [230], who solved a jet flow from a funnel (Fig. 242). If the diameter AA_1 of the orifice is 2, then the equation of the wall in the meridian half-plane xOy has the form

$$y = 1 - x \tan \beta \ . \qquad (11.24)$$

On the surfaces of the funnel and the jet, Salamatov distributed rings of vortices instead of sources. The result is a more workable equation for the stream function.* If on the arc element $d\ell_1$ of the boundary there is a vorticity $\gamma(x_t)d\ell_t$, then in cylindrical coordinates the stream function ψ has the form

$$\psi = \frac{y_s}{4\pi}\int_{-\infty}^{\infty}\left\{y_t\gamma(x_t)\int_0^{2\pi}\right.$$

$$\left.\cdot\ \frac{\cos\omega\, d\omega}{\left[(x_s - x_t)^2 + y_t^2 + y_s^2 - 2y_s y_t \cos\omega\right]^{1/2}}\right\} d\ell_t \quad . \qquad (11.25)$$

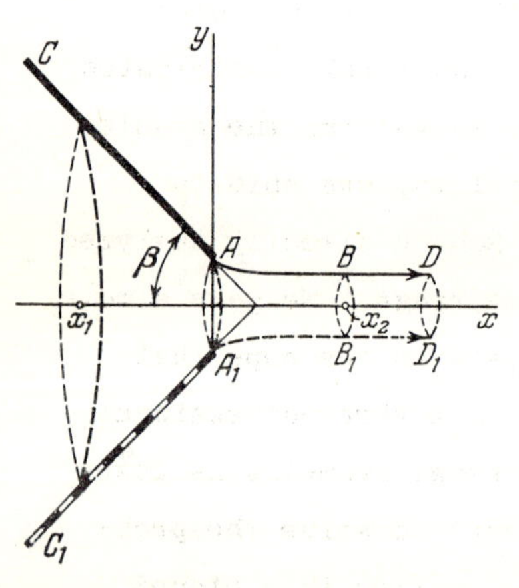

Fig. 242

On the surface of the jet, γ is constant and can be set equal to unity—i.e., $\gamma = 1$. Salamatov, unlike Trefftz, does not bound the flow on the left and right. Instead, he assumes that far enough downstream $(x_t \geqq x_2)$ the shape of the jet is practically cylindrical, while far enough upstream $(x_t \leqq x_1)$ the function $\gamma(x_t)$ is given by

$$\gamma(s_t) = \gamma_1\left(\frac{y_1}{y_t}\right)^2 \quad , \qquad (11.26)$$

where $\gamma_1 = \gamma(x_1)$, $y_1 = y(x_1)$. This equation arises from the continuity condition. Accordingly, the stream function is

*For the source rings the stream function is not single-valued, while for the vortex rings the velocity potential is not single-valued [5, in which additional literature is listed].

split into three parts: $\psi = \psi_1 + \psi_2 + \psi_3$, where ψ_1 is produced by upstream vortices $(x_t < x_1)$ and ψ_3 is produced by downstream vortices $(x_t > x_2)$. The functions ψ_1 and ψ_3 are completely known when the radius y_o of the jet at infinity and the value of γ_1 at point x_1 are known. The function ψ_2, produced by the action of vortices located between x_1 and x_2, is not known. To determine ψ_2, it is sufficient to find the shape of the jet (in $0 \leqq x_t \leqq x_2$) and $\gamma(x_t)$ (in $x_1 \leqq x_t \leqq 0$).

Since CAD (Fig. 242) is a streamline, the boundary condition

$$v_y - v_x \frac{dy}{dx} = 0 \qquad (11.27)$$

must be satisfied there. Salamatov solves the problem by the method of successive approximations; however, his suggested method of selecting the successive approximations is rational, even if its convergence has not been demonstrated. First, the shape of the jet is chosen arbitrarily. From knowledge of its shape we may replace v_y and v_x in the boundary condition Eq. (11.27) by expressions involving the stream function ψ, which is a function of $\gamma(x_t)$. Thus, we obtain an integral equation for $\gamma(x_t)$ in $x_1 \leqq x_t \leqq 0$, which is solved numerically. The values of γ are determined at different specific points on the cone, and the solution of the integral equation is reduced to the solution of a system of linear equations with the unknown values $\gamma_1, \gamma_2, \ldots, \gamma_n$.

Knowing the function ψ, we can find v_x and v_y from Eqs. (11.1). Knowing v_x and v_y, we find dy/dx on the free surface from Eq. (11.27). Then, a second approximation for the shape of the jet is obtained as

$$y = 1 + \int_0^x \frac{dy}{dx}\,dx \quad . \tag{11.28}$$

Once the second jet-shape approximation has been found, the entire process is repeated.

Salamatov computed results for the case $\beta_1 = \pi/4$ and obtained 0.75 as the contraction coefficient of the jet. This result differs only slightly from the contraction coefficient in the plane problem (see Chapter II).

B. A SURVEY OF REFERENCES ON AXISYMMETRIC JET FLOWS

In addition to Trefftz's numerical method, several others have been suggested, to which we refer briefly here.*

Bauer [231] computed an approximation for the drag coefficient of a sphere by summing the pressures on the corresponding front part of a half-body produced by placing a source in a uniform flow. The drag coefficient $C_x = 2X/(\rho\pi R^2 v^2) = 0.27$ (here X is drag, ρ is density, R is the radius of the sphere, and v is the velocity of sphere motion). Earlier, Bauer had found experimentally that this coefficient was 0.3 (Ann. der Physik, 80, 11, 1926).

Garabedian [232] found the drag on a disk in a flow by using the Riabouchinsky model. Garabedian expanded ψ in terms of series of particular solutions of Eq. (11.3). The coefficients of the series were determined so that the average quadratic error in the satisfaction of the boundary conditions was a minimum.

Vandrey [233] solved an axisymmetric Borda-nozzle flow by a finite-difference method, which is based on finite-difference

*Additional references, accompanied by a short survey, are found in Ref. [5].

representations of the equation of motion [Eq. (11.2) or Eq. (11.3)] and the boundary conditions. Using this method, we would find that the computed drag coefficient of a disk is 0.8 [234, Introduction].

The finite-difference equation is also used in the rational method based on the analogy between fluid flow and strain-stress in a membrane. The relaxation method has also been used to solve a whole series of plane- and axisymmetric-jet problems [234, 236].

The electro-hydrodynamic analogy (a method that permits solution of hydrodynamic problems by using an electrolytic tank) has been employed by several investigators (Rouse and Abul-Fetouh, Leclerc). Rouse and Abul-Fetouh [237] used this technique to solve the flow of a circular jet from an infinitely long circular vessel (Fig. 243a). They computed the pressure distribution on the walls of the vessel, the contraction coefficient, and the shape of the jet; then they compared their

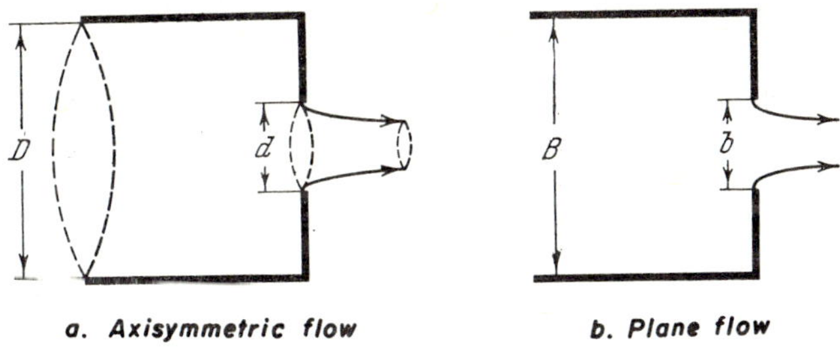

a. *Axisymmetric flow* b. *Plane flow*

Fig. 243

computations with those of Trefftz [227], von Mises [14], Southwell and Vaisey [235], and Kretzschmer [228], as well as the experimental results of Weisbach and others. In particular, for a vessel of infinite width, the jet shapes obtained by Rouse and Abul-Fetouh, Trefftz, Southwell and Vaisey, and Kretzschmer are very similar. From among all the computations in [227] we present only a small sample, Table 30. There the contraction coefficients k_P and k_A for plane and axisymmetric vessels respectively are given for the cases when $b/B = d/D$ (Figs. 243a and b). The data for the plane vessel were taken from von Mises's work. The table clearly indicates that the plane and axisymmetric contraction coefficients are practically identical. Dumitresku [238] determined the contraction coefficient for an axisymmetric flow of a jet from the bottom of an infinitely large axisymmetric vessel. He used an expansion of the velocity potential in a series of Bessel functions and found the first few coefficients of the series approximately.

TABLE 30

$(b/B)^2 = (d/D)^2$	0	0.25	0.50	0.75	1
k_P	0.611	0.644	0.689	0.757	1
k_A	0.612	0.644	0.691	0.757	1

Now we describe a simple method of computing the drag on an axisymmetric body with a jet flowing around it; however, while the method gives good practical results, it is not rationally based on theory.

Figure 244 shows an axisymmetric body in a separated flow. If p_o is the pressure in the cavity behind the body, we easily find that the drag of the body X is

$$X = 2\pi \int_0^{y_1} (p - p_o)\, y\, dy \quad , \tag{11.29}$$

where y is the distance from the axis of symmetry and y_1 is the radius of the base of the body (Fig. 244). We now assume that the pressure distribution p is equal to that on

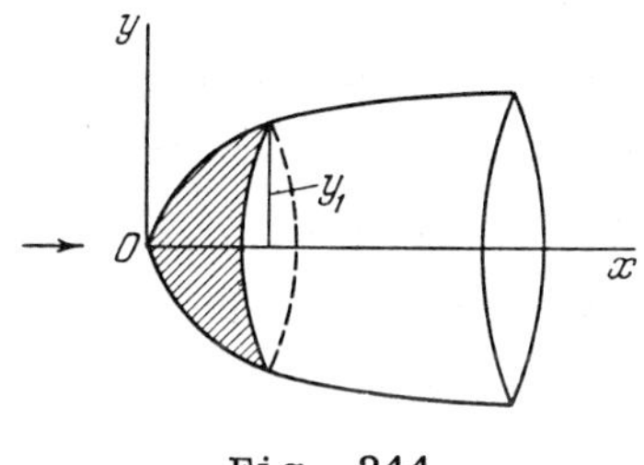

Fig. 244

a plane contour (in a jet flow), the shape of which is the same as that of the meridian section of the axisymmetric body. The drag coefficients $C_x = 2X/(\rho\pi y_1^2 v^2)$ of a sphere and a disk computed in this way were approximately 0.81 and 0.28, respectively [234, Introduction]. Detailed computations for the drag of a cone as a function of cavitation number were made by Plesset and Shaffer [99, 239]. Their results agreed quite well with experiments [239]. The results from [99] for zero cavitation number are given in Table 31. Here, 2β is the included angle of the cone. For a disk, $\beta = 90$ deg. When $\beta > 90$ deg, the flow approaches the interior of a cone.

TABLE 31

β (deg)	C_x	β (deg)	C_x
15	0.2045	105	0.8646
30	0.3758	120	0.9101
45	0.5181	135	0.9442
60	0.6350	150	0.9643
75	0.7296	165	0.9874
90	0.8053		

Birkhoff and Zarantonello [5] also give other approximate results derived from various methods for the drag coefficients of spheres and cones. For example, for the sphere they give Bauer's result $C_x = 0.34$ computed by a method employing sources. The cone results—$C_x = 0.50$ for $\beta = 45$ deg and $C_x = 0.15$ for $\beta = 15$ deg—are also cited. The first of these cone results is too small, however, while the second differs considerably from the results of Plesset and Shaffer.

To this point we have been concerned with only the two classical problems of jet theory: jet flow about a body and jet flow from an orifice. Now we shall discuss problems of a different sort. First, we recall the work of Khmelnik [155, 157], mentioned in Chapter VIII. He studied the jet flow of a thin sheet of fluid on a cone. In his dissertation, Khmelnik formulated a general problem about thin jet flows over a surface, which was based on the work of Golubev [156]. Another formulation of this problem was given by Volterra [240] and Pérès [241]. Volterra sought flows with active inertial forces under which the given surface was a free surface. The flow was extended inside the fluid from the free surface by use of a series. In particular, Volterra investigated a thin, free-fluid sheet and a thin fluid sheet flowing along a solid wall.

An interesting attempt to obtain an exact solution to jet problems was made by Garabedian [242], who wrote the equations for the stream function ψ of a symmetric flow in the form

$$\frac{\partial^2 \psi}{\partial z\, \partial \bar{z}} + \frac{1}{2(z - \bar{z})} \frac{\partial \psi}{\partial z} - \frac{1}{2(z - \bar{z})} \frac{\partial \psi}{\partial \bar{z}} = 0 \quad , \qquad (11.30)$$

where $z = x + iy$ and $\bar{z} = x - iy$. Using Riemann's functions, Garabedian constructed the solution to Eq. (11.2) which possessed the characteristic that the arc of an arbitrary curve is a free streamline in the meridian plane. However, Garabedian was not able to construct interesting physical examples in which the flow region would have a correct form as a whole.

On the other hand, in contrast to the preceding attempts, much progress has been made on the questions of the existence and uniqueness of axisymmetric jet flows. Gilbarg [243] and Serrin [244] built upon the ideas of Lavrentiev [70] and applied them to prove the uniqueness of, and to develop comparison theorems for, basic classes of axisymmetric jet flows. An excellent summary of these and other results is found in [85]. Many of these results were generalized by Gilbarg [243] and Serrin to a compressible fluid flow [245, 246]. The flow in channels was studied also.

Garabedian, Lewy, and Schiffer [247] proved the existence of an axisymmetric flow of the Riabouchinsky type—i.e., where the axisymmetric body is followed by a cavity—bounded by a free surface and closed by a mirror image of the first body. The whole flow is then symmetric with respect to a perpendicular to the longitudinal axis of symmetry x. The existence proof is based on minimizing the expression, obtained in [247],

$$M - (v_o - 1)V \quad ,$$

where M and V are the virtual mass and volume of the "body"—bounded by the surfaces of the real bodies and the free surface of the cavity—v_o is the velocity on the free surface, and the velocity of the approaching flow $v_\infty = 1$. This proof includes, as a special limiting case, the existence of a solution to a Kirchhoff-type flow around an axisymmetric body (infinite cavity).

C. THE ASYMPTOTIC LAW OF JET SHAPE WITH APPLICATIONS

The complete solution to a flow problem is achieved when the velocity potential Φ and the forces acting on the body are found. The calculation of forces can always be carried out by summing the pressure components acting along the surface of the body; however, this summation involves tedious work and, in many cases, no simple computational equation is available. In plane problems the theory of complex variables is available, and in Chapter IV we derived the very useful Levi-Civita equation—Eq. (4.22)—for the resultant force acting on a contour around which fluid is flowing.

Another method may be used to calculate the drag in plane problems. It is known—see Eq. (4.24)—that, in a separated jet flow around a contour, the free surface behind the contour expands to infinity according to a parabolic law. By using the momentum theorem (applied to the mass of fluid confined between the contour, the free surface, and a circle of infinite radius) we can express the drag of the body in terms of a parameter of the parabola. Thus, the drag depends only on the asymptotic law of expansion of the cavity at infinity; the contour's drag is equal then to the drag of a corresponding parabola, which is a half-body with finite drag in a plane.

If we assume for a moment that the free surface of a half-body is frozen, then the pressure on it will not change; we now have a half-body of finite drag. But deforming the front (finite) part of the half-body does not change its total drag because all half-bodies with the same expansion law at infinity have the same drag. Thus, finding a half-body of finite drag is equivalent to finding the law of expansion of the cavity at infinity. While a single, exact solution to a separated flow around an axisymmetric body has not been found, the law of jet expansion at infinity has been determined and the body's drag has been expressed in terms of a parameter on which the law depends [234, 248, and 249].

In [249] the asymptotic jet expansion is found by analyzing the integro-differential equation obtained directly for the jet theory problem. The same asymptotic law for the jet shape at infinity is obtained [234, 248] by constructing a half-body of finite drag. Our discussion below covers the methods employed in these two references. The investigation is divided into three parts. First, axisymmetric bodies with different power-expansion laws are considered, and it is shown that none of these bodies is a half-body with finite drag. Second, the expansion law for an axisymmetric jet of incompressible fluid is found. Third, the influence of compressibility is considered for subsonic gas flow.

We begin with an incompressible fluid and consider the particular solutions to the Laplace equation*

$$\varphi^* = r^n P_n(\cos\theta) = r^n P_n(z) \quad ,$$

where r and θ are polar coordinates in an arbitrarily chosen meridian plane (Fig. 245), $z = \cos\theta$ and $P_n(z)$ is the Legendre function that satisfies**

$$n(n+1)\, P_n(z) = \frac{d}{dz}\left[(z^2-1)\,\frac{dP_n(z)}{dz}\right] . \qquad (11.31)$$

For brevity we will use P_n for $P_n(z)$ below. It is well known that Legendre functions satisfy a series of recurrence formulas

---

*Sedov has suggested using these solutions.

**Legendre functions are discussed in many source books—e.g., see Sagan, H., Boundary and Eigenvalue Problems in Mathematical Physics, Wiley, New York, 1961, or Whittaker, E.T., and Watson, G. N., A Course of Modern Analysis, 4th Ed., Cambridge Univ. Press, London, 1962.

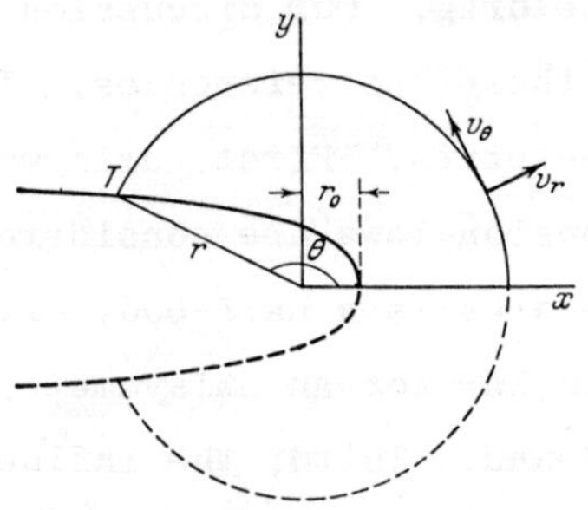

Fig. 245

$$\left.\begin{aligned} &P'_{n+1} - zP'_n = (n+1)P_n \qquad P'_{n+1} - P'_{n-1} = (2n+1)P_n \\ &\frac{(z^2-1)P'_n}{n(1+n)} = \frac{P_{n+1} - P_{n-1}}{2n+1} = \frac{zP_n - P_{n-1}}{1+n} = \frac{P_{n+1} - zP_n}{n} \end{aligned}\right\} . \quad (11.32)$$

In addition to these recurrence relations we also need an expansion of P_n in the neighborhood of $z = -1$. This expansion was found by Hill* as

$$P_n = \frac{\sin n\pi}{\pi} \ln \frac{1+z}{2} + \frac{\sin n\pi}{\pi} [\lambda(n) + \lambda(-n-1) + 2C]$$

$$+ O[(1+z)\ln(1+z)] \quad , \qquad (11.33)$$

where C is the Euler constant, and

$$\lambda(n) = -C - \sum_{k=1}^{\infty} \left(\frac{1}{n+k} - \frac{1}{k}\right) .$$

*See, e.g., Hobson, E. W., The Theory of Spherical and Ellipsoidal Harmonics, Cambridge Univ. Press, London, 1931.

From Eq. (11.33) it follows that if $z \approx -1$, then

$$P_{n-1} - P_n \approx -\frac{2 \sin n\pi}{\pi} \ln \frac{1+z}{2} \tag{11.34}$$

$$P_{n-1} + P_n \approx \frac{\sin n\pi}{\pi} [\lambda(n) + \lambda(-n-1) - \lambda(n-1) - \lambda(-n)]$$

$$= \frac{2 \sin n\pi}{n\pi} \quad . \tag{11.35}$$

Superposing a flow with constant velocity $-v_\infty$, directed in the negative x-direction, on a flow with a velocity potential φ^* produces

$$\varphi = A(r^n P_n - 1) - v_\infty r \cos \theta \quad , \tag{11.36}$$

where A is a constant but is dependent on n. From Eq. (11.36) we obtain the velocity components in the flow

$$\left.\begin{aligned} v_r &= \frac{\partial\varphi}{\partial r} = -\frac{1}{r^2 \sin\theta}\frac{\partial\psi}{\partial\theta} = nAr^{n-1}P_n - v_\infty \cos\theta \\ v_\theta &= \frac{\partial\varphi}{r\,\partial\theta} = \frac{1}{r\sin\theta}\frac{\partial\psi}{\partial r} = -A\sin\theta r^{n-1}P_n' + v_\infty \sin\theta \end{aligned}\right\} . \tag{11.37}$$

The stream function ψ is easily found now from Eq. (11.37) as

$$\psi = \frac{1}{2} v_\infty r^2 \sin^2\theta - A(P_n \cos\theta - P_{n+1}) r^{n+1} \quad . \tag{11.38}$$

The validity of Eq. (11.38) is verified by differentiation and use of the recurrence Eqs. (11.32).

The velocity potential φ, from Eq. (11.36), or the stream function ψ, from Eq. (11.38), determines a flow around some axisymmetric body. In order to find the shape of the body, we shall set $\psi = 0$ in Eq. (11.38); then, by using Eqs. (11.32), we obtain

$$r^{1-n} = \frac{2A}{v_\infty} \frac{P_n z - P_{n+1}}{1 - z^2} = \frac{2A}{v_\infty} \frac{P'_n}{1 + n} .$$

We determine A in terms of the distance r_o from the coordinate origin to the nose of the body. Obviously, at the nose $\theta = 0$ or $z = 1$. On expressing P_n in terms of the hypergeometric function, we have

$$P_n(z) = F\left(n + 1; \quad -n; \quad 1; \quad \frac{1 - z}{2}\right)$$

$$= 1 + \frac{(n + 1)(-n)}{1 \cdot 1} \frac{1 - z}{2} + O[(1 - z)^2] .$$

By differentiating this last equation with respect to z and setting $z = 1$, we find

$$P'_n(1) = \frac{n(n + 1)}{2} , \qquad (11.39)$$

from which

$$A = \frac{v_\infty r_o^{1-n}}{n} . \qquad (11.40)$$

When r_o is finite and $n \neq 0$, A is finite. The case $n = 0$ is examined by using a limiting process in Eq. (11.36) [234, 248]. Chaplygin found that $n = 0$ corresponds to a flow around a paraboloid.

Now we find the asymptotic law of expansion at infinity—i.e., as $z \to -1$. From Hill's expansion, Eq. (11.33), it follows that

$$P'_n \approx \frac{\sin n\pi}{\pi(1 + z)} \quad . \tag{11.41}$$

From Eqs. (11.39) and (11.41) we obtain

$$\frac{r}{r_o} \sim \left[\frac{2 \sin n\pi}{\pi n(1 + n)(1 + z)}\right]^{1/(1-n)} \quad , \tag{11.42}$$

Not all values of n are useful for our purposes. Clearly, when $n \geq 1$, the perturbed velocities do not tend to zero as $r \to \infty$ [cf., Eq. (11.37)]. A special investigation [234] shows that when $n \leq -2$, the considered contour crosses the x-axis more than once (i.e., not only at the nose of the body). Thus, for n to give the class of infinite half-bodies, n is limited to $-2 < n < 1$.

Now, as we go along the body's contour to infinity, $\theta \to \pi$ and $z \to -1$. Therefore, using Cartesian coordinates, we obtain

$$\left.\begin{aligned} r &\approx |x| \\ 1 + z = 1 + \cos\theta &= \frac{\sin^2\theta}{1 - \cos\theta} \approx \frac{y^2}{2|x|^2} \end{aligned}\right\} \quad . \tag{11.43}$$

From Eqs. (11.42) and (11.43),

$$y \approx \left[\frac{4 \sin n\pi r_o^{1-n}}{\pi n(1 + n)}\right]^{1/2} |x|^{(1+n)/2} \quad , \tag{11.44}$$

i.e., the bodies of the considered family expand at infinity according to different power laws.

Next, we compute the drag force. We define an absolute motion as that motion in which the fluid is at rest at infinity and the body moves along the x-axis with a positive velocity

v_∞. The components of the absolute velocity are designated by V with appropriate subscripts. For example, V_x is the x-component of the absolute velocity, V_r is the radial component of the absolute velocity, etc. The velocity components v_r and v_θ introduced above [see Eq. (11.37)] are designated the components of the relative velocity. We now apply the momentum theorem to the mass of fluid bounded by the body and part of a spherical control surface. The front of the body is that portion of the main body which has been cut by the control surface. The drag X of the front is then

$$X = 2\pi r^2 \int_0^\theta (p - p_\infty) \cos\theta \sin\theta \, d\theta$$

$$+ 2\rho\pi r^2 \int_0^\theta (-v_\infty + V_x) v_r \sin\theta \, d\theta \quad . \tag{11.45}$$

Here p is the local pressure, p_∞ is the pressure at infinity, and the integral limit θ is the value of the polar angle θ corresponding to the end of the front part of the body—i.e., to the upper point T at the intersection of the body and the control surface. Because there are no sources in the fluid, we have

$$\int_0^\theta v_r \sin\theta \, d\theta = 0 \quad . \tag{11.46}$$

According to the Lagrange integral,

$$p - p_\infty = \rho v_\infty V_x - \frac{1}{2} \rho \left(V_r^2 + V_\theta^2\right) \quad ,$$

where

$$V_r = v_r + v_\infty \cos\theta \qquad \text{and} \qquad V_\theta = v_\theta - v_\infty \sin\theta \quad .$$

Thus, by using Eq. (11.46), we have from Eq. (11.45)

$$X = \pi r^2 \rho \int_0^\theta \left[\left(V_r^2 - V_\theta^2\right) \cos\theta - 2V_r V_\theta \sin\theta\right] \sin\theta \, d\theta \quad . \tag{11.47}$$

On introducing V_r and V_θ, given by Eq. (11.37), into Eq. (11.47) and replacing $\cos\theta$ by z, we obtain

$$X = -\rho\pi r^{2n} A^2 \int_1^z \left[zn^2 P_n^2 + z(z^2 - 1)P_n'^2 - 2n(z^2 - 1)P_n' P_n\right] dz \quad . \tag{11.48}$$

We evaluate

$$I_{n,m} = \int_1^z \left[z(1 - z^2)P_n' P_m' - nmP_n P_m - (1 - z^2)(nP_n P_m' + mP_m P_n')\right] dz \tag{11.49}$$

and the result is

$$I_{n,m} = -\frac{nm}{n + m}(P_m P_n - P_{m-1} P_{n-1}) \quad . \tag{11.50}$$

When $z = 1$, the right-hand side is 0 because $P_n(1) = 1$. Differentiation of Eq. (11.50) gives

$$\frac{dI_{n,m}}{dz} = -\frac{nm}{n + m}(P_m P_n' + P_m' P_n - P_{m-1} P_{n-1}' - P_{m-1}' P_{n-1}) \quad . \tag{11.51}$$

Using the recurrence relations, Eqs. (11.32), to express P_{n-1}, P_{n-1}', P_{m-1}, and P_{m-1}' in terms of P_n, P_n', P_m, and P_m' leads to

$$P_{n-1} = zP_n + \frac{P'_n}{n}(1 - z^2) ; \qquad P'_{n-1} = zP'_n - nP_n, \ \ldots \ .$$

By introducing these expressions into Eq. (11.51) on the right-hand side, we easily transform it into the form of the integrand in Eq. (11.48). It is now easy to see that the integral in Eq. (11.48) is the same as $-I_{m,n}$. Thus, by putting $n = m$ in Eq. (11.50), we find

$$X = \frac{\pi}{2} \rho r^{2n} A^2 n \left(P^2_{n-1} - P^2_n\right) . \tag{11.52}$$

The asymptotic drag formula of the front part of the body is found as $z \to -1$—i.e., as $\theta \to \pi$. We use the asymptotic expansions of Eqs. (11.34), (11.35), (11.40), and (11.42). After introducing the appropriate values in Eq. (11.52) we have

$$X \approx \frac{\pi}{2} \rho v_\infty^2 r_o^2 \left[\frac{2 \sin n\pi}{\pi n(1 + n)^n (1 + z)^n}\right]^{2/(1-n)} \ln \frac{2}{1 + z} . \tag{11.53}$$

It follows that when $-2 < n < 0$, the drag of the entire half-body $X_\infty = \lim_{z\to -1} X = 0$ and when $0 \leq n < 1$, the drag of the half-body is infinite. Therefore, a half-body with finite drag does not expand at infinity according to a power law, but expands at a rate located somewhere between the rate for half-bodies expanding at $y = O(|x|^{1/2})$ and $y = O(|x|^{1/2-\epsilon})$, where $\epsilon > 0$ and as small as desired.

We seek a half-body with a finite drag among bodies whose flow is given by a velocity potential of the form

$$\varphi = \int_{-N}^{0} a(n)\left(r^n P_n - 1\right) dn - r v_\infty \cos\theta , \tag{11.54}$$

where the constant $N > 0$. Then, we have

$$\left.\begin{aligned} v_r &= \frac{\partial\varphi}{\partial r} = \frac{1}{r^2 \sin\theta}\frac{\partial\psi}{\partial\theta} \\ &= \int_{-N}^{0} na(n)r^{n-1} P_n dn - v_\infty \cos\theta \\ v_\theta &= \frac{\partial\varphi}{r\,\partial\theta} = \frac{1}{r\sin\theta}\frac{\partial\psi}{\partial r} \\ &= -\int_{-N}^{0} a(n)\sin\theta r^{n-1} P'_n dn + v_\infty \sin\theta \end{aligned}\right\} . \qquad (11.55)$$

By using the recurrence Eqs. (11.32), it is easy to find a stream function

$$\psi = \frac{1}{2} v_\infty r^2 \sin^2\theta - \int_{-N}^{0} a(n)r^{n+1}(zP_n - P_{n+1})\, dn \qquad (11.56)$$

that satisfies Eqs. (11.55).

The shape of the body is determined by the equation $\psi = 0$ or, in the expanded form after using the recurrence formulas, by

$$\frac{1}{2} v_\infty r = \int_{-N}^{0} \frac{a(n)r^n P'_n}{1+n} dn \quad . \qquad (11.57)$$

By using Eq. (11.39) we find that the distance r_o from the front of the body to the coordinate origin satisfies the equation

$$v_\infty r_o = \int_{-N}^{0} na(n)r_o^n\, dn \quad . \qquad (11.58)$$

The coefficient $a(n)$ is most conveniently given so that r_o will be finite. If we choose a linear scale so that $r_o = 1$, then

$$v_\infty = \int_{-N}^{0} na(n)\, dn \quad . \qquad (11.59)$$

We place the following conditions on $a(n)$:

1. The integral in Eq. (11.59) converges absolutely.
2. When $-\epsilon \leqq n < 0$, where ϵ is a sufficiently small constant, $a(n)$ does not change sign.

We now find the asymptotic shape of the body at infinity. By introducing P_n' from Eq. (11.41) into Eq. (11.59), we obtain

$$r^{\frac{1+z}{2}} v_\infty \approx \int_{-N}^{0} r^n a(n) \frac{\sin n\pi}{\pi(1+n)}\, dn \quad . \qquad (11.60)$$

Now we must transform this asymptotic equation. We split the interval of integration into two parts: one from $-N$ to $-\epsilon$ and the other from $-\epsilon$ to 0. Then it is intuitively obvious that the asymptotic law, Eq. (11.60), can be replaced by*

$$r^{\frac{1+z}{2}} v_\infty \approx \frac{1}{\pi} \int_{-\epsilon}^{0} r^n a(n) \sin n\pi\, dn \quad . \qquad (11.61)$$

The drag force on the front part of the body is now found by using Eq. (11.47). Introducing into it the absolute velocities $V_r = v_r + v_\infty \cos\theta$ and $V_\theta = v_\theta - v_\infty \sin\theta$, where v_r and v_θ are taken from Eqs. (11.55), and replacing the products of integrals by a double integral gives

*More rigorous reasoning is found in [234] and [248].

$$X = -\rho\pi \int_1^z dz \int_{-N}^0 dn \int_{-N}^0 dm r^{n+m} \Big\{ znma(n)a(m)P_n P_m$$

$$- za(n)a(m)(1 - z^2)P_n'P_m'$$

$$+ (1 - z^2)[na(n)a(m)P_n P_m' + ma(n)a(m)P_m P_n'] \Big\} \quad .$$

By changing the order of integration, we find

$$X = \rho\pi \int_{-N}^0 \int_{-N}^0 dn\, dm r^{n+m} a(n)a(m) I_{n,m} \quad , \qquad (11.62)$$

where $I_{n,m}$ is given by Eq. (11.49). Using Eq. (11.50) gives

$$I_{n,m} = \frac{nm}{2(n + m)} [(P_{m-1} + P_m)(P_{n-1} - P_n) + (P_{n-1} + P_n)(P_{m-1} - P_m)] \; ,$$

from which, together with the asymptotic expansions (11.34) and (11.35), we find

$$I_{n,m} \approx \frac{2}{\pi^2} \sin n\pi \sin m\pi \; \ell n \frac{2}{1 + z} \quad .$$

By introducing this expression for $I_{n,m}$ into the drag Eq. (11.62), we see that the double integral is a product of two equal integrals. Thus, the drag formula becomes

$$X \approx \frac{2\rho}{\pi} \ell n \frac{2}{1 + z} \left(\int_{-N}^0 r^n a(n) \sin n\pi \, dn \right)^2 \quad .$$

It is obvious that this asymptotic expression for X can be replaced by

$$X \approx \frac{2\rho}{\pi} \ln \frac{2}{1 + z} \left(\int_{-\epsilon}^{0} r^{n} a(n) \sin n\pi \, dn \right)^{2} \quad ; \qquad (11.63)$$

the integral in this formula, however, can be evaluated through the use of Eq. (11.61). Thus,

$$X \approx \frac{\pi}{2} \rho v_{\infty}^{2} r^{2} (1 + z)^{2} \ln \frac{2}{1 + z} \quad ,$$

from which, after a change to Cartesian coordinates, according to Eqs. (11.43), we obtain

$$\frac{8X}{\rho \pi v_{\infty}^{2}} \approx \frac{y^{4}}{x^{2}} \ln \frac{x^{2}}{y^{2}} \quad .$$

But the drag of the entire half-body $X_{\infty} = \lim_{x \to -\infty} X$ is, as assumed, finite. Thus, we obtain the following asymptotic law for the jet expansion:

$$\frac{8X_{\infty}}{\rho \pi v_{\infty}^{2}} \approx \frac{y^{4}}{x^{2}} \ln \frac{x^{2}}{y^{2}} \quad , \qquad (11.64)$$

or

$$y \approx \left[\frac{8X_{\infty}}{\rho \pi v_{\infty}^{2}} \right]^{1/4} |x|^{1/2} \left[\ln \frac{x^{2}}{y^{2}} \right]^{-1/4} \quad .$$

It is easily noted that $\ell n\ x^2/y^2 \approx \ell n\ |x|$, and thus we obtain the final asymptotic law in the form*

$$y \approx \left[\frac{8X_\infty}{\rho\pi v_\infty^2}\right]^{1/4} |x|^{1/2}\ [\ell n\ |x|\,]^{-1/4} \tag{11.65}$$

As noted above, our third subject is a compressible fluid flow [234]. Consider a subsonic, ideal, compressible-fluid flow approaching an axisymmetric half-body. We study the case when the pressure p is a function only of the density ρ. Since we are interested only in the flow at infinity (where the perturbation velocities tend to zero) we shall use the linearized equation of continuity. This is not a rigorous approach since we will solve a problem for the

*This same asymptotic law, but with an undetermined constant coefficient C, i.e.,

$$y \approx C|x|^{1/2}\ [\ell n\ |x|\,]^{-1/4} ,$$

can be obtained simply in several different ways. To the author's knowledge, Logvinovich was the first to derive such a result, which he gave in a hydrodynamics seminar at Moscow State University. For this Logvinovich proceeded from the assumption that the cavity behind the body expands at infinity as a result of inertia. Later, the same result was obtained independently by Galin, who considered the cavity a thin body. His report was made in an aero-hydrodynamics seminar at the Institute of Mechanics, Academy of Sciences, USSR. An axisymmetric, thin body in unsteady motion through a gas with separation of the flow at small cavitation numbers was studied by Grigorin in his doctoral dissertation (Moscow State University, 1956).

asymptotic equation, when it would be more correct to solve the more difficult problem: to find the asymptotic solution to the exact equations of gas dynamics.

Neglecting higher-order small terms in Bernoulli's equation, we find that distant from the body

$$\left.\begin{aligned} p - p_\infty &\approx \rho_\infty v_\infty V_x - \frac{\rho_\infty}{2}\left[V_x^2\left(1 - \mathbf{M}_\infty^2\right) + V_y^2 + V_z^2\right] \\ \rho &\approx \rho_\infty\left[1 + \frac{V_x}{v_\infty}\mathbf{M}_\infty^2\right] \end{aligned}\right\} . \qquad (11.66)$$

where p_∞, ρ_∞, and $\mathbf{M}_\infty$ are the pressure, density, and Mach number at infinity.

To determine the drag of the front part of the body, we apply the momentum theorem to a fluid control volume, bounded by the body and a control surface. Obviously,

$$X = \int (p - p_\infty) \cos (n,x) \, dS + \int \rho V_x v_n \, dS \quad , \qquad (11.67)$$

where the integrals are along the control surface, dS is an element of the surface (an elementary ring), and v_n is the component of the relative velocity on the outward normal—i.e.,

$$v_n = (-v_\infty + V_x) \cos (n,x) + V_y \cos (n,y) \quad . \qquad (11.68)$$

From Eqs. (11.67), (11.66), and (11.68) we obtain for a meridian section $z = 0$, where $V_z = 0$,

$$X = \frac{\rho_\infty}{2} \int \left\{\cos (n,x) \left[V_x^2\left(1 - \mathbf{M}_\infty^2\right) - V_y^2\right] + 2V_x V_y \cos (n,y)\right\} dS \quad . \qquad (11.69)$$

We shall choose as a control surface (Fig. 246) an ellipsoid of revolution with semi-axes a and b, where $b = a\left[1 - \mathbf{M}_\infty^2\right]^{-1/2}$. For an ellipse in the plane $z = 0$ (with semi-axis a and b), we obtain

$$\left.\begin{aligned} \cos(n,x) &= b^2 x\left[a^4 y^2 + b^4 x^2\right]^{-1/2} \\ \cos(n,y) &= a^2 y\left[a^4 y^2 + b^4 x^2\right]^{-1/2} \\ dS = 2\pi y\, ds &= 2\pi y\left[dx^2 + dy^2\right]^{1/2} \\ &= -2\pi\left[a^4 y^2 + b^4 x^2\right]^{1/2}\frac{dx}{a^2} \end{aligned}\right\} . \qquad (11.70)$$

The velocity potential Φ of the absolute flow satisfies the asymptotic equation

$$\frac{\partial^2\Phi}{\partial x^2}\left(1 - \mathbf{M}_\infty^2\right) + \frac{\partial^2\Phi}{\partial y^2} + \frac{\partial^2\Phi}{\partial z^2} = 0 . \qquad (11.71)$$

This equation is reduced to the Laplace equation by the substitutions

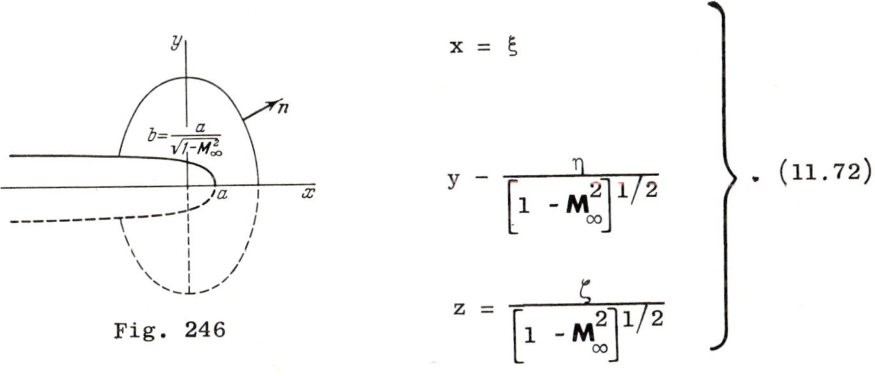

Fig. 246

$$\left.\begin{aligned} x &= \xi \\ y &= \frac{\eta}{\left[1 - \mathbf{M}_\infty^2\right]^{1/2}} \\ z &= \frac{\zeta}{\left[1 - \mathbf{M}_\infty^2\right]^{1/2}} \end{aligned}\right\} . \qquad (11.72)$$

As a result, it follows from Eq. (11.71) that $\Phi(\xi,\eta,\zeta)$ is a harmonic function that can be studied as the potential of some fictitious flow of an incompressible fluid in the space (ξ,η,ζ). The relations between the velocities at corresponding points in the compressible and incompressible flows are given according to the changes of variables Eqs. (11.72) as

$$\left.\begin{aligned} V_x &= \frac{\partial\Phi}{\partial x} = \frac{\partial\Phi}{\partial\xi} = V_\xi \\ V_y &= \frac{\partial\Phi}{\partial y} = \frac{\partial\Phi}{\partial\eta}\left[1 - \mathbf{M}_\infty^2\right]^{1/2} = V_\eta\left[1 - \mathbf{M}_\infty^2\right]^{1/2} \end{aligned}\right\} . \qquad (11.73)$$

Accordingly, from Eqs. (11.40), (11.72), and (11.73), the drag, Eq. (11.68), takes the following form:

$$X = -\pi\rho_\infty \int \left[\xi\left(V_\xi^2 - V_\eta^2\right) + 2V_\xi V_\eta \eta\right] d\xi \quad .$$

We introduce in the plane $\zeta = 0$ of the incompressible flow the polar coordinates $\cos\theta = \xi/r$ and $r = [\xi^2 + \eta^2]^{1/2}$. Then,

$$\xi\left(V_\xi^2 - V_\eta^2\right) + 2V_\xi V_\eta \eta = r\left[\cos\theta\left(V_r^2 - V_\theta^2\right) - 2V_r V_\theta \sin\theta\right] ,$$

from which we obtain

$$X = \pi\rho_\infty r^2 \int \left[\cos\theta\left(V_r^2 - V_\theta^2\right) - 2V_r V_\theta \sin\theta\right] \sin\theta \, d\theta \quad . \qquad (11.74)$$

Let the velocity potential of the absolute fluid flow have the form

$$\Phi = \int_{-N}^{0} a(n)\left[r^n P_n(\cos\theta) - 1\right] dn \quad . \tag{11.75}$$

Since Eqs. (11.47) and (11.74) for the drag X are the same and Eq. (11.75) and (11.54) for the velocity potentials of the absolute and relative motion are equivalent, we have, as above for an incompressible flow,*

$$X \approx \frac{2\rho_\infty}{\pi}\left[\ell n \frac{2}{1+\cos\theta}\right]\left[\int_{-\epsilon}^{0} r^n a(n) \sin n\pi \, dn\right]^2 . \tag{11.76}$$

However, the streamlines in the x- and y-plane deform under transformation to the ξ- and η-plane and do not remain streamlines. We must now express the right-hand side of the asymptotic Eq. (11.76) in terms of the coordinates (x,y) of the half-body in the real flow plane. By neglecting small values of higher order in the streamline equation, we obtain

$$dx = -\frac{V_\infty}{\Phi_y} dy \quad .$$

We now find the asymptotic formula for Φ_y as $-x \to r \to \infty$. It is easy to see that

$$r = \left[x^2 + y^2\left(1 - \mathbf{M}_\infty^2\right)\right]^{1/2} \qquad \frac{\partial r}{\partial y} = \frac{y\left(1 - \mathbf{M}_\infty^2\right)}{r}$$

$$\frac{\partial \cos\theta}{\partial y} = -\frac{x}{r^2}\frac{\partial r}{\partial y} \quad ,$$

*See Eq. (11.63).

from which

$$\Phi_y = \int_{-N}^{0} \left[nr^{n-1} P_n - P_n' \frac{x}{r^2} \right] \frac{y\left(1 - \mathbf{M}_\infty^2\right)}{r} a(n)\, dn$$

or

$$\Phi_y \approx \frac{y\left(1 - \mathbf{M}_\infty^2\right)}{r^2} \int_{-\epsilon}^{0} a(n)\, r^n (nP_n + P_n')\, dn \quad . \qquad (11.77)$$

But, as $\theta \to \pi$,

$$P_n \approx \frac{\sin n\pi}{\pi} \ell n \frac{1 + \cos\theta}{2} \qquad P_n' \approx \frac{\sin n\pi}{\pi(1 + \cos\theta)}$$

and

$$1 + \cos\theta \approx \frac{y^2}{2x^2}\left(1 - \mathbf{M}_\infty^2\right)$$

according to Eqs. (11.33) and (11.41). Thus, it is clear that nP_n is small compared to P_n', and, from Eq. (11.77),

$$v_\infty y\, dy \approx -\frac{2}{\pi} dx \int_{-\epsilon}^{0} a(n)\, r^n \sin n\pi\, dn \quad ,$$

where we use $-x \approx r$ or $1 + n \approx 1$; we find from the above equation that

$$v_\infty \frac{y^2}{2} \approx -\frac{2}{\pi} x \int_{-\epsilon}^{0} a(n)\, r^n \sin n\pi\, dn \quad .$$

Comparing this equality with Eq. (11.76) and, after discarding relatively small terms, we finally find

$$X_\infty = \lim_{x \to -\infty} X \approx \rho_\infty \frac{\pi}{8} v_\infty^2 \frac{y^4}{x^2} \ln \frac{x^2}{y^2} \quad ;$$

this last expression for X_∞ does not depend on $\mathbf{M}_\infty$ and agrees precisely with Eq. (11.64) for an incompressible fluid. Therefore, in the case of subsonic axisymmetric flow, compressibility does not influence the asymptotic law for the jet expansion.

The results are somewhat different in a plane flow. As shown in [234], a half-body of finite drag in a gas, as well as in an incompressible fluid, expands at infinity according to the parabolic law $-2qx \approx y^2$, where q is the parameter of the parabola. However, the drag of such a half-body now depends on the Mach number—i.e.,

$$X_\infty = \frac{\pi}{2} \rho_\infty v_\infty^2 \frac{q}{\left[1 - \mathbf{M}_\infty^2\right]^{1/2}} \quad .$$

If the drag X_∞ is given, then the parameter of the parabola depends on the Mach number—viz., in the plane case compressibility influences the parameter of the asymptotic parabola.

$$X_n = \lim_{\lambda \to \infty} S = [illegible]$$

This last expression for X_n does not depend on [illegible] and agrees precisely with Eq. (7.54) for an incompressible fluid. Therefore, in the case of subsonic [illegible] compressibility does not influence the [illegible] for the jet expansion.

The results are somewhat different [illegible]. As shown in [284], a rigid body of finite size in a gas jet [illegible] in an incompressible fluid [illegible] the particle [illegible] the particles. However, the [illegible] on the [illegible].

[illegible]

If the drag X_n is given, then the [illegible] of the [illegible] depends on the Mach number [illegible]. In the [illegible] case compressibility influences the [illegible].

CHAPTER XII. FLOW OF A HEAVY FLUID AND THE EFFECTS OF SURFACE TENSION

A. EXACT SOLUTIONS

A complete discussion of free-surface flows would include both jet theory and gravity-wave theory. However, because a large, well developed body of characteristic methods and techniques for wave analysis exists as a separate field in hydrodynamics, only those flows of heavy fluids in which surface waves are absent are considered in this chapter. In addition, since jet theory problems are invariably characterized by non-linear boundary conditions, we must first consider the available methods of problem solution before examining any specific problems. We shall assume in the following that the fluid has significant weight and that g denotes the acceleration due to gravity.

For heavy fluids, the continuity equation and wall boundary conditions are the same as for weightless fluids. Given a horizontal x-axis and a vertical y-axis, then, in accordance with the Bernoulli integral, the boundary condition on a free surface where p is constant will be

$$v^2 + 2gy = \text{const.} \tag{12.1}$$

The first work on the jet flow of heavy fluids was done by Zhukovskii [250]. If we transform Eq. (12.1) as Zhukovskii did and then differentiate it, we obtain

$$v\,dv = -g\,dy = -g \sin\theta\,ds = -\frac{g \sin\theta\,d\varphi}{v},$$

where ds is the differential arc length on the free surface. It follows that

$$v^3 = -3g \int \sin\theta \, d\varphi \, . \tag{12.2}$$

By defining

$$\omega = \ln \frac{v_o dz}{dw} = \ln \frac{v_o}{v} + i\theta = \tau + i\theta \, ,$$

where v_o is some constant velocity, we obtain, from Eq. (12.2),

$$\tau = \ln \frac{v_o}{v} = -\frac{1}{3} \ln \left(-\frac{3g}{v_o^3} \int \sin\theta \, d\varphi \right) \tag{12.3}$$

on the free surface. Zhukovskii then mapped the complex potential $w = \varphi + i\psi$ and the variable ω onto the upper half-plane of the parametric variable u so

$$\left. \begin{aligned} \varphi + i\psi &= w(u) \\ \tau + i\theta &= \omega(u) = \Phi(u) + i\Phi_1(u) \end{aligned} \right\} \, . \tag{12.4}$$

Since the boundary conditions $\psi = \text{const.}$ for the complex potential are the same for a heavy fluid as for a weightless fluid, the calculation of $w(u)$ is the same in both cases.

We first assume that all the bounding walls of the flow are rectilinear. This condition is satisfied if $\operatorname{Re} \Phi_1(u) = \text{const.}$ and $\operatorname{Im} \Phi(u) = \text{const.}$ on the walls. We next assume that, on the free surface, $\Phi_1(u)$ is real and $\Phi(u)$ either is entirely real or has an imaginary part equal to $\pm\pi i$. Then we try to choose $\Phi(u)$ and $\Phi_1(u)$ in such a way that they fulfill the boundary condition (12.3).

If the substitution $\Phi_1(u) = -\arcsin[f(u)]$ is made, then we obtain from Eqs. (12.3) and (12.4) the boundary condition on the free surface in the new form

$$\Phi(u) = -\frac{1}{3}\,\ell n\left[\frac{3g}{v_o^3}\int f(u)\,\frac{dw}{du}\,du\right] . \tag{12.5}$$

If we assume that Eq. (12.5) is valid in the entire upper half of the u-plane, then

$$\omega = \tau + i\theta = -\frac{1}{3}\,\ell n\left[\frac{3g}{v_o^3}\int f(u)\,\frac{dw}{du}\,du\right] - i\arcsin f(u) . \tag{12.6}$$

Thus, the problem is reduced to the proper choice of $w(u)$ and $f(u)$.

We can now review Zhukovskii's example [250]. Let

$$\left.\begin{aligned} f(u) &= u \\ w(u) &= \frac{v_o^3}{2g}\,u^2 \end{aligned}\right\} . \tag{12.7}$$

From Eq. (12.6) we have

$$\omega = -\frac{1}{3}\,\ell n\left[\frac{3g}{v_o^3}\int u\,\frac{v_o^3}{g}\,u\,du\right] - i\arcsin u .$$

By choosing the integration constant so that when $u = 1$, $v = v_o$ (i.e., $\tau = 0$, and $\theta = -\pi/2$), we obtain

$$\omega = -\ell n\,u - i\arcsin u , \tag{12.8}$$

or

$$\omega = \ln \frac{v_o dz}{dw} = -\ln u - \ln \left[(1 - u^2)^{1/2} + iu\right] . \quad (12.9)$$

The complex velocity is

$$\frac{dw}{dz} = v_o u \left[(1 - u^2)^{1/2} + iu\right] . \quad (12.10)$$

Our results must now be examined. First we check to see if the general conditions imposed on $\Phi(u)$ and $\Phi_1(u)$ are satisfied. On the positive real u-axis, $\Phi(u) = -\ln u$ is real, while on the negative real axis, $\text{Im}\ \Phi(u) = -\pi$. Finally, $\Phi_1(u) = -\arcsin u$ is real when $|u| \leqq 1$. On this segment of the real axis, boundary condition (12.5) is satisfied. Now we need only to determine whether $\text{Re}\ \Phi_1(u) = \text{const.}$ when $|u| > 1$. With $|u| < 1$ we have

$$\Phi_1(u) = -\arcsin u = i \ln \left[(1 - u^2)^{1/2} + iu\right] .$$

As we pass around the point $u = 1$ in a clockwise direction (Fig. 247), the argument of $(1 - u^2)^{1/2}$ becomes $-\pi/2$; hence $\Phi_1(u) = i\{\ln [u - (u^2 - 1)^{1/2}] + i\pi/2\}$—i.e., $\text{Re}\ \Phi_1 = -\pi/2 = \text{const.}$ In an analogous way it is possible to prove that $\text{Re}\ \Phi_1 = \text{const.}$ for $u < -1$. From the second equation in Eq. (12.7) it follows that the real axis in the u-plane corresponds to the streamline $\psi = 0$ and that this streamline bifurcates at $u = 0$ (see, e.g., Chapter I, Section E or F). From the above, we can conclude that Eqs. (12.7) and (12.8) or (12.9) give the solution to problems in which the real axis segment $-1 \leqq u \leqq 1$ corresponds to the free surface, and the segments $u > 1$ and $u < 1$ correspond to solid rectilinear walls.

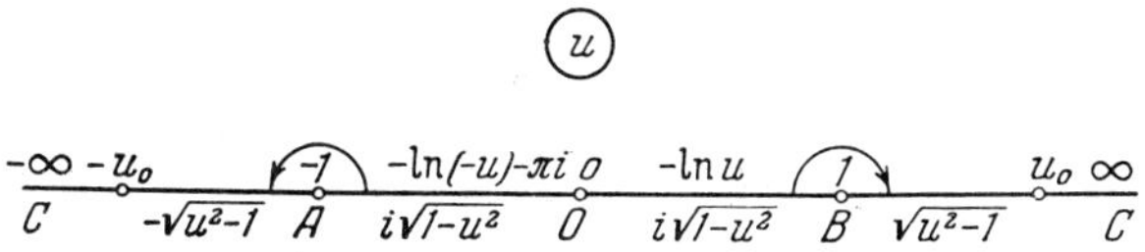

Fig. 247

We are now prepared to study the flow picture in greater detail. From Eq. (12.8) we find that, as u varies from 0 to 1, the angle θ changes from 0 to $-\pi/2$. The corresponding part of the free surface is illustrated in Fig. 248 (curve OB). The parametric equations of the free surface can be easily obtained from Eqs. (12.10) and (12.7), and

$$dz = \frac{dw}{v_o u\,[(1-u^2)^{1/2} + iu]} = \frac{v_o^2}{g}\,du\,[(1-u^2)^{1/2} - iu] \quad . \tag{12.11}$$

But, from the expressions for ω, we see that $\theta = -\arcsin u$, and therefore that

$$dx = -\frac{v_o^2}{g}\cos^2\theta\,d\theta \qquad dy = -\frac{v_o^2}{g}\cos\theta\sin\theta\,d\theta \quad .$$

Hence

$$x = -\frac{v_o^2}{2g}\left[\theta + \frac{\sin 2\theta}{2}\right] \qquad y = -\frac{v_o^2}{2g}\sin^2\theta \quad . \tag{12.12}$$

It follows that, at point $B(\theta = -\pi/2)$,

$$x_B = \frac{v_o^2\pi}{4g} \qquad y_B = -\frac{v_o^2}{2g} \quad .$$

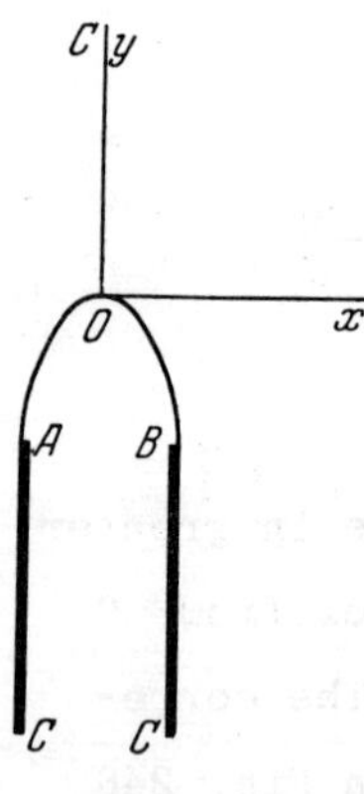

Fig. 248

From Eq. (12.11) for $u > 1$--i.e., on BC--

$$dz = -\frac{iv_o^2}{g}\left[(u^2 - 1)^{1/2} + u\right] du \quad .$$

On integrating this expression, we find that BC represents a vertical wall extending down to infinity. It is not difficult to show that the flow is symmetric with respect to the y-axis. The complete flow picture is illustrated in Fig. 248.

From Eq. (12.10) the complex velocity on BC—i.e., $u \geqq 1$—can be expressed as

$$\frac{dw}{dz} = iv_o u\left[u - (u^2 - 1)^{1/2}\right] = \frac{iv_o u}{u + (u^2 - 1)^{1/2}} \quad . \tag{12.13}$$

From Eq. (12.13) we obtain the absolute value of the velocity $v = |dw/dz| = v_o$ at B. At infinity $(u = \infty)$ we have $dw/dz = iv_o/2$. From the Bernoulli equation it follows that, as we move up or down on the y-axis to infinity, the pressure decreases or increases respectively without limit. Although of interest as the first exact solution of a jet problem for heavy fluids, this example by Zhukovskii is not physically realistic.

Richardson [251] presented a method similar to Zhukovskii's. He gave the complex velocity in the form

$$\frac{dw}{dz} = qe^{-i\theta} = \frac{\mu[G(w)]^{1/3}}{[1 - G'^2(w)]^{1/2} + iG'(w)} \quad . \tag{12.14}$$

If along some streamline the quantities $[G(w)]^{1/3}$, $G'(w)$, and $[1 - G'^2(w)]^{1/2}$ are real and finite, then, from Eq. (12.14), it follows that

$$y = \frac{3}{2\mu} \{C + [G(w)]^{2/3}\} \tag{12.15}$$

and

$$v^2 = \left|\frac{dw}{dz}\right|^2 = \mu^2 [G(w)]^{2/3} \quad . \tag{12.16}$$

By comparing Eqs. (12.15) and (12.16), we find that $v^2 + 2gy = -\mu^2 C$ for $\mu^3 = -3g$—i.e., the condition on the free surface, $p = \text{const.}$, is satisfied. By choosing different functions $G(w)$, Richardson found exact solutions to certain problems; unfortunately, these problems are no less artificial than Zhukovskii's example. In the fourth of Richardson's examples, $G(w) = B + \tanh \alpha w$, where $B > 1$, $\alpha < 1$. Richardson obtained a flow with finite depth and distorted bottom in this case, in which the main defect lies in the deformed bottom.

In addition to the abovementioned works of Zhukovskii and Richardson, the work by Bervi [252] should be considered briefly. In the first part of his work (Chap. VI) a solution is found in the form

$$\left.\begin{aligned} w &= \varphi + i\psi = \int \tau(\tau^2 + \tau'^2)\, du \\ z &= x + iy = k \int (\tau - i\tau')^2\, du \\ &= k \int (\tau^2 - \tau_1'^2)\, du - ik\tau^2 + \text{const.} \end{aligned}\right\} , \tag{12.17}$$

where τ is a function of u. The proper choice of τ gives us the solution to certain as yet undefined problems.

The boundaries of the flow consist of the curves ψ = const. The real axis of u, or those parts of it where τ is real when $k = (2g)^{-1/3}$, corresponds to the free surface. Actually, from (12.17) we have

$$y = -k\tau^2 + \text{const.}$$

$$v^2 = \left(\frac{d\varphi}{ds}\right)^2 = \frac{(d\varphi/du)^2}{(dx/du)^2 + (dy/du)^2} = \frac{\tau^2(\tau^2 + \tau'^2)^2}{(\tau^2 - \tau'^2)^2 + 4\tau^2\tau'^2}\frac{1}{k^2} = \frac{\tau^2}{k^2} .$$

Hence $y = -k^3v^2$ + const., and for $1/k^3 = 2g$ we have $v^2 = -2gy$ + const.—i.e., the boundary condition Eq. (12.1) on the free surface is satisfied.

By choosing $\tau = e^{au}$, where a is a constant, Bervi found the solution to a problem with a rectilinear free surface AO (Fig. 249). The free surface is inclined at an angle of 30 deg to the horizontal. On the right, the free surface is covered with a wall that also has an inclination of 30 deg. Along the wall the pressure is constant, and if we remove the wall we obtain a wave with a 120-deg included angle at the vertex.

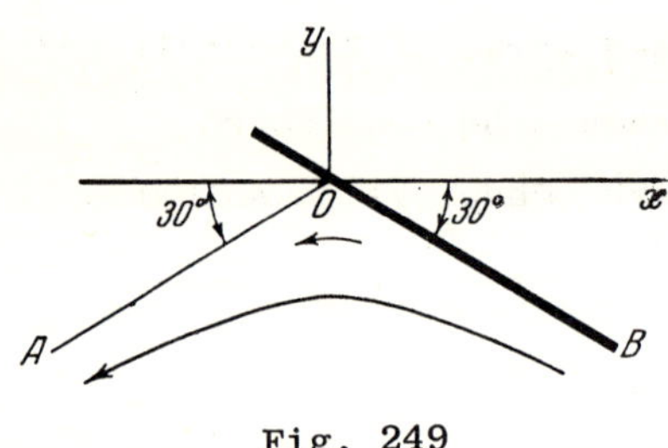

Fig. 249

Richardson [251], obviously without knowing of Bervi's work, obtained a solution to the same problem by putting $G(u) = -w/2$. Any arbitrary streamline below the free surface can be chosen as a bottom (Fig. 249).

In the second part of his work [252, Chap. VII], Bervi solved a group of problems, in particular the Zhukovskii problem discussed above. Bervi's waterfall problem (Fig. 250) deserves special mention. However, as in Richardson's example, the resulting bottom shape is unfortunately complicated. His solution to these problems is given as

$$\left.\begin{aligned} w &= \varphi + i\psi = \ln u \\ z &= x + iy = \int \left[\frac{1}{u^2(c + 2g\tau)} - \left(\frac{d\tau}{du}\right)^2\right]^{1/2} du - i\tau \end{aligned}\right\} . \quad (12.18)$$

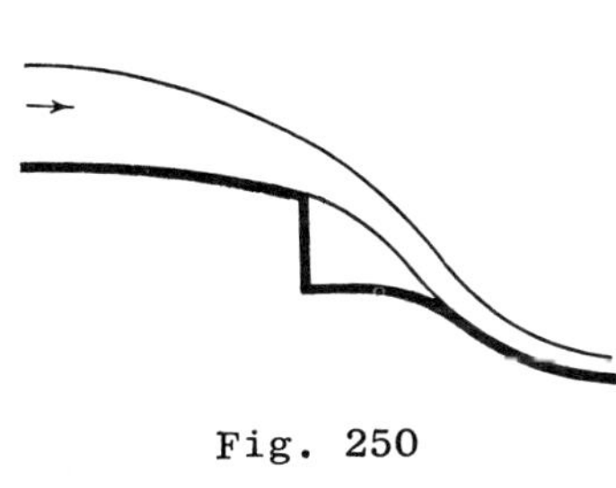

Fig. 250

Here w varies over the horizontal slit $0 \leqq \psi \leqq \pi$, and u varies correspondingly over the upper half-plane. Various solutions are obtained by appropriate choices of $\tau(u)$. It is readily verified that, in those regions of the real u-axis on which $\tau(u)$ is real and the expression under the root is positive, the free-surface boundary condition Eq. (12.1) is satisfied. Bervi gave special attention to the analysis of the singularities of $\tau(u)$ and to the behavior of the function under the integral in Eq. (12.18).

The methods described above solve only a limited number of problems. In the final section of the book it will be shown that certain simple problems of the jet flow of heavy fluids can be solved approximately. Our first concern, however, is with exact methods, and we consider next the action of surface-tension forces. These methods are closely related to those described above, which account for the action of gravity.

B. THE INFLUENCE OF SURFACE TENSION ON FREE SURFACE FLOWS

Only a few investigations, notably by Zhukovskii [250] and McLeod [253], have been carried out on the influence of surface tension in dynamic flows. To isolate the effects, we consider surface-tension force effects on the flow of weightless fluids only.

Assume that at the free surface the pressure in the fluid is p, and the pressure in the air is p_1, both being in equilibrium with the normal force resulting from the cohesion tension in the surface of the fluid. Let α denote the surface tension coefficient [177] and R the radius of curvature of the surface. Then

$$p_1 = p + \frac{\alpha}{R} , \qquad (12.19)$$

where the radius of curvature is considered positive if the center of curvature lies on the air or p_1 side of the surface.

By applying Bernoulli's equation $p = \text{const.} - (\rho v^2/2)$ to Eq. (12.19), Zhukovskii [250] obtained

$$\frac{1}{R} = a + bv^2 , \qquad (12.20)$$

where $a = (p_1 - \text{const.})/\alpha$, $b = \rho/(2\alpha)$. But the radius of curvature can be expressed as $1/R = \pm\, d\theta/dS = \pm\, v d\theta/d\varphi$. Therefore, $d\theta/d\varphi = \pm[(a/v) + bv]$, or

$$\theta = \pm \int \left(\frac{a}{v} + bv\right) d\varphi \quad . \qquad (12.21)$$

In this equation the signs, according to [250], are chosen in the following way: for positive R, plus if θ increases in the direction of flow, minus if θ decreases in the direction of flow; for negative R, the reverse.

As in the case of heavy fluids, Zhukovskii, using Eqs. (12.4), expressed the complex potentials $w = \varphi + i\psi$ and $\omega = \ln\,[v_o dz/dw]$ in terms of u, where u varies over the upper half-plane. On the real u-axis we have $\text{Im}\ w = \text{const.}$

and $\operatorname{Im} \Phi(u) = 0$. On the sections of the real axis corresponding to rectilinear walls, $\operatorname{Re} \Phi_1(u) = \text{const.}$ or $\operatorname{Re} \Phi_1(u) = \pi$; and on the section of the real axis corresponding to the free surface, $\operatorname{Im} \Phi_1(u) = 0$. Furthermore, in accordance with Eq. (12.3) the relation

$$\omega = \Phi(u) \pm i \int \left(\frac{a}{v_o} \exp\left[\Phi(u)\right] + bv_o \exp\left[-\Phi(u)\right] \right) \frac{dw}{du} \, du \tag{12.22}$$

should be satisfied on the free surfaces. Zhukovskii studied an example in which

$$\Phi(u) = -\frac{1}{2} \ln (1 - u^2) \quad . \tag{12.23}$$

Here, by choosing the plus sign in front of the integral in Eq. (12.22), we obtain

$$\omega(u) = -\frac{1}{2} \ln (1 - u^2) + i \int \left[\frac{a}{v_o (1 - u^2)^{1/2}} + bv_o (1 - u^2)^{1/2} \right] \frac{dw}{du} \, du$$

or

$$\omega(u) = -\frac{1}{2} \ln (1 - u^2) - ibv_o \int \frac{u^2 - u_o^2}{(1 - u^2)^{1/2}} \frac{dw}{du} \, du \quad , \tag{12.24}$$

where $u_o^2 = 1 + (a/bv_o^2) > 1$. In [250] it was assumed that

$$\frac{dw}{du} = \frac{1}{bv_o (u^2 - u_o^2)} \tag{12.25}$$

and then Eq. (12.24) gives

$$\omega(u) = \ell n \frac{v_o dz}{dw} = -\frac{1}{2} \ell n (1 - u^2) + i \arccos u$$

$$= -\frac{1}{2} \ell n (1 - u^2) + \ell n [u + i(1 - u^2)^{1/2}] \quad . \tag{12.26}$$

Hence

$$\frac{v_o dz}{dw} = \frac{u}{(1 - u^2)^{1/2}} + i \quad . \tag{12.27}$$

The upper half-plane of the variable u (Fig. 247) corresponds to the right part of a stream that flows between two parallel walls and around the gas bubble AOBO' (Fig. 251). The segment of the real axis $-1 \leqq u \leqq 1$ corresponds to the free surface AOB. On the free surface, according to Eqs. (12.25) and (12.27) for dw/du and $v_o dz/dw$,

$$dx + i\ dy = \frac{du}{bv_o^2} \left[\frac{u}{(1 - u^2)^{1/2}(u^2 - u_o^2)} + \frac{i}{u^2 - u_o^2} \right] ,$$

or since, according to Eq. (12.26), $\theta = \arccos\ u$,

$$bv_o^2\, dx = \frac{\cos\theta\, d\theta}{u_o^2 - \cos^2\theta} \qquad bv_o^2\, dy = \frac{\sin\theta\, d\theta}{u_o^2 - \cos^2\theta} \quad . \tag{12.28}$$

By integrating these expressions for dx and dy, we get the free-surface equation in a parametric form:

$$\left.\begin{aligned} x &= \frac{1}{bv_o^2} \frac{1}{(u_o^2 - 1)^{1/2}} \arctan \frac{\sin\theta}{(u_o^2 - 1)^{1/2}} \\ y &= \frac{1}{bv_o^2} \frac{1}{2u_o} \ln \frac{u_o - \cos\theta}{u_o + \cos\theta} \end{aligned}\right\} . \quad (12.29)$$

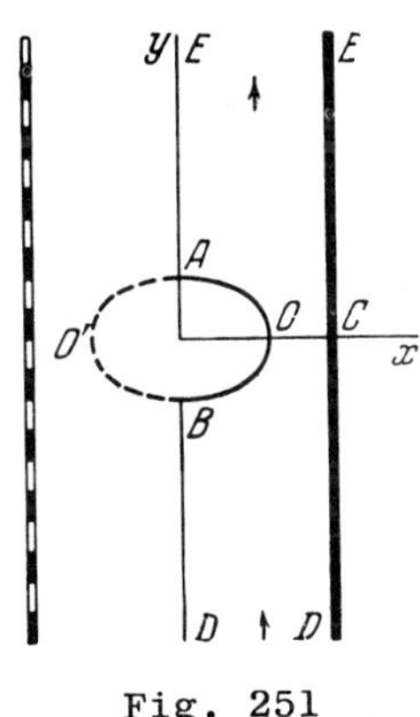

Fig. 251

The following is the correspondence between walls and segments on the real axis: to wall AE, $-u_o < u < -1$; to wall EC, $-\infty < u < -u_o$; to wall CD, $u_o < u < \infty$; to wall BD, $1 < u < u_o$.

By using conformal transformation, McLeod [253] solved the problem of infinite flow around a gas bubble. He mapped the regions of change of the complex potential and

$$q(z) = \frac{\partial z_o}{\partial s} + \lambda \int_{z_o}^{z} \left(\frac{dw}{dt}\right)^2 dt$$

(where z_o is a fixed point on the free surface and λ is a complex constant), onto the exterior of a unit circle in the plane of a parametric variable ζ. As a result, one determines $z(\zeta)$. In addition, McLeod thus reduced a jet-theory problem to a problem in the calculus of variations.

C. APPROXIMATE SOLUTIONS FOR HEAVY FLUID FLOWS

We now return to heavy fluids in which cohesion forces are absent on the free surface. Since 1953, several papers have demonstrated the value of approximate methods for solving problems involving heavy fluids. These methods are better than the known exact ones for solving certain simple practical problems.

Mark [254] solved the following problem: a heavy, ideal, incompressible fluid flows between parallel horizontal walls AC and AOB (Fig. 252). The lower wall AOB coincides with the abscissa x. The upper wall AC ends on the right with the plate CD inclined at an angle α to the x-axis. A jet

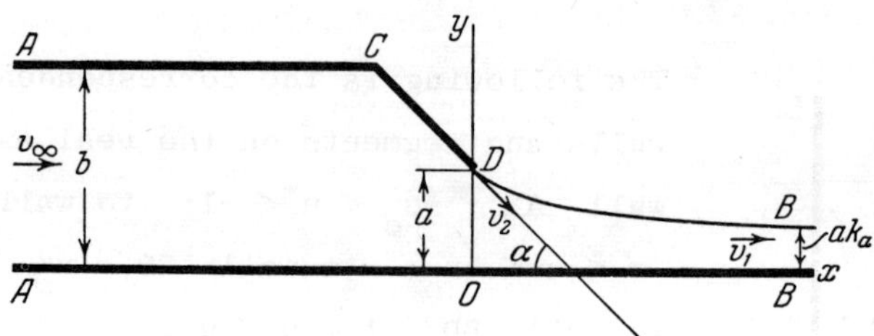

Fig. 252

with the free surface DB flows out from under the inclined plate. The problem is solved by mapping the complex potential plane $w = \varphi + i\psi$ and the complex velocity $dw/dz = v_x - iv_y$ onto the plane of the variable u. The mapping of dw/dz is done approximately. The region of change of the complex velocity is illustrated in Fig. 253. The free surface BD becomes, in this figure, an arc of complex form. The region of change of dw/dz is mapped by

$$\eta = \left(\frac{dw}{dz}\right)^{\pi/2\alpha} \tag{12.30}$$

onto a region (Fig. 254) in which the segments CB and CD are perpendicular to each other. We define the length of segments CB and CD in the η-plane as η_1 and η_2 respectively.

After the transformations

$$\frac{1}{\eta} = \frac{\eta_m}{\eta_1\eta_2}\left(u - \frac{\epsilon}{u}\right), \qquad \eta_m = \frac{\eta_1 + \eta_2}{2} \qquad \text{and} \qquad \epsilon = \frac{\eta_1 - \eta_2}{\eta_1 + \eta_2}, \tag{12.31}$$

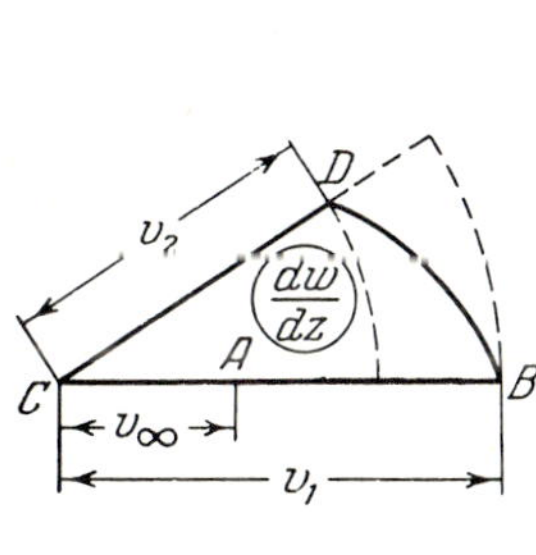

Fig. 253

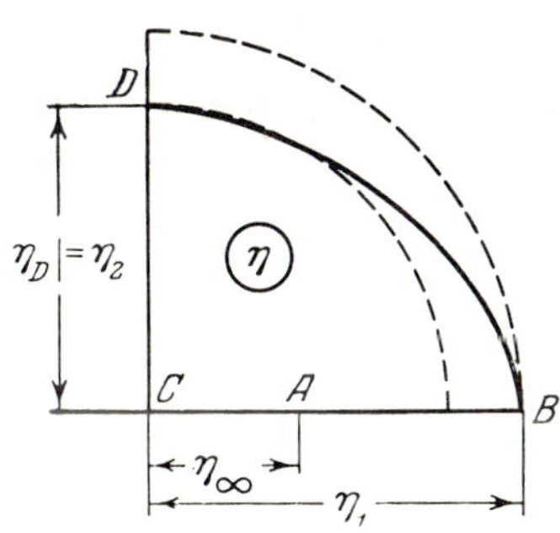

Fig. 254

Mark introduces his approximation by assuming that the arc BD becomes an arc of a circle. Obviously, under the transformations Eqs. (12.31), CB and CD do remain straight, but the point $C(\eta = 0)$ goes to infinity. We must determine the position of the arc BD in the η-plane. To do this we put $u = e^{i\sigma}$ and allow the real variable σ to range from 0 to $\pi/2$. We obtain

$$\frac{1}{\eta} = \frac{\eta_1 + \eta_2}{2\eta_1\eta_2}\left(e^{i\sigma} - \frac{\eta_1 - \eta_2}{\eta_1 + \eta_2}\, e^{-i\sigma}\right) = \frac{1}{\eta_1}\cos\sigma + \frac{i}{\eta_2}\sin\sigma \quad .$$

Under Mark's hypothesis, the arc BD in the η-plane is represented by the inverse of an elliptic arc with semi-axes $1/\eta_1$ and $1/\eta_2$.

The region of change of w is a strip (Fig. 255) of width q, where q is the flowrate. The mapping of this strip onto the lower half of the ζ-plane is given by

$$w = \frac{q}{\pi}\,\ln\frac{\zeta - k^2}{1 - k} \quad , \tag{12.32}$$

where the points $\zeta = k^2$ and $\zeta = 1$ correspond to the points at infinity A (source) and B (sink).

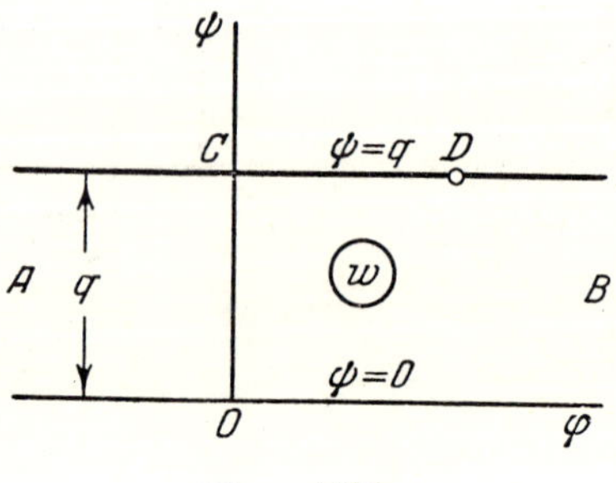

Fig. 255

It is readily verified that the mapping of the lower half of the ζ-plane onto the exterior of a quarter circle in the u-plane can be accomplished by

$$\zeta = \frac{1}{2}\left(u^2 + \frac{1}{u^2}\right) , \tag{12.33}$$

where

$$k^2 = \frac{1}{2}\left(m^2 + \frac{1}{m^2}\right) \qquad m - \frac{\epsilon}{m} = \frac{\eta_1\eta_2}{\eta_m\eta_\infty} \qquad \eta_\infty = v_\infty^{\pi/2\alpha} . \tag{12.34}$$

In the last equations v_∞ is the velocity of the moving jet at infinity—i.e., at $A(u = m)$.

Obviously,

$$z = \int \frac{dw}{dw/dz} + \text{const.}$$

By using the above results we can express z as a function of u by

$$z = \frac{4q(k^2 - 1)}{\pi}\left(\frac{\eta_m}{\eta_1\eta_2}\right)^{2\alpha/\pi}\int \frac{u[u - (\epsilon/u)]^{2\alpha/\pi}(u^2 + 1)\,du}{(u^4 + 1 - 2k^2u^2)(u^2 - 1)} + \text{const.} \tag{12.35}$$

The above equations give the general solution to the stated problem. We must now calculate numerical results; the most important of the unknown quantities is the contraction coefficient of the jet k_a, which is equal to the ratio of the jet width at infinity to the width a of the opening (Fig. 252).

For weightless fluids the flow is completely determined if the following are given: the angle of inclination α of plate CD, the width of the opening a, the distance b between the parallel walls, the difference between the pressure p_∞ under the upper wall at infinity and the pressure p_o at the free surface, and the density ρ of the liquid. The coefficient of contraction k_a is dimensionless and can depend only on dimensionless combinations of the parameters $p_\infty - p_o$, a, b, α. It follows that k_a is a function of only a/b and α. This result is in complete agreement with the results of Chapter II.

For heavy fluids, the acceleration g due to gravity must also be included among the above parameters in accordance with the Bernoulli integral of the boundary condition at the free surface. As a result, for heavy fluids we form another important dimensionless combination $(p_\infty - p_o)/(\rho g b)$, and the contraction coefficient becomes a function of three dimensionless combinations:

$$k_a = f\left(\alpha, \frac{a}{b}, \frac{p_\infty - p_o}{\rho g b}\right).$$

The same result can be obtained from an analysis of the general solution to the problem given above. Mark carried out computations for the case of small ϵ [cf. Eq. (12.31] for $\alpha = \pi/2,\ \pi/4,\ \pi/3,\ \pi/6$ under the condition that $p_\infty - p_o = 0$. The values of the coefficient $\mu = k_a[1 + (ak_a/b)]^{-1/2}$ are given in Table 32. Also presented in that table are the values of the same coefficient obtained from a recomputation of von Mises' results [14], noted previously in Chapter II, Section D, and the results of Gentilini's experiments [255]. The coefficients obtained by von Mises are indicated by μ_1, and the experimental ones by μ_*.

TABLE 32

α	Coeff.	b/a					
		2	3	5	7	10	∞
$\pi/2$	μ	0.536	0.552	0.571	0.581	0.589	0.611
	μ_1	0.560	0.568	0.581	0.589	0.595	0.611
	μ_*	0.547	0.563	0.580	0.590	0.598	---
$\pi/3$	μ	0.578	0.609	0.640	0.654	0.664	0.692
	μ_1	0.608	0.628	0.651	0.662	0.671	0.692
	μ_*	0.583	0.612	0.644	0.659	0.672	---
$\pi/4$	μ	0.614	0.653	0.687	0.704	0.716	0.747
	μ_1	0.641	0.670	0.699	0.712	0.722	0.747
	μ_*	0.615	0.654	0.690	0.708	0.722	---
$\pi/6$	μ	0.654	0.707	0.747	0.765	0.778	0.814
	μ_1	0.687	0.722	0.755	0.770	0.783	0.814
	μ_*	0.659	0.707	0.747	0.767	0.784	---

Independently of Mark, Melkonan [256] solved in an analogous manner the same problem of flow under a plate, but with $\alpha = \pi/2$. In Melkonan's work the region of change of dw/dz was approximated by a quarter of an ellipse, which was mapped onto the interior of a rectangle. The complex potential in the rectangle was constructed by source-sink methods. Mark's method for solving the problem when $\alpha = \pi/2$ was also applied by Benjamin [257], who included some experimental data in his paper.

We turn now to the works of Woronetz [258, 259], who considered jet flows in which gravity has a small, but not negligible, influence. Assume that we have solved some jet problem for weightless fluids by the use of a conformal transformation of the complex potential w_o and $\omega_o = \ln (dz_o/dw_o)$ onto some proper region of change of the parametric variable t. For heavy fluids as for weightless fluids, the boundary conditions require that the imaginary parts of the complex potential be constant along flow boundary lines. Since the boundary conditions for $w(t)$, the complex potential of the heavy fluid flow, and $w_o(t)$, the complex potential of weightless fluid flow, are the same, the two potentials are equal.

For $\omega(t) = \ln (dz/dw)$, the boundary condition on the walls does not differ from the one for $\omega_o(t)$. However, on the free surface the boundary conditions for $\omega(t)$ and $\omega_o(t)$ are different.

Woronetz [258, 259] gives the velocity of the flow of heavy fluids in the form $v = v_o[1 + \delta\lambda(x,y)]$ where v_o is the flow velocity of a weightless fluid (on the free surface, v_o has a constant value), and δ is a small, constant, dimensionless parameter. The Bernoulli integral leads to

$$p = \rho \frac{v^2}{2} + \rho g y = p_o + \rho \frac{v_o^2}{2} + \rho g Y_o \quad . \tag{12.36}$$

where the y-axis is oriented vertically upward, p is the pressure, and p_o is the pressure at the level Y_o. On the free surface the pressure is constant and we have, from the last equation, $v_o^2[1 + \delta\lambda]^2 + 2g(y - Y_o) = v_o^2$, from which, neglecting terms containing δ^2, we obtain

$$\lambda = -\frac{g(y - Y_o)}{\delta v_o^2} \quad . \tag{12.38}$$

If, in lieu of the true function $y(t)$, we take as a first approximation $y_o(t)$ that is obtained from solution of the corresponding problem for weightless fluids, then on the free surface λ becomes a known function of t.

Furthermore, by introducing the notation $\omega = \omega_o + \delta\omega_1$, we obtain on the free surface

$$\omega = \omega_o + \delta\omega_1 = - \ell n\ v_o\ (1 + \delta\lambda) + i\theta \approx - \ell n\ v_o - \delta\lambda + i\theta \quad .$$

Thus, for the determination of the additional function ω_1, we have the following boundary conditions:

1. On those parts of the boundaries of the region t corresponding to solid walls, $\text{Im}\ \omega_1 = 0$.
2. On that part of the boundaries corresponding to the free surface, $\text{Re}\ \omega_1 = -\lambda$.

If we choose the upper half-plane as the region of change of t, then the resulting boundary problem can be solved by using the Keldysh-Sedov formula [4, 24]. Woronetz indicates that it is not always necessary to restrict the problem to a first approximation. By expanding the unknown functions in a series of powers of δ, it is possible to determine successively the higher-order approximations.

As an example of the application of his method, Woronetz solved in first approximation the problem of a jet flowing from a vertical wall (Fig. 256). For weightless fluids, the jet's surface is horizontal at infinity. However, even though the correction for the action of gravity is small everywhere, the jet actually must turn down and fall vertically at infinity. Therefore, the Woronetz theory as applied to this problem can give a representative form of the jet only in the region close to the aperture.

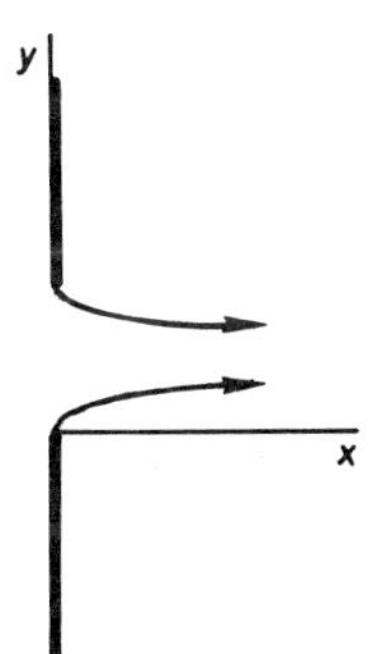

Fig. 256

Mark's problem for the case of $\alpha = \pi/2$ was solved in first approximation using Woronetz's method by Gurevich and Pykhteev [260]. As a numerical example, they solved the problem for the case when $p_\infty - p_o = 0$ and $a/b = 0.161$. Under these conditions the coefficient

$$\mu = k_o[1 + (k_a a/b)]^{-1/2} = 0.574 \quad .$$

This result is in good agreement with Mark's computations presented above.

In general, Woronetz's method is more general and accurate in the first approximation than Mark's. Essentially the latter's method is restricted to the first approximation. However, while in Mark's problem the first approximations found by both methods are equivalent, in Kochin's problem [261] about flow over a channel bottom with a step (Fig. 257), Mark's first approximation is substantially more precise than Woronetz's [260]. In

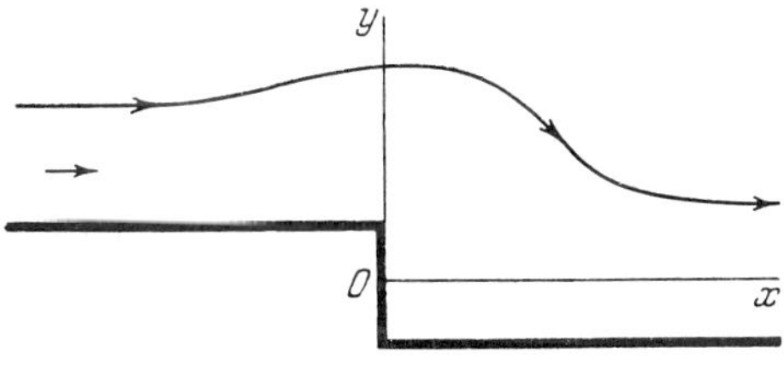

Fig. 257

this case even Kochin's method, which is not discussed here because it deals with linearized wave theory, gives substantially more accurate values of the flow depths and velocities* downstream than does Woronetz's method.

*These quantities can be computed exactly from Bernoulli's integral and the continuity condition.

In Mark's method, to take into account the influence of gravity we have available only one parameter—i.e., the relation of the semi-axes of the bounded ellipse in the plane $1/\eta$. Duisheev [163], in solving the problem of a flow of a fluid over an obstacle, suggested a method in which an unlimited number of parameters are available to satisfy the boundary conditions of the free surface.

A sketch of the flow is shown in Fig. 258. The problem is solved by mapping the region of change of the complex potential w and $\omega = \ln(dw/dz) = \ln v - i\theta$ onto the upper half-plane of the parametric variable t. The correspondence of various points is shown in Figs. 258 and 259.

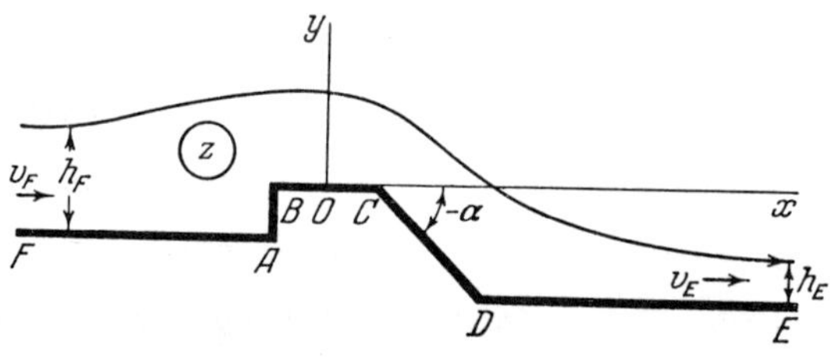

Fig. 258

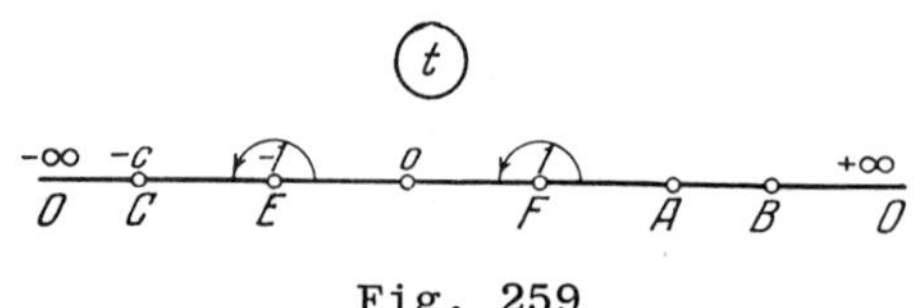

Fig. 259

Obviously, the region of change for w is a strip (Fig. 260) of width q, where q is the discharge of fluid in the flow. The image of this region of change is constructed in an elementary way by placing a source and a sink at points E and $F(t = \pm 1)$. In this way we obtain

$$w = \frac{q}{\pi} \ln \frac{t - 1}{t + 1} \quad . \tag{12.38}$$

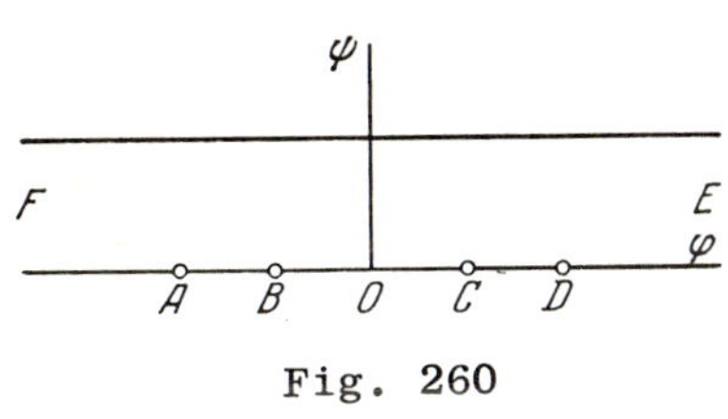

Fig. 260

To find the image of the region of change of ω—i.e., to find $\omega(t)$—we introduce an auxiliary function

$$F(t) = \frac{\omega(t)}{(t^2 - 1)^{1/2}} = \frac{\ln v - i\theta}{(t^2 - 1)^{1/2}} . \tag{12.39}$$

It is easy to see that, on OBAF, the imaginary part of $F(t)$ is known, because on the bottom of the channel the angle $\theta(t)$ is known everywhere, if, of course, the parameters a and b are known (Fig. 259); hence

$$\operatorname{Im} F(t) = -\frac{\theta(t)}{(t^2 - 1)^{1/2}} \qquad (t \geqq 1) . \tag{12.40}$$

As we pass around point F in a counter-clockwise direction on an infinitesimal semicircle (Fig. 259), the argument of $(t^2 - 1)^{1/2}$ increases to $\pi/2$, and because of this, on EOF,

$$\operatorname{Im} F(t) = -\frac{\ln v}{(1 - t^2)^{1/2}} \qquad (-1 \leqq t \leqq 1) . \tag{12.41}$$

Finally, on BCE,

$$\operatorname{Im} F(t) = \frac{\theta(t)}{(t^2 - 1)^{1/2}} \qquad (t \leqq -1) . \tag{12.42}$$

If we know $\ln v(t)$ on the free surface $(-1 \leqq t \leqq 1)$ and the parameters a, b, c, then $F(t)$ is easily determined by using the known solution to the problem of determination of a complex function in the upper half-plane from its given imaginary part [4]:

$$F(t) = \frac{1}{\pi} \int_{-\infty}^{\infty} \frac{\operatorname{Im} F(\xi)\, d\xi}{\xi - t} . \tag{12.43}$$

If we know $F(t)$, it is also possible to determine immediately that $\omega(t) = F(t)(t^2 - 1)^{1/2}$. Duisheev represents $\ell n\ v(\xi)$ on the free surface in the form

$$\ell n\ v(\xi) = \sum_{k=0}^{n} a_k(\xi - 1)^k \quad , \tag{12.44}$$

where $a_o = \ell n\ v_F$ is the logarithm of the velocity at point F, and the coefficients $a_1, a_2, \ldots, a_n$ are unknown real constants. To determine the $n + 1$ constants $a_o, a_1, \ldots, a_n$ and the three constants a, b, and c, with a given* flow-rate q, we have, first of all, three conditions arising from the fact that the dimensions AB, BC, and CD are known. Furthermore, and most important, we need to satisfy the boundary condition Eq. (12.2) on the free surface. In a differential form this condition can be written as

$$v^2 \frac{dv}{d\varphi} = -g \sin \theta \quad . \tag{12.45}$$

Obviously, with a limited number of parameters we can satisfy this condition only at a limited number of points. If we decide to try to solve the problem exactly, then it is worthwhile to express the angle θ in terms of $\ell n\ v$ for $|\xi| < 1$. Then Eq. (12.45) gives an integro-differential equation for the determination of $\ell n\ v(\xi)$.

If we limit ourselves to the approximate solution, as Duisheev did, then in addition to using Eq. (12.45) to determine some of the constants, it is convenient to take advantage

*Instead of the discharge q, we may prescribe some other physical parameter—e.g., the depth of the water at infinity before the obstacle or the velocity of the flow at infinity.

of the Bernoulli integral in its first form, applied at points F and E,

$$\frac{v_F^2}{2} + gh_F = \frac{v_E^2}{2} + gh_E \tag{12.46}$$

and the continuity relation

$$h_F v_F = h_E v_E = q \quad . \tag{12.47}$$

In Eqs. (12.46) and (12.47), h_F and h_E represent the depths of the flow at infinity (Fig. 258). Duisheev found that solutions achieved by his method compared satisfactorily with experimental data.

A method that is quite similiar in concept to Duisheev's is applied very successfully in the monograph by Birkhoff and Zarantonello [5]. Under the guidance of one of the authors, Wilson studied the problem of a symmetric jet flow from an aperture in a plate (Fig. 261). The problem is solved by mapping the region of change of w and dw/dz onto a unit circle in the plane of the parametric variable $\tau(|\tau| \leqq 1;$ $\mathrm{Im}\,\tau \geqq 0)$ in such a way that the plate is mapped onto the diameter of the semicircle and the free surface onto the upper half of the semicircle (Fig. 262). It can be easily seen that

$$w(t) = \frac{q}{\pi} \ell n \frac{\tau + \tau^{-1}}{-2} \quad , \tag{12.48}$$

where q is the flowrate. Because $\zeta(\tau) = dw/dz$ is real on the diameter BCA, we can continue it into the lower half of the circle. At point $C(\tau = 0)$ the velocity is 0 and in the vicinity of C, because of the symmetry of the flow, $\zeta(\tau)$ can be represented inside the circle $|\tau| < 1$ by a series of the form

$$\zeta(\tau) = C_1\tau + C_3\tau^3 + C_5\tau^5 + \dots , \tag{12.49}$$

where C_1, C_3, C_5, ... are real constants. In accordance with Lewy's theorem [262] concerning the analyticity of the free surface of the flow of heavy fluids, $\zeta(\tau)$ is analytic on the

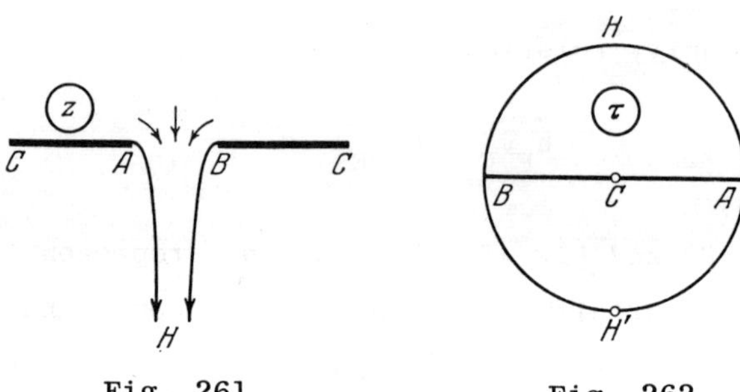

Fig. 261

Fig. 262

circumference $\tau = e^{i\sigma}$ of the unit circle except at the separation points of the jet $\tau = \pm 1$ and the points $\tau = \pm i$ at which $\zeta(\tau)$ is infinite. Since the jet, during its fall toward infinity, becomes vanishingly thin, we must have asymptotically, in the vicinity of H,

$$\frac{dw}{dz} = \zeta = i(2giz)^{1/2} .$$

Thus,

$$w = \int i(2giz)^{1/2} dz = \frac{(8g)^{1/2}}{3}(iz)^{3/2} \qquad z \approx -i\left[\frac{3w}{(8g)^{1/2}}\right]^{2/3} .$$

In the vicinity of H the complex potential, in accordance with Eq. (12.48), is of the order of $\ln(1 + i\tau)$ (a sink). Therefore, near H,

$$\zeta = i(2giz)^{1/2} = O(w^{1/3}) = O\{[\ln(1 + i\tau)]^{1/3}\} . \tag{12.50}$$

At $H'(\tau = -i)$, in accordance with the principle of symmetry, ζ is of the order of $[\ell n\ (1 - i\tau)]^{1/3}$. As a result of this analysis of the singularities of $\zeta(t)$, it is possible to set

$$\zeta = \tau[-\ell n\ C(1 + \tau^2)]^{1/3}\ e^{\Omega(\tau)}\ , \qquad (12.51)$$

where C is a real constant between 0 and 0.5 and $\Omega(\tau) = \Omega(\tau, C)$ can be represented in the series form

$$\Omega(\tau) = a_o + a_2\tau^2 + a_4\tau^4 + \ldots$$

inside the unit circle $|\tau| < 1$. By using the expression for the imaginary part of a function of complex variable in terms of its real part, we can, in a manner analogous to that used in Chapter IV, Section C, obtain from Eq. (12.45) an integro-differential equation for $d[\mathrm{Re}\ \Omega]/d\sigma$ on the circumference $\tau = e^{i\sigma}$.

To conclude, we remark that in a new, as yet unpublished work, Pykhteev, in considering Mark's problem, also arrives at a nonlinear integro-differential equation, which he has solved by the method of decomposition by a parameter. In addition, Pykhteev proves the existence and uniqueness of his solution.*

---

*Translator's Note: Additional work on the subject of this chapter has been accomplished by Professor Gurevich: M. I. Gurevich, "Influence of Capillary Forces upon the Coefficient of Contraction of a Jet," J. Appl. Math. Mech., 25, 6 (1961).

M. I. Gurevich and G. N. Pykhteev, "Approximate Solution of the Problem of Flow of a Heavy Ideal Incompressible Fluid from under a Sluice Gate," PMTF (Akad. Nauk), 2, 1960, pp. 3-14.

REFERENCES

1. N. E. Kochin, I. A. Kibel, N. V. Roze, Theoretical Hydromechanics, 5th ed., trans by Boyanovitch, Interscience Publishers, New York, 1964.
2. H. Lamb, Hydrodynamics, 6th ed., Dover Publications, New York, 1945.
3. I. I. Privalov, Introduction to the Theory of Functions of a Complex Variable, 6th ed., Moscow, 1940.
4. M. A. Lavrentiev and B. V. Shabat, The Methods in the Theory of Functions of Complex Variables, 2nd ed., Fizmatgiz, Moscow, 1958.
5. G. Birkhoff and E. H. Zarantonello, Jets, Wakes, and Cavities, Academic Press, New York, 1957.
6. S. A. Chaplygin, Gas Jets, Scientific Memoirs, Moscow Univ., 1962; trans. as NACA TM 1063, 1944; also in Collected Works, Vol. II, Gostekhizdat, Moscow, 1948.
7. G. Kirchhoff, J. reine u. angew. Math., 70, 1869, pp. 289-298.
8. G. Kirchhoff, Vorles. über Math. Phys., 21, V, 1876.
9. H. Helmholtz, Monatsber. Berlin Akad., 1868, pp. 215-228; reprinted in Phil. Mag., 36, 1868, pp. 337-346, and in Wiss. Abh., 1, 1882.
10. N. E. Zhukovskii, Math. Coll., 15, 1890; also Collected Works, 2, 3, Gostekhizdat, Moscow, 1949.
11. J. Michell, Phil. Trans. Roy. Soc. Lond., Ser. A, 181, 1890, pp. 389-431.
12. V. V. Golubev, Trudy Tsent. AGI, No. 393, 1940.
13. Lord Rayleigh, Phil. Mag., II, Ser. 5, 1876.
14. R. von Mises, Zeits., Ver. dtsch. Ing., 61, 21, 1917.
15. K. Pearson, Tables of Incomplete Beta Function, Cambridge University Press, London, 1934.
16. I. M. Konovalov, "Opredelenie szhatiya strui ...," Trudy Leningrad for Water-Transport. Engineering, No. 15, 1949.

17. I. M. Konovalov, "Opredelenie koeffitsienta ...," Trudy Leningrad for Water-Transport. Engineering, No. 15, 1949.

18. V. N. Taliev, Doklady Akad. Nauk SSSR, **94**, 4, 1954.

19. S. N. Numerov, Paper No. 2385, J. Papers in Mechanics, **5**, May 1955, p. 36.

20. D. K. Bobylev, J. Russ. Phys-Chem. Soc., **13**, 63, 1881.

21. M. Rethy, Ann. Math., **46**, 1895, pp. 249-272.

22. Gerlach, Civilingenieur, **31**, 1885.

23. I. V. Meshcherskii, J. Russ. Phys-Chem. Soc., **18**, 1886.

24. L. I. Sedov, Two-Dimensional Problems in Hydrodynamics and Aerodynamics, Interscience Publishers, 1965.

25. P. W. Ketchum, Q. Appl. Math., **1**, 2, Jul 1943.

26. G. H. Bryan and R. Jones, Proc. Roy. Soc. Lond., Ser. A, **91** A630, Jun 1918, pp. 354-369.

27. V. P. Alekseevskii, J. Appl. Math. and Mech., **22**, 6, 1958.

28. E. P. Borisova, P. P. Koriavov, N. N. Moiseev, J. Appl. Math. and Mech., **23**, 2, 1959.

29. S. A. Chaplygin, Collected Works, Vol. 1, Gostekhizdat, Moscow, 1948, pp. 5-18.

30. V. I. Smirnov, A Course in Higher Mathematics, Vol 3, Ch. 2, Gostekhizdat, Moscow, 1951.

31. T. Levi-Civita, Rend. Circ. Mat., Palermo, **23**, 1, 1907, pp. 1-37.

32. S. A. Chaplygin and A. L. Lavrentiev, Trudy Tsent. AGI, 123, 1933.

33. Ya. I. Serkerzh-Zenkovich, Trudy Tsent. AGI, 170, 1934.

34. R. V. Churchill, Complex Variables and Applications, 2nd ed., McGraw-Hill Book Co., Inc., New York, 1960.

35. Lord Kelvin, Mathematical and Physical Papers, Vol. IV, Cambridge University Press, London, 1910; also in Nature, **50**, 1894.

36. H. Villat, Lecons sur l'hydrodynamique, Paris, 1929.

37. I. M. Belenkii and E. K. Zelenskii, Khark. Aviats. In.-T., 1936.

38. V. M. Abramov, Trudy, the Math. Congress, **II**, 1934.

39. E. V. Zarantonello, J. math. pures et appl., **33**, 1, 1954.

40. H. Villat, Annales de l'Ecole Normale Super. (3), **28**, 1911.

41. S. A. Chaplygin, Trudy Tsent. AGI, 240, 1935.

42. V. V. Golybev, Lectures on Wing Theory, Gostekhizdat, Moscow, 1949.

43. G. I. Taylor, Phil. Trans. Roy. Soc. Lond., Ser. A., 225, 1925.

44. M. Brillouin, Annales de chim. et phys., 23, 1911, pp. 145-230.

45. H. Villat, J. math pures et appl., 10, 1914.

46. C. Jacob, Mathematica, 11, 1935, pp. 149-175.

47. S. Brodetsky, Proc. Roy Soc. Lond., Ser. A, 102, A718, 1923.

48. C. Schmieden, Ingr.-Arch., 1, 1, 1929, pp. 104-109.

49. G. Darboux, Lecons sur la theorie generale des surfaces, Paris, 1894.

50. L. Rosenhead, Proc. Roy. Soc. Lond., Ser. A, 117, 777, 1928.

51. U. Cisotti, Idromeccanica piana, Milano, 1, 1921; 2, 1922.

52. A. I. Nekrasov, Izv. Inst. Ivan Voznesensk, Politekh. 5 (Math issue), 1922.

53. Ya. I. Serkerzh-Zenkovich, Trudy Tsent. AGI, 299, 1937.

54. P. P. Kufarev, Prikl. Mat. Mekh., 16, 5, 1952.

55. A. Weinstein, Compt. rend. Acad. Sci., 196, 5, Paris, 1933.

56. Ya. I. Serkerzh-Zenkovich, Trudy Tsent. AGI, 354, 1938.

57. A. Weinstein, "Sur les jets...," Rend. R. Accad. Lincei, 1926.

58. A. Weinstein, "Sur le theoreme d'existence...," Rend. R. Accad. Lincci, 1926.

59. A. Weinstein, Proc. Symp. Appl. Math., Vol I, New York, 1949.

60. R. Finn, J. d'Anal. Math., 4, 2, 1956, pp. 246-291.

61. K. Friedrichs, Math. Ann., 109, 1933/34, pp. 60-82.

62. D. Riabouchinsky, Compt. rend., 185, 1927, Paris, pp. 840-841.

63. J. Leray, Comm. Math. Hel., 8, 2, 3, 1935-36.

64. M. A. Lavrentiev, Mat. Sbornik, New Series, 4(46), 3, 1938, pp. 391-458.

65. J. Leray and J. Schauder, Ann. Sci. de l'Ecole Normale Super., 51, 1934, pp. 45-78.

66. N. I. Muskhelishvili, Singular Integral Equations, trans. by Radok, P. Noordhoff, Holland, 1953.

67. J. Kravtchenko, J. math. pures et appl., Ser. 9e, 20, 1941, pp. 35-239.

68. A. Oudart, J. math. pures et appl., 22, 1943; 23, 1944.

69. J. Kravtchenko, Ann. Sci. de l'Ecole Normale Super., Ser. 3e, 63, 1, 1946; 62, 1945.

70. M. A. Lavrentiev, Trudy Steklov Phys.-Mat. Inst., AN SSSR, 5, 1934, pp. 159-246.

71. L. I. Sedov, Trudy Tsent. AGI, 342, 1938, (Teoret. Sbornik Tsent AGI, 5).

72. G. N. Pykhteev, Prikl. Mat. Mekh., 19, 4, 1955.

73. G. N. Pykhteev, Prikl. Mat. Mekh., 20, 3, 1956.

74. G. N. Pykhteev, Doklady Akad. Nauk SSSR, 108, 1, 1956.

75. L. A. Epshtein, Zhur. Tekh. Fiz., 6, 1946.

76. S. W. Barnaby, Trans. Inst. Naval Arch., 1897.

77. A. Betz and E. Petersohn, Ingr.-Arch., 2, 1931, pp. 190-211.

78. O. Walchner, Hydromech. Prob. des Schiffsantriebs (conference), Hamburg, 1932.

79. L. Prandtl, Essentials of Fluid Dynamics, Hafner Publishing Co., New York (Blackie & Son, Glasgow), 1952.

80. L. Prandtl and Q. G. Tietjens, Hydro- and Aeromechanics, 2 vols., Dover Publications, New York, 1957.

81. G. Birkhoff, Hydrodynamics, A Study in Logic, Fact, and Similitude, 2nd ed., Princeton University Press, 1962.

82. R. Eppler, J. Rational Mech. and Analysis, 3, 1954, pp. 591-644.

83. M. Kolscher, Luftfahrforsch, 17, 5, May 1940.

84. D. A. Efros, Doklady Akad. Nauk SSSR, 51, 4, 1946, pp. 267-270.

85. D. Gilbarg, "Jets and Cavities," Handbuch der Physik, 9, Springer, Berlin, 1960.

86. M. I. Gurevich, Trudy Tsent. AGI, 612, 1947.

87. M. I. Gurevich, Izv. Akad. Nauk SSSR, OTN, 2, 1947.

88. A. Betz, Proc. Third Intern, Congr. Appl. Mech., Stockholm, 1930.

89. L. A. Epshtein, Trudy Tsent. AGI, 1950.

90. L. C. Woods, Proc. Roy. Soc. Lond., Ser. A., 227, 1170, 1955, pp. 367-386.

91. I. Mimura, J. Phys. Soc. Japan, 13, 11, 1958.

92. D. Riabouchinsky, Proc. Lond. Math. Soc., 19, Ser. 2, 1920, pp. 206-215.

93. F. Weinig, Hydromech. Prob. des Schiffsantriebs (Conference), Hamburg, 1932.

94. B. Demtchenko, Compt. rend. 3rd Int. Congr. Mech. Appl., Stockholm, 1930.

95. D. Gilbarg and J. Serrin, J. Math. Phys., 29, 1, 1950, pp. 1-12.

96. D. Gilbarg, Proc. Nat. Acad. Sci., 35, 1949.

97. A. Roshko, J. Aero Sci., 22, 2, 1955.

98. M. I. Gurevich, Proc. of A. I. Mikoyan Moscow Tech. Inst. of Fishing Indus. and Econ., V, 1953.

99. M. S. Plesset and P. A. Shaffer, J. Appl. Phys., 19, 10, 1948, pp. 934-939.

100. A. D. Cox and W. A. Clayden, J. Fluid Mech., 3, 6, 1958, pp. 615-637.

101. D. A. Efros, Izv. Akad. Nauk SSSR, OTN, 9, 1947.

102. J. Serrin, J. Rational Mech. and Analysis, 1, 1952, pp. 1-48.

103. T. Y.-t. Wu, J. Math. Phys., 35, 3, 1956, pp. 236-265.

104. I. Mimura, J. Phys. Soc. Japan, 13, 9, 1958.

105. A. Fage and F. C. Johansen, Proc. Roy. Soc. Lond., Ser. A, 116, 773, 1927, pp. 170-197.

106. G. Birkhoff, M. Plesset, and N. Simmons, Part I, Q. Appl. Math., 8, 2, 1950; Part II, Q. Appl. Math., 9, 4, 1952.

107. A. P. Kotelnikov, Proc. Sec. on Phys.-Mat. Nauk Kazan, 8, 1889.

108. J. Bonder, Ann. Acad. Sci. Tech. Warsaw, III, 1936.

109. S. A. Chaplygin and A. P. Minakov, (Suppl. to 3rd vol. Collected Works Zhukovskii), Trudy Tsent. AGI, 41, 1930.

110. G. F. Proskura, Hydrodynamics of Turbo-Machinery, 1954.

111. N. V. Lambin, Prikl. Mat. Mekh., 8, 3, 1944.

112. M. G. Ernst, Techn. et Sci. Aeronaut., 2, 1953.

113. N. I. Akhiezer, Nauch. Zap. KhAI, 2, 1934.

114. I. M. Belenkii and E. K. Zelenskii, Prikl. Mat. Mekh., 1, 2, 1937.

115. G. Yu. Stepanov, Prikl. Mat. Mekh., 17, 5, 1953.

116. Ya. R. Berman, Prikl. Mat. Mekh., 13, 5, 1949.

117. G. Birkhoff, H. H. Goldstine, and E. H. Zarantonello, Rend. Sem. Mat. Univ. Politec. Torino, 13, 1953.

118. M. I. Gurevich, Izv. Akad. Nauk SSSR, OTN, 4, 1946; also Rensselaer Polytechnic Institute Math. Trans. 4, 1959.

119. H. Cohen and R. Gilbert, J. Appl. Mech., 24, 2, 1957.

120. M. P. Tulin, J. Ship Res., 7, 3, Jan 1964, pp. 16-37.

121. L. I. Sedov, Trudy Tsent. AGI, 252, 1936.

122. L. I. Sedov, Proc. Conf. on Wave Resistance, Izd. Ts AGI, 1937.

123. H. Wagner, Z. angew. Math. u. Mech., 12, 4, 1932, pp. 193-215.

123a. M. I. Gurevich and A. R. Yanpolskii, Tekhnika Vozdushnovo Flota, 10, Dekabr, 1933.

124. Handbook of Aviation Construction, Vol. II, Hydroplane Hydromechanics, Moscow, 1938.

125. N. Kalinin, Study Notes, Saratovsk State University, 1, (14), Ser. FMI, 1, 1938.

126. M. I. Gurevich, Tekh. Zametki Tsent. AGI, 48, 1935.

127. A. E. Green, Proc. Cambridge Phil. Soc., 31, 1935, p. 4; 32, 1936, p. 1; 34, 1938, p. 2.

128. Yu. S. Chaplygin, Prikl. Mat. Mekh., 5, 2, 1941.

129. E. T. Whittaker and G. N. Watson, A Course of Modern Analysis, 4th ed., Cambridge University Press, London, 1962.

130. F. Weinig, Zur theorie des Unterwassertragflugels und der Gleitflache, luftfahrtforschung (Ser. 314), 1937.

131. A. Franke, Z. angew, Math. u. Mech., 18, 3, 1938.

132. Voight, Math. Annal., 28, 1886.

133. U. Cisotti, Ann. di mat. pura ed appl., Milano, 23, 1914.

134. Boggio, Atti della Accad. di Torino, 50, 1915.

135. Caldonazzo, Ann. di mat. pura ed appl., Milano, 26, 1916.

136. Caldonazzo, Rend. del Reale Instituto Lombardo, 52, 1919.

137. A. Palatini, Atti. del R. Instituto Venetto di Sc. L. ed. Arti, 75, 1916.

138. G. Birkhoff, D. P. MacDougall, E. Pugh, and G. Taylor, J. Appl. Phys., 19, 1948.

139. V. Ivanova and V. Rozantseva, Mekhanika, 4, 20, 1953.

140. M. A. Lavrentiev, Progress in Math. Sci. (Russ), 12, 4, Jul-Aug 1957, p. 76.

141. B. Hopkinson, Proc. Lond. Math. Soc., 29, 1898.

142. N. Simmons, Q. J. Math. Oxford, Dec 1939.

143. N. Simmons, Phil. Mag. and J. Sci. (7s), 31, 205, Feb 1941.

144. A. A. Nikolskii, Prikl. Mat. Mekh., 8, 6, 1944.

145. L. C. Woods, Proc. Roy. Soc. Lond., Ser. A, 229, 1177, 1955.

146. L. G. Whitehead, Aero. Res. Coun. Rep. and Memo. No. 2802, London, Jun 1950.

147. G. Greenhill, Aero. Res. Coun. Rep. and Memo No. 19, London, 1910.

148. F. F. Ehrich, J. Aero. Sci., 20, 2, Feb 1953.

149. C. Schmieden, Z. angew. Math. u. Mech., 12, 5, Oct. 1932.

150. N. T. Nazarov, Trudy Kuibyshevskovo Inh.-Stpoitel. In-ta., 3, 1956.

151. J. C. Gibbings and J. R. Dixon, Q. J. Mech. Appl. Math., 10, Pt. 1, Oxford, Feb 1957.

152. B. A. Lighthill, Aero. Res. Coun. Rep. and Memo. No. 2105, London, Sep 1945.

153. L. C. Woods, Q. J. Mech. Appl. Math., 7, 3, 1954.

154. J. B. Keller, J. Appl. Phys., 28, 8, Aug. 1957.

155. M. I. Khmelnik, "Nekotorye..," Lecture Notes MOPI, J. Dept. Theo. Phys., 75, 4, 1958.

156. O. V. Golubev, Lecture Notes MOPI, J. Dept. Theo. Phys., 18, 2, 1951.

157. M. I. Khmelnik, "Struinse...," Lecture Notes MOPI, J. Dept. Theo. Phys., 75, 4, 1958.

158. F. Weining, Ingr.-Arch., 11, 4, 1940.

159. T. von Karman, Annali di math. pura ed appl., 29, S4, 1949.

160. D. Gilbarg, Z. angew. Math. u. Phys., 3, 1, 1952.

161. L. C. Woods, Aero. Res. Coun. Curr. Pap. No. 149, 1954.

162. M. I. Gurevich, Prikl. Mat. Mekh., 16, 1, 1952.

163. E. Duisheev, Izv. Vyssh. Uchebn. Zavedenii, Matem., 2(3), 1958.

164. Ya. R. Berman, Prikl. Mat. Mekh., 20, 3, 1956.

165. S. I. Parkhomovskii, J. App. Math. Mech., 22, 4, 1958.

166. S. I. Parkhomovskii, Prikl. Mekh., 4, 4, 1958.

167. S. I. Parkhomovskii, Izv. Vyssh. Uchebn. Zav., Mat., 6(7), 1958.

168. S. I. Parkhomovskii, J. Appl. Math. Mech., 23, 3, 1959.

169. G. Birhoff, Q. Appl. Math., 10, 1, Apr 1952.

170. J. L. Fox and G. W. Morgan, Q. Appl. Math., 11, 4, 1954.

171. M. I. Gurevich and M. D. Khaskind, Prikl. Mat. Mekh., 17, 5, 1953.

172. L. C. Woods, Proc. Roy. Soc. Lond., Ser. A., Math. Phys. Sci., 229, 1177, Apr. 1955.

173. C. M. Ablow and W. D. Hayes, Grad. Div. Appl. Math, Brown University, T.R. No. 1, 1951.

174. N. Curle, Proc. Roy. Soc. Lond., Ser. A, 235, 1202, May 1956.

175. Durand, Aerodynamic Theory, Vol II, Dover Publications, New York, 1963.

176. Lord Lelvin, Math. Phys. Pap., 4, Cambridge, 1910; Phil. Mag., 42, Nov. 1871.

177. L. D. Landau and E. M. Lifshitz, Fluid Mechanics, trans. from Russian, Pergamon Press, New York, 1959.

178. L. I. Sedov, Similarity and Dimensional Methods in Mechanics, trans. by Holt and Friedman, Academic Press, New York, 1959.

179. A. S. Povitskii, Trudy Tsent. AGI, 423, 1939.

180. L. I. Sedov, (Coll. Gen. Theoret. Grp. Ts AGI), Techn. Notes Tsent. AGI, 52, 1932.

181. L. I. Sedov, Trudy Tsent. AGI, 187, 1934.

182. J. Pierson, IAS Fund Paper, No. FF-3, 1950.

183. M. Schiffman and D. C. Spencer, Comm. Pure Appl. Math., 4, 1951.

184. P. R. Garabedian, Comm. Pure Appl. Math., 6, 2, May 1953.

185. L. S. Liebenzen, Doklady Akad. Nauk SSSR, 3, 9, 1935.

186. Contemporary State of Large Aerodynamic Construction, Vol. 1, Ch. VII, gen. ed. L. Khouart, trans. from English., Moscow, 1955.

187. A. Arynov, Doklady Akad. Nauk SSSR, 123, 1, 1958

188. Ya. I. Serkerzh-Zenkovich, Prikl. Mat. Mekh, 21, 6, 1957.

189. L. M. Ovsiannikvov, Prikl. Mat. Mekh., 13, 5, 1949.

190. Yu. V. Rudnev, Lecture Notes, National Correspondence Institute of Transportation Engineering, No. 1, 1960.

191. S. V. Falkovich, Prikl. Mat. Mekh., 21, 4, 1957.

192. T. M. Cherry, Proc. Roy. Soc. Lond., Ser. A, 202, 1950.

193. S. K. Aslanov and V. A. Legkova, J. Appl. Math. and Mech., 23, 1, 1959.

194. L. N. Sretenskii, Doklady Akad. Nauk SSSR, 119, 6, 1958.

195. L. N. Sretenskii, J. Appl. Math. and Mech., 23, 2, 1959.

196. A. G. Mackie, Proc. Cambridge Phil. Soc., Math Phys. Sci., 54, Pt. 4, 1958.

197. N. A. Slezkin, Doklady Akad. Nauk SSSR, 2, 8-9, 1935.

198. A. I. Bunimovich, Lecture Notes MGU, 3, 152 (Mechanics), 1951.

199. A. Busemann, Z. angew. Math. u. Mech., 17, 2, 1937.

200. C. Jacob, Portugalial Math., 1, 3, 1939.

201. L. I. Sedov, Vestnik. Mosk. Univ., 9, 1949.

202. S. A. Khristianovich and I. M. Yurev, Prikl. Mat. Mekh., 11, 1, 1947.

203. T. von Karman, J. Aero, Sci., 8, 9, 1941.

204. H. S. Tsien, J. Aero. Sci., 6, 10, 1939.

205. C. Jacob, C. R. Acad. Sci., 123, 714, 1946.

206. B. Demtchenko, Publ. Math. Univ. de Belgrade, 2, 1933, pp. 85-105.

207. C. Jacob, C. R. Acad. Sci., 203, 1936.

208. C. Jacob, Ed. Acad. Rep. Pop., Romône, 1952.

209. R. Sauer, Sitz. bayer Akad. Wiss. Math.-naturw, Klasse, 9, 1951.

210. J. Peres, C. R. Acad. Sci., 219, 20, 1944.

211. G. A. Dombrovskii, Doklady Akad. Nauk SSSR, 103, 1, 1955.

212. G. A. Dombrovskii, Doklady Akad. Nauk SSSR, 111, 2, 1956.

213. F. Tricomi, Rend. Reale. Accad. Lincei, Ser. 5, 14, 1923, pp. 134-247.

214. N. Coburn, Q. Appl. Math., 3, 1945, pp. 106-116.

215. F.-K. Chuang, Acta Sci. Sinica, 4, 2, 1955.

216. S. A. Khristianovich, Prikl. Mat. Mekh., 11, 2, 1947.

217. Z. Hasimoto, J. Phys. Japan, 8, 3, 1953.

217a. K. Jaeckel, Z. angew. Math. u. Mech., 34, 112, 1954.

218. K. C. Shin, C. R. Acad. Sci., 225, 17, 1947.

219. I. M. Yurev, Prikl. Mat. Mekh., 19, 3, 1955.

220. O. S. Vorobiev, Doklady Akad. Nauk SSSR, 122, 5, 1958.

221. A. Shapiro, The Dynamics and Thermodynamics of Compressible Fluid Flow, Vol. 1, Ronald Press, 1953.

222. L. Prandtl, Phys. Zeit. I Okt., 19, 1904, p. 599.

223. G. A. Dombrovskii, Doklady Akad. Nauk SSSR, 113, 1, 1957.

224. F. I. Frankl, Izv. Akad. Nauk SSSR, Ser. Mat., 9, 1945.

225. N. A. Skripkin, Prikl. Mat. Mekh, 19, 1, 1955.

226. S. I. Tomotika and K. Tamada, "Two-Dimensional Mixed Compressible Flow," Ch. III, Collected Trans. in Mechanics., No. 2, Russia, 1952,

227. E. Trefftz, Z. Math. Phys., 64, 1, 1916.

228. F. Kretzschmer, V.D.I., Forschungsheft, 381, 1936.

229. W. Schach, Ingr-Arch., 6, 1, Feb 1935.

230. Dzh. Salamotov, J. Appl. Math. and Mech., 23, 2, 1959.

231. W. Bauer, Ann. Phys., 82, 7, Pt. 4, 1927.

232. P. R. Garabedian, Bull. Amer. Math. Soc., 62, 3, May 1956, p. 642.

233. F. Vandrey, Ingr.-Arch., 11, 1940.

234. M. I. Gurevich, Trudy Tsent. AGI, 653, 1947.

235. R. V. Southwell and G. Vaisey, Phil. Trans. Roy. Soc. Lond., Ser. A, 240, 815, 1946.

236. D. M. Young, L. D. Gates, R. J. Arms, and D. F. Eliezer, NAVORD Proving Ground Rept. No. 1413, Dec 1955.

237. H. Rouse and A. H. Abul-Fetouk, J. Appl. Mech., 17, 4, Dec 1950.

238. D. Dumitreskii, Science in Rumanian Rep., Vol. 2, 1953.

239. M. S. Plesset and P. A. Shaffer, Revs. Mod. Phys., 20, 1, Jan 1949.

240. V. Volterra, J. math. pures et appl., Ser. 9, 11, 1, 1932.

241. J. Peres, J. math. pures et appl., Ser. 9, 2, 1, 1932.

242. P. R. Garabedian, Stud. Math. Mech., Academic Press, New York, 1954.

243. D. Gilbarg, J. Rational Mech. and Analysis, 1, 2, 1952.

244. J. Serrin, Amer. J. Math., 74, 1952.

245. D. Gilbarg, J. Rational Mech. and Analysis, 2, 2, 1953.

246. J. Serrin, J. Math. Phys., 23, 1, Apr 1954.

247. P. R. Garabedian, H. Lewy, and M. Schiffer, Annals Math., 56, 3, Nov 1952.

248. M. I. Gurevich, Prikl. Mat. Mekh., 11, 1, 1947.

249. N. Levinson, Ann. Math., 47, 1946.

250. N. E. Zhukovskii, J. Russ. Phys.-Chem. Soc., 22, 1891; also in Collected Works, Gostekhizdat, Moscow, 1949.

251. A. R. Richardson, Phil. Mag., Ser. 6, 235, Jul 1920.

252. N. Bervi, Trudy Otd. Phys. Nauk imp. Obshch. Lyubitel. Estest., 6, 7, Moscow, 1894.

253. E. B. McLeod, J. Rational Mech. and Analysis, 4, 4, 1955.

254. E. Marchi, Ann. mat. pura ed appl., 35, 1953.

255. B. Gentilini, L'Energia Electrica, 1941.

256. G. I. Melkonyan, Izv. Akad. Nauk Armenian SSR, Ser. Phys.-Mat. Nauk, 10, 3, 1957.

257. T. B. Benjamin, J. Fluid Mech., 1, Pt. 2, Jul 1956.

258. K. Woronetz, K. R. Acad. Sci. T., 236, 3, 1953.

259. K. Woronetz, Publs. Inst. Math. Acad. Serbe Sci., 5, 1953.

260. M. I. Gurevich and G. N. Pykhteev, Proc. of A. I. Mikoyan Moscow Tech. Inst. of Fishing Indus. and Econ., 8, 1957.

261. N. E. Kochin, Collected Works, Izv. Akad. Nauk SSSR, 1949.

262. H. Lewy, Proc. Amer. Math. Soc., 3, 1, Feb. 1952.

SUBJECT INDEX

SUBJECT INDEX

SUBJECT INDEX

SUBJECT INDEX